CHEMICAL ELEMENTS: THEIR SYMBOLS, ATOMIC NUMBERS, AND ATOMIC MASSES—1961

Name	Symbol	Number	Mass[a]	Name	Symbol	Number	Mass[a]
Actinium	Ac	89	(227)	Mercury			
Aluminum	Al	13	26.9815	Molybdenum			
Americium	Am	95	(243)	Neodymium			
Antimony	Sb	51	121.75	Neon			
Argon	Ar	18	39.948	Neptunium	Np		
Arsenic	As	33	74.9216	Nickel	Ni	28	58.71
Astatine	At	85	(210)	Niobium	Nb	41	92.906
Barium	Ba	56	137.34	Nitrogen	N	7	14.0067
Berkelium	Bk	97	(249)	Nobelium	No	102	(253)
Beryllium	Be	4	9.0122	Osmium	Os	76	190.2
Bismuth	Bi	83	208.980	Oxygen	O	8	15.9994
Boron	B	5	10.811	Palladium	Pd	46	106.4
Bromine	Br	35	79.909	Phosphorus	P	15	30.9738
Cadmium	Cd	48	112.40	Platinum	Pt	78	195.09
Calcium	Ca	20	40.08	Plutonium	Pu	94	(242)
Californium	Cf	98	(249)	Polonium	Po	84	210.
Carbon	C	6	12.01115	Potassium	K	19	39.102
Cerium	Ce	58	140.12	Praseodymium	Pr	59	140.907
Cesium	Cs	55	132.905	Promethium	Pm	61	(145)
Chlorine	Cl	17	35.453	Protactinium	Pa	91	231.
Chromium	Cr	24	51.996	Radium	Ra	88	226.05
Cobalt	Co	27	58.9332	Radon	Rn	86	222.
Copper	Cu	29	63.54	Rhenium	Re	75	186.2
Curium	Cm	96	(245)	Rhodium	Rh	45	102.905
Dysprosium	Dy	66	162.50	Rubidium	Rb	37	85.47
Einsteinium	Es	99	(251)	Ruthenium	Ru	44	101.07
Erbium	Er	68	167.26	Samarium	Sm	62	150.35
Europium	Eu	63	151.96	Scandium	Sc	21	44.956
Fermium	Fm	100	(253)	Selenium	Se	34	78.96
Fluorine	F	9	18.9984	Silicon	Si	14	28.086
Francium	Fr	87	(223)	Silver	Ag	47	107.870
Gadolinium	Gd	64	157.25	Sodium	Na	11	22.9898
Gallium	Ga	31	69.72	Strontium	Sr	38	87.62
Germanium	Ge	32	72.59	Sulfur	S	16	32.064
Gold	Au	79	196.967	Tantalum	Ta	73	180.948
Hafnium	Hf	72	178.49	Technetium	Tc	43	(99)
Helium	He	2	4.0026	Tellurium	Te	52	127.60
Holmium	Ho	67	164.930	Terbium	Tb	65	158.924
Hydrogen	H	1	1.00797	Thallium	Tl	81	204.37
Indium	In	49	114.82	Thorium	Th	90	232.038
Iodine	I	53	126.9044	Thulium	Tm	69	168.934
Iridium	Ir	77	192.2	Tin	Sn	50	118.69
Iron	Fe	26	55.847	Titanium	Ti	22	47.90
Krypton	Kr	36	83.80	Tungsten	W	74	183.85
Lanthanum	La	57	138.91	Uranium	U	92	238.03
Lawrencium[b]	Lw	103		Vanadium	V	23	50.942
Lead	Pb	82	207.19	Xenon	Xe	54	131.30
Lithium	Li	3	6.939	Ytterbium	Yb	70	173.04
Lutetium	Lu	71	174.97	Yttrium	Y	39	88.905
Magnesium	Mg	12	24.312	Zinc	Zn	30	65.37
Manganese	Mn	25	54.9380	Zirconium	Zr	40	91.22
Mendelevium	Md	101	(256)				

[a] The numbers in parentheses are the mass numbers of the most stable isotopes.
[b] The existence of this element has not yet been confirmed.

SOURCE: *Journal of the American Chemical Society*, **84**:4175, 1962.
Journal of Chemical Education, **38**:625, 1961.

ARNOLD E. BEREIT

KENNETH BORST

LEALLYN B. CLAPP

JAMES V. DEROSE

ROBERT K. FITZGEREL

EDWARD FULLER

ERIC GRAHAM

ARTHUR H. LIVERMORE

RICHARD MILLER

H. A. NEIDIG

HENRIETTA PARKER

ROBERT SHEWBERT

LAURENCE E. STRONG

WENDELL H. TAYLOR

FRANK H. VERHOEK

PAUL WESTMEYER

HAROLD WIK

M. KENT WILSON

CHEMICAL BOND APPROACH PROJECT

In 1959 a group of nine high school and nine college chemistry teachers set up the Chemical Bond Approach Project. The group prepared a preliminary draft of an introductory chemistry course during the summer of 1959. Members of this group and others have continued to evaluate and to revise instructional materials. This work has resulted in the publication of Chemical Systems *and* Investigating Chemical Systems. *Throughout the trial and revision program, the work of the group has been supported by grants from the National Science Foundation.*

CBA CHEMICAL BOND APPROACH PROJECT

WEBSTER DIVISION
McGRAW-HILL BOOK COMPANY

CHEMICAL SYSTEMS

St. Louis · New York · San Francisco · Dallas · Toronto · London · Sydney

This book is dedicated to
HARRY F. LEWIS *who suggested*
the study and whose continued
support, enthusiasm, and wise
counsel have been of immeasurable
value in the writing of this book.

Published by Webster Division
McGraw-Hill Book Company

345678910 RM 7372717069686766

PREFACE

CHEMISTRY COMBINES imaginative ideas and a great many facts into an intelligible whole, from which a student can get an introductory view of a modern science. It is the process of weaving together ideas and facts that should occupy the attention of the student of chemistry— a process in which he can participate.

Chemical Systems provides an introduction to chemistry as a modern science. The book is divided into five parts. In Part One the nature of chemical change is discussed with emphasis on the interaction of substances which compose a system. Interaction can be observed in the laboratory. To understand interaction, the idea of atoms is introduced along with the idea that atoms are arranged to give a structure. Atomic mass, molecular mass, chemical formulas, and equations are introduced.

Part Two develops a basis for understanding how atoms can interact to form structures. Part Two proceeds by examining systems that undergo chemical reactions and produce electric energy. Experimental evidence indicates that electricity is related to all matter. The study of the nature of interactions of electrostatic charges leads to the conclusion that matter may be considered to have a structure with atoms as building blocks while the atoms in turn are electric structures. Each atom consists of a central positively charged nucleus surrounded by negatively charged electrons.

Two different mental models in which nuclei and electrons are assumed to be the structural units of atoms are the center of attention in the third part of the book. The first mental picture of the arrangement of nuclei and electrons is called the charge cloud model and the second the atomic orbital model. Both models assume that electric forces of attraction hold atoms together in molecules and in crystals. The roles of kinetic-molecular theory and enthalpy as mental models are also discussed in Part Three.

Structural models provide a way of thinking about the arrangement of electrons and nuclei to give a three-dimensional picture for each substance in a system. In Part Four, substances are classified as covalent, metallic, or ionic. These three classes are based in part on the properties of the substances and in part on ideas about the structure of each substance. In Part Four the ideas developed in Part One about the nature of reactions are related to the study in Part Three of structural models of substances.

For many systems chemical reactions proceed to a final state in which both reactants and products are present in the system, yet further reaction fails to occur. To understand this phenomenon, the idea of chemical equilibrium is introduced in Part Five. The study of electrical systems begun in Part Two is carried further to develop criteria for equilibrium. Electric potential energy, concentration, and free energy are shown to be interrelated. This interrelation is expressed by an equilibrium constant which describes the concentrations of the components of a system in an equilibrium state.

Although the equilibrium state is a description of a system for which no further spontaneous change in state is possible, systems not in an equilibrium state can undergo change. The rate at which reactions occur is considered in Part Five. The rate of reactions provides a basis for thinking about how atoms rearrange as substances react.

Throughout *Chemical Systems,* emphasis is placed upon ideas and experiments, both of which are necessary in an effective study of chemistry. Experiments directly related to chemical systems are presented in *Investigating Chemical Systems.* Throughout these two books, stress is placed on operational and conceptual definitions and on how to think about chemical reactions.

There are many introductory books on chemistry. Why should there be another? Many teachers have felt a need for a book which presents chemical reactions in the light of modern ideas. A book that meets this need must be totally new in organization. *Chemical Systems* is the first thoroughgoing effort to show the interrelated roles of ideas and facts in chemistry.

The major questions with which this book deals are (1) What is the nature of a chemical system—how do we recognize it, and how do we interpret it? (2) When a chemical reaction occurs, how does the change alter the surroundings of the system? (3) Why do chemical elements form certain compounds but not others? (4) What determines the conditions under which a chemical change is complete? (5) Why do reactions take time to occur?

Throughout the book many questions are raised. Some are raised and discussed in the text itself, while others are raised for the student to discuss. A few questions are raised to point out aspects of chemistry for which chemists do not yet have satisfactory understanding. Chemistry continues to be a development which is incomplete and in which many people participate.

An experimental procedure was used in the development of this book. Members of the Chemical Bond Approach staff prepared trial versions of text and laboratory guide. These were used by over 200 cooperating teachers and over 10,000 students. Information supplied by teachers and students led to revision and further improvement of the materials.

A number of expert scientists reviewed the materials and provided critical analyses. The principal consultants were

D. MURRAY ALEXANDER, Foothill College, Mountain View, California

WAYNE BOOTH, University of Chicago, Chicago, Illinois

D. COMPTON, University of Illinois, Urbana, Illinois

C. A. COULSON, Oxford University, Oxford, England

A. B. GARRETT, Ohio State University, Columbus, Ohio

R. M. GASCOIGNE, University of New South Wales, Sydney, Australia

FRANK HALLIWELL, University of North Staffordshire, North Staffordshire, England

GEORGE KIMBALL, A. D. Little Company, Cambridge, Massachusetts

S. P. MCGLYNN, Louisiana State University, Baton Rouge, Louisiana

ROBERT MARSCHNER, American Oil Company, Whiting, Indiana

ROBERT MAYBURY, University of Redlands, Redlands, California

R. S. NYHOLM, University College, London, England

GEORGE SCATCHARD, Massachusetts Institute of Technology, Cambridge, Massachusetts

ROBERT SHERMAN, Roger Williams Junior College, Providence, Rhode Island

E. B. WILSON, Harvard University, Cambridge, Massachusetts

The final assembling of this edition was the major responsibility of

O. T. BENFEY, *Earlham College*
L. B. CLAPP, *Brown University*
J. V. DEROSE, *Marple-Newtown Senior High School*
W. E. HUNTER, *Rich Township High School*
A. H. LIVERMORE, *Reed College*
H. A. NEIDIG, *Lebanon Valley College*
M. H. SCHEER, *Nashua High School*
E. S. SCOTT, *Ripon College*
L. E. STRONG, *Earlham College*
M. K. WILSON, *Tufts University*

CONTENTS

THE SCIENCE OF CHEMICAL CHANGE

WHAT IS chemistry? Chemists agree that chemistry is a science. Like physics, it is one of the physical sciences. The physical sciences are members of a larger group of sciences known as the natural sciences. The natural sciences include not only the physical sciences but also the biological sciences and the earth sciences.

Boundaries between these sciences are not at all clearcut. Between physics and chemistry, for example, there is a large area in which scientists from both fields work. Other similar overlapping areas are found, for example, between chemistry and biology, between chemistry and geology, between physics and biology. Though the borderlines may not be agreed upon, the sciences themselves are nonetheless still distinct. The situation is not unlike that of two adjoining countries which are distinct even though they may disagree about their common boundary.

But to call chemistry one of the physical sciences is only the beginning of an answer to the question, "What is chemistry?" What does it mean, after all, to call chemistry a science?

1-1   WHAT IS SCIENCE?

The work of Ernest Rutherford provides an excellent example of science. Rutherford would certainly be regarded as a scientist by all who have studied his life. Early in the twentieth century he became interested in the properties of a variety of radioactive materials,

1

including radium, which had been discovered by Marie and Pierre Curie only a short time before. Through a series of laboratory studies he showed that any amount of radium steadily decreased in quantity. Quite unlike all changes in matter observed up to that time, the alteration of radium went on entirely independently of how the radium was treated. Rutherford was able to show that one product of the change in radium was a stream of tiny particles traveling at high speed away from the radium. These tiny high-speed particles were called alpha particles.

After making these observations, Rutherford was led to explore the effect of the alpha particles on a variety of substances under different circumstances. His experiments included some in which a beam of alpha particles was aimed at a thin metal sheet of uniform thickness. He expected to find that all the alpha particles would pass through the thin sheet and emerge on the other side traveling a bit more slowly and in a slightly different direction compared to their initial speed and direction. The results of these experiments were unexpected, however. A tiny fraction of the particles were actually found to have reversed their direction as if they had bounced off some part of the sheet. Most of the particles seemed to go through the sheet as if it were a sieve rather than a nearly continuous solid material that current theories of the nature of matter had assumed (Fig. 1-1).

Before Rutherford began his experiments with radium and metal foils, he had already assumed that the metal was made up of atoms packed closely together. Guided by experimental data on how alpha particles were affected by metal foils, he proposed, in 1911, the idea that each atom in a metal is composed of a tiny, massive nucleus surrounded by large, almost massless electrons. The tiny fraction of particles that reversed direction from the thin foil were thought by Rutherford to have hit the massive nucleus in a head-on collision.

Now what does this example show about the nature of science? The question has at least two different answers. One is derived from the

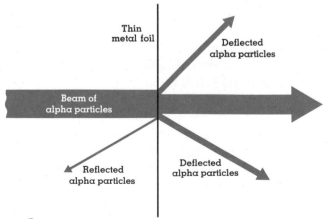

Fig. 1-1 *Rutherford's experiment with a beam of alpha particles aimed at a thin metal foil. Most alpha particles pass directly through the foil, but some are deflected and a few are reflected toward the source of alpha particles.*

ERNEST RUTHERFORD   *1871–1937*

*A British scientist born in New Zealand. He was a Nobel
Prizewinner in chemistry (1908) as well as a Fellow and
president of the Royal Society. A scholarship brought him
to England in 1895, where he was one of the first students
in the new Cavendish Laboratory of Cambridge University,
working under J. J. Thomson. He began investigations
on radioactive substances that had just been discovered
by Becquerel and the Curies. From 1898 to 1907, he taught
at McGill University, Canada, and developed, with
Frederick Soddy, the laws of nuclear disintegrations. The
next twelve years he was a professor at Manchester, where
with H. Geiger and E. Marsden he worked on the nuclear
structure of the atom* (Philosophical Magazine, **21**:669, 1911). *During World
War I, he studied underwater acoustics to cope with submarines. In 1919
he became professor of experimental physics at the Cavendish Laboratory,
Cambridge, doing his major work on the artificial transmutation of the
elements,* The Newer Alchemy—*as he entitled one of his books. Described
as a man of volcanic energy, intense enthusiasm, and immense capacity
for work, he influenced a remarkable group of students and colleagues,
among them N. Bohr; J. Chadwick, who discovered the neutron; and
H. G. J. Moseley, who obtained experimental evidence for atomic numbers.*

*So significant were Rutherford's contributions to human understanding
that at his death in 1937 he was buried in Westminster Abbey beside
Newton and Kelvin. In this way, England gave Rutherford a recognition
extended to only a few scientists.*

sequence of laboratory work and thinking that Rutherford carried
out. His experiments raised questions which led to ideas, while thinking about the ideas raised questions which led to experiments. As
Rutherford's work was followed further by subsequent experimenters,
still other ideas and experiments emerged. Rutherford's work thus
illustrates a process in which successive experiments and ideas are
interwoven with questions and answers. In this view, science is a
process of inquiry.

Rutherford wrote out and published descriptions of his experiments
and his conclusions. Other scientists repeated his work, while still
others tried out related work that was suggested by Rutherford's
experiments. In the planning of later research, his written record is
accepted as reliable by scientists. A scientist today goes on to other
experiments without repeating these earlier experiments, confident

that new experiments must, if correctly interpreted, be consistent with the recorded behavior of alpha particles as they pass through metal sheets. These written records of the experiments and ideas developed by earlier scientists are of great value to the present-day scientist, not only because new experiments and ideas may be suggested by the earlier work, but also because today's scientist does not have to repeat the experiments and the development of ideas.

Much of the science to be studied in this course will have to be taken from the records of the work of other scientists, but we hope that you will take every opportunity to get involved in the process as well. Reading about science leaves you only a spectator. The more personally you become involved in the chain of experiments and ideas as you study this course, the more you will be proceeding as a scientist. Possibly some of you will find this so satisfying that you will want to continue as scientists later on.

There is no completely definite answer available as to whether Rutherford's work should be called physics or chemistry. He did most of his work in the Cavendish Physics Laboratory at Cambridge, England, so on this basis he was a physicist. Yet the work briefly described here won him a Nobel Prize (1908) in chemistry. Probably many scientists would classify his laboratory work as physics, but the great idea of the nuclear atom which he developed so convincingly is of tremendous assistance in every branch of science. The precise label applied to his work is much more a matter of human choice than of logical necessity and is not very important.

All this description of scientific inquiry can be summed up by saying that science is both experimental and mental. It is both doing and thinking. It is observation and imagination.

1-2 WHO IS A SCIENTIST?

A scientist is, obviously enough, someone who works at science. Rutherford carried on the process of science both as an experimenter and as an originator of ideas. Actually he operated a laboratory with a number of students and colleagues associated with him. Many of these associates did primarily experimental work. They are considered to be scientists, even though they may not have made any outstanding contributions of ideas.

Albert Einstein's contribution to science, in contrast to Rutherford's, was in the realm of ideas, not experiments. As a man who generated some of the great ideas on which much other scientific work is based, he was a most distinguished scientist.

There are relatively few people whose scientific work is the creation of great ideas. Ideas usually arise because scientists are intrigued by experimental facts. Also, the best single measure of the importance of an idea in science is the extent to which the idea suggests new experiments to be performed. Most scientists make their contribution to science by doing laboratory experiments. For laboratory results to be significant, the scientist not only has to think about his own work, but he also has to see as clearly as possible the relation of his work to the ideas and to the results of the work of others.

1-3 EXPERIMENTAL SCIENCE

Everyone makes many observations every day, but only a few people make scientific observations. Yet scientific observations are simply carefully made observations. What, then, is it that distinguishes between ordinary observations and those called scientific?

Scientific observations are made to obtain information. With the information, the scientist attempts to answer questions raised by ideas. In most cases the questions require special procedures to get the most appropriate information. Such special procedures for making observations are usually called **experiments.**

There are two major features which distinguish scientific experimentation from ordinary observations—isolation and control. The scientist attempts to separate or *isolate* from everything else the materials that he desires to study. If he wishes to study the chemistry involved in the rusting of iron, he will not ordinarily work with any old piece of iron as he finds it in a junk pile. Instead he will deliberately separate the iron from all other materials. In this way, he tries to rule out from his experiment all materials except those which, along with the iron, are found essential for the production of iron rust. The particular collection of materials and the portion of the immediate environment which are isolated for experimental study are called a **system.**

Ordinarily, in an experiment, a chemist is interested in whether any feature of a system changes. As an illustration, iron exposed to air in a room might be observed over a period of time. Initially the iron is a shiny and tough solid. As the system of air and iron is examined for several hours or days, a red powder appears while the shiny solid and some of the air disappear. The final description of the system will therefore differ from the initial description. Everything that goes into a description of a system at a given instant is called the **state** of that system. The description of the system before a change is called the **initial state** and the description after the change is called the **final state.** In these terms, then,

$$\text{Change} \begin{pmatrix} \text{is described} \\ \text{by comparing} \end{pmatrix} \text{the Final State} \begin{pmatrix} \text{to} \end{pmatrix} \text{the Initial State} \\ \text{of the System}$$

Once it is established that a change occurs, a chemist is almost certain to be curious about what is responsible for the change. For the rusting of iron, this curiosity might take the form of the question, "Is the moisture present in the air of the room necessary in the rusting of iron?" To answer this question requires that two systems be compared.

A system of iron and dry air could be compared over a time interval with another system formed from an identical piece of iron in air known to contain moisture. As each system is observed, it may be found that the moisture-containing system produces iron rust while the dry system does not. If the system of iron and dry air is called the first system, and the iron and moist air the second system, there are two changes to be described.

$$\text{First Change} \left(\text{is described by comparing} \right) \text{the Final State of the First System} \left(\text{to} \right) \text{the Initial State of the First System}$$

$$\text{Second Change} \left(\text{is described by comparing} \right) \text{the Final State of the Second System} \left(\text{to} \right) \text{the Initial State of the Second System}$$

In this way the change to be associated with the difference between the two systems is given by the following expression.

$$\text{Change produced by added moisture} \left(\text{is described by comparing} \right) \text{the Second Change} \left(\text{to} \right) \text{the First Change}$$

It is customary to call a system of the first type (iron and dry air) a control. Every other system to be compared with the control will differ from it only in some definite way, for example, in the materials present or in temperature or air pressure. The purpose of a **control** in an experiment is to determine whether a change in the state of a system is the result of a known difference between the experimental system and the control.

A **controlled experiment** of this kind is the most common way of determining what factors produce the observed change. Usually the scientist attempts to be certain that only one of the things used to describe a system is altered at any one time. He can then say that the change he observed happens only when the one alteration is made. Although this, at first sight, seems simple to do, it often is surprisingly difficult.

Since the study of change is tied to the observations that make up the state of a system, this points to a third major feature of scientific experimentation. So far as intelligent discussion is concerned, the state of a system is what is said about it in words or pictures. Not only is it necessary to observe systems carefully, but it is also necessary to record what is observed. Indeed, a quite general feature of scientific experimentation is the writing of an accurate, precise, and complete record of observations, thoughts, and ideas. Some of the consequences of this were referred to in connection with the description of Rutherford's work. You should form the habit of writing in your laboratory notebook all information about any experiment you do. This should include the problem to be investigated, exactly what you do in the laboratory, the observations that you make, and your interpretation and analysis of the meaning of these results. Suggestions for keeping a reliable record of your experimentation are presented in the laboratory guide, *Investigating Chemical Systems*. The best single test of a reliable record is that someone else can take the record and repeat or extend the work reported.

In Experiment 1 in the laboratory guide, *Investigating Chemical Systems,* chemical systems are isolated in test tubes. The procedure asks the experimenter to make observations of properties of these systems in their initial and final states and to draw some conclusions from these observations.

1-4 THINKING ABOUT EXPERIMENTS

The success of an experiment will depend in large part on the amount of thought given to it. Little is gained from an experiment unless considerable thinking is done about the problem to be investigated before and during the actual laboratory work. Of equal importance are the considerations given to the experimental data obtained. Following the directions of a recipe without thought or theoretical considerations is not experimentation.

At the same time, the value of the ideas and concepts presented must be tested by seeing whether they do help you understand available experimental information. As the ideas of chemistry are presented, the role of experimentation will be emphasized. In some cases, the consideration of experimental data will support the development of a theoretical concept. On the other hand, ideas will be tested by considering related experimental evidence. In both situations, you will be asked to think about the ideas and the data and the relationships between them.

Throughout this course, much will be said about ideas appropriate to chemistry and how to think about them. Whether in the classroom or in the laboratory, ideas, thoughts, and experiments will be considered as interrelated parts of scientific inquiry. This should illustrate for you the way in which scientists work.

Experiment 2 in *Investigating Chemical Systems* shows the experimental approach to chemistry. A scientific experiment can be considered to be in some ways similar to observations made about a sealed box. If a sealed box with a loose object inside is examined, it is possible to make a number of observations about the behavior of the contents of the box. This behavior is likely to provide hints about the nature of the object inside the box. Without opening the box, one might imagine some device which should logically produce a behavior similar to what has been observed. A sealed container, left unopened as its behavior is studied, is often referred to as a **black box.**

The ability to draw any conclusions about what is inside a sealed box is, in part, a result of ideas we already have in mind. We believe that an unsupported object will fall toward the earth. We believe it is always more difficult to stop a heavy object than a light object after both have fallen the same distance. It is on the basis of these and other ideas that rather specific questions are asked. "What will happen if the box is tipped?" "What will happen if the box is shaken?"

In much the same spirit a chemist does an experiment. Instead of a black box he may use a test tube or a more complex piece of equipment. He begins because he has a question. His experiments are suggested by the nature of the question. From the experiments come results. This experimental information by itself is not necessarily an answer to the question. Answers are obtained only by thinking about the results of the experiments.

Some of the questions that a chemist asks are best put in the form, "What happens?" Others can be put in the form, "How much?" Answers for the first question are **qualitative;** those for the second are **quantitative.** Both qualitative and quantitative answers to the same question may be obtained, depending on how the experiment is conducted. For example, when a few crystals of sodium chloride are placed in water, they are observed to disappear. Qualitatively, then, it can be said that sodium chloride dissolves in water. The amount of sodium chloride that will dissolve in a measured volume of water can be determined by weighing. This is a quantitative observation.

Experimenters have obtained a considerable amount of information about the dissolving of sodium chloride in water. What happens when the crystals are stirred or ground or shaken in the water are qualitative questions of great practical importance. The quantitative questions about how much sodium chloride will dissolve in water with stirring, grinding, standing, temperature changes, or other circumstances are also items for which the laboratory worker wants information. Experience shows, however, that answers to these questions do not by themselves reveal why sodium chloride and water behave as they do. In this sense, the system made up of sodium chloride and water is a black box.

The scientific process has proved enormously productive. It has expanded our knowledge of the earth and the heavens. It has given man the ability to produce materials never known before. In the pursuit of science, man has developed some striking and imaginative ideas about the universe.

The most important results by far are an understanding of the nature of the world in which we live and the development of the mental habits useful in the exploration of our world. If you are ever intrigued by puzzles or riddles, some of the most intriguing are provided in science. The struggle to solve them continues to be an exciting adventure.

In the search for understanding, men have developed the atomic theory into a particularly effective aid. The idea that matter is made up of **atoms** (small parts) is very old. When or to whom it first occurred is not known, but we do know that men have used the idea of atoms for more than 2,000 years. The Roman poet Lucretius wrote a poem, *De Rerum Natura*, which referred to it, and even with him the idea was not new. Down through the centuries many great thinkers—including Plato, René Descartes, Robert Boyle, John Dalton, and Ernest Rutherford—refined the idea of atomicity until today, in a greatly modified form, it is useful in thinking about a great variety of experimental observations. No doubt the idea that all things are made of atoms will continue to play a significant role in man's future thinking, though unquestionably it will be further modified. Well-developed ideas which provide ways of interrelating many different phenomena are usually called **theories.** An example is the atomic theory.

Though theories are probably the most important product of science, scientific ideas and observations often provide solutions for practical problems with far-reaching consequences. As a result of the activities of many scientists working in many fields, each year it is possible to do and to know things that had not been done or known the year before. Not so many years ago diabetes was an incurable disease. Through the discovery of insulin, doctors learned how to control the disease. More recently, the complex arrangement of atoms within insulin has been worked out by painstaking experimentation. It is even possible that sometime in the future insulin may be made in the laboratory or the factory. Further study may eventually lead from control of diabetes to actual cure.

Forty years ago, clothes were made from natural fibers such as wool and cotton. Tires were made from natural rubber. Food was wrapped only in paper. Then scientists learned how to make certain large molecules, called polymers, and now we have synthetic fibers for clothes, synthetic rubber which wears better than natural rubber, and polyethylene bags for packaging foods. The term **synthetic** as used here means that the material is made by man rather than in the natural processes of living plants and animals.

Developments in technology and engineering also contribute to the development of science. In the seventeenth century, pump makers worked out several improvements in water pumps. Their interest was mainly directed to the practical problems of pumping water from deep mine shafts. Following the improvement in pumps, it became possible for Robert Boyle to experiment more effectively with gases. He used this advance in the technology of pumps as a basis for a most significant piece of scientific work on the nature of gases.

At the present time chemical reactions are used to put objects in orbit outside the earth's atmosphere. As a result, a number of scientific studies can be pursued that were not practical before. One example is the detailed study of the surface of the sun. With a telescope in orbit outside the earth's atmosphere, it is now possible to take photographs of the sun's surface which are much sharper than any obtained with telescopes on the ground. In this way, further information can be obtained about the nature of the sun's surface and a better concept can be formed about the nature of the sun's interior.

The account of the activities of a scientist given here is much too brief to reveal the details of the development of such things as synthetic fibers and, indeed, of most other scientific achievements. In every scientific discovery many individuals are involved. One person suggests an idea, others collect observations, and still others compare ideas and observations. Some will modify and improve the original idea. What is now known by scientists is the result of the work, the thought, and even the wrong ideas of many different people. You, yourself, may contribute something further to this enterprise—perhaps a new fact, a new technique, or a powerful idea.

1-6 WHAT IS CHEMISTRY?

Following this discussion of the general question of what science is, a more nearly complete answer to the original query, "What is chemistry?" can be attempted. Since the whole book deals with this question, a short, concise answer may well be misleading. With this risk in mind, however, **chemistry** can be defined as the science of changes in matter (from initial to final state).

Change has been described as the difference found when a system is compared in two different states. A ball may move from the top of a hill to the bottom. An ice cube in a warm room turns into a puddle of liquid and still later the liquid vanishes. A piece of shiny iron, when exposed to moist air, becomes covered with a dull red powder. The transparent white of an egg becomes opaque and tough as it is heated in a frying pan. Everyone is familiar with many other examples of change, but chemists refer to only certain of these changes as chemical changes.

Any decision as to which changes are chemical and which are not is, to some extent, arbitrary. That is, people simply decide to recognize certain changes as chemical and proceed to call themselves chemists as they study them. However, a few rules are usually followed. When the ball moves from the hilltop to the valley, its change in position and the effects which accompany the change are not considered to be chemical changes. But the change of iron from a hard, tough, shiny metal to a red, loose powder is an example of chemical change. Chemists are very much interested in chemical changes.

Is the melting of ice sufficiently similar to the rusting of iron to be called a chemical change? If you consult books by chemists, you will certainly find them interested in the melting of ice and of all sorts of things. There is a distinction, however, between the melting of ice and the rusting of iron. Ice exposed to a high temperature melts to give liquid water, which, exposed to a low temperature, turns again to ice. The high and low temperatures may be so chosen that their difference is as small as desired and they still produce the cycle of melting and freezing. When iron rusts, no particularly noticeable change in temperature need accompany the change, but, even more important, simply raising or lowering the temperature will not turn the rust back to iron. A chemist will say that ice and liquid water are different forms of the same material, water, and thus they have a number of common properties. Iron and iron rust are considered to be different materials with distinctly different properties. Therefore, the formation of iron rust is a chemical change.

1-7 PROPERTIES AND CHANGE

Chemistry has been defined as a study of changes for which the initial state of a system is different from the final state. An important part of the observations that make up the state of a system is the identity of each material composing the system. This means that the properties of each material in the system should be considered before and after change takes place.

Perhaps the most striking of properties is described when the physical state of a material is specified. The *physical state* of a material is specified when the material is said to be a solid, a liquid, or a gas. The specification of the physical state of a material is included in the state of a system. The three physical states of the substance water have been observed by all of us. Most gases (vapors) are colorless and therefore transparent for all colors of visible light, although a few are visibly colored and therefore not transparent for all colors of light. When water boils, the gaseous state of water is represented by the clear space (apparently empty) between the surface of the liquid and the white cloud. This colorless, transparent gas is commonly called steam.

When water is heated until it boils, bubbles of gas rise through the hot liquid as shown in Fig. 1-2a. When an electric current passes through water (an example of a process called electrolysis), bubbles of gas rise through the liquid as shown in Fig. 1-2b. Superficially, the two events appear the same. Are they?

If the steam produced when water is boiled is cooled to room temperature, a liquid is formed which is indistinguishable from the original water at the same temperature. In the electrolysis experiment, gas is produced at two different parts of the apparatus and both samples remain as gases when they are cooled to room temperature. They remain gases even at the temperature at which the vapor from boiling water turns to a solid. These two processes, boiling and electrolysis, have resulted, then, in products with quite different properties.

In the process of boiling, it appears that the gas does not represent a new material but only a different physical state of the original material. The electrolysis, on the other hand, has generated a product which is at least one and possibly more than one new material, but in any case, which is different from either water or steam. A change in the state of a system which goes from liquid to gas without the production of new materials is called a **physical change.** For this reason the term physical state is applied to the solid, liquid, and gas states. Whenever a process takes place with the production of one or more

Fig. 1-2 *Gases are produced when water is boiled and when it is electrolyzed. (a) Water boils at the surface of a wire which is heated electrically. (b) Bubbles of gas are produced at each electrode when electricity is passed through water.*

(a)   (b)

Fig. 1-3 *A gas is produced when vinegar is poured onto baking soda.*

new materials, the system within which the process takes place is called a **chemical system.** The process itself within a chemical system is called a **chemical change** or a **chemical reaction.** In a chemical reaction, the initial materials (or **reactants**) are replaced by a new set of materials (or **products**).

Many chemical reactions are familiar to all of us. Gasoline and wood burn. Silver metal turns to black tarnish; tough iron turns to red powdery rust. Fluid milk turns to semisolid curd; solid baking soda and liquid vinegar produce a gas. Many other commonly encountered changes are also chemical. These include the growth of plants and animals and the cooking of food.

This discussion of change has brought into sharp focus the need to recognize the nature of the material from which a given object is made. *Material* is a general term used to designate one or several substances which make up an object. The features by which the material in an object is identified are called the **properties of matter.** Are different properties equally valuable in identifying and distinguishing different materials?

Ex. 1-1   What is the white cloud that is visible above the spout of a kettle in which water is being boiled?

1-8   MASS AND VOLUME OF MATTER

Matter is the stuff of which the materials of the universe are made. It fills space and has mass. To measure the space-filling property of a piece of matter, we determine its volume. A volume measurement is made by comparing the object with a standard measure of volume.

(In scientific work the metric system of measures is used. The basic relationships among units are presented in handbooks.)

To measure the mass of a piece of matter, the mass of the object is compared with a known mass. Most commonly, in the laboratory the comparison is carried out with an equal-arm balance using a set of objects of known mass. The operation in which mass is measured on a balance is called **weighing. Weight,** which refers to the gravitational attraction of the earth for an object, is perhaps most simply measured on a spring scale. **Mass** is a fixed property of a particular object, whereas weight varies slightly from one part of the earth to another and varies drastically as the object moves away from the earth. Chemists are generally not concerned with weight but rather with mass.

A standard mass has been agreed upon by an international organization of scientists. This arbitrarily chosen standard is a specially selected metal in the form of a block called a kilogram mass. It is kept in a laboratory near Paris, France. In this laboratory equal-arm balances are available which permit the comparison of the standard with other similar blocks of metal. These blocks are shipped to other parts of the world to be used in producing objects of known mass for laboratory and industrial application.

Can the two properties, mass and volume, be used to identify and distinguish different pieces of matter? Do they, for instance, permit one to distinguish between iron and marble which we can easily see are

Fig. 1-4 (a) *The triple-beam balance, and* (b) *the equal-arm balance. Of these balances, the triple-beam balance gives more precise measures of masses.*

(a)

(b)

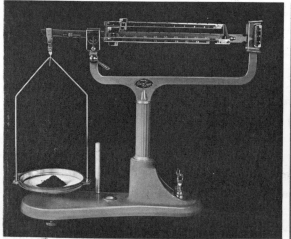
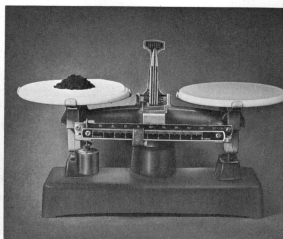

TABLE 1-1 MASSES AND VOLUMES OF SAMPLES OF THREE MATERIALS

Marble Chips		Iron Filings		Lead Shot	
Mass, expressed in grams	Volume, expressed in milliliters	Mass, expressed in grams	Volume, expressed in milliliters	Mass, expressed in grams	Volume, expressed in milliliters
27.5	9.2	34.5	5.1	64.6	5.8
42.2	14.8	80.8	12.2	104.9	9.9
53.5	18.8	139.0	20.2	179.4	17.0
69.9	24.0	164.9	24.5	261.3	24.1

different? At first sight the answer seems to be "No." After all, a piece of marble can have any mass and volume from a tiny (almost invisible) fragment to a block as big as a house. However, before this possibility is abandoned entirely, let us look a bit further. We do find that it is not possible for a piece of marble to have small mass and large volume. There appears to be some way in which mass and volume are related.

An investigation of a possible relation between mass and volume requires experimental data. Mass and volume are but two of many properties of matter which can be described and measured. These two have been chosen because they are relatively easy to measure, and they form the basis of a great variety of laboratory experiments. Marble chips, iron filings, and lead shot, three solids conveniently available in a laboratory, were investigated. The masses of four samples of the three different solids were determined by direct comparison with standard masses. Their volumes were determined by difference. To do this, a volume of water was placed in a graduated cylinder and then the weighed solid was totally immersed in the water. The volume for the combination of water and solid was read off the scale of the graduated cylinder. Subtracting the initial water volume from the final volume of the combination gave the volume of solid which is recorded in Table 1-1 in milliliters (ml).

Measurements of mass and volume for samples of marble chips, iron filings, and lead shot are recorded in Table 1-1. The data for Table 1-1 were obtained in the laboratory with a trip balance and a graduated cylinder. The smallest division on the scale of the trip balance is 0.1 gram (g). The graduated cylinder has a maximum volume of 100.0 ml, and the smallest division is 1.0 ml. Do the data reveal anything about the relation of mass and volume or the nature of the three materials?

Much experimental work in science results in the collection of measurements represented by numbers. Table 1-1 is one example of such a collection. If the collection remains only a jumble of numbers, little is gained. Experiments become significant only to the extent that we can see relationships among the data obtained.

Just the process of writing down the numbers can often show some relations. In the horizontal rows of Table 1-1, each pair of mass and volume data corresponds to a single system and is therefore directly related. The vertical columns of numbers in the table are arranged so that the smallest masses are at the top and the largest masses at the bottom. This permits you to run your eye down parallel columns to see whether mass and volume vary together or independently.

Often it is more revealing to present the data in pictorial form. Figure 1-5 does this by means of a graph. The center of each circle is placed on the graph so that it corresponds to one pair of values for mass and volume in Table 1-1. Each pair of values plotted on the graph is called a **point.** By this method of plotting, each point represents a single determination for a system. A smooth curve or line is drawn to pass as closely as possible through all the points corresponding to one material. It is sometimes found that not all the points will lie accurately on a smooth curve, and in this case the line is drawn so that an almost equal number of points is on either side. Even a glance at the graph then can often show if the plotted numbers are related in a particular way.

Although a graph is usually plotted with only

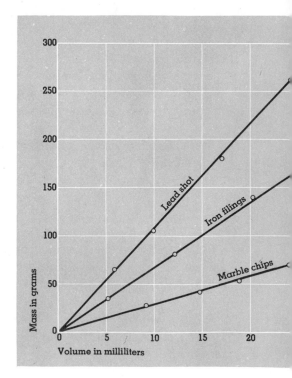

Fig. 1-5 *Graphical comparison of mass and volume.*

a few points on it, whenever a smooth curve can be drawn, it is quite possible to get other values from the graph. For example, Fig. 1-5 can be used to show that 100 g of iron filings should have a volume of 14.6 ml. The volume occupied by 100 g of iron can be experimentally determined and compared with the value read from the graph.

Many graphs will be used in this book to aid you in seeing relationships. You will be well repaid to refresh your knowledge of the preparation and analysis of these aids to thought. *Investigating Chemical Systems* contains an appendix devoted to a further discussion of graphing.

What do the straight lines drawn in Fig. 1-5 suggest for the data in Table 1-1? Experience with matter suggests that for zero mass the volume must also be zero. The point on the graph where both values are zero is called the **origin.** In Fig. 1-5 each line goes through the origin.

When the straight line not only passes close to all the points representing measured data but also through the origin of the graph, the data have an unusually simple relationship. Thus, according to the graph, 20.0 ml of lead shot has a mass of 216 g, which is just twice the mass of 108 g found for 10.0 ml of shot. Similarly, for the volume of 5.0 ml of lead, the mass is 54.0 g or one-quarter the mass of 216 g. The ratio of these masses, 216 g/108 g, is 2:1. Similarly the ratio of the volumes, 20.0 ml/10.0 ml, is 2:1. If, as in this case, the ratio of two masses is the same as the ratio of the corresponding volumes, then the masses and the volumes are said to be proportional to each other. That is, 216 g/108 g is equal to 20.0 ml/10.0 ml. The ratio of mass to volume is widely used and is called **density.**

To see if the data in Table 1-1 do imply a constant ratio for each material, ratios can be calculated directly. As an example, this is done in Table 1-2 for the lead shot. For each material, all the calculated ratios have nearly the same numerical value. The more closely the points lie along a straight line, the more closely the ratios come to being the same.

TABLE 1-2   RATIOS OF MASS TO VOLUME FOR LEAD SHOT

Mass, g	Volume, ml	Mass/Volume Ratio, g/ml[a]
64.6	5.8	11.1
104.9	9.9	10.6
179.4	17.0	10.6
261.3	24.1	10.8

[a] Measured in grams per milliliter (g/ml).

TABLE 1-3 MASS/VOLUME RATIOS (densities) FOR THREE MATERIALS

	Mass/Volume, g/ml
Marble chips	2.9
Iron filings	6.8
Lead shot	10.8

From the lines in Fig. 1-5 it is possible to read directly a pair of mass and volume values for each of the three materials. Ratios can be calculated for each of these pairs, and the results are given in Table 1-3. In the case of lead, the value obtained from the line for the ratio is the same as the average of the four values listed in Table 1-2. The calculated value of the ratio based on the line is a value which best fits all the experimental data for each substance.

For a straight-line graph of the type shown in Fig. 1-5, the ratio for each line listed in Table 1-3 is called the **slope** of the line in the graph. The more nearly vertical the line is, the larger is the value of the slope; whereas the more nearly horizontal the line, the smaller the slope. *Investigating Chemical Systems* gives a procedure for determining the slope when the line does not go through the origin on the graph. In *Investigating Chemical Systems*, Experiment 3 is an investigation of the mass/volume ratios for several samples of a material.

Ex. 1-2   From Fig. 1-5 estimate the volume of 50.0 g of marble.

Ex. 1-3   From the data in Table 1-1 for marble and iron filings, prepare tables similar to Table 1-2. What are the average values of the mass/volume ratios for lead, marble, and iron filings?

Ex. 1-4   For the purest iron a volume of 50.0 ml has a mass of 393 g. Compare the mass/volume ratio for this iron with the value for iron filings in Table 1-3.

Ex. 1-5   Plot the data in Exercise 1-4 and in Table 1-1 (for iron filings) on the same graph. Do all the points lie on a line passing through the origin? Compare your graph with Fig. 1-5.

1-10 CHARACTERISTIC PROPERTIES

One important feature of density is that it is independent of the amount of material involved. Thus a chemist might order iron filings and specify, whatever the quantity, that their density be 6.8 grams per milliliter (g/ml). At the least, he could then be quite sure it was not a piece of lead, and in fact, such a description will distinguish it from many other materials. Density is one example of the properties of matter which chemists find useful.

Density is a property, then, that must be computed from measurements in the laboratory. It is defined by the operations of weighing and measuring volume. From the data provided by these two operations, a density value is calculated as the ratio of mass to volume. Most commonly, the mass will be measured in grams, and the volume in milliliters; and so the density calculated from the mass and volume of an object will be described in grams per milliliter.

A single lead shot has a certain mass and volume, while a section of lead pipe may have quite different values. The lead itself from which each object is made can thus have any value for its mass and volume but only one certain value for its density. These properties which are determined by the nature of a particular material but not by the amount of the material examined will be called **characteristic properties.** Among these are density, color, odor, hardness, electric conductivity, and ability to flow. Mass and volume, on the other hand, are properties of material which vary from one object to another.

1-11   IS TEMPERATURE A CHARACTERISTIC PROPERTY?

When a thermometer is placed in contact with an object, the reading on the thermometer is called the **temperature** of the object. There are a number of temperature scales in use. For this course most measurements of temperature will be based on the Celsius scale (°C), also called the centigrade scale. A discussion of temperature scales is given in Chapter 8.

You might wonder whether the temperature of an object is at all useful for identification. Mass was not useful as an identifying property of a substance because the value for mass varies, depending upon how much material is taken. Temperature for an object, on the other hand, does not vary in this way. If two objects made of the same material and at the same temperature are put together, the temperature remains unchanged and does not become twice the value found for one of the objects alone.

Experience suggests that the temperature of an object can be varied over a considerable range. Values obtained for particular properties usually alter with change in temperature. So it must be that some properties are in some way connected with the temperature. One way of varying the temperature of an object is to place it in contact with a second object at a temperature different from that of the first. As an example, if samples of hot and cold water are mixed in a container, the final temperature is found to be intermediate between the two initial temperatures.

Another way to raise the temperature of a material, such as water, is to place it in contact with a source of heat. Figure 1-6 shows an

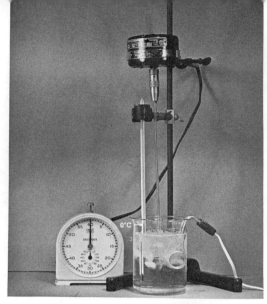

Fig. 1-6 *Crushed ice and water in a beaker equipped with a heater, thermometer, and stirrer, ready to start the experiment described in Section 1-11.*

apparatus for doing this simply by means of a small electric heating coil. With the heater connected to a suitable electrical source, it seems reasonable to assume that the amount of heat given out by the heater increases in direct proportion to the length of time the heater is on. That is, twice as much heat is given off in two minutes as in one minute.

In one experiment some crushed ice and a little water were placed in the apparatus (Fig. 1-6). With heater connected and a thermometer immersed in the ice and water, a record was made of the temperature of the water at various times. Figure 1-7 is a plot of the data obtained.

It does not appear reasonable to draw a single straight line through all the points. You can attempt to draw either a smooth curve through most of the points or three straight lines. The reason for the choice of the second strategy will become clear in the next few paragraphs. In the middle portion of the curve, the temperature increases steadily as

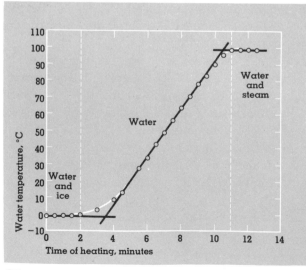

Fig. 1-7 *The relationship between the temperature of water and the time of heating.*

heat is added by the heater; but at either end, the temperature changes only slightly or not at all.

Visual observation of the ice–water mixture during the experiment showed that, for the left-hand horizontal portion of the graph, ice and water were present and that the length of this line depended only on how much ice was initially present. In the central rising portion only liquid water was present; in the right-hand horizontal portion both steam and liquid were present. The length of the top horizontal line depended only on how much water was converted to steam. The relation between the curve and the system is shown in Fig. 1-8. Many other materials behave in much the same way, although the observed temperatures may be much different from those in the experiment with water.

In the heating curve in Fig. 1-7, the temperature remains constant for about two minutes with both solid and liquid present. Other

Fig. 1-8 *When a mixture of ice and water is heated, the ice melts first, then the temperature of the liquid water increases. Finally the system consists of liquid water and steam.*

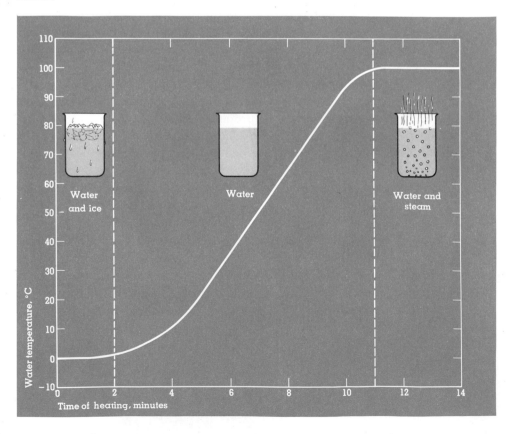

TABLE 1-4 CHARACTERISTIC PROPERTIES FOR SOME MATERIALS

Material	Density at 20°C,[a] g/ml	Melting Point,[a] °C	Boiling Point,[a] °C	Liquid Range,[a] °C
Carbon monoxide	0.0012	−207	−192	15
Oxygen	0.0013	−219	−183	35
Carbon dioxide[b]	0.0018	−56		
Water	1.00	0	100	100
Naphthalene	1.15	80	218	138
Magnesium	1.74	650	1120	469
Sodium chloride	2.16	808	1465	657
Iron	7.86	1535	2800	1265
Lead	11.34	328	1620	1292

[a] All data are for a pressure of 1 atmosphere except for carbon dioxide whose melting point was measured at 5 atmospheres.

[b] At 1 atmosphere pressure, solid carbon dioxide changes directly from solid to gas at −78.5°C without formation of liquid.

amounts of solid would change the time but not the temperature. This constant temperature is referred to as the **melting point** of a solid. At the upper portion of the curve, the temperature remains constant for at least 1½ minutes while both liquid and gas are present. This constant temperature is referred to as the **boiling point** of a liquid. Thus, although the temperature and the amount of energy possessed by an object are not, by themselves, properties suitable for identification, the constant temperatures corresponding to the melting and boiling points are highly useful and are considered to be characteristic properties. In addition, the temperature interval between the melting point and the boiling point of a material is not altered by changing the amount present and is a characteristic property called the **liquid range.** For water the graph indicates a liquid range of 100°C (Fig. 1-7).

Does the exploration of matter thus far give any aid in trying to see inside chemicals? Through the determination of mass and volume, densities are available. Temperature studies provide melting and boiling points. Such data for several materials discussed in this chapter are collected in Table 1-4. What conclusions about matter and about chemistry do such data suggest? Taken by themselves such data provide little insight. Now a more careful comparison of different materials is needed.

Ex. 1-6   When the data in Table 1-4 are compared, does there appear to be any relation between density and melting point?

Ex. 1-7   Mercury has a density of 13.5 g/ml and a melting point of −38.9°C. Does this information alter your answer to Exercise 1-6?

Ex. 1-8   The melting point of benzene is 5.5°C and the boiling point is 80.1°C at 1 atmosphere pressure. How would the heating curve for benzene compare with the heating curve for water shown in Fig. 1-7?

Ex. 1-9   From the heating curve in Fig. 1-7, calculate the slope for the interval from six to eight minutes; compare with the slope calculated for the interval from eight to ten minutes.

Ex. 1-10   Which of the materials listed in Table 1-4 are solids at 20°C? Which are liquids? Which are gases?

Ex. 1-11   Which of the materials listed in Table 1-4 will float on water at room temperature?

1-12   UNIFORMITY OF PROPERTIES

In large part, conclusions about the nature of materials are determined by the amount of detail that can be seen. Often the amount of visible detail is determined by how close the object of study is. Thus the brick wall in Fig. 1-9a and b appears uniform at a distance but quite nonuniform at closer range.

At a considerable distance the brick wall would appear to be composed of a single grayish-red material. Closer inspection would suggest two components, red bricks and white mortar, arranged in a repeating pattern. Still closer inspection reveals the individual bricks as made up of materials of different colors and different hardnesses.

(a)

(c)

Fig. 1-9 *Homogeneous and heterogeneous systems.* (a) *From a distance a brick wall appears to be homogeneous.* (b) *Close up, a brick wall appears to be heterogeneous.* (c) *Some rocks are homogeneous with respect to color.* (d) *Some rocks are heterogeneous with respect to color.*

(b)

(d)

At a distance, the two rocks in Fig. 1-9c and d would appear to be identical except for shape. A closer look reveals certain visible differences. One of the rocks is uniform in color and the other is nonuniform. To be more certain of this, each rock could be broken into small pieces which can be compared with one another. When all such pieces are the same, or uniform, in properties, the material is classified as **homogeneous with respect to subdivision.** A material in which some portions differ in properties from other portions is classified as **heterogeneous with respect to subdivision.** Heterogeneous materials are commonly called **mixtures.**

A material can be homogeneous in processes other than subdivision. It will often be useful in the identification of a material to specify that it is homogeneous with respect to such properties as color, density, and hardness. If a material consists of tiny particles, microscopic examination may be necessary to determine whether there is more than one kind of particle. Under the microscope, materials that appeared to be homogeneous to the naked eye may be heterogeneous. As with the brick wall, homogeneity may disappear when the eye gets closer.

1-13 SUBSTANCES AND SOLUTIONS

Some materials are not only homogeneous when one portion is compared with another by color, density, hardness, and subdivision, but also in another way. When a sample of steam (water vapor) is cooled and condensed to liquid, each drop of liquid water has the same set of characteristic properties as every other drop. If the water is cooled until it freezes into ice, each particle of ice has the same set of characteristic properties as every other particle. When each part of a sample of material behaves in a uniform way during all possible changes in physical state (that is, from gaseous state to liquid state or solid state to gaseous state, and so forth), the chemist calls the sample a pure or single **substance.** Some materials are known to behave homogeneously with respect to one type of change in physical state but not with respect to another. Such materials are not likely to be single substances.

Each piece of a particular pure substance must have the same characteristic properties as every other piece. Even by microscopic examination, this uniformity must be evident. In addition, when the substance is changed in state, all of any one portion and all portions must change in the same way. In the case of pure water, if half the liquid is allowed to evaporate and then condense (as water vapor does on a cold glass), the remaining half must have all of the same characteristic properties as the condensed liquid or, indeed, as the original liquid.

When you examine seawater from which all visible suspended material has been removed, it is obvious that it is clear throughout and that samples have the same density. If the seawater is divided into two samples of equal size and if heat is applied to each in a suitable container, the water will distill, leaving the same quantity of solid in each container. When a liquid distills, it changes to a gas and then condenses to a liquid. In other ways, the samples, whether small or large, can be shown to have the same properties. Therefore, it is said that seawater is homogeneous with respect to subdivision. If the seawater is boiled and the steam cooled to produce liquid again, every drop of liquid collected has the same properties as every other drop. When this collected liquid is compared with the original material, however, the two samples are not the same.

When water is boiling in the distilling flask, the space above the water contains steam (water vapor) at a temperature of 100°C. In the condenser the steam is cooled by the cooling water which flows through the condenser jacket. The condensed steam is collected in the receiving flask (Fig. 1-10). If a sample of the condensed steam is cooled, it freezes at 0°C as does pure water. The seawater has characteristics different from those of pure water. For example, it freezes at a lower temperature than does water, and the boiling point is higher that that of pure water. Seawater is an example of a material that is homogeneous with respect to subdivision but heterogeneous with respect to change in physical state. Such materials are called **solutions.** The diagram in Fig. 1-11 outlines the process for examining the seawater.

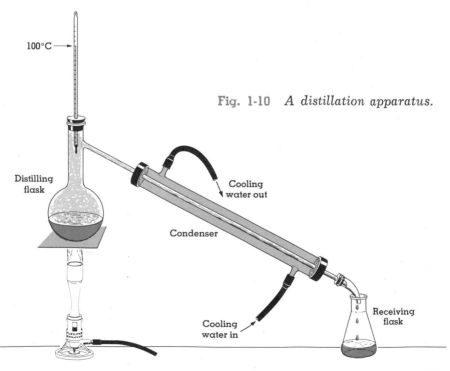

100°C →

Fig. 1-10 *A distillation apparatus.*

Distilling flask

Cooling water out

Condenser

Cooling water in

Receiving flask

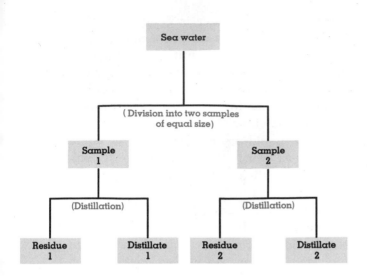

Fig. 1-11 *Flow sheet for the examination of seawater. Two samples of seawater of equal size were evaporated. Comparison of the samples with each other shows that they behave identically or uniformly. On the other hand, for any one sample, for example, sample 1, the nature and quantities of residue and distillate are different. The properties of the liquid distillate also differ from those of the liquid seawater.*

1-14 PROPERTIES OF COMPOUNDS AND ELEMENTS

Substances have been defined as materials that behave uniformly and hence are homogeneous with respect to all possible changes in physical state. Naphthalene, for example, widely used as moth balls, can be obtained readily as a substance quite free of impurities. Thus when solid lumps of naphthalene are heated, each portion melts at the same temperature.

If a small portion of naphthalene is heated to a sufficiently high temperature, it changes from solid to gas, bursts into flame, and burns. Several things can be observed about the changes that take place during burning. As the naphthalene burns, a great quantity of voluminous, black solid particles and some gas are produced. When the burning is complete, none of the original white solid remains. By cooling the gaseous product down to room temperature, a colorless liquid is obtained. At the same time, a third material can be isolated which is a gas at room temperature but different from air. In other words, at least three different materials are found: a black solid, a colorless liquid, and a colorless gas. This can be summarized in a brief form with plus signs to connect those substances present together in the system and an arrow to indicate the change from reactant on the left to product on the right.

Naphthalene + air → black solid + colorless liquid + colorless gas

Careful control of the burning process can result in the formation of less soot and, with a plentiful supply of air, even complete elimination of the black soot. Such a change has little or no effect on the amount of liquid formed, but it greatly increases the amount of gas formed. All the properties of the liquid correspond to those of water, whereas the properties of the gas correspond to those of a substance called carbon dioxide. This reaction can be expressed as follows.

Naphthalene + air → water + carbon dioxide

No evidence is available to suggest that water can be converted to carbon dioxide or vice versa. In short, for the burning of naphthalene, the products are never fewer than two different substances.

This process of burning naphthalene is an example of a chemical reaction. Further experiments show that the entire reaction can be produced using only naphthalene and oxygen as reactants. In this chemical reaction, an initially homogeneous material reacts with oxygen to give products which consist of at least two substances, each different from either reactant.

Naphthalene + oxygen → water + carbon dioxide

The final substances not only differ from each other in properties, but one substance cannot be converted into the other. Since neither water nor carbon dioxide can be produced from oxygen alone, naphthalene must contribute in some way to each. Naphthalene is then to be regarded as a substance which is homogeneous with respect to change in physical state but heterogeneous with respect to at least one chemical change.

There are reactions in which naphthalene produces but a single substance. It is possible to have naphthalene react with hydrogen so as to produce a single substance called decahydronaphthalene.

Naphthalene + hydrogen → decahydronaphthalene

Fig. 1-12 *Naphthalene sublimes* **(a)** *when it is heated above room temperature. When naphthalene is heated to higher temperatures in air, it burns* **(b)** *to produce black solid particles and some gas.*

(a)   (b)

Naphthalene provides other examples of chemical changes in which it reacts to give a single product, but nevertheless the fundamental lack of homogeneity of naphthalene has been adequately demonstrated by a reaction producing two products.

Most substances known to chemists behave in essentially the way described for naphthalene. They are not homogeneous with respect to one or more chemical changes. Of at least four million known substances, only 103 have been found so far which are homogeneous with respect to every change in state in which they participate and never undergo reaction to produce two or more substances that cannot be converted into one another. These 103 substances are called the **chemical elements.** (A list of the elements arranged alphabetically by name is given in Chapter 10.) When magnesium, for example, reacts with oxygen under specified conditions, magnesium reacts as an element to form a single pure substance, magnesium oxide. Similar behavior is characteristic for other reactions of magnesium, and magnesium is recognized as a chemical element.

A material like naphthalene which is a pure substance but which in a single reaction can contribute to two or more products is called a **compound.** If naphthalene is heated to above 1000°C in the absence of air, it undergoes a reaction in which a black solid and a gas are the sole products. Each of these materials proves to be physically and chemically homogeneous and is therefore an element. The black solid is called carbon, and the gas formed is called hydrogen. Naphthalene is therefore shown to be composed of the elements carbon and hydrogen.

1-15 ANALYSIS AND SYNTHESIS

Analysis is the process of identifying and determining the elements that make up a compound. Seldom can the analysis of a compound be carried out simply by raising the temperature. More commonly, the unknown compound is made to react to give products whose composition is already known. Thus any substance which reacts with oxygen to produce water and carbon dioxide can be analyzed in this way, once it is recognized that water is a compound of hydrogen and oxygen and that carbon dioxide is composed of carbon and oxygen. An additional step would be necessary to decide whether or not the compound contained oxygen as well as carbon and hydrogen.

Fig. 1-13 *The process of identifying and determining the elements that make up a compound is called analysis.*

| Naphthalene (white solid) | Heat → | Carbon (black solid) | + | Hydrogen (colorless gas) |

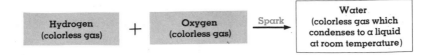

Fig. 1-14 *The process of preparing a compound from elements is called synthesis.*

In contrast to analysis by breaking a compound down into its elements, elements can enter into reactions which result in compounds. A reaction in which a compound is produced from other substances is called **synthesis.** Information obtained from the synthesis of compounds from elements provides knowledge about the composition, and so syntheses are useful in analysis.

1-16 **DEFINITION OF COMPOUND AND ELEMENT**

There are conditions in which an element produces more than one compound in a single reaction. An example is the burning of carbon either in air or in pure oxygen. With a limited supply of air and a high temperature, a gas is produced which can be drawn off and, if desired, caused to burn in a supply of additional air. This combustible gas is called carbon monoxide.

Carbon + oxygen → carbon monoxide

Carbon monoxide is toxic. Carbon can also be burned to give a gas neither combustible nor toxic, called carbon dioxide.

Carbon + oxygen → carbon dioxide

This is the substance used in soda water and other carbonated drinks. Quite commonly, when carbon burns, both gaseous substances are found together as simultaneous products of the chemical change.

Carbon + oxygen → carbon monoxide + carbon dioxide

Experimental study of the carbon monoxide and carbon dioxide mixtures shows one important difference from the case of naphthalene. If the mixture is heated to a temperature above 1000°C, the carbon dioxide changes to carbon monoxide and oxygen.

Carbon dioxide → carbon monoxide + oxygen

Alternatively, if more oxygen or air is added to the mixture at a temperature somewhat below 1000°C, all the carbon monoxide changes to carbon dioxide.

Carbon monoxide + oxygen → carbon dioxide

In the naphthalene–oxygen system, no amount of changing temperature or adding other reagents results in converting water to carbon

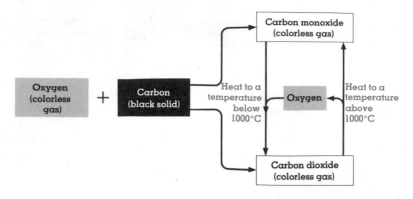

Fig. 1-15 *An element may produce more than one compound in a single reaction. In this case, the compounds that are produced are completely interconvertible.*

dioxide or carbon dioxide to water. On the contrary, the products obtained in the reaction of carbon and oxygen are completely interconvertible without adding or removing any of the carbon used. This implies that a compound like naphthalene reacts in a fundamentally different way from carbon. When any portion of naphthalene reacts with oxygen, both water and carbon dioxide are produced together.

On the basis of this discussion, it is necessary to modify the earlier simple statements concerning compounds and elements. A compound is a substance that enters into at least one chemical change in which two or more noninterconvertible products are formed. Some elements, on the other hand, enter into reactions in which interconvertible sub-

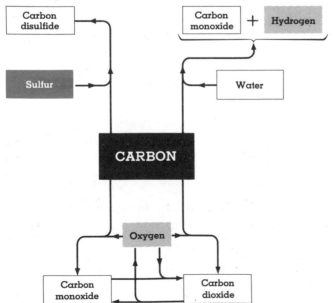

Fig. 1-16 *Carbon is an element. Carbon reacts with sulfur to give a single product. Carbon reacts with water to form two products, but only one of them contains carbon. Oxygen and carbon react to produce two products, but these are completely interconvertible.*

stances are formed. Carbon is an element and naphthalene is a compound.

Another reaction of carbon must be considered in the discussion before we can define an element precisely. Steam passed over hot carbon produces a material called water gas, a mixture of two gases which, according to all available evidence, cannot be converted into each other. When cooled to a sufficiently low temperature, the mixture separates into liquid carbon monoxide and gaseous hydrogen.

Carbon + steam → carbon monoxide + hydrogen

In this reaction of carbon with steam, two substances are produced— only one of which contains carbon. This is a common type of reaction between an element and a compound.

A **chemical element** may now be defined as a substance which always enters into chemical change to produce a single product, interconvertible products, or products of which only one is a compound of the substance. By this definition, carbon is a chemical element.

The conclusions reached about mixtures, solutions, compounds, and elements are summarized in Fig. 1-17.

Fig. 1-17 *Classification of matter.*

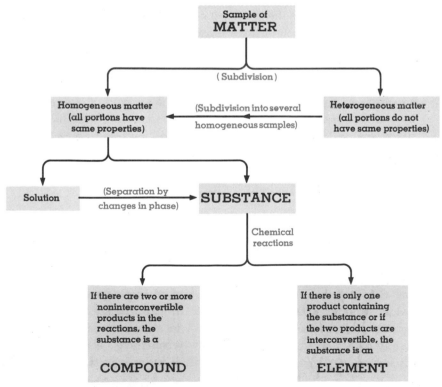

It may be asked at this point why so much care with definitions is required. It is important to understand that distinctions between different compounds and between compounds and elements are based on consistent, uniform laboratory experience. If they were not, the distinctions would be of no use to us whatever. The elements are, in fact, simply those substances that have acted in the way described above. The list of 103 elements was initially compiled through generations of experience in separating compounds into other substances that in the end fit one of the parts of the three-part definition of an element.

1-17 OF WHAT IS THE UNIVERSE MADE?

A most remarkable feature of the universe is revealed by a study of the chemical elements. Of all the millions upon millions of different objects found in the universe—people, rats, lice, plants, planets, meteorites, and so forth—none seems to be made of anything but this one set of 103 elements. The tremendous variety of things as they are can be reduced to combinations in various amounts of just 103 different substances.

If by a substance is meant a material that can be separated from other substances, examined in isolation, and put in a bottle for storage, then the separation of compounds into elements is the end of the separation process. All experiments which chemists have done so far point to the conclusion that the chemical elements cannot be separated into still other substances different from the 103 presently known elements. Notice that so far each of the elements is completely and utterly different from every other one of the 103.

It is worth puzzling a bit over one implication suggested by the above conclusion. The term universe comes from two Latin words which mean one part. A universe, then, has a kind of oneness about it. In some sense or other, a universe is all one or can be reduced to some single entity. If there are 103 elements, do we live in a universe?

This question about the universe will lurk in the background as this study proceeds. For some it is a question of crucial importance, but others may not be troubled by it.

1-18 DEFINITIONS

Several terms have been defined so far: mixture, solution, compound, element, chemical change. New terms are not introduced as an exercise merely to increase your vocabulary but primarily to simplify and clarify the discussion. Thus instead of having to describe a material as homogeneous with respect to the comparison of different portions but heterogeneous with respect to change in physical state, it is simply called a solution. Several new terms have been introduced by a discussion of their meaning rather than by a definition. You may find it helpful to work out short definitions in a form which you find easy to remember.

So far, considerable use has been made of a particular kind of definition. The definition of substance was stated thus: When a sample of material behaves in a uniform way during all changes in physical state, the chemist calls the sample a pure substance. Notice that in this defining statement there is a description of what should be done in the laboratory in order to decide whether or not a particular sample is a substance. To define a term by giving a set of directions for what should be done experimentally to test the statement is called an **operational definition.** Such statements are of great value in a scientific discussion because they carry with them the precision gained by including a set of directions. An operational definition tells you what to do to apply the term used to any particular system.

Operational definitions are not the only way of ensuring effective use of language. Some terms can be defined in other ways to advantage. Considerable use will be made of conceptual definitions. Properly formulated, conceptual definitions are invaluable for clear thinking. In Section 1-19 an example will be presented which is central to a chemist's thinking about chemistry.

1-19   ATOMS AND MOLECULES

Central to the whole fabric of modern chemical theory is the imaginative concept that matter is made up of atoms. We have already mentioned the slow development of this idea over a period of more than 2,000 years. For more than 100 years now, chemists have accepted and used this idea. However, as recently as 1902, a famous German chemist, Wilhelm Ostwald, warned his fellow chemists not to take the concept of atoms too seriously. Before Ostwald's warning is passed off as nonsense, it is well to consider that modifications in the present concept of the atom may yet be made. Too often, facts tend to be confused with concepts, and it was this confusion that Ostwald was warning against. Although the facts about chemicals as described by their physical properties and chemical changes cannot be altered, the atoms which chemists imagine to make up each substance are concepts designed to aid in understanding. This concept of atoms may be altered in order to provide a more effective basis for understanding the unalterable physical and chemical facts.

William Higgins, an Irishman, in the late eighteenth century and John Dalton, an Englishman, about twenty years later, put the idea of the atomic nature of matter into a form which proved useful to chemists. Dalton concluded that all matter is composed of **atoms** which cannot be further subdivided and that in any given element all the atoms are alike with respect to mass and in all other ways, whereas

JOHN DALTON *1766–1844*

An English chemist, physicist, and meteorologist. Dalton, a Quaker, began teaching school at age twelve and seven years later became principal of a school in Kendal. In 1793 he moved to Manchester to teach mathematics and natural philosophy at New College. Finding that his duties interfered with his scientific studies, he chose in 1799 to become a public and private teacher of mathematics and chemistry. Largely self-trained, he kept a meteorological diary for fifty-seven years. He described the nature of color blindness, of which he was a victim. Through his studies of the atmosphere and other gases, he developed the atomic hypothesis of Galileo, Newton, and Boyle into a form useful in chemistry and assigned different masses to the atoms of different elements. His earliest table of relative atomic masses dates back to 1803. Thereby he enunciated and developed the law of multiple proportions, explaining, for instance, the simple numerical relation between the compositions of the two oxides of carbon.

A powerful thinker but indifferent experimenter, he refused to accept J. L. Gay-Lussac's careful studies on the volumes of reacting gases, because he did not see how they could be fitted into his theory. Although he was honored at home and abroad, he maintained a simple and methodical way of living.

atoms of different elements differ in mass. In a chemical combination the atoms of different elements join together in various simple ratios, but in these combinations each atom maintains its mass.

A major question, then, is whether the idea of an atom can give insight into the observed behavior of substances defined as chemical elements and compounds. Thus the homogeneity characteristic of a chemical element might be accounted for if it is said that any sample of a particular element is made up of identical units repeated over and over a sufficient number of times to extend throughout the sample. Homogeneity could then be, in the case of elements, the reflection of the repetition of identical units, and these identical units are atoms.

In a compound, however, there must be at least two different atomic units. If they are arranged in some regular pattern, this might give the best explanation of the observations of uniformity in properties. Two

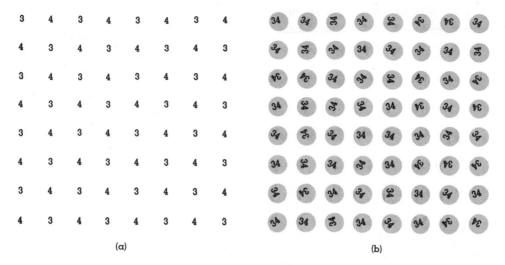

3	4	3	4	3	4	3	4
4	3	4	3	4	3	4	3
3	4	3	4	3	4	3	4
4	3	4	3	4	3	4	3
3	4	3	4	3	4	3	4
4	3	4	3	4	3	4	3
3	4	3	4	3	4	3	4
4	3	4	3	4	3	4	3

(a)   (b)

Fig. 1-18 *Two possible regular patterns for the arrangement of the structural units of compounds. In (a) each 4 is surrounded by 3's and each 3 by 4's. In (b) the individual unit is a combination of a 3 and a 4 and the units are arranged in a regular pattern.*

different types of digit patterns are shown in Fig. 1-18. In the first type the digits 3 and 4 are arranged in a regular repetition which provides a pattern. Within this pattern a particular 4 is surrounded by 3's and a particular 3 is surrounded by 4's. A different pattern is exhibited in the second case with individual units joined in pairs to form a more complex unit enclosed in a circle. This more complex unit is then repeated to form a pattern.

Patterns similar to both possibilities in Fig. 1-18 are found in compounds, but with atoms as units instead of digits. In the second type, atoms are joined together to form units called **molecules.** The molecular units may also be arranged in a pattern. Although Fig. 1-18 represents the simplest possibilities with a 1:1 ratio of two different units, other ratios of units are found. Matter always extends in three dimensions. You must therefore imagine that the patterns in Fig. 1-18 extend above and below the plane of the page so as to add a third dimension to the structure.

The idea that elements and compounds are made up of atoms arranged in particular ways suggests a definition of chemical change. In a **chemical change** the reactants and products contain the same atoms but differ in the pattern in which the atoms are arranged.

The definition of a chemical change in terms of atomic theory differs from the earlier operational definition of chemical change as alteration in observable properties. Such a **conceptual definition** tells you what to think about rather than what to do. Chemical change may thus be given either an operational or a conceptual definition. These two definitions suggest that changes in properties are associated with changes in arrangement of atoms.

It is important to note that the two kinds of definitions will sometimes refer to a given change in the same way and sometimes not. When liquid water changed to steam, the operational definition labeled this as a physical rather than chemical change. Comparison of the arrangement of the molecules in liquid water with that in gaseous water suggests that at least this physical change does not differ in principle from the changes ordinarily called chemical.

Although it is sometimes convenient to try to distinguish sharply between physical changes of state and chemical changes, we shall, for the most part, give little attention to the differences. To most scientists it is of little importance to distinguish between chemical and physical changes. To reduce the possibility of confusion between the term physical state and other aspects of the state of a system, the term **phase** is used to refer to the gas, liquid, or solid form of matter. Therefore, the description of the state of a system includes information concerning the phase or phases in which the matter is present in the system.

WILLIAM HIGGINS   1766–1825

An Irish chemist, educated at Oxford. Higgins preceded Dalton in the application of the atomic hypothesis to chemistry and was the first chemist to use chemical bond diagrams. As a supporter of the views of Antoine Lavoisier, he wrote in 1789 A Comparative View of the Phlogistic and Antiphlogistic Theories. *The latter theories he expounded by means of atomic conceptions; for instance, "Let A be a particle of water and I and D its constituent principles, I inflammable air [hydrogen] and D dephlogisticated air [oxygen], combined with the force of 6⅝."*

$$I \overset{6\frac{5}{8}}{\rule{2cm}{0.4pt}} D$$

Thus Higgins not only represented bonds as lines joining atoms but even attempted to assign quantitative values to the forces between them. He also suggested that the differences between the oxides of nitrogen lie in the number of oxygen atoms attached to one nitrogen atom.

Higgins was appointed professor of chemistry and mineralogy to the Royal Dublin Society in 1800. In 1814 he made a formal claim to have preceded John Dalton in the use of the atomic theory in chemistry. Dalton's contribution lay in his emphasis on the relative masses of atoms with all the quantitative conclusions derivable from such masses.

THE CENTRAL PROBLEM IN CHEMISTRY

The preliminary view of chemical substances and their reactions presents a puzzle. We have suggested that chemical compounds can be formed from the reaction of chemical elements in an appropriate series of steps and that, hence, the compounds are composed of elements. Yet the properties of the compounds are different from the properties of the elements. How can this be possible? Why does a compound not have a set of properties which is simply the sum of the properties of the constituent elements?

It seems most strange, for example, that opaque, silvery, soft metallic sodium reacts explosively with clear, greenish, gaseous chlorine to produce hard white or colorless salty crystals of sodium chloride (ordinary table salt). If the properties of sodium are added to the properties of chlorine when the compound sodium chloride is formed, it is a most remarkable kind of addition.

The central problem in chemistry is to account for or explain such mysterious facts as the changes which occur when sodium reacts with chlorine. The initial materials undergo a change to form a final product whose components are, in some way, the initial materials but whose properties appear to be unrelated to those of the initial materials. The remainder of this course will be concerned with some of the experiments and ideas that provide explanations of how each element contributes to the properties of the compounds in which it is found.

But what does it mean to explain? When a chemist seeks to explain a property of a substance, he seeks to connect that property with other properties of the same substance and of other substances. As an example, a chemist wonders why a hard diamond can be converted to soft graphite or why table salt dissolves in water and diamonds do not. Or he wonders if there is any connection between the fact that sodium reacts directly with either chlorine or oxygen, whereas chlorine and oxygen do not react with each other directly.

The explanation of facts found by experiments is thus the demonstration of interconnections among the facts. It is a curious feature of human experience that when we are confronted with two or more facts, we cannot ordinarily see any connection between them by simply looking at them. However closely we may observe, they remain just isolated facts. To achieve interconnections among seemingly isolated facts, the chemist makes use of imaginative ideas, called theories. These ideas are developed by human beings and in a sense can be called inventions. For many facts chemists have found interconnections and, hence, explanations. There are still other facts whose connections remain to be established. Chemistry is somewhat like a fine piece of cloth in the process of being woven. Some threads are interconnected and form a pattern, while other threads run off into loose ends.

Ex. 1-12 Rutherford used the idea that metal foils were composed of closely packed atoms. Is this analogous to saying that a building is made of bricks?

Ex. 1-13 Some of the great ideas in science were developed by J. Willard Gibbs. Most of his work was concerned with interpreting experimental data or with predicting the results of experiments that might be done. In his work he used mathematical equations rather than laboratory equipment. On the basis of this information, would you consider that J. Willard Gibbs was a scientist?

Ex. 1-14 Match terms with statements.

Terms	*Statements*
1. Controlled experiment	*a.* A collection of materials isolated for scientific study
2. Change in a system	*b.* A precise and complete record of scientific experimentation
3. State of a system	*c.* A casual collection of data on numerous topics
4. System of substances	*d.* Description of a system at a particular instant
5. Scientific report	*e.* A scientific experiment designed to permit the study of the effect of one variable
	f. Final state of a system compared to the initial state of a system

Ex. 1-15 In what way does a chemical system resemble a black box?

Ex. 1-16 Are the following observations qualitative or quantitative?

a. A match burns in pure oxygen, but not in carbon dioxide.

b. Twelve grams of carbon reacts with oxygen to form 44 g of carbon dioxide.

c. The boiling point of water is 100°C at 1 atmosphere pressure.

Ex. 1-17 Because an object can have any mass and any volume, mass and volume are not considered to be characteristic properties. How can the mass and volume of an object be combined to become a characteristic property?

Ex. 1-18 The ratio of volume to mass is defined as specific volume. How is specific volume related to density? Are both density and specific volume characteristic properties? Calculate the specific volume of lead shot.

Ex. 1-19 Defend or refute the following statements.

a. The product of mass times volume is a characteristic property.

b. The texture of a substance is a characteristic property.

c. Characteristic properties are independent of environment.

d. Temperature is a characteristic property.

Ex. 1-20 Does methane classify as a compound or a chemical element on the basis of these observations? Melting point, −182.5°C. Boiling point, −161.5°C. Burns in oxygen to produce water and carbon dioxide.

Ex. 1-21 Classify the following processes as either analysis or synthesis.

a. If 2.17 g of a red powder is heated strongly, 2.01 g of mercury metal and 0.16 g of oxygen gas are produced.

b. If 2.43 g of magnesium metal is ignited in pure oxygen gas, it reacts rapidly to produce 4.03 g of magnesium oxide.

Ex. 1-22 A red substance burns in pure oxygen to produce two interconvertible compounds. Is the red substance an element? Explain.

Ex. 1-23 As completely as is justified, classify the following materials as mixture, substance, solution, compound, or element.

a. Material X in its initial state is homogeneous with respect to subdivision. Material X is placed in a test tube and heated. The system, in its final state after heating, is composed of a colorless gas and a silver-colored metal. The gas and the metal are elements.

b. Material Y is homogeneous with respect to subdivision. Y melts and sublimes at the same time to form a dark liquid and a violet gas. Both the dark liquid and the violet gas can be condensed to material Y. Reaction of Y with hydrogen produces only one product, but reaction of Y with copper can produce two interconvertible products.

c. Material Q, a gray powder, is heterogeneous with respect to subdivision. Material Q is easily separated by a magnet into a black powder and a yellow powder. When Q is heated, it changes to a dark material R which is not attracted by a magnet. R is a solid, is homogeneous with respect to subdivision, and melts completely to form a liquid which is homogeneous with respect to subdivision.

d. Material A is a clear liquid with a boiling point of 82°C. Heating of A produces a colorless gas and leaves a white solid (B) as a residue. The colorless gas can be condensed to form a third material, C (a clear liquid). B melts at 135°C, and C boils at 80°C.

Ex. 1-24 Which of the following are operational definitions? conceptual definitions?

a. System—a collection of materials isolated for scientific study

b. Mixture—heterogeneous with respect to subdivision

c. Element—homogeneous with respect to subdivision, with respect to change in physical state, and with respect to chemical change

d. Molecule—a unit containing two or more atoms

e. Compound—a substance composed of at least two kinds of atoms combined in a definite ratio by mass

f. Temperature—position of the top of a mercury column in a thermometer

g. Sodium chloride—substance produced by the reaction of sodium and chlorine

MIXTURES AND CHEMICAL CHANGE

GASOLINE CAN BE CHANGED into water and carbon dioxide when air is present. This change is an example of burning or combustion. Coal, air, and water can be converted to gasoline and many other products. Such changes can have great practical importance. In some cases, the changes provide ways to produce materials that have properties of great utility. In other cases, the changes can be used to produce further changes (for example, the burning of gasoline to lift an automobile from the bottom to the top of a hill). Chemists study changes in materials to shed light on the nature of matter.

Systems may consist of one substance or many substances isolated for study. In either case each substance has a set of properties which contribute to the state of the system. In Chapter 1 a few of these properties have been discussed. Every substance can be identified by a unique set of properties. Moreover, during a chemical change the reactants, which have one set of properties, are replaced by the products, which have another set of properties. Chemists are most interested in the circumstances that determine when and how systems can undergo change in state.

Is there any way in which the state of a system determines whether a particular change can or cannot occur?

2-1 SYSTEMS FOR THE STUDY OF CHANGE

Before detailed study of changes in the states of systems is undertaken, it would be profitable to consider some specific examples of changes. In Chapter 1 a variety of systems was examined. Operational procedures were developed with which a system can be classified as to whether it is a mixture, a solution, a compound, or an element. In this chapter you will study examples of the preparation of mixtures, solutions, and compounds to see how the properties of the substances finally present in a system differ from those of substances initially selected for the experiments.

Several different systems will be examined. Each of the substances in a system is referred to as a **component.** Both reactants and the products in the system are referred to as components.

2-2 SODIUM BROMIDE AND SUCROSE

In the first system to be studied, the two components are sodium bromide and sucrose. According to the operational definitions developed in Chapter 1, each of these components is both a substance and a compound. The nature of changes in states of the systems will be explored primarily by measurements of masses and volumes.

Sodium bromide is a white solid similar in many ways to table salt. It is used as a medicine instead of as a food. Sucrose is familiar as table sugar. The procedure described in Section 1-10 was followed to find the masses and volumes of several portions of both the sodium bromide and the sucrose. A weighed sample of each separate solid substance was immersed in a known volume of liquid. A liquid that did not alter the solid was chosen for immersion. From the volume of the solid and liquid together and the volume of the liquid alone, the volume of the solid was found by subtraction.

Experimental data for the masses and volumes of samples of the two substances are presented in graphical form in Fig. 2-2. From these data a density can be calculated for each substance (Section 1-9).

Fig. 2-1 *Crystals of* (a) *sucrose,* (b) *sodium bromide,* *and* (c) *a mixture of sucrose and sodium bromide.*

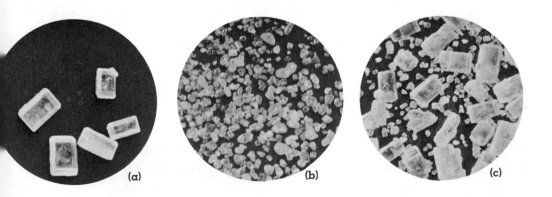

(a)   (b)   (c)

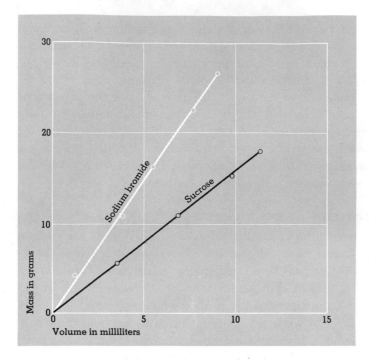

Fig. 2-2 *The relationship between mass and volume for sodium bromide and sucrose at 25°C.*

Ex. 2-1   From Fig. 2-2, estimate the volume that 10 g of sodium bromide will occupy, that 10 g of sucrose will occupy, that 18 g of sodium bromide will occupy, and that 18 g of sucrose will occupy.

Ex. 2-2   What would be the mass of 6 ml of solid sodium bromide? of 6 ml of solid sucrose?

Ex. 2-3   What is the density of sodium bromide (from the slope of the curve in Fig. 2-2)? of sucrose?

A complete description of a system containing both sodium bromide and sucrose must include a statement of the quantity of each substance present. A statement that indicates how much of each substance is present is called the **composition** of the system.

The densities of the initial components can be compared with the densities of several mixtures of the two substances. The comparison will indicate whether systems composed of the two substances initially separate differ from the same systems when the two substances are finally mixed together. A consideration of the results of this comparison will be helpful in understanding the nature of any changes that may occur.

For the first survey of the possibility of change, several mixtures of varying composition were prepared. A simple way to do this is to mix known masses of the two substances to prepare a series of mixtures

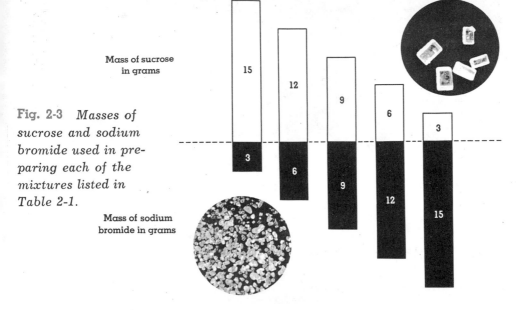

Mass of sucrose
in grams

Fig. 2-3 *Masses of
sucrose and sodium
bromide used in pre-
paring each of the
mixtures listed in
Table 2-1.*

Mass of sodium
bromide in grams

ranging from pure sodium bromide through a 1:1 mixture to pure sucrose. The composition is described by the ratio of masses used. The ratios chosen are listed in the third column of Table 2-1.

The fifth column of Table 2-1 shows the volume measurements for each system in its final state. The density of each system in the final state was calculated by dividing the mass by the volume. Density values are listed in the sixth column of Table 2-1.

Inspection of the data in Table 2-1 indicates that each system has a mass whose final value is experimentally the same as the sum of the

TABLE 2-1 DENSITIES OF MIXTURES OF SODIUM BROMIDE AND SUCROSE[a]

Mass of Sucrose, g	Mass of Sodium Bromide, g	Mass Ratio[b]	Mass of Mixture, g	Volume of Mixture, ml	Density of Mixture, g/ml
15.00	3.00	5:1	18.00	10.58	1.70
12.00	6.00	2:1	18.00	9.60	1.88
9.00	9.00	1:1	18.01	8.68	2.07
6.00	12.00	$\frac{1}{2}$:1	18.00	7.78	2.31
3.00	15.00	$\frac{1}{5}$:1	17.99	6.88	2.61

[a] The tabulated data were obtained in the laboratory. Masses were measured with a balance sensitive to 1 centigram (cg). A 25-ml graduated cylinder was used to measure volumes to the nearest 0.02 ml.
[b] The mass ratio was calculated by dividing the mass of sucrose by the mass of sodium bromide and is listed to one significant figure.

43

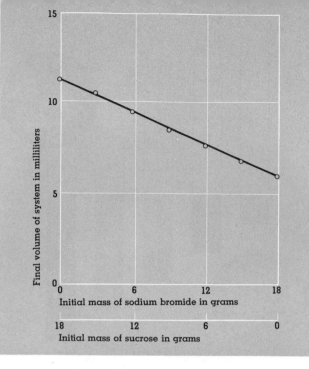

Fig. 2-4 *The relationship between volume and composition of sucrose–sodium bromide systems.*

masses of the separate initial components. How is the final volume of each system related to the volumes of the separate materials initially taken? One way to see the relation is to plot values for the final volume and the corresponding mass of either sucrose or sodium bromide. This was done in Fig. 2-4 using the data in Table 2-1. A straight line comes close to connecting the successive points. The mass of sodium bromide is plotted on the horizontal axis. For each mass of sodium bromide there is also, according to Table 2-1, a corresponding mass of sucrose. The mass of sucrose is indicated by a second scale below the first. The volumes of 18.0 g of sucrose and of 18.0 g of sodium bromide were obtained from Fig. 2-2. What does Fig. 2-2 signify?

In thinking about the experiment, consider the data in Fig. 2-2 which gives values for the volumes of known masses of sodium bromide and sucrose initially present. From the graph, the volume of 9.0 g of sucrose is 5.7 ml and the volume of 9.0 of sodium bromide is 3.0 ml. Added together these give a total initial volume of 8.7 ml for a system containing 9.0 g of sucrose and 9.0 g of sodium bromide. In Table 2-1, the final volume of the same system is 8.68 ml. Since these two volumes (8.7 ml and 8.68 ml) are the same within the error of the experiment, the difference between final and initial volumes is zero. (Errors of measurement are discussed in the Appendix of *Investigating Chemical Systems.*)

In terms of the description for a change in property (Section 1-3),

Final Value $\begin{pmatrix} \text{compared} \\ \text{to} \end{pmatrix}$ Initial Value $\begin{pmatrix} \text{describes} \\ \text{the} \end{pmatrix}$ Change in the
for a Property   for a Property   Property

The property being studied this time (volume) can be determined quantitatively, and the change can be expressed arithmetically.

Final volume — initial volume = change in volume
8.7 ml — 8.7 = 0.0 ml

No change in volume is found for mixtures of every other possible composition. The mixing of sodium bromide and sucrose therefore results in no change in volume.

Further examination of the system indicates that no other change occurs upon mixing the two substances. Figure 2-1 shows enlarged views of the grains of sodium bromide in (b), of sucrose in (a), and of a 1:1 mass ratio mixture in (c). Visual examination shows that the separate particles of sodium bromide and sucrose exist in the system in its final state without having had any observable effect upon each other.

The line drawn in Fig. 2-4 implies that, regardless of what mass ratio of sucrose to sodium bromide might be taken, the volume of any system containing a total mass of 18.0 g would lie on the line. In other words, Fig. 2-4 describes the behavior of all systems having a total mass of 18.0 g but varying mass ratios of the two components, sodium bromide and sucrose.

When a chemist measures some property common to a series of systems prepared from the same components in all possible mass ratios, the procedure is called the *method of continuous variation*. Usually this leads to a graph of some observed property of the systems against composition such as that in Fig. 2-4. A single straight line in the graph of data obtained by continuous variation methods means that, for the particular property being measured, the same value is obtained either by adding the measured values for the separate components or by measuring the final value for the entire system. Since the initial state ordinarily includes statements of the magnitudes of the properties of the separate components, the final state must also include statements of the magnitudes of the corresponding property of the system in its final state. When the magnitudes of the measured property are the same for both the initial and final states, the graph is a straight line. When a straight-line graph is obtained, the property is said to be *additive*. In the case of the sodium bromide–sucrose systems, the volume is additive.

Ex. 2-4   How do the initial and final masses compare for the systems in Table 2-1?

Ex. 2-5   From the graph in Fig. 2-4, estimate the volume that 18.0 g of a 3:1 sucrose–sodium bromide mixture would occupy.

RANDOM MIXTURES OF SOLIDS

To what extent does the presence of a grain of sodium bromide in the 1:1 mixture in Fig. 2-1c determine whether the grain next to it will be sodium bromide or sucrose? Or to ask the question in another way: Does the knowledge of the position of one type of particle give information that will help predict where any other one will be? If the two materials are thoroughly mixed and then any small portion is examined, a grain of sodium bromide may be next to another grain of sodium bromide or to a grain of sucrose. This can be verified by examining a large number of samples under a microscope.

When there is no repeating pattern of arrangement of particles in a system, the distribution of particles is said to be **random.** In other words, it is a matter of chance whether two grains next to each other are the same or different. If all the particles were crushed to make them still smaller, the material would appear to be more uniform but the particles would still retain this random or haphazard pattern of arrangement.

It is possible to prepare mixtures of sodium bromide and sucrose that have all compositions from nearly pure sucrose to nearly pure sodium bromide. All these mixtures are collections of particles having a random arrangement.

These systems have five general characteristics.

1. They are heterogeneous with respect to visual comparison of different portions.

2. The final total mass is equal to the sum of the initial masses of the separate components.

3. The final total volume is equal to the sum of the initial volumes of the separate components.

4. The components can be present in any ratio.

5. The particles of the separate components are arranged at random with respect to each other in the final state of the system.

Any system with these five characteristics will be called a **mixture.**

Ex. 2-6 Estimate the density of a mixture containing sucrose and sodium bromide in the mass ratio of 3:1.

Ex. 2-7 One of the mixtures of sucrose and sodium bromide was immersed in a cylinder containing ethylene dibromide. The density of ethylene dibromide is 2.2 g/ml, and neither sodium bromide nor sucrose will dissolve in the

Fig. 2-5 *A mixture of sucrose, sodium bromide, and ethylene dibromide.*

liquid. When the cylinder and its contents were examined, two white solids were seen. Figure 2-5 shows that one solid floated at the surface of the liquid and that the other rested on the bottom. Explain.

2-4 MIXTURES OF LIQUIDS

When gasoline is mixed with water, the total volume of the mixture is always the same as the sum of the volumes of the separate liquids. In this respect the mixture of gasoline and water behaves as does the mixture of sodium bromide and sucrose. The two liquids do show one difference from the two solids in that the liquids tend to separate rather rapidly from each other and do not remain randomly mixed. The liquid of lower density (gasoline) is found on top, and the liquid of higher density (water) is found on the bottom of their common container. Two liquids that separate into two layers are said to be immiscible, and two liquids that form a homogeneous final state when they are mixed are said to be miscible. Methanol and ethanol, for example, are miscible.

The mixing of methanol (methyl alcohol) and ethanol (ethyl alcohol) produces a system whose total volume is always the same as the sum of the volumes of the separate liquids. Unlike the system of gasoline and water, which is heterogeneous, the methanol–ethanol system is homogeneous. Methanol and ethanol form a solution according to the operational definition of a solution developed in Section 1-13. Measurements made on the system before and after mixing indicate that, within an error of 0.1 percent, there is no difference in volume between the initial and final states.

Comparisons of volume can be made rather simply for ethanol–water systems. Measured amounts of each liquid were delivered from a buret so that the initial total volume was 44.00 ml. The combined liquids were placed in another buret to determine the final volume of the mixed system. The precision of each volume measurement was about 0.02 ml. The sum of the volumes of the unmixed liquids was taken as the volume of the system in its initial state. (Precision of measurement is discussed in the Appendix of *Investigating Chemical Systems*.) The measured volume of the combined liquids was taken as the volume of the system in its final state. The difference between these two volumes is then the observed volume change.

In Fig. 2-6 data are presented for a series of ethanol–water systems with the volume change plotted against the amount of ethanol in the system. The initial total volume of each successive system was kept constant by decreasing the volume of water as the volume of ethanol was increased. This investigation of ethanol and water is another example of the continuous variation method.

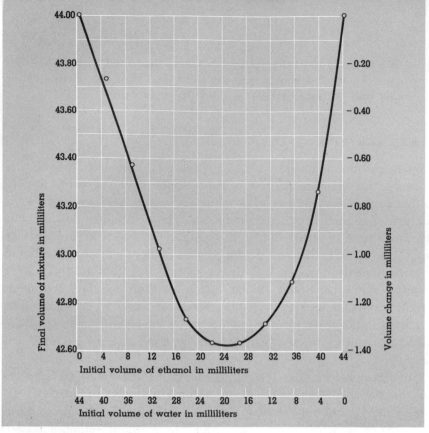

Fig. 2-6 *Relationship between volume and composition of ethanol–water systems.*

No matter what relative amounts of water and ethanol are in the initial state, the system in its final state is homogeneous and fits the operational definition of a solution. If you examine the volume of the system in relation to the sum of the volumes of the separate components, you will find a behavior different from that observed for the gasoline–water and methanol–ethanol systems.

For the systems of sodium bromide and sucrose discussed in Section 2-2, the final volume and initial volume were the same for every mass ratio used. Essentially the same result is obtained for gasoline–water mixtures and methanol–ethanol systems. These are three examples of a quite general behavior. When the component parts of a system do not interact, properties such as volume are additive. Each component contributes to the properties of the system in its final state as if the other components were absent.

The components of the ethanol–water system described in Fig. 2-6 show a different behavior. The final volume differs from the sum of the volumes of the components. Thus a mixture of 22.00 ml of ethanol and 22.00 ml of water has a final volume of 42.63 ml or 1.37 ml less than the sum of the initial volumes, 44.00 ml. In other words, each component appears to contribute to the properties of the system in its final state in a way that is influenced by the other component.

The properties of a system of substances assembled but unmixed are taken as the properties of the system in its initial state. The properties of the system in its final state can have one of two possible relations to the properties of the system in its initial state.

1. The value for some initial property is the same as the value for that same property of the system in its final state. In this case, the property is said to be additive.

2. The value for some initial property differs from the value for that same property of the system in its final state. In this case, the property is said to be nonadditive.

In a system for which a property is nonadditive, the indicated change is said to be caused by an *interaction* of the components. Thus, for the sodium bromide–sucrose system and for the methanol–ethanol system, there was no interaction of the components in terms of volume measurements. On the other hand, for the ethanol–water system, volume measurements indicated an interaction of ethanol and water.

The method of continuous variation is often a convenient way to study a set of systems which differ in relative amounts of the same components for detecting the presence or absence of interaction. Whenever a property varies in a straight-line relationship for a set of compositions arranged according to the continuous variation method, one concludes that so far as the measured property is concerned there is no interaction. If, on the other hand, the data for the set of systems are plotted in a graph (Fig. 2-6) and are not fitted by a straight line, interaction is implied.

Ex. 2-8 What is the final volume of a mixture containing 60 ml of ethanol and 40 ml of water?

Ex. 2-9 What volume ratio of the ethanol–water system undergoes the greatest volume contraction?

2-5 POTASSIUM CHLORIDE AND WATER

When certain solids are added to a liquid, some of the solid disappears into the liquid to form a homogeneous product. This process is called **dissolving.** A homogeneous material which separates into two materials during a change in phase is called a solution. A solution may exist as a solid, a liquid, or a gas. For the most part, this textbook will discuss solutions that are liquid.

Potassium chloride, a substance very similar to sodium chloride, will form solutions in water. A series of mixtures containing various amounts of water and potassium chloride can be prepared and then allowed to stand until no further solid dissolves. Hours or even days may be required for some of these systems to reach a state in which no more potassium chloride dissolves. Experience has shown that grinding the solid before adding the liquid, stirring the mixture, or heating systems of this type will often shorten the time required to complete the dissolving process.

Figure 2-7 shows the volumes occupied by several different masses of potassium chloride. In Fig. 2-7a, the test tubes contain various masses of potassium chloride arranged in sequence to show how the volume of potassium chloride samples increases with increasing mass. Of course, the apparent volume of the powdered solid includes not only the solid but also the air between the particles. In Fig. 2-7b, 15.00 ml of toluene has been added to each tube, in order to displace the air. The amount of solid is not affected by the addition of toluene. The upper liquid level now represents the total volume of solid and liquid together. Since the first tube on the left contains only toluene and no solid, it can be used for comparison with the others. The difference between the volume in the second tube and the volume in the first tube must then represent the volume of the solid in the second tube.

When the tubes containing only solid are compared with those containing solid and toluene together, there is no visible difference in the amount of solid. If all the liquid is poured out of the tubes so as to separate solid and liquid, the solid that remains is, when dried, indistinguishable in mass and other properties from the original potassium chloride sample used. This confirms the literature reports that potassium chloride is not affected by toluene.

The set of tubes in Fig. 2-8b is the same as the set of tubes in Fig. 2-7a except that 15.00 ml of water has been added to each potassium chloride sample. In the set of tubes containing water and potassium chloride, the solid has completely dissolved in three of the tubes (2, 3, and 4). In their final states these systems are homogeneous with respect

Fig. 2-7 *Mass and volume of solid potassium chloride. Reading from left to right the successive tubes in both* **(a)** *and* **(b)** *contain 0.0, 1.5, 3.0, 4.5, 6.0, 7.5, 9.0, 10.5, and 12.0 g of potassium chloride.*

(a)   (b)

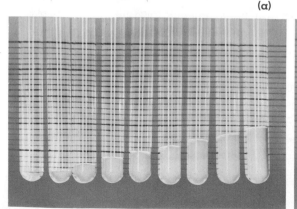
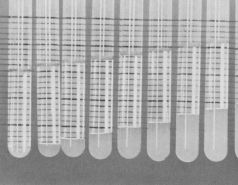

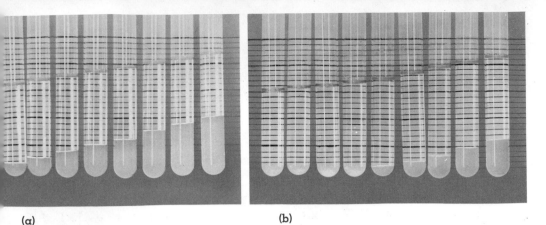

(a)   (b)

Fig. 2-8   *Potassium chloride in* (a) *toluene and in* (b) *water at*
25°C. Each tube in (a) *contains 15 ml of toluene, and the tubes*
from left to right contain 0.0, 1.5, 3.0, 4.5, 6.0, 7.5, 9.0, 10.5,
and 12.0 g of potassium chloride (see Fig. 2-7). The set of nine
tubes in (b) *is the same as the set of tubes in* (a), *except that*
each tube contains 15 ml of water instead of 15 ml of toluene.

to light transmission. Even in the other five tubes (5, 6, 7, 8, and 9) of
Fig. 2-8b, a substantial portion of the initial solid has dissolved. The
upper liquid level indicates that the systems containing potassium
chloride and water have volumes greater than that of the water alone,
that is, greater than 15 ml. Because toluene produces no change in the
amount of potassium chloride, each of the tubes in Fig. 2-8a represents
a system in its initial state for visual comparison with the corresponding tube in Fig. 2-8b which contains potassium chloride and water. The
interval between successive horizontal lines in the background represents about 1 ml in volume within the tubes.

The scale of black background lines permits the comparison of the
volume in various tubes. Thus, tube 9 containing potassium chloride
and toluene in Fig. 2-8a can be compared with the corresponding tube
containing water and potassium chloride in Fig. 2-8b. The two volumes
differ by about 0.8 of the distance between successive lines on the
scale behind the tubes, or by about 0.8 ml.

Each system of potassium chloride and toluene in Fig. 2-8a represents a situation in which mixing without dissolving has occurred to
give results completely analogous to the systems containing sodium
bromide and sucrose. Since the toluene appears to be without effect on
the solid, it will be assumed that the volumes are additive. Each of the
tubes pictured in Fig. 2-8b represents a system containing potassium
chloride and water in its final state. Each system in its initial state
is represented by the tubes in Fig. 2-8a. Although Fig. 2-8a shows systems of potassium chloride and toluene, the tubes can be assumed also

TABLE 2-2 VOLUMES AND MASSES OF POTASSIUM CHLORIDE–WATER SYSTEMS[a]

| System | Initial State | Final State | | | |
	Mass of Potassium Chloride, g	Mass of System, g	Total Volume, ml	Volume of Solution, ml	Mass of Solution, g
1	6.01	106.0	101.7	101.7	106.0
2	12.00	112.1	103.5	103.5	112.1
3	18.01	117.9	106.8	106.8	117.9
4	23.98	124.0	109.3	109.3	124.0
5	29.98	130.0	111.8	111.8	128.8
6	35.97	135.9	114.8	111.5	129.9
7	42.00	142.1	117.6	111.3	130.9
8	48.0	148.0	120.7	111.5	130.9
9	54.0	154.0	123.9	111.8	131.6

[a] Initially each system contains 100.0 g of water at 25°C.

to represent the situation at the instant water was mixed with the solid and before any dissolving had occurred. Therefore, in systems containing water and potassium chloride, not only does the amount of solid change as a result of the dissolving process, but also the total volume of the system changes when the final and initial states are compared.

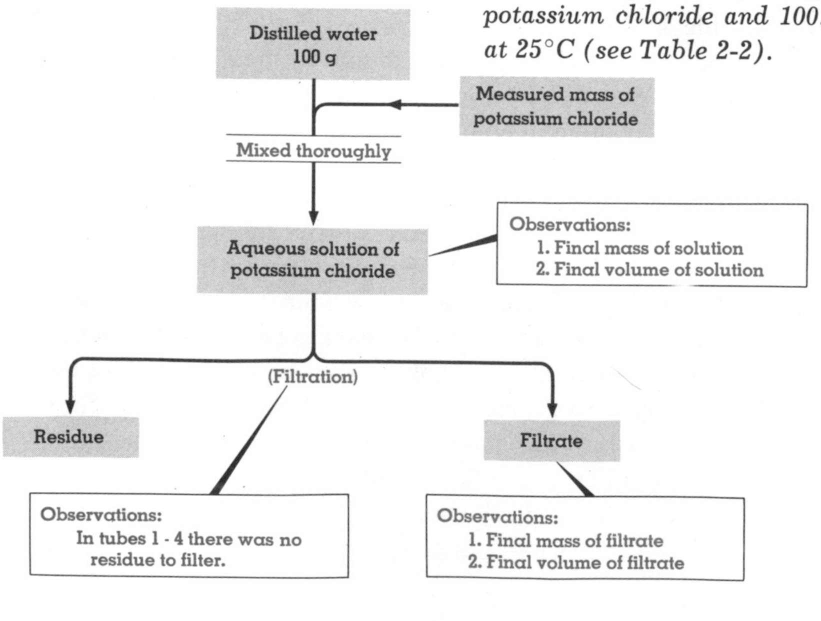

Fig. 2-9 *Flow sheet for determination of volumes of systems of different masses of potassium chloride and 100.0 ml of water at 25°C (see Table 2-2).*

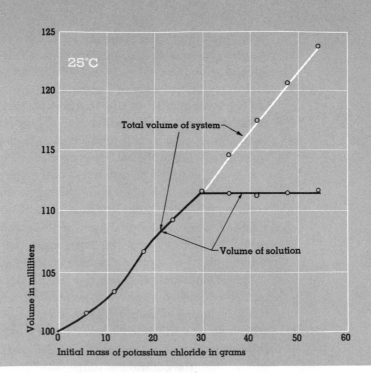

Fig. 2-10 *Volumes of systems of potassium chloride and 100 ml (100 g) of water at 25°C.*

More precise data on the changes in volume which seem to accompany the dissolving of potassium chloride in water require measurements more precise than those presented so far. Additional experiments were therefore carried out using systems of larger volume. Various masses of potassium chloride were mixed with 100.0 g of water kept at 25°C until dissolving was complete. The final total mass and final total volume were measured. Volumes were measured in a graduated cylinder that could be read with a precision of 0.1 ml. In addition, for the final states of those systems which contained some solid, the liquid and solid were separated as completely as possible by filtration. This permitted the measurement of the mass and volume of each phase present in the system in its final state. The data obtained are listed in Table 2-2.

The relationships implied by the data in Table 2-2 are more evident when they are plotted in Fig. 2-10. In Fig. 2-10 the black lines apply only to the solution that has been separated from any visible solid. The white line shows the final volume of systems containing both solid and solution simultaneously.

Inspection of the graph shows that, as more and more potassium chloride is added to water, there is first a steady increase in the volume of the solution. However, after about 30 g of potassium chloride has been added to 100.0 g of water, the volume of the solution remains approximately constant as more potassium chloride is added. According to the sixth column of data in Table 2-2, the mass of the solution is approximately the same for all those systems in which the solution volume remains the same. The data allow the conclusion that up to 30 g of potassium chloride dissolves in 100 g of water at 25°C but that no potassium chloride in excess of 30 g dissolves.

One consequence of the observation just stated is that all the solutions represented by the horizontal line in Fig. 2-10 should have the same composition. This can be tested experimentally by analyzing samples of each of the solutions used. For systems of potassium chloride and water, analysis of a sample can be simply performed by evaporating the water. The potassium chloride remains as a nonvolatile solid residue. The dry solid residue of potassium chloride can then be weighed. The results of these analyses show that each solution represented by points along the horizontal line of the graph does contain about 30 g of potassium chloride and 100 g of water.

The composition of a solution is usually referred to as the **concentration** of the solution. Concentrations are sometimes expressed in terms of grams of **solute** (the material dissolved) per gram of **solvent** (the material in which dissolving occurs). In systems of potassium chloride and water there are two different types of observed effects. In one type, the addition of more potassium chloride produces a change in concentration of the solution. In the other type, the addition of more potassium chloride produces no change in concentration of the solution. The additional potassium chloride remains undissolved. The solution in which the second type of effect is observed is called a **saturated solution,** and the solution of the first type is called an **unsaturated solution.**

Fig. 2-11 *Potassium chloride and water at 25°C and at 50°C. The set of nine tubes in* (**a**) *is the same as the set in Fig. 2-8b with potassium chloride and water at 25°C. The set of tubes in* (**b**) *contains systems having the same composition as those in the left-hand set but at a temperature of 50°C. Tube 5 in the 25°C set contains visible solid, whereas tube 5 in the 50°C set does not contain visible solid.*

(a)   (b)

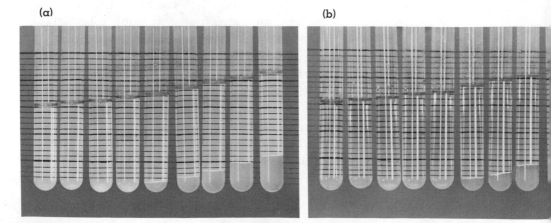

When a saturated solution of potassium chloride and water is prepared at 25°C, the concentration can be expressed as 30.0 g of potassium chloride solute per 100.0 g of water solvent. Alternatively, since volumes are measured more quickly, the concentration may be conveniently expressed in terms of a ratio of mass to volume. For a mass/volume ratio the data give

$$\frac{30.0 \text{ g of potassium chloride}}{111.8 \text{ ml of solution}}$$

or a numerically equivalent form is

$$\frac{30.0 \text{ g of potassium chloride}}{111.8 \text{ ml of solution}} = \frac{26.8 \text{ g of potassium chloride}}{100.0 \text{ ml of solution}}$$

Figure 2-11 shows the effect of changing the temperature of the potassium chloride–water systems shown in Fig. 2-8b from 25°C to 50°C. Figure 2-12 is a graph of the masses and volumes of the systems described in Table 2-2 and Fig. 2-10, but at a temperature of 50°C instead of at 25°C. The mass of water used was the same at 50°C as at 25°C, but the volume at 50°C is 101.3 ml instead of 100.0 ml. The volume changes resulting from the addition of potassium chloride to the water at the higher temperature were the same as those resulting at 25°C. The composition of a saturated solution has also changed from a concentration of 30 g of potassium chloride per 100 g of water at 25°C to a concentration of 40 g of potassium chloride per 100 g of water at 50°C. The concentration of potassium chloride in the saturated solution therefore increases when the temperature increases. This

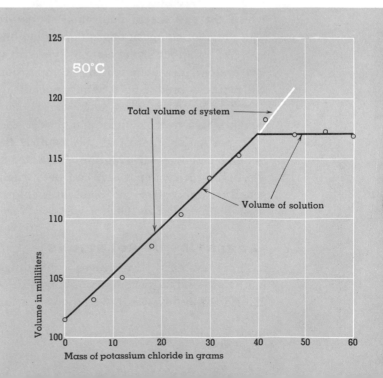

Fig. 2-12 *Volumes of systems of potassium chloride and 101.3 ml (100 g) of water at 50°C.*

conclusion is true of saturated solutions for nearly all substances, although the concentrations of some substances decrease when the temperature increases.

Ex. 2-10 Express the concentration of the potassium chloride solutions in systems 1, 5, 7, and 9 of Table 2-2 in grams per milliliter of solution and in grams per 100 g of water.

Ex. 2-11 Which expression in Exercise 2-10 is more useful if you want to obtain a definite mass of potassium chloride from a solution of known concentration?

Ex. 2-12 In Table 2-2, observe that 29.98 g of potassium chloride added to 100 g of water forms a solution whose volume is 111.8 ml. What was the volume of the initial components separately? Account for the change in volume.

Ex. 2-13 Compare the mass obtained by adding the mass of each item (second column) in Table 2-2 and 100 g of water with the corresponding mass of each system in its final state (third column). Does dissolving produce a change in total mass of the system?

2-6 CHARACTERISTICS OF THE POTASSIUM CHLORIDE–WATER SYSTEMS

Systems of potassium chloride and water have five characteristics.

1. The final total mass is equal to the sum of the masses of the separate components.

2. The final volume is not equal to the sum of the volumes of the separate components.

3. There is a range of compositions for which the systems have final states that are not only different from their initial states, but also for which the systems in their final states are completely homogeneous. The range of compositions is dependent on the temperature.

4. Within the range of compositions for which completely homogeneous systems are obtained, the composition can be varied entirely at will without producing a heterogeneous system.

5. The homogeneous systems can be separated into the initial components by a suitable change in phase.

Of particular interest at this point is the fourth characteristic. For systems of potassium chloride and water at 25°C, the range of values through which composition can be varied without producing heterogeneity extends from no potassium chloride up to about 30 g of potassium chloride per 100 g of water.

2-7 PROPERTIES OF SOLUTIONS

Three systems of mixtures containing one or more liquids, the methanol–ethanol system, the ethanol–water system, and the potassium chloride–water system, have now been examined. These systems fit the operational definition of a solution (Section 1-13); that is, they are homogeneous with respect to subdivision but can be separated partially (methanol–ethanol, ethanol–water) or completely (potassium chloride–water) during a change in phase. From these studies some general conclusions can be stated.

1. The mass of a solution is equal to the sum of the masses of the separate components.

2. The volumes of the components of some solutions are additive, whereas the volumes of others are nonadditive.

3. A change in composition produced by altering the relative amounts of the components has one of two consequences: (*a*) the system remains homogeneous for all compositions (methanol–ethanol and ethanol–water), or (*b*) there is a critical temperature-dependent composition below which the system is homogeneous and above which it is heterogeneous (potassium chloride–water).

Ex. 2-14 Compare the properties of the sodium sulfate–water systems (Experiment 4) with those of the potassium chloride–water systems (Section 2-6).

2-8 ARE SOLUTIONS RANDOM MIXTURES?

Besides the three general properties of solutions (Section 2-7), do solutions have other properties common to mixtures? For example, to what extent do the properties of potassium chloride solutions match the characteristics of random mixtures developed in Section 2-3?

No amount of magnification by a microscope permits a view of a solution with enough detail to see individual particles, whereas mixtures are ordinarily visibly heterogeneous. Therefore, visual inspection, aided or unaided by magnification, provides no information on which to base a decision as to whether or not a solution is made up of particles in a random arrangement. Even if a mixture of sodium bromide and sucrose were crushed to an extremely fine powder which appears uniform when viewed directly, a sample viewed under a microscope can be seen to consist of two different types of small grains. On the other hand, solutions remain homogeneous with respect to visual examination even with the help of the most powerful microscopes. This does not, however, preclude the possibility of random arrangement of particles; the particles are simply too small to be visible as separate units with the magnifying instruments now available. The fact that solutions, like mixtures, can be varied in composition tempts us to infer that random arrangement of particles is a characteristic common to both solutions and mixtures.

Ex. 2-15 Is the lead nitrate–water system (Experiment 4 of *Investigating Chemical Systems*) a random mixture? Explain your answer.

2-9 INTERACTION IN SOLUTIONS

In the methanol–ethanol system, the experimental evidence indicates that volume of components is an additive property. On the basis of measurements of this property, no interaction (defined in Section 2-4) between the components is evident. Systems of ethanol and water as well as systems of potassium chloride and water behave in a way that indicates at least some interaction.

Why are some systems of potassium chloride and water visibly heterogeneous in their final states? This is another indication that systems of potassium chloride and water are not exactly comparable to systems of the sodium bromide and sucrose type. Indeed potassium chloride–water systems behave as if, in some way, there were a limited predictable number of places for potassium chloride to go when it dissolves in water. When all these places are filled, no further dissolving can occur. However, if the potassium chloride does fit into the water, this would suggest a structural relation between the two rather than an entirely random relation.

Although it is easy to raise questions about whether solutions are random or structural arrangements, it is not easy to answer the questions. On the basis of the information presented in Chapters 1 and 2, solutions are somewhat puzzling systems, largely because of the problem of interaction. Systems for studying different kinds of interaction are provided by two examples, the potassium chloride–water system (Exercise 2-16) and the copper–sulfur system (Section 2-10).

Ex. 2-16 Compare the interaction in solutions of potassium chloride with the interaction in solutions of silver nitrate and sodium chloride (Experiment 5 of *Investigating Chemical Systems*).

2-10 COPPER AND SULFUR

Copper is one example of a large number of elements called metals. Copper is commonly used to make pennies, ornaments, and wire for conducting electricity. Like many other metals, copper can be drawn into wires; that is, it is ductile.

Sulfur, another chemical element, is a rather hard but brittle solid; that is, it is not ductile. Neither will it conduct electricity. One common form of sulfur, called flowers of sulfur, is a powder. In fact, the properties of sulfur are so different from those of metals that chemists refer to it as a nonmetal. Its main industrial use is in the preparation of sulfuric acid. Since sulfuric acid is widely used by industry, sulfur is a crucial chemical element in modern society.

Some properties of these two substances are given in Table 2-3. In addition to the differences recorded here, there are other differences that can be pointed out. For example, how do copper and sulfur behave

TABLE 2-3 SOME PROPERTIES OF COPPER AND SULFUR

	Copper	Sulfur
Color	"Copper"	"Yellow"
Melting point	1083°C	112.8°C
Boiling point	2582°C	444.6°C
Liquid range	1500°C	332°C
Density of solid	8.92 g/ml	2.07 g/ml

when they are heated separately? With a bunsen burner flame in the laboratory it is possible to heat an object to about 800°C. The data in Table 2-3 indicate that sulfur will not only melt but will also turn to a gas when it is heated by a bunsen burner and that copper will remain a solid. Materials that easily change to gases are said to be **volatile.** At temperatures attainable with a bunsen burner in the laboratory, then, sulfur is said to be volatile and copper nonvolatile.

If these two elements are mixed at room temperature, the resulting mixtures are initially quite comparable in their behavior to that of the mixtures of sodium bromide and sucrose. It is possible to separate these mixtures into the starting substances by physical means. If the mixture is allowed to stand for a period of days, however, the copper will be observed to lose its initial color and become black. Although the change is slow, it indicates that the copper–sulfur systems are quite unlike the mixtures of sodium bromide and sucrose which do not change in any observable way on standing. This slow change can be made to occur more rapidly by raising the temperature of the mixture.

When sulfur is heated to about 200°C, it turns to a dark reddish-brown liquid, whether or not the copper is present. When both copper (in the form of a flexible wire) and sulfur are present at about 200°C, the temperature of the system suddenly rises, even when the source of heat is removed, and the sulfur boils. If the system is in a test tube, the boiling sulfur produces a vapor which will condense to solid sulfur again on the upper (cooler) parts of the tube. After a short time, the product is observed to be in the form of a wire but is no longer flexible; instead the wire is hard, brittle, and black.

To explore the copper–sulfur system in more detail, it is possible to use a procedure which is similar to that already employed for the earlier types of systems. For systems of sodium bromide and sucrose, various amounts of the two substances were used in order to include examples of all possible compositions from pure sodium bromide to pure sucrose. This method was referred to as the continuous variation method. For systems of potassium chloride and water, various amounts of potassium chloride were used with a fixed amount of water. Either procedure can be used with copper and sulfur. As a start, the continuous variation method (Section 2-2) was tried.

Plate 1a shows the components of a series of systems of copper and sulfur in their initial states. The mass ratio of copper to sulfur is different in each system. The copper is in the form of short pieces of wire, and the sulfur is in the form of a powder. Table 2-4 lists the masses of each initial component (Columns I and II).

Each of the copper–sulfur mixtures was heated so that in a period of about five minutes the temperature rose to about 200°C. The temperature suddenly increased so that the sulfur began to turn to vapor and traveled up the tube. With continued heating, all the sulfur that would vaporize was driven away from the remaining nonvolatile solid. In this way, each system was separated into a volatile and a nonvolatile portion. Plate 1b shows nine systems of copper and sulfur; Plate 1c shows the same nine systems after they were heated. The volatile material has condensed as a yellow solid on the upper portion of several of the tubes. Tests indicated that the volatile yellow solid was sulfur. Note that in systems 1, 2, and 3 there is evidence of little or no sulfur. Further study of the changes in the systems hinges upon the selection of some property that could be measured before and after heating. Although volume could be measured, the changes in volume are quite small. It was easier to weigh the nonvolatile portion of the system in its final state and compare this mass with the mass of the original copper.

The nonvolatile material finally left at the bottom of each tube was removed and weighed to determine by what amount its mass differed from that of the corresponding initial copper. Table 2-5 lists the experi-

TABLE 2-4   INITIAL COMPOSITIONS FOR NINE SYSTEMS OF COPPER AND SULFUR

System	I Mass of Copper, g	II Mass of Sulfur, g	III Total Mass, g	IV Mass Ratio, Copper/Sulfur
1	5.72	0.32	6.04	17.9:1
2	5.09	0.64	5.73	8.0:1
3	4.45	0.96	5.41	4.6:1
4	3.81	1.28	5.09	3.0:1
5	3.17	1.60	4.77	2.0:1
6	2.54	1.92	4.46	1.3:1
7	1.91	2.24	4.15	0.9:1
8	1.27	2.56	3.83	0.5:1
9	0.64	2.88	3.52	0.2:1

System	Final Masses			Mass Changes	
	V Total Mass,[a] g	VI Nonvolatile Mass,[b] g	VII Volatile Sulfur Mass,[c] g	VIII,[d] g	IX,[e] g
1	6.08	6.08	0.00	0.04	0.36
2	5.78	5.77	0.01	0.05	0.68
3	5.40	5.40	0.00	—0.01	0.95
4	4.98	4.92	0.06	—0.11	1.11
5	4.71	4.09	0.62	—0.06	0.92
6	4.42	3.20	1.22	—0.04	0.66
7	4.15	2.52	1.63	0.00	0.61
8	3.86	1.63	2.23	0.03	0.36
9	3.53	0.89	2.64	0.01	0.25

[a] These masses were measured after the systems were heated without allowing sulfur to escape the tube.

[b] After data in Column V were obtained, the nonvolatile material was removed from the tube and weighed.

[c] Final mass of volatile sulfur, Column VII, was obtained by subtracting Column VI from Column V.

[d] Column VIII was obtained from the expression: Mass change = final mass — initial mass (V — III in Table 2-4).

[e] Column IX was obtained from the expression: Nonvolatile mass change = final nonvolatile mass — initial copper mass (VI — I in Table 2-4).

mental data found for the mass of nonvolatile products in each of the tubes.

To show more clearly the nature of the changes indicated by the data, the initial and final nonvolatile masses and the nonvolatile mass changes are plotted in two ways in Fig. 2-13. Two intersecting straight lines can be drawn to connect the points fairly satisfactorily.

Data for the total mass of each system before (Column III, Table 2-4) and after heating (Column V, Table 2-5) indicate small, irregular changes (Column VIII). Other experiments designed to exclude air and to prevent any accidental loss of sulfur give a total mass change of zero. This means that the decreases in mass indicated in Column VIII are the result of small losses of sulfur vapor, while the increases in mass are probably the result of reaction with a little air. In short, it is proper to conclude that mass was conserved within the error of the experiment as was true of the systems studied earlier. Nonvolatile mass changes are plotted against initial masses of copper and sulfur in Fig. 2-14.

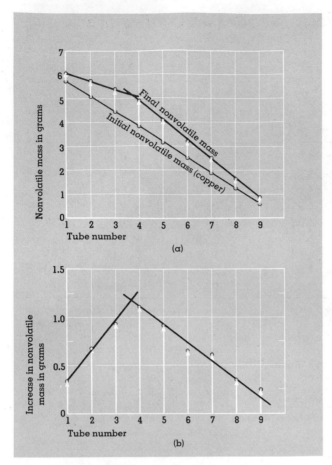

Fig. 2-13 *The increase in nonvolatile mass resulting from heating copper–sulfur systems is indicated by the vertical arrows in* (a) *and* (b). *The increase is plotted in a different manner and on a different scale in* (b).

Careful inspection of Fig. 2-14 shows that the intersection of the two lines would occur for a system containing 4.07 g of copper. The change in mass of nonvolatile material at this point on the graph is 1.17 g. If the mass of the copper is not altered by heating it, then the increase in mass must be the result of some change that made the sulfur nonvolatile. In other words, the greatest change in mass of nonvolatile matter would occur in a system having a copper/sulfur ratio of

$$\frac{4.07 \text{ g of copper}}{1.17 \text{ g of sulfur}} = \frac{3.48 \text{ g of copper}}{1.00 \text{ g of sulfur}}$$

Figure 2-15 is a flow sheet diagram showing the procedure followed in studying the systems of copper and sulfur.

Visual and chemical examination of each of the materials in tubes 1, 2, and 3 showed that the product consists of a copper wire surrounded by a brittle shell of some material other than copper. In tubes 1, 2, and 3 the diameter of the remaining copper wire became progressively smaller. The copper disappeared completely in tubes 4 to 9. In tube 4 the first trace of sulfur appeared. In tubes 5 to 9 the products consisted of nonvolatile solid in the bottom of each tube and sulfur near the top. The final components of the copper–sulfur systems are shown in Plates 1d and 2a.

The several evidences of change can be summarized.

1. The system in its initial state was a mixture of two substances, one of copper color and one of yellow color, whereas the system in its final state was either copper color and black, black and yellow, or black.

2. Initial nonvolatile solid (copper) was ductile, whereas some of the final nonvolatile solid was brittle.

3. Initial mass of nonvolatile solid (copper) was less than final mass of nonvolatile material.

4. Initial mass of volatile solid (sulfur) was more than final mass of volatile solid (sulfur).

Still another aspect of the systems must be considered. Initially each mixture of copper and sulfur was heterogeneous. After the systems were heated, heterogeneity was altered. In tube 3 careful examination revealed only a trace of a solid identifiable as copper, whereas the bulk of the solid was homogeneous with respect to such properties as color and density. In tubes 1 to 3, the initially heterogeneous mixtures changed to products having no evidence of sulfur. Also, the greater the

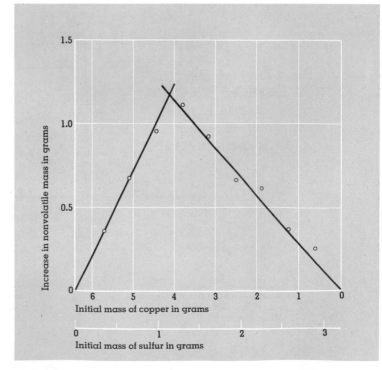

Fig. 2-14 *The increase in nonvolatile mass plotted against initial masses of copper and sulfur.*

relative amount of initial sulfur, the smaller the amount of final copper and the more homogeneous the system in its final state. On the other hand, in tubes 4 to 9 the initially heterogeneous mixtures changed to products with no detectable copper. The smaller the relative amount of initial sulfur, the more nearly homogeneous was the system in its final state. The intersection point in Fig. 2-14 must correspond to the system with an initial ratio of copper to sulfur so that chemical reaction gives only a single homogeneous solid as the final product.

The copper–sulfur systems differ from the two systems considered earlier. All systems of sodium bromide and sucrose were initially and finally heterogeneous. All systems of potassium chloride and water were finally heterogeneous if the compositions represented systems containing more than enough potassium chloride needed to produce a saturated solution. But in contrast to this, all systems of potassium chloride and water were homogeneous if the concentration was less than the value corresponding to a saturated solution. For copper and sulfur there appears, however, to be just one composition which gives a homogeneous system, whereas all others are heterogeneous.

The homogeneity and heterogeneity comparisons are summarized in general terms in Table 2-6.

It is possible then to introduce a simplification in describing the system under study here. This is done by saying that copper and sulfur form a compound called copper sulfide. This permits a division of

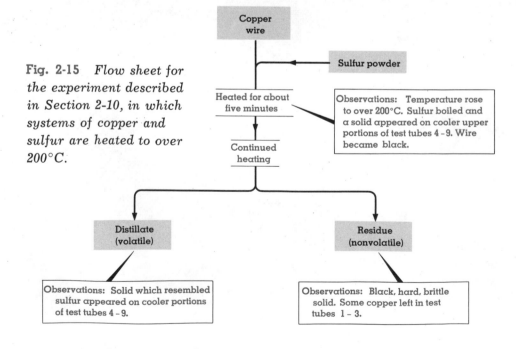

Fig. 2-15 *Flow sheet for the experiment described in Section 2-10, in which systems of copper and sulfur are heated to over 200°C.*

TABLE 2-6   COMPARISON OF HOMOGENEITY
IN THREE TYPES OF SYSTEMS

Type of System	Action in the System	Homogeneity Observed
Mixture	Mixing	None
Solution	Dissolving	For all systems with concentration less than saturation
Compound	Chemical reaction	For only a single composition

copper–sulfur systems (Plate 1c) into three groups. The division is described in the composition diagram shown in Fig. 2-16. The great utility of this division hinges upon the fact that the composition of the compound is constant. In a sense this reduces a complex interaction of two substances to a simple case of mixtures of three separate substances, copper, sulfur, and copper sulfide. The value of this point of view has been demonstrated by chemists in thousands of cases.

If the copper–sulfur systems react at different temperatures, new sets of data can be collected for the masses and changes in masses. If this is done and the data are plotted as in Fig. 2-14, the inter-

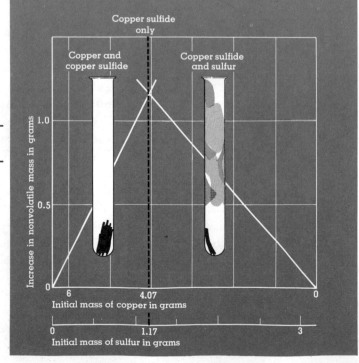

Fig. 2-16 *Relationship between composition of the final product and the relative amounts of copper and sulfur used in each of the copper–sulfur systems.*

(a)   (b)

Fig. 2-17   *Some natural crystals.* (**a**) *Sulfur,* (**b**) *quartz,* (**c**) *gypsum,*
and (**d**) *fluorite.* (American Museum of Natural History)

section will be at the same copper/sulfur mass ratio as before, over
a considerable temperature range. This behavior is in contrast to
the behavior of systems of potassium chloride and water in which the
concentration of a saturated solution varies with temperature.

For copper and sulfur, then, the mass ratio of 3.48:1 does not change
with temperature or with initial composition of the system. The product
appears to be a single substance different from either copper or sulfur
and hence a compound of the two.

Measurements of volume were used to indicate changes that might
have occurred in the states of the systems considered earlier. Volume
measurements have been made of, the copper–sulfur system. Plate
2b shows the various amounts of initial copper in tubes as used
before, with each tube holding 7 ml of toluene. The difference between
the volume of toluene (7 ml) and the total volume in each of the tubes
is the volume of copper. With these volumes of copper are to be compared the volume of the nonvolatile product in Plate 2c where again,
7 ml of toluene has been added to each tube.

In the study of the copper–sulfur system, two solids were mixed and
heated. As a result, a chemical reaction occurred, but it was found
that homogeneity of the system was observed for only a single composition. Would this also be the case if two solutions, each containing a
different substance, were mixed and a chemical reaction occurred? To
answer this question, the reaction of solutions of lead nitrate and
potassium iodide are studied in Experiment 6.

Ex. 2-17   In Experiment 6, what substances correspond to copper, sulfur, and copper
sulfide, respectively?

(c)   (d)

Ex. 2-18 Compare the conclusions you drew from your data obtained in Experiment
6 with those conclusions given for the copper–sulfur system.

2-11 DISTRIBUTION OF ELEMENTS IN A COMPOUND

Mixtures behave in a way which can be understood as the result of
a random mixing of two or more different substances. Solutions possess
some features of random arrangement and some suggestions of a regular structure, but no convincing evidence for either has yet been
developed. How are systems to be interpreted when a chemical change
takes place and a new substance is formed?

In systems that form solutions, initial mixtures of widely different
composition can each produce a solution as their sole product. In contrast, when a compound is the sole product for a change in state of a
system, the system can have only a single or fixed composition in its
final state. Earlier the idea was proposed that a single element consists
of a collection of atoms identical in every way, including mass. Compounds must be made up of two or more different kinds of atoms.

If you assume that the atoms of a compound are present so that the
relative numbers of different atoms can be expressed as a fixed ratio,
this will account for the experimental observations. That is, if the ratio
of copper atoms to sulfur atoms in copper sulfide is 1:1 or 2:1 or 1:2
or 3:2 or some other such ratio, it would be possible to account for the
fixed mass ratios. A way of determining the atomic ratios will be discussed in Chapter 3.

It is also desirable to understand why a compound is homogeneous.
The assumption that atoms are present in fixed ratios and that the
atoms are arranged in a regular pattern would fit in with the observation of homogeneity. An assumption that atoms are arranged in a pattern is essentially a statement that a compound has a structure. What
other evidence for structure in nature is there?

2-12 CRYSTALS

Among naturally occurring objects, crystals are conspicuous because they have visible structure. Quite a few varieties of crystals of different substances are found in many places on the earth. Figure 2-17 shows four examples of different crystal forms. Crystals can also be produced in the laboratory and in the factory. In an enlarged view of grains of table salt, it is possible to see the remarkable way in which each grain has exactly the same cubic shape as every other. Although the grains of table salt may differ greatly in size and may not always be actual cubes, the angles between adjoining faces are always quite accurately right angles. Some substances that form crystals in which the faces do not intersect at right angles are shown in Fig. 2-17. Whatever the angles between the faces of a particular substance may be, the form of the crystal appears to be a characteristic property of that substance. This property is referred to as **crystal habit**.

The crystalline nature of some substances and the fact that a given substance has a particular and characteristic crystal habit have fascinated scientists for a long time. Such regular geometric forms strongly suggest some kind of internal architecture or structure. If the theory of atoms and molecules is extended to a consideration of crystals, the characteristic shapes of crystals could be assumed to be a result of regular geometrical relationships among the atoms and molecules which are imagined to be inside the crystal. In short, crystals imply that atoms and molecules in crystals are arranged in a regular structure instead of in a random fashion.

2-13 REACTION OF CARBON WITH OXYGEN

Another kind of evidence for structure in substances can be obtained from a comparison of certain chemical changes. One example is provided by a study of the reactions of graphite and diamond with oxygen. Both graphite and diamond occur naturally, and they are also produced industrially. Some properties characteristic of these two materials are listed in Table 2-7. Each material, in addition, can be demonstrated to be a chemical element.

TABLE 2-7 SOME PROPERTIES OF GRAPHITE AND DIAMOND

	Graphite	Diamond
Color	Black	Colorless
Crystal form	Hexagonal plates	Cubic
Hardness	Soft	Hardest natural substance known
Density at 20°C	2.26 g/ml	3.51 g/ml
Melting point	Above 3000°C	Above 3000°C

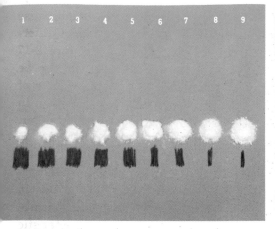

(a) *Systems of copper and sulfur. The masses of copper and sulfur are given in Table 2-4.*

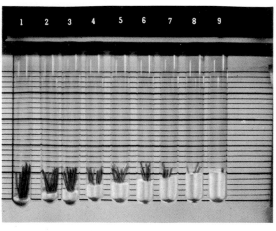

(b) *Systems of copper and sulfur shown in Plate 1a placed in test tubes. The tubes have not been heated.*

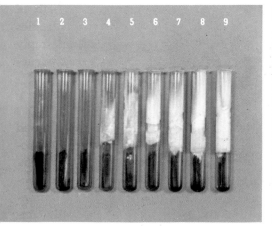

(c) *Systems of copper and sulfur after heating to over 200°C for more than five minutes.*

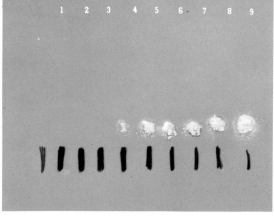

(d) *Systems of copper and sulfur after heating. Products have been removed from the tubes. Some unheated copper wire is shown at the left for comparison with the nonvolatile products.*

PLATE 1

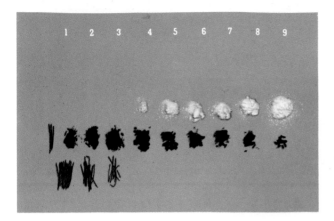

(a) *The nonvolatile products shown in Plate 1d have been broken up to show that the products in tubes 1, 2, and 3 contain some copper.*

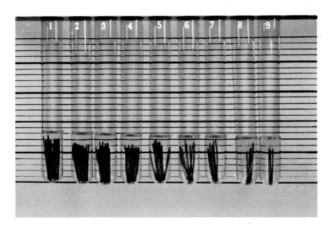

(b) *Nine tubes showing the height of liquid (7 ml of toluene) above the nine samples of copper shown in Plate 1a.*

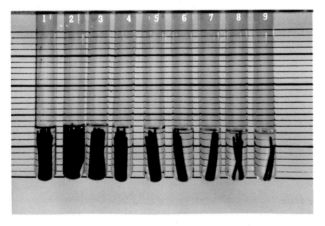

(c) *Nine tubes showing the height of liquid (7 ml of toluene) above the nine products shown in Plate 2a.*

PLATE 2

TABLE 2-8 PROPERTIES OF OXYGEN AND GASES FROM THE REACTION OF GRAPHITE AND DIAMOND WITH OXYGEN

	Oxygen	Gas 1[a]	Gas 2[b]
Color	Colorless	Colorless	Colorless
Melting point	−218.8°C	−78.5°C[c]	−78.5°C[c]
Boiling point	−183.0°C		
Density[d]	1.31 g/liter	1.81 g/liter	1.81 g/liter

[a] Gas produced by reaction of graphite and oxygen.
[b] Gas produced by reaction of diamond and oxygen.
[c] Changes directly from solid to gas at −78.5°C without formation of liquid.
[d] Densities of gases are expressed in grams per liter (g/liter) at 25°C and 1 atmosphere pressure.

The data in Table 2-7 certainly indicate that these two substances are different.

When they are heated to temperatures above 500°C, both graphite and diamond react rapidly with oxygen gas, so that the solid substances disappear and leave only a gas as product. The gases formed in the two reactions have identical properties. These are listed in Table 2-8.

Magnesium, a chemical element, reacts with all three gases described in Table 2-8. Hot magnesium and oxygen react to give a white solid compound called magnesium oxide. Hot magnesium reacts with each of the other two gases to give identical products which are simply mixtures of a white solid and a black solid. The white solid is magnesium oxide and the black solid is graphite. These reactions can be summarized as

Magnesium + oxygen → magnesium oxide
Magnesium + gas 1 → magnesium oxide + graphite
Magnesium + gas 2 → magnesium oxide + graphite

A compound reacts to form two or more products that are noninterconvertible. Because the gases produced by the reaction of graphite and diamond with oxygen react with magnesium to form magnesium oxide and graphite which are noninterconvertible, it can be concluded that gases 1 and 2 are compounds. The mass ratios of the elements in the two compounds are:

for the graphite and oxygen product,

$$\frac{1 \text{ g of graphite}}{2.67 \text{ g of oxygen}}$$

and for the diamond and oxygen product,

$$\frac{1 \text{ g of diamond}}{2.67 \text{ g of oxygen}}$$

Observations of the physical and chemical behavior of the product from burning graphite in oxygen (gas 1) indicate that it is the same as the product from burning diamond in oxygen (gas 2). How can any sense be made of these observations of the identical behavior of substances so obviously different as are graphite and diamond?

The chemical reactions presented thus far can most easily be explained if graphite and diamond are really the same element. All other known chemical evidence agrees with such a conclusion. Chemists call this element carbon. But if graphite and diamond are the same element, how can the differences in their properties shown in Table 2-7 be explained?

The only explanation available is provided by the conclusion that the atoms of carbon are arranged in different patterns in diamond and graphite. Two or more forms of an element which behave similarly in chemical reactions but which have different properties are called **allotropic forms** of the element. An alternative definition for allotropic forms of an element is that they differ in having different structural arrangements of a single kind of atom. In a later chapter a more detailed description of the structures of graphite and diamond will be discussed.

Graphite has many uses. These include the lead in pencils, crucibles for steel making, and brushes for electric motors. Considerable quantities of natural graphite, plus efficient industrial methods for producing graphite from coal and oil, ensure a plentiful supply at a low price. Diamonds, on the other hand, are much less plentiful and are relatively expensive. For many years, attempts have been made to convert graphite into diamond since this would change an inexpensive form of carbon into a more expensive form. Within the past few years, laboratories in the United States and in South Africa have developed techniques for doing this. Diamonds suitable for industrial use as abrasive material are now manufactured on a considerable scale.

2-14 SUMMARY

This chapter began with questions about the nature of the changes in state which a system may undergo. In explorations of several examples, certain particularly striking features were developed. Common to all the systems examined so far is the fact that the mass of a system after change is experimentally the same as the mass of the individual components before the change. Such experimental evidence is a major basis for an assumption about chemical change called the **law of conservation of mass.** According to this law, the total mass of components does not change during a change in the state of a chemical system.

One type of system has been called a mixture. Five characteristics of mixtures were found.

1. The mixture is heterogeneous with respect to subdivision and to visual comparison of different portions.

2. The final total mass is equal to the sum of the initial masses of the separate components.

3. The final total volume is equal to the sum of the initial volumes of the separate components.

4. The components can be present in any ratio.

5. The particles of the separate components are randomly arranged with respect to each other in the final state of the system.

A second type of system involves the production of a solution.

1. The mass of a solution is equal to the sum of the masses of the separate components.

2. A solution is homogeneous with respect to subdivision.

3. The volumes of the components of some solutions are additive, whereas the volumes of others are nonadditive. Nonadditivity of volumes of components can be one evidence of interaction.

4. In all cases where the concentration of a solution is less than that corresponding to a saturated solution, the composition of the solution is identical to the composition of the initial state of the system. A solution of this type is an example of a system that is homogeneous in its final state.

5. The homogeneous system can be separated into the initial components by a suitable change in phase.

In a third type of system, one or more substances are produced which are different from the initial substances. This is called a **chemical change** or a **chemical reaction.** Five characteristics of chemical reactions were discussed.

1. The final total mass is equal to the sum of the masses of the separate components.

2. The volume change in the chemical reaction discussed was not great enough to be useful as an indication of change. Another property (increase in nonvolatile mass) was examined instead.

3. A final component or product is formed whose composition remains constant for many different mass ratios of initial components.

4. When the initial components are elements, there is a particular composition for which the product is a single substance.

5. The composition of the final single substance remains constant through a temperature range of at least a few degrees.

In the study of chemical systems, one feature of the experimental data is of particular importance. In its initial state a system is a collection of separate components. The final state is reached after a change in state following the mixing of the components. Any difference between the initial and final states indicates interaction of the components.

In the study of mixtures and their changes, two major ideas prove useful. The components of a system whose composition can be varied at will without changing its homogeneity or heterogeneity probably have a disorderly or random arrangement. When variation in composition produces some systems that are heterogeneous and others that are homogeneous, it is assumed that these systems have some orderly arrangement of components or structural feature. Simple mixtures appear to be random arrangements; solutions have properties that suggest random arrangements which are modified by interactions; and elements and compounds seem to have structural arrangements. More information on the nature of the interactions is needed to provide an adequate basis for ideas about the nature of solutions and compounds.

A distinction may now be drawn between the operational definition of a compound given in Chapter 1 and the conceptual definition formulated from the discussion in this chapter. Operational definition—A compound is a substance that enters into at least one chemical change in which two or more products are formed that are noninterconvertible. Laboratory operations are necessary to match a substance with the definition. Conceptual definition—A compound is a substance made up of structural units, all alike, which contain atoms of more than one element. This definition makes us think about the tiny units of which matter consists.

Ex. 2-19 Is the following definition of a compound operational or conceptual? A compound is a substance of constant composition even when it is separated from systems whose overall compositions are different.

Ex. 2-20 A series of two-component systems of sand particles and iron filings was set up in the laboratory. The total mass of the mixture was the same in each system. Defend or refute the following statements regarding these systems.

a. The particles of sand and iron are arranged in regular patterns with respect to one another.

b. The total mass of the system is equal to the sum of the masses of the iron and the sand.

c. The final volume of the system is equal to the sum of the initial volumes of the iron and the sand.

d. The density of any system made up of sand particles and iron filings has a value between that of iron and that of sand.

Ex. 2-21 A series of two-component systems consists initially of the separate substances methanol and water (methanol and water are soluble in each other). The total mass of methanol and water was the same in each system. Defend or refute the following statements regarding these systems.

a. In their final states the systems are homogeneous with respect to subdivision.

b. The total mass of each system is always equal to the mass of the methanol plus the mass of the water, and the total volume of each system is always equal to the volume of the methanol plus the volume of the water.

c. The density of each of the methanol–water systems is greater than the density of either methanol or water.

Ex. 2-22 The table lists mass in grams and volume in milliliters for various mixtures of sand particles and iron filings. The components of these systems are subdivided into particles of nearly uniform size.

Mass of Sand, g	Mass of Iron Filings, g	Mass Ratio, Sand/Iron	Total Mass, g	Total Volume of Mixtures, ml
30.0	0.0	(pure sand)	30.0	11.35
25.0	5.0	5:1	30.0	10.80
20.0	10.0	2:1	30.0	8.83
15.0	15.0	1:1	30.0	7.59
10.0	20.0	1:2	30.0	6.34
5.0	25.0	1:5	30.0	5.10
0.0	30.0	(pure iron)	30.0	3.85

Make a graph similar to the one in Fig. 2-4, plotting the total volume on the ordinate and the mass of iron filings on the abscissa. Use your graph to answer the following questions.

a. What volume is occupied by a mixture consisting of 18 g of iron filings and 12 g of sand particles?

b. What conclusions are implied by the straight-line character of the plotted points?

c. What volume is occupied by 30 g of sand? by 30 g of iron?

d. What is the density of the iron filings used? What is the density of a 1:1 mixture of sand particles and iron filings?

Ex. 2-23 Refer to Fig. 2-16. Give the rectangular coordinate (the numerical value of the abscissa related to a given value of the ordinate) which corresponds to the following:

a. The point where two straight lines intersect

b. One point where the system in its final state is heterogeneous with respect to subdivision

c. The point where the final nonvolatile mass is a maximum

d. One point where two separate components, homogeneous with respect to subdivision, remain in the system.

Ex. 2-24 Defend or refute these statements regarding the copper–sulfur system described in the text.

a. The initial mass of nonvolatile copper is less than the final mass of non-volatile product.

b. The final mass of sulfur is always less than the initial mass of sulfur.

c. In each case the heterogeneity of the system in its initial state is altered by heating.

d. The copper sulfur mass ratio necessary to produce just one product that is homogeneous with respect to subdivision is 3.48:1 (refer to Fig. 2-16).

Ex. 2-25 Data obtained from a handbook for a series of sucrose–water systems are shown in the table.

Mass of Sucrose, g	Mass of Water, g	Mass Ratio, Sucrose/Water	Total Mass, g	Total Volume, ml
0.0	100.0		100.0	100.0
10.0	90.0	1:9.00	100.0	96.5
20.0	80.0	1:4.00	100.0	92.0
30.0	70.0	1:2.33	100.0	88.5
40.0	60.0	1:1.50	100.0	85.5
60.0	40.0	1:0.75	100.0	77.0
70.0	30.0	1:0.43	100.0	74.3
80.0	20.0	1:0.25	100.0	70.8
90.0	10.0	1:0.11	100.0	67.6

Prepare a graph similar to the one in Fig. 2-4, plotting the total volume of the sucrose–water solution on the ordinate and the mass of the sucrose on the abscissa.

Defend or refute these statements regarding the sucrose–water systems.

a. According to the data given, the densities of sucrose–water solutions are always greater than the density of either the water or the sucrose.

b. On the basis of the data given in the table, it can be concluded that a large amount of heat is absorbed when sucrose dissolves in water.

c. The volume of 100 g of a mixture having a 1:1 mass ratio of sucrose to water is equal to 85.0 ml.

d. Sucrose does not dissolve in carbon tetrachloride. Nevertheless, a graph of total volume versus mass of sucrose for a series of sucrose–carbon tetrachloride systems would be similar to the graph for the sucrose–water systems.

Ex. 2-26 *a.* Propose chemical evidence which supports the idea that graphite and diamond are allotropic forms of the same element.

b. Propose evidence that would be needed to show that red and yellow phosphorus are allotropic forms of the same element.

Ex. 2-27 Give an operational definition and a conceptual definition for the phrase "allotropic forms of an element."

GASES, MOLECULES, AND MASSES

ON THE BASIS of some knowledge of the relative masses of substances that react to form chemical compounds (the lead nitrate–potassium iodide system in Experiment 6 in *Investigating Chemical Systems* and the copper–sulfur system in Section 2-10), we have considered the possibility that the atoms in each chemical compound may be arranged in a characteristic pattern. It is easy to guess that many of the properties of a substance are related to the pattern of arrangement of the atoms. To verify such a speculation, however, information about the structures and properties of particular substances is needed. As a first guess, you might imagine that each compound is composed of two or more known elements. The atoms of these elements are present in a compound in a characteristic atomic ratio.

John Dalton was the first chemist to make reasonable headway in working out atomic ratios for the elements in compounds. He assumed that a chemical element was composed of atoms identical in all respects, including mass, whereas different elements contained different atoms. Compounds were formed when the atoms of two different elements joined together. He also assumed that, in most cases, the atoms of the elements making up a compound were present in a 1:1 ratio. The latter assumption was chosen primarily because of its simplicity. Although important modifications have since been necessary, Dalton's work did establish in the minds of other chemists the idea of relating atomic ratios and mass ratios of elements in compounds. Thus, although several of the details Dalton published in the early nineteenth century are now considered to be misleading, his overall idea has continued to be enormously effective.

Another line of work and reasoning was begun about the same time as Dalton's by Joseph Gay-Lussac, a French chemist. He made rather extensive studies, comparing the volumes of pairs of gases before and after they reacted with each other. His experimental data led Amadeo Avogadro to create an idea which provided a method for the determination of atomic masses.

3-1 REACTIONS IN SYSTEMS CONTAINING GASES

All the systems studied in Chapter 2 contained either solid or liquid components. Gases were omitted, partly because their masses are somewhat difficult to determine. This difficulty arises solely because the densities of most gases are quite small under ordinary circumstances. In Table 3-1 experimentally determined densities and other properties of some gases are listed.

Although it is convenient to express densities of solids and liquids in units of grams per milliliter, it is more convenient to work with large volumes of gases. Roughly speaking, gas densities are only about one-thousandth of the densities of solids and liquids. Table 3-1 lists the gases in order of increasing density, but this is not at all the order observed for boiling or melting points.

The approximate volume of a sample of gas which does not dissolve in water is quite easily measured in a graduated cylinder held upside down and under water. The method is illustrated in Fig. 3-1.

TABLE 3-1 PROPERTIES OF SEVERAL GASES

	Density,[a] g/liter	Boiling Point, °C	Melting Point, °C
Hydrogen	0.0825	−252.7	−259.1
Helium	0.1637	−268.9	−272.2
Methane	0.657	−161.5	−182.5
Carbon monoxide	1.145	−191.5	−207.0
Nitrogen	1.146	−195.8	−209.9
Oxygen	1.309	−183.0	−218.8
Hydrogen chloride	1.491	−84.9	−114.8
Carbon dioxide[b]	1.811		
Chlorine	2.90	−34.1	−101.0

[a] The densities tabulated were determined at 25°C and 1 atmosphere pressure.
[b] Solid carbon dioxide changes into carbon dioxide gas without forming a liquid at a pressure of 1 atmosphere at −78.5°C.

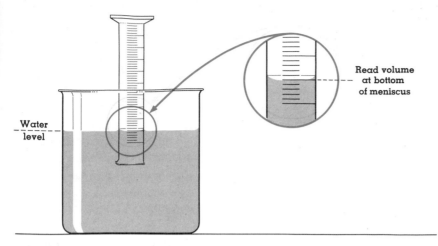

Fig. 3-1 *Measuring the volume of a gas. The water level should be read from the bottom of the meniscus.*

A mixture of hydrogen and oxygen gases is an example of a system that can react. The reaction of the two gases will produce a high-temperature flame that can be used for welding. The only product of the reaction of hydrogen and oxygen at the high temperature of the welding flame is the compound water. A mixture of hydrogen and oxygen reacts immeasurably slowly at room temperature, but if a mixture is heated to red heat (about 500°C), the reaction is likely to proceed with such rapidity that the whole volume of gas explodes. By mixing and heating the gases a little at a time, as is done in a burner, however, the violence of the reaction can be controlled.

Now examine the hydrogen–oxygen system (two gases) as you did the copper–sulfur system (two solids) and the lead nitrate–potassium iodide system (two solutions). When hydrogen and oxygen are mixed, they form a homogeneous colorless mixture. By cooling the mixture sufficiently, one gas can be separated from the other by changing it to a liquid. The gaseous mixture is a solution because it can be separated into its components by a change in phase. The mixtures of hydrogen and oxygen can be handled over water since both gases are insoluble in water (Fig. 3-2).

Various mixtures of hydrogen and oxygen were ignited with a small coil of wire heated to red heat by an electric current. Any final component that was present in the gas phase remained in an inverted test tube (Fig. 3-2). A graduated cylinder with 0.2-ml divisions was used to measure the volume of remaining gas, so that volume could be read to ±0.1 ml. In Fig. 3-3 the volumes of gases before reaction are shown on the scales below the test tubes, while the volumes of gas remaining after reaction are shown in the test tubes.

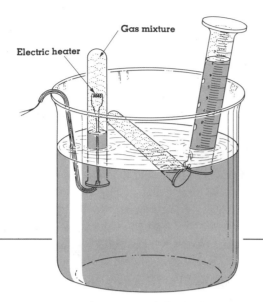

Electric heater

Gas mixture

Fig. 3-2 *Apparatus for investigating the reaction of hydrogen and oxygen. In the left side of the beaker, a test tube containing a gas mixture has the electric heater inserted. In the right side of the beaker, the gas in a test tube is being transferred to a water-filled graduated cylinder so that the volume of the gas can be measured.*

The measured total initial volume of the gas mixtures in the third column of Table 3-2 is identical with the sum of the volumes of the unmixed gases. The volumes of hydrogen and oxygen used in the mixtures were chosen to extend from a system containing nine times as much oxygen as hydrogen to a system containing nine times as much hydrogen as oxygen. For each case, the volume change during reaction was calculated by subtracting the initial volume of the system from the final volume of the system.

**TABLE 3-2   REACTIONS OF MIXTURES OF
HYDROGEN AND OXYGEN AT 20°C**

	Initial State		*Final State*	
Volume of Hydrogen, ml	*Volume of Oxygen, ml*	*Total Volume, ml*	*Volume of Residual Gas, ml*	*Volume Change, ml*
1.0	9.0	10.0	8.6	—1.4
2.0	8.0	10.0	7.1	—2.9
3.0	7.0	10.0	5.7	—4.3
4.0	6.0	10.0	4.0	—6.0
5.0	5.0	10.0	2.6	—7.4
6.0	4.0	10.0	1.2	—8.8
7.0	3.0	10.0	1.5	—8.5
8.0	2.0	10.0	4.0	—6.0
9.0	1.0	10.0	7.0	—3.0

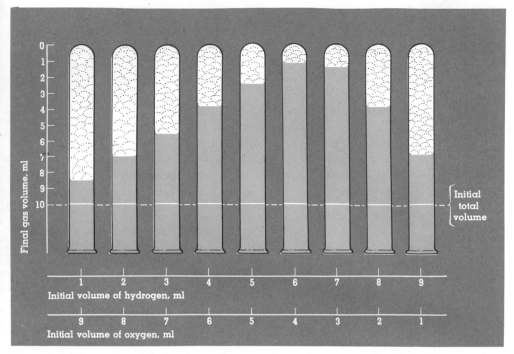

Fig. 3-3 *Gaseous products from the reactions of systems of hydrogen and oxygen. Volumes of each gas before reaction are shown on the scales below the test tubes.*

Volume change = final volume of system — initial volume of system

A plot of the volume changes against composition of the initial mixtures shows a striking relation (Fig. 3-4). In general, the continuous variation plot for hydrogen–oxygen systems has the same appearance, except for being inverted, as the plot obtained from data found for the copper–sulfur systems (Fig. 2-13). The data used to plot Fig. 2-13 were entirely concerned with masses, whereas those in Fig. 3-4 are entirely concerned with volumes. Inspection of Fig. 3-4 shows that the lines intersect where the initial gas volumes are 6.7 ml of hydrogen and 3.3 ml of oxygen, so that at this point the volume ratio is given approximately ($\cong$) by

$$\frac{6.7 \text{ ml of hydrogen}}{3.3 \text{ ml of oxygen}} \cong \frac{2.0 \text{ volumes of hydrogen}}{1 \text{ volume of oxygen}}$$

The more carefully the experiments are conducted, the more closely the ratio approaches 2:1. In the system represented by the intersection of the lines on the graph, the volume decrease is equal to the initial gas volume. This means that all the gas in the initial mixture is converted to the reaction product (water), which is not a gas at room

79

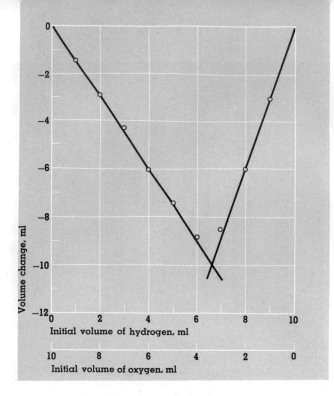

Fig. 3-4 *Volume change, measured at 20°C, for the reaction of mixtures of hydrogen and oxygen.*

temperature. The liquid portions of the systems in their final states were not recoverable because the water produced obviously merged with the larger volume of water used in collecting the gases. The reaction product, water, occupies nearly zero volume by comparison with the initial volume of gases. The experimental evidence leads to the conclusion that 2 volumes of hydrogen reacts completely with 1 volume of oxygen to produce water. When the volume ratio of reactants is 2:1, neither hydrogen nor oxygen is present in the products.

Ex. 3-1 Refer to Table 3-2 and Fig. 3-4.

a. What is the significance of the point of intersection of the two straight lines on the continuous variation graph in Fig. 3-4?

b. If 4.0 ml of hydrogen and 6.0 ml of oxygen are mixed in the immersed graduated cylinder and ignited, what gas remains unreacted in the cylinder? What is the volume of the unreacted gas?

c. What would happen if 10.0 ml of pure hydrogen were placed in the immersed cylinder and the coil of wire then heated to red heat by an electric current?

3-2 DECOMPOSITION OF WATER

In Section 3-1, study of the reaction between hydrogen and oxygen provided data that could be used to reach a conclusion about the composition of water. Can a similar conclusion be reached by decomposing water?

One possible way to break up a compound is to raise its temperature. Although this method is satisfactory for decomposing some substances, water cannot be decomposed easily by heating it. Even at 1000°C only about 0.1 percent of a sample of water decomposes to hydrogen and oxygen. It has been found, however, that when electricity passes through water, a reaction occurs in which the liquid water is converted to gases even at room temperature.

An apparatus for producing this change in water is pictured in Fig. 3-5. Arrangements for passing electricity through the water are provided by two pieces of platinum metal dipped into the water and connected to a battery or other source of electricity. If pure water is placed in the apparatus, the reaction proceeds quite slowly, but following the addition of sulfuric acid to the water, passing of electricity produces a rapid reaction. In Fig. 3-5a, the inverted test tubes contain water to which some sulfuric acid has been added. The platinum electrodes (black squares) in the water are attached to the wires in the bent glass tubes hooked over the edge of the beaker. To start the reaction (Fig. 3-5b), the wires are connected to the positive (+) and negative (−) terminals of the dry cells. Electricity has passed through the apparatus, and gas has collected in the tube above each platinum electrode.

As electricity flows, both metal plates become covered with gas bubbles which rise to the surface of the liquid. Test tubes filled with water and inverted over the electrodes can be used to collect the gases over water. With care to see that gas bubbles from one metal plate are kept separate from the bubbles formed at the other metal plate, each

Fig. 3-5 *Apparatus for electrolysis of water.* (**a**) *Before electricity has passed.* (**b**) *After electricity has passed.*

(a)

(b)

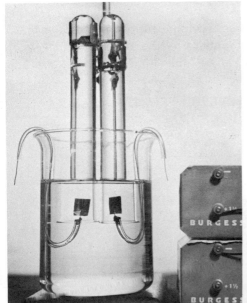
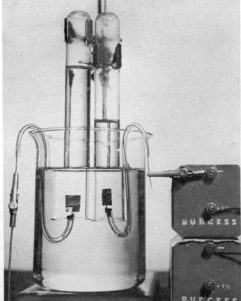

gas can be tested for properties and proves to be a pure substance. One is oxygen and the other is hydrogen. Figure 3-5 shows the apparatus after it has operated for a time and gases have collected. Note that the volume of one gas appears to be about twice that of the other gas. The gas present in larger volume is hydrogen, and the gas present in smaller volume is oxygen.

The presence of both sulfuric acid and water leads to some uncertainty about which compound decomposes to liberate hydrogen and oxygen. Several lines of evidence indicate that the sulfuric acid does not contribute to the hydrogen and oxygen.

1. Changing the concentration of sulfuric acid has no effect on the identity or volume ratio of the gases.

2. One addition of sulfuric acid is sufficient for the decomposition of an unlimited amount of water.

3. Several other substances can be added to water to produce the same effect, for example, sodium sulfate, phosphoric acid, and sodium nitrate.

The evidence leads to the conclusion that the hydrogen and oxygen gases are produced by the decomposition of water.

A number of experimental investigations of the decomposition of water have been made. Edward Morley at Western Reserve University, Cleveland, Ohio, made an extensive study that indicated a volume ratio of

$$\frac{\text{Hydrogen gas volume}}{\text{Oxygen gas volume}} = \frac{2.000}{1}$$

This volume ratio agrees with the value found by the synthetic procedure described in Section 3-1. Thus, the conclusion is that 2 volumes of hydrogen gas and 1 volume of oxygen gas react to form a product consisting solely of water.

3-3 OTHER GAS VOLUME RATIOS

For other pairs of reacting gases, volume ratios can be determined for complete reaction and are found to be the ratios of small whole numbers. Several results are listed in Table 3-3. Experiment also indi-

TABLE 3-3 VOLUME RATIOS FOR SEVERAL REACTING GASES

Components	Gas Volume Ratios for Reactants
Hydrogen + oxygen → water	2:1
Hydrogen + chlorine → hydrogen chloride	1:1
Carbon monoxide + oxygen → carbon dioxide	2:1
Methane + oxygen → water + carbon dioxide	1:2

cates that within reasonable limits these ratios do not change with temperature, provided only that the volumes of the two gases represented by the ratio are measured at the same temperature and pressure. Thus the ratios of the volumes of gaseous reactants appear to be as fundamental as the mass ratios of reactants in chemical reactions. In addition, scientists are always intrigued by experiments that suggest small whole numbers, although caution must be the watchword for fear of forcing data to appear as whole numbers when unprejudiced conclusions suggest more complex ratios. It is the hope of scientists that such numerical relations point the way toward some simple explanation. Does the fact that the volume ratios for the gaseous reactants in Table 3-3 are small whole numbers imply that the mass ratios for the reaction of these particular substances are equally simple numerically?

3-4 MASSES OF REACTING GASES

The mass of 10.0 ml of oxygen is about 0.014 g. The direct measurement of the mass of 10.0 ml of gas is not particularly easy because most usable containers would have a mass many times that of the gas within the container. A small difference in measurement between two measured numbers that are large is notably unreliable. The densities of gases listed in Table 3-1 have been calculated from experimentally measured relations between the mass and volume for several gases, however.

The *densities of gases* are expressed in terms of the mass in grams of one liter (g/liter). If the densities of two different gases are divided by each other, the result will be the ratio of the masses of equal volumes of the two gases. In Table 3-3, the volume ratio of the gaseous reactants hydrogen and chlorine is listed as 1:1. Therefore, for hydrogen and chlorine, the ratio of the masses which have equal volumes must also be the ratio of the masses which will react completely and is given by

$$\frac{0.0825 \text{ g/liter of hydrogen}}{2.90 \text{ g/liter of chlorine}} = \frac{\text{density of hydrogen}}{\text{density of chlorine}}$$

$$= \frac{1 \text{ g of hydrogen}}{35.2 \text{ g of chlorine}} = \text{mass ratio of reactants}$$

The mass ratio of equal volumes of hydrogen and oxygen is 1:15.87 The volume ratio for hydrogen and oxygen reacting to form water is 2:1, however. The ratio for reacting masses must then be

$$\frac{2 \times 1}{15.87} = \frac{2}{15.87} = \frac{1}{7.93}$$

Mass ratios for the gases making up the systems listed in Table 3-3 have been determined and are presented in Table 3-4.

TABLE 3-4   MASS RATIOS FOR SEVERAL REACTING GASES

Gases	Mass Ratios
Hydrogen–oxygen	1:7.93
Hydrogen–chlorine	1:35.2
Carbon monoxide–oxygen	1:0.572
Methane–oxygen	1:3.99

A comparison of Table 3-3 with Table 3-4 shows that even though the volume ratios are accurately represented by small whole numbers, the mass ratios are not. Even the most precisely conducted experiments offer no hope that mass ratios can ever be turned into ratios of small whole numbers. How are these data for mass ratios and volume ratios to be interpreted?

3-5   AVOGADRO'S HYPOTHESIS

By 1808 Gay-Lussac had published gas volume ratios for a number of reacting gases. In 1811 an Italian chemist, Amedeo Avogadro, provided an explanation for the small whole numbers. In effect, he proposed that, wherever different gas samples are compared at a given temperature and pressure, equal volumes of the gas samples contain equal numbers of molecules. He proposed that this was true for different samples of the same gas and for samples of different gases. This bold assumption provides a way to interpret the data for mass and volume discussed in Sections 3-3 and 3-4.

Two volumes of hydrogen, according to Avogadro, must contain twice as many molecules as 1 volume of oxygen. That is, if the ratio of volumes is 2:1, then the ratio of the numbers of molecules is also 2:1. Of course, this does not give a method for actually counting molecules, but only a method for determining the ratio of the numbers of molecules in two different gas samples. Application of the assumption proposed by Avogadro to the data for water in Tables 3-3 and 3-4 leads to the conclusion that oxygen molecules are about sixteen times as massive as hydrogen molecules.

If there were some way of deciding how many atoms are present in a molecule, then the molecular mass ratio could be converted to an atomic mass ratio. Avogadro's hypothesis gives the clue to this problem as well.

3-6   OXYGEN MOLECULES

To apply Avogadro's hypothesis to the water data, you need to know the relationship between the volume of water formed from known volumes of hydrogen and oxygen. The experimental data in Fig. 3-3

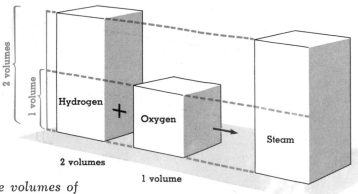

Fig. 3-6 *Relative volumes of reactants and product in the synthesis of gaseous water from hydrogen and oxygen.*

will not give this information since the product of the reaction described there disappeared into the collecting system. It was a liquid, water. But Avogadro's assumption about molecules applies only to gas volumes and not at all to volumes of liquids or solids. If 2 volumes of hydrogen and 1 volume of oxygen react at some temperature high enough so that all the water produced is in the form of a gas, then it is found that 2 volumes of hydrogen and 1 volume of oxygen produce 2 volumes of steam. The relationship is indicated by the diagram in Fig. 3-6.

JOSEPH LOUIS GAY-LUSSAC   *1778–1850*

A French chemist and physicist. Gay-Lussac was professor of physics at the Sorbonne, Paris, from 1808 to 1832. To this position, the post of professor of chemistry at the École Polytechnique was added in 1809. In 1804 he made the highest balloon ascent of the time (21,000 ft) to collect meteorological and magnetic data. He rediscovered Charles's law relating gas volumes and temperatures and, in 1804 and 1809, published the famous papers on the law of combining gas volumes. He discovered new methods for preparing potassium and boron and made important contributions to organic chemistry, chemical analysis, acid-base theory, and industrial methods of synthesis.

Gay-Lussac was elected to the French Academy of Sciences in 1806 and to the Chamber of Deputies (French House of Representatives) in 1831.

Application of Avogadro's hypothesis to this information produces the conclusion that there are twice as many hydrogen as oxygen molecules and, similarly, there are twice as many steam as oxygen molecules. Without any direct knowledge of the number of molecules in any particular volume, however, volume data cannot be translated into a count of molecules. Nonetheless, the molecular relationship is accurately described by

$$\text{2 molecules of hydrogen} \left(\begin{array}{c}\text{react}\\\text{with}\end{array}\right) \text{1 molecule of oxygen} \left(\begin{array}{c}\text{to}\\\text{produce}\end{array}\right) \text{2 molecules of steam}$$

Multiplication of each term of the above statement by any common factor does not change the $2:1:2$ relation, whatever the total number of molecules involved may be.

It has already been assumed that all of the molecules must be identical in a single substance made up of molecules. This means that, in the case of water, every water molecule contains oxygen. If this is reasonable, then it has to mean that each oxygen molecule must divide into two equal parts in order to supply oxygen to each of two molecules of water. An oxygen molecule could split in this way if it is made up of two structural units, that is, two oxygen atoms. Any other even number of oxygen atoms in the molecule would lead to the same possibility, but the simplest arrangement is a two-atom molecule. No reaction has ever been found which requires an assumption that oxygen molecules subdivide into more than two parts. A molecule composed of two atoms is called a **diatomic molecule.**

If the symbol O is used for an oxygen atom, then the oxygen molecule can be designated by O_2. Unfortunately, the formation of water from hydrogen and oxygen does not, by itself, permit any conclusion about the composition of a hydrogen molecule. Are there reactions in which hydrogen gas behaves as if it contains molecules with more than one atom?

The essence of Avogadro's thinking in devising a mental model of a molecule is the kind of thinking you did in Experiment 2 in *Investigating Chemical Systems*. Avogadro developed a concept picturing a molecule capable of being divided. In Experiment 2, you conceived a mental model of an object which would account for the behavior that your black box exhibited.

3-7 COMPOSITION OF HYDROGEN MOLECULES

The reaction of hydrogen with chlorine to form hydrogen chloride is a useful one to explore the character of the hydrogen molecule. At room temperature, each of these three substances is a gas, and the experimentally determined volume relations during the reaction are pictured in Fig. 3-7.

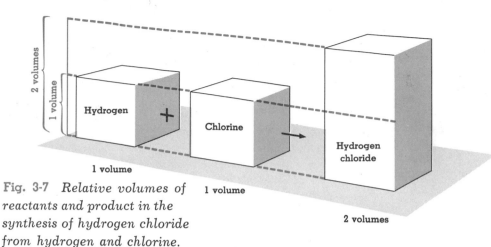

Fig. 3-7 *Relative volumes of reactants and product in the synthesis of hydrogen chloride from hydrogen and chlorine.*

When the reasoning just used for oxygen is applied here, both hydrogen molecules and chlorine molecules must be divisible into two equal parts and are presumably diatomic. If this is the proper conclusion, then it also requires that a molecule of hydrogen chloride have equal numbers of hydrogen atoms and chlorine atoms, so that the atomic composition of the molecule could be represented most simply by combining the symbols to give HCl. All of the preceding interpretation can be combined into one statement for the reaction of hydrogen and chlorine. In words, the statement is

1 diatomic molecule of hydrogen and
1 diatomic molecule of chlorine react to give
2 diatomic molecules of hydrogen chloride

Symbolically this can be compactly written as

$$H_2 + Cl_2 \rightarrow 2HCl$$

The symbolic statement is called a **chemical equation.** A chemist would read the equation aloud by saying, "H-two reacts with Cl-two to yield two HCl."

If these deductions are correct, the gas volume relations in the previous case of hydrogen, oxygen, and water are compatible, provided that the atomic ratio of H/O in water is $2:1$. The information about the volume relations among the gases hydrogen, oxygen, and water can be put into symbolic form.

$$2H_2 + O_2 \rightarrow 2H_2O$$

Ex. 3-2   Does the argument given in Section 3-7 exclude the composition of hydrogen molecules shown in the expression below?

$$H_4 + Cl_4 \rightarrow 2H_2Cl_2$$

AMEDEO AVOGADRO *1776–1856*

An Italian physicist and lawyer. Avogadro received a doctorate in ecclesiastical law at the age of twenty, practiced law for three years, and then turned to science. In 1809 he was appointed professor of physics at the Royal College of Vercelli, Italy; in 1820 he became the first to occupy the chair of mathematical physics at the University of Turin. When the university was closed for a decade for political reasons, he practiced law and continued his scientific studies, then returned to teach at the university until he was seventy-four. During his lifetime, Avogadro held many public offices dealing with education and technology.

In 1811, Avogadro published a paper attempting to reconcile Dalton's atomic theory with the simple relations among the volumes of reacting gases established by Gay-Lussac. He proposed his now famous hypothesis that, at the same temperature and pressure, equal volumes of any two gases contain the same number of molecules. Since this hypothesis led to the conclusion that the molecules of oxygen, hydrogen, nitrogen, and chlorine were diatomic and since it was not possible to explain why two identical atoms should join to form a molecule, the paper was largely ignored. Only after several alternative theories had been tried unsuccessfully by chemists, did Stanislao Cannizzaro, in 1860, succeed in establishing Avogadro's view as the only one satisfactorily accounting for the experimental observations.

Ex. 3-3   Predict the composition of molecules of carbon dioxide and methane using:

a. The information in Section 3-7 on the composition of oxygen, hydrogen, and water molecules

b. The data in Table 3-3

c. The formula for carbon monoxide—CO

d. The experimental evidence that 2 volumes of carbon monoxide combines with 1 volume of oxygen to produce 2 volumes of carbon dioxide.

3-8   ATOMIC MASSES

Can the conclusions about atoms and molecules now be coupled with the data on mass ratios of reacting substances? If the mass ratio for oxygen to hydrogen in water is

$$\frac{\text{Hydrogen mass in water}}{\text{Oxygen mass in water}} = \frac{1}{7.93}$$

and if the atomic ratio is

$$\frac{\text{Hydrogen atoms in water}}{\text{Oxygen atoms in water}} = \frac{2}{1}$$

a conclusion may be made that the hydrogen mass in water refers to twice as many atoms as does the oxygen mass. It is more generally useful to know the mass ratio for the same number of atoms. This will be

$$\frac{\text{Hydrogen mass per atom}}{\text{Oxygen mass per atom}} = \frac{1}{7.93} \times \frac{1}{2} = \frac{1}{15.87}$$

In the case of hydrogen chloride, the mass ratio is

$$\frac{\text{Hydrogen mass in hydrogen chloride}}{\text{Chlorine mass in hydrogen chloride}} = \frac{1}{35.2}$$

while the atomic ratio is

$$\frac{\text{Hydrogen atoms in hydrogen chloride}}{\text{Chlorine atoms in hydrogen chloride}} = \frac{1}{1}$$

This means that the mass ratio for the elements in hydrogen chloride is also numerically the same as the ratio of the atomic masses. By similar laboratory techniques, it is possible to determine the atomic mass ratios for pairs of many of the known elements. Can some method be developed so that all the elements are related to each other in terms of mass?

Such a question could be answered by constructing a numerical scale on which each element could be experimentally assigned a characteristic value for its atomic mass. In the laboratory, the masses of objects are quite commonly measured in grams. Such a procedure compares, by means of a balance, the mass of an object with a carefully selected block of metal that has been assigned by choice, rather than by logical necessity, a mass of 1 kilogram (kg). This particular metal block is the standard against which the masses on a balance are compared. Can you then proceed to compare the masses of various atoms with the standard kilogram?

There is no procedure available to chemists by which atomic masses can be weighed on a balance. What can be done is to find the mass of one element that will react with a given mass of a second element. From these experimental data, calculation and theory lead to a relationship between the mass of one atom and that of a second atom that can react chemically with the first.

What we finally hope to find is the connection between the combining ratios, both mass and volume, (a laboratory operation) and the formulas for molecules (a conceptual scheme).

3-9 A SCALE OF ATOMIC MASSES

Comparisons of the atomic masses of various elements that will react with each other offer another possibility. Scientists have found it convenient to select the mass of one of the elements as a standard for the comparison of atomic masses. At various times, hydrogen, oxygen, and carbon have been proposed and used as standards.

Just as with the metric mass scale, so with the **atomic mass scale,** it is only necessary to decide two things to establish the scale.

1. The substance for the standard must be chosen.

2. The size of a unit on the relative mass scale must be specified.

Around the middle of the nineteenth century the oxygen atom was selected as the standard of mass. A value of 16 for the atomic mass of oxygen as it occurred in nature was assigned. The number system then dictates one-sixteenth of the mass of an oxygen atom as the **atomic masses unit (amu)**.

Only straightforward arithmetic is needed to place hydrogen and chlorine on the scale. The ratio of the atomic mass of hydrogen to that of oxygen can be expressed as

$$\frac{\text{Mass per hydrogen atom}}{\text{Mass per oxygen atom}} = \frac{1}{15.87}$$

What is wanted, however, is the comparison of the mass of one hydrogen atom with the mass of one-sixteenth of an oxygen atom, not with the mass of one oxygen atom.

$$\frac{\text{Mass per hydrogen atom}}{\text{Mass per 1/16 oxygen atom}} = \frac{1}{15.87 \times 1/16} = 1.008 \text{ amu}$$

This locates hydrogen on the atomic mass scale.

With the data already discussed, it is possible to compare chlorine with oxygen.

$$\frac{\text{Mass per chlorine atom}}{\text{Mass per hydrogen atom}} = \frac{35.2}{1} \qquad \text{(Section 3-8)}$$

$$\frac{\text{Mass per hydrogen atom}}{\text{Mass per oxygen atom}} = \frac{1}{15.87}$$

If these two ratios are multiplied together,

$$\frac{\text{Mass per chlorine atom}}{\text{Mass per hydrogen atom}} \times \frac{\text{mass per hydrogen atom}}{\text{mass per oxygen atom}}$$

$$= \frac{35.2}{1} \times \frac{1}{15.87}$$

the term mass per hydrogen atom can be canceled. This leaves

$$\frac{\text{Mass per chlorine atom}}{\text{Mass per oxygen atom}} = \frac{35.2}{15.87}$$

Chlorine can be put onto the atomic mass scale by relating it to one-sixteenth of the mass of an oxygen atom.

$$\frac{\text{Mass per chlorine atom}}{\text{Mass per 1/16 oxygen atom}} = \frac{35.2}{15.87 \times 1/16} = 35.5 \text{ amu}$$

The comparison of the masses of reacting elements has thus provided values for the atomic masses of three elements on a single scale.

Hydrogen   1.008 amu
Oxygen   16.00   amu
Chlorine   35.5   amu

Through the analysis of compounds, the determination of mass ratios for reacting elements, and the measurement of the volumes of reacting gases, most other elements can be assigned appropriate positions on the same scale.

In Chapter 10, the accepted values for atomic masses are listed for all the known elements. In Fig. 3-8 many of the elements are located pictorially on the atomic mass scale.

Each value listed tells, for the atom of each element, how many times more massive it is than one-sixteenth of an oxygen atom. These values

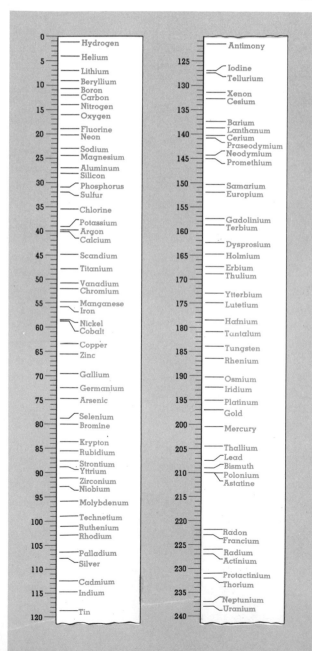

Fig. 3-8 *The scale of atomic masses.*

91

are reviewed periodically by an international committee of scientists and revised when more reliable data from improved experiments justify it. In 1883, Lothar Meyer and Karl Seubert, after a critical evaluation, chose hydrogen as a basis for the atomic mass scale. They set the atomic mass of hydrogen at 1 amu. Wilhelm Ostwald at the same time chose oxygen (16.000). In 1897, the German Chemical Society recommended oxygen (16.000) as the standard. Between 1903 and 1905, the International Atomic Weight Commission gave two sets of international atomic masses based on oxygen (16.000) and hydrogen (1.000), respectively. From 1906 to 1961, only oxygen was accepted as the standard. In 1961, the standard of the atomic mass scale was changed by international agreement from the oxygen atom to the carbon atom, and the values in the table in Chapter 10 are on this newer basis. The change in standards is important in precise scientific work.

3-10 **COUNTING MOLECULES**

Although a procedure has been described for determining the numerical ratios of atoms in compounds, no mention has been made of the problem of the numbers of atoms or molecules in a given object or piece of matter. The solution to this problem is important in connection with a variety of scientific questions whose answers require knowledge of the actual number of atoms or molecules in a system.

To find the number of the atoms or molecules in a piece of matter, it is first necessary to select a known amount of a single substance. These choices can be made in any way that is convenient. Since oxygen was selected as the standard for comparison in the scale of atomic masses, it seems reasonable to attempt a count of oxygen atoms or molecules. Although any amount of oxygen could be used, 32 g of oxygen might be selected because 32 amu is the mass for one molecule of oxygen, O_2. This mass for a molecule of oxygen is obtained by combining the deduction that oxygen is diatomic with the assignment of a mass of 16 amu to one atom of oxygen.

$$\frac{16 \text{ amu}}{1 \text{ atom of oxygen}} \times \frac{2 \text{ atoms of oxygen}}{1 \text{ molecule of oxygen}} = \frac{32 \text{ amu}}{1 \text{ molecule of oxygen}}$$

How many molecules are in 32 g of oxygen? The count of molecules in 32 g of oxygen can be extended to other gases through the application of Avogadro's assumption. Equal volumes of gases at the same temperature and pressure are assumed to contain equal numbers of molecules.

Among the ways available for relating numbers of molecules and their masses, a procedure used by Rutherford is the simplest to describe. During his study of radium and polonium, Rutherford found that each of these elements gave off alpha particles. When captured in a container, each alpha particle produced one helium atom. Further-more, he found that the alpha particles were discharged from the ra-dium or polonium with such energy that each particle produced a visi-ble flash of light on a screen of zinc sulfide. The flashes of light could be counted to give the number of alpha particles given off in a known time. This would give a count of the number of helium atoms formed. The accumulated helium gas could then be collected and weighed.

Experiments of this nature were carried out by Rutherford and his students beginning around 1903. They found that 1 g of radium pro-duced about 7.7×10^{-6} g of helium in one year. They estimated that during this same time 11.6×10^{17} alpha particles were produced by 1 g of radium. If each alpha particle produces one helium atom, then the number of helium atoms in 1 g of helium must be

$$\frac{11.6 \times 10^{17} \text{ atoms of helium per gram per year}}{7.7 \times 10^{-6} \text{ g of helium per gram per year}}$$
$$= 1.51 \times 10^{23} \text{ atoms per gram of helium}$$

To answer the question of how many helium atoms are in a molecule, you can proceed in much the same way as you did in studying the reactions and molecular compositions of hydrogen and oxygen. This is possible because helium is also a gas.

Experiments show that helium does not form compounds that are comparable to those formed by other elements. This suggests that helium atoms do not join with each other to form diatomic molecules. If the simplest assumption possible is made about a helium molecule, there should be but one atom per molecule. Other lines of experimen-tation also confirm such a choice.

From the density values for helium and oxygen in Table 3-1, the mass ratio of helium molecules to oxygen molecules in equal volumes can be calculated.

$$\frac{0.1637 \text{ g/liter of helium}}{1.309 \text{ g/liter of oxygen}} = \frac{0.1250 \text{ g of helium}}{1 \text{ g of oxygen}}$$

A container whose volume is sufficient to hold 32 g of oxygen will, at the same temperature and pressure, hold a mass of helium given by

$$32 \text{ g of oxygen} \times \frac{0.1250 \text{ g of helium}}{1 \text{ g of oxygen}} = 4.00 \text{ g of helium}$$

Rutherford's experiment gave 1.51×10^{23} helium atoms per gram, which means that there would be 6.0×10^{23} helium atoms in 4.00 g of helium. According to Avogadro's assumption, then, there would be 6.0×10^{23} molecules of oxygen in 32 g of oxygen. Since oxygen mole-cules are diatomic, it follows that 6.0×10^{23} atoms of oxygen must have a mass of 16 g. The same number of hydrogen atoms will have a mass of 1.008 g.

On the basis of this information, it is possible to calculate the masses of individual oxygen atoms or molecules in grams. If 6.0×10^{23} atoms weigh 16 g, each atom of oxygen would weigh

$$\frac{16 \text{ g}}{6.0 \times 10^{23} \text{ atoms of O}} = 2.7 \times 10^{-23} \text{ g/atom of O}$$

If 6.0×10^{23} molecules weigh 32 g, each molecule would weigh

$$\frac{32 \text{ g}}{6.0 \times 10^{23} \text{ molecules of O}_2} = 5.3 \times 10^{-23} \text{ g/molecule of O}_2$$

3-11 THE AVOGADRO NUMBER

A large number of the magnitude of 6.0×10^{23} is not to be compared with any of the numbers we encounter in everyday life. Even a count of all the people presently living on the earth comes to only about 3×10^9 persons. Written out in numbers, 6.0×10^{23} is 6 followed by 23 zeros:

$$600,000,000,000,000,000,000,000$$

In words, this number is six hundred sextillion. This number is much larger than any number we are accustomed to thinking about.

Fig. 3-9 *Some magnitudes compared.*

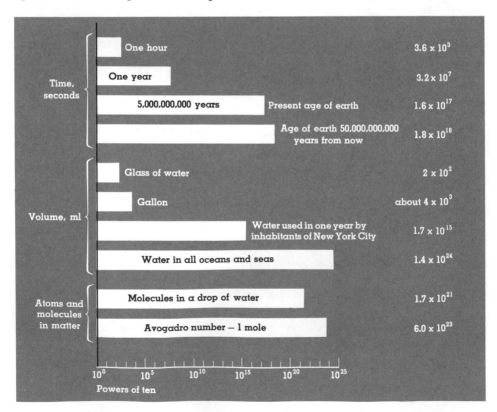

As a suggestion of the magnitude of 6.0×10^{23}, consider the volume of water on the earth's surface in all the oceans and seas. These contain about 3.4×10^8 cubic miles of water. In the metric system this volume is equivalent to 14×10^{23} ml. If, while at the seashore, you remove about 2 ml of seawater, you will have removed from the sea a fraction of the water whose magnitude is just about the same as if you were to remove one molecule of oxygen from the molecules in 32 g of oxygen.

Although the number of molecules in 32 g of oxygen is extremely large, it is nonetheless a number that can be determined in the laboratory. It has been measured in a variety of ways with considerable precision, and the presently accepted value is 6.024×10^{23}. In honor of Avogadro's contributions to science, this number is referred to as the **Avogadro number.** Rutherford's estimate in 1903 (6.0×10^{23}) is remarkably little changed by today's measurements, a great tribute to his excellent experimental work.

Ex. 3-4   Suppose that all the people in the world (3×10^9 people) were set to work counting oxygen molecules at the rate of one per second. How long would it take them to count the molecules in 32 g of oxygen?

Ex. 3-5   If there are 6.0×10^{23} molecules in 18 g of water, in how many grams of water are there as many molecules of water as there are milliliters of water in all the oceans?

3-12   MOLECULAR MASSES AND NUMBERS

The development which made it possible to assign an atomic mass for each element also more clearly revealed what a molecule must be. A **molecule** can be defined as a collection of atoms which behaves as a connected unit. It is possible to combine experimental data and ideas to provide information about the atomic composition of the molecules believed to be present in gases. Each molecule of the gases studied thus far (hydrogen, oxygen, and chlorine) consists of two atoms.

Just as the masses of atoms of elements can be experimentally compared on the atomic mass scale, so can the masses of molecules be compared on the same scale. The **molecular mass** of a substance is the mass of a molecule of the substance on the atomic mass scale.

The ratio of densities of two gases is the ratio of masses of equal volumes of the two gases. For several gases, the mass ratios of equal volumes (based on oxygen) are given in the third column of Table 3-5. To place the gases on the scale of atomic masses, it is necessary only to multiply each mass ratio by 32, the number of atomic mass units per molecule of oxygen. The molecular masses which result from this calculation are given in the fourth column of Table 3-5.

It has proved helpful to chemists to look at the situation from a different viewpoint. If 32 g of oxygen contains 6.0×10^{23} molecules,

TABLE 3-5 MOLECULAR MASSES OF SEVERAL GASES

	Density,[a] g/liter	Mass Ratio [b]	Molecular Mass,[c] amu
Hydrogen	0.0825	0.0631	2.02
Helium	0.1637	0.1250	4.00
Methane	0.657	0.502	16.06
Carbon monoxide	1.145	0.875	28.0
Nitrogen	1.146	0.876	28.0
Oxygen	1.309	1.000	(32)
Hydrogen chloride	1.491	1.140	36.5
Carbon dioxide	1.811	1.385	44.4
Chlorine	2.90	2.22	71.0

[a] Densities are for gases at 25°C and 1 atmosphere pressure.
[b] The mass ratio is found by dividing the gas density by oxygen density.
[c] Mass ratio multiplied by 32 which gives the molecular mass in atomic mass units.

so also does 2 g of hydrogen or 44 g of carbon dioxide. Or, in general, when a sample of a molecular substance has a mass in grams which is numerically equal to the molecular mass of that substance, the sample contains 6.0×10^{23} molecules.

Ex. 3-6   *a.* What is the mass (in grams) of a single molecule of water? *b.* in atomic mass units?

3-13 THE MOLE AS A UNIT

For all chemical systems it is assumed that the fundamental units necessary to account for mass relations are atoms or molecules. Whenever water is formed by the reaction of oxygen and hydrogen, the number of atoms that combine can only be such as will correspond to the atomic ratio characteristic of water. We have already seen that, for chemical reactions, the absolute number of atoms is not particularly important, but the relative numbers are of crucial importance.

Chemists frequently indicate relative numbers of atoms by expressing them in terms of multiples of the Avogadro number of atoms. The mass of matter which contains the Avogadro number of structural units is called a **mole** of matter. It is convenient in some cases to use atoms as units; in other cases, molecules; and in still different cases, some other particular set of atoms as units. Usually the context will make clear which choice of unit is best.

Because the Avogadro number was determined by finding the number of molecules in 4 g of helium and was shown to be the same in 32 g of oxygen, the mole can be defined in another way. A mole is the mass of a substance which contains as many structural units as there are molecules in exactly 32 g of oxygen. By definition, 32 g of oxygen is 1 mole of oxygen molecules (O_2). The mass of a mole of a material is specified if it can have its units located on the atomic mass scale.

Oxygen atoms were assigned a mass of 16 amu on the atomic mass scale, so 16 g of oxygen contains an Avogadro number of atoms. In similar fashion, 44 g of carbon dioxide must contain an Avogadro number of molecules, and 1 mole of carbon dioxide contains 1 mole of carbon atoms and 2 moles of oxygen atoms.

In theoretical discussion of the properties of matter, it is often convenient to think in terms of a small number of atoms and molecules. In most practical problems, however, it is much more convenient to experiment with one or more moles of material. In establishing the relative numbers of atoms or molecules that are involved in a reaction, either procedure gives the same result.

Ex. 3-7   At 25°C the volume of 1 mole of water is 18.0 ml. What is the volume occupied by a single molecule of water?

Ex. 3-8   If the water molecule in Exercise 3-7 were spherical, what is the radius of a water molecule in centimeters (cm)?

3-14   SYMBOLS

Before the behavior of other chemical systems is considered, it will be advantageous to discuss some chemical shorthand in order to save time in talking and writing about reactions. In Section 1-14 it was pointed out that 103 chemical elements are now known. These are listed on page 98. Because the names of the elements may contain up to twelve letters each, chemists have found it convenient to represent these names by *symbols* of one or two letters. Thus C is used to mean the element carbon, and Cl the element chlorine. With these symbols you can save time and space in writing statements which describe systems of chemicals.

In Section 1-19 the idea was introduced that each sample of a particular element consists of a collection of identical atoms. In addition to its use to designate the element, then, the symbol for an element also stands for one atom and for the mass of one atom in atomic mass units. Quite commonly in experimental work the symbol is used to refer to 1 mole of the element. The several meanings of the symbol for an element are discussed in Section 3-17. Usually the context in which the symbols are used will make clear the most appropriate meaning.

Both names and symbols for the elements have, for many years, been subject to international agreement as worked out by chemists through the International Union of Pure and Applied Chemistry.

ALPHABETICAL LIST OF SYMBOLS OF ELEMENTS

Symbol	Name	Symbol	Name	Symbol	Name
Ac	Actinium	Ge	Germanium	Po	Polonium
Ag	Silver	H	Hydrogen	Pr	Praseodymium
Al	Aluminum	He	Helium	Pt	Platinum
Am	Americium	Hf	Hafnium	Pu	Plutonium
Ar	Argon	Hg	Mercury	Ra	Radium
As	Arsenic	Ho	Holmium	Rb	Rubidium
At	Astatine	I	Iodine	Re	Rhenium
Au	Gold	In	Indium	Rh	Rhodium
B	Boron	Ir	Iridium	Rn	Radon
Ba	Barium	K	Potassium	Ru	Ruthenium
Be	Beryllium	Kr	Krypton	S	Sulfur
Bi	Bismuth	La	Lanthanum	Sb	Antimony
Bk	Berkelium	Li	Lithium	Sc	Scandium
Br	Bromine	Lu	Lutetium	Se	Selenium
C	Carbon	Lw	Lawrencium	Si	Silicon
Ca	Calcium	Md	Mendelevium	Sm	Samarium
Cd	Cadmium	Mg	Magnesium	Sn	Tin
Ce	Cerium	Mn	Manganese	Sr	Strontium
Cf	Californium	Mo	Molybdenum	Ta	Tantalum
Cl	Chlorine	N	Nitrogen	Tb	Terbium
Cm	Curium	Na	Sodium	Tc	Technetium
Co	Cobalt	Nb	Niobium	Te	Tellurium
Cr	Chromium	Nd	Neodymium	Th	Thorium
Cs	Cesium	Ne	Neon	Ti	Titanium
Cu	Copper	Ni	Nickel	Tl	Thallium
Dy	Dysprosium	No	Nobelium	Tm	Thulium
Er	Erbium	Np	Neptunium	U	Uranium
Es	Einsteinium	O	Oxygen	V	Vanadium
Eu	Europium	Os	Osmium	W	Tungsten
F	Fluorine	P	Phosphorus	Xe	Xenon
Fe	Iron	Pa	Protactinium	Y	Yttrium
Fm	Fermium	Pb	Lead	Yb	Ytterbium
Fr	Francium	Pd	Palladium	Zn	Zinc
Ga	Gallium	Pm	Promethium	Zr	Zirconium
Gd	Gadolinium				

The vast majority of substances are compounds made up of two or more elements. Combinations of the symbols for the elements in each particular compound are called **formulas.** Thus, the major constituent of common table salt is a compound produced by the reaction of sodium and chlorine and called sodium chloride. The experimentally determined mass ratio of sodium to chlorine agrees closely with the atomic mass ratio of sodium to chlorine; that is, the atomic ratio is $1:1$. These ratios are then represented by the formula NaCl.

When the atomic ratio is other than $1:1$, subscript numerals are used following the symbols to indicate the proper ratio. If a compound of carbon and oxygen is found to have a mass ratio of $12:32$, this means that the atomic ratio is $1:2$, so the formula is CO_2. For pure substances which are known to be in the form of molecules, the formula can also represent the molecule, as is the case for CO_2. In the case of molecular substances such as CO_2, the subscripts are a characteristic set of numbers determined by experimental evidence. The subscripts are not reduced to the lowest common denominator. Thus, because of experimental evidence, hydrogen peroxide is represented by H_2O_2, not HO. The **molecular formula** gives the total number of atoms of each element in a molecule of a molecular substance. Several elements have already been shown to exist in the form of molecules containing more than one atom. For ordinary oxygen, then, the molecular formula is O_2. Some other examples are nitrogen, N_2; chlorine, Cl_2; phosphorus vapor, P_4; and sulfur vapor, S_8.

Solid sodium chloride is one of a considerable number of substances which do not appear to exist as a collection of separate molecules. In this case, the formula represents the atomic ratio of the elements in the compound, but not a molecule of sodium chloride. Whenever experimental knowledge suggests that compounds do not exist in molecular form or when the evidence is incomplete, formulas can still be useful to indicate the mass ratio and the atomic ratio of the elements in the compound. The subscripts in the formulas for compounds of this type are chosen to be the smallest numbers possible. The resulting formula is referred to as an **empirical formula.**

Even though NaCl does not represent a molecule of sodium chloride, it is quite proper to refer to a mole of sodium chloride since chemists have agreed to write its formula as NaCl. One mole of sodium chloride will contain 6×10^{23} sodium atoms and 6×10^{23} chlorine atoms, but not 6×10^{23} molecules of sodium chloride. One mole of NaCl will have a mass equal to the sum of the masses of 1 mole of Na and 1 mole of Cl.

$$23.0 \text{ g/mole of Na} + 35.5 \text{ g/mole of Cl} = 58.5 \text{ g/mole of NaCl}$$

For any substance whose formula is known, a mass corresponding to the formula can be computed. This calculation is made simply by adding together the atomic masses for each of the elements in the formula. Thus for water with the formula H_2O, the **formula mass** is obtained by

H_2	atomic mass is	$2 \times 1.008 =$	2.02
O	atomic mass is	$1 \times 16.00 =$	16.00
H_2O	formula mass is		18.02

or for copper sulfate with the formula $CuSO_4$,

Cu	atomic mass is	$1 \times 63.54 =$	63.54
S	atomic mass is	$1 \times 32.07 =$	32.07
O_4	atomic mass is	$4 \times 16.00 =$	64.00
$CuSO_4$	formula mass is		159.61

or for ammonium phosphate with the formula $(NH_4)_3PO_4$,

N_3	atomic mass is	$3 \times 14.01 =$	42.03
H_{12}	atomic mass is	$12 \times 1.008 =$	12.10
P	atomic mass is	$1 \times 30.98 =$	30.98
O_4	atomic mass is	$4 \times 16.00 =$	64.00
$(NH_4)_3PO_4$	formula mass is		149.11

Strictly speaking, formula mass is restricted to atomic mass units; but in practical laboratory work, the term is taken to mean the same mass in units of grams or a mole.

Handbooks of chemistry list the names, formulas, and several of the physical properties of many compounds. You will find these lists of considerable value for reference.

Ex. 3-9   Find the formula mass for each of the following: $CaSO_4$, PbI_2, KNO_3.

3-16 NAMES

Although formulas are used as precise, short statements about the composition of compounds, chemists also use words to name substances. Word names are desired wherever written statements in prose are made about substances. At the same time, it is convenient to have the names provide as much information about each substance as possible.

Because nearly four million different substances have been named by many people during a period of several thousand years, various naming systems have been devised. In addition, there are numbers of substances, such as sugar or salt, which have not been named according to any system. A name such as sugar does not refer directly to the

TABLE 3-6 NAMES OF SOME CHEMICAL COMPOUNDS

Trivial Name	Formula	Systematic Name
Galena	PbS	Lead sulfide
Iron rust	Fe_2O_3	Iron oxide
Litharge	PbO	Lead oxide
Quicklime	CaO	Calcium oxide
Salt	NaCl	Sodium chloride
Zinc blende	ZnS	Zinc sulfide
Ammonia	NH_3	Ammonia
Methane	CH_4	Methane
Water	H_2O	Water
Soda	$NaHCO_3$	Sodium hydrogen carbonate
Caustic soda	NaOH	Sodium hydroxide
Soda ash	Na_2CO_3	Sodium carbonate

composition of the substance, and chemists therefore call it a **trivial name.** A trivial name sometimes becomes the base for a **systematic name** and is not necessarily unimportant, as the word trivial may imply. For example, methane and ammonia are trivial as well as systematic names.

Many of the compounds discussed in this book are composed of just two elements. Where the pair of elements consists of a metal and a nonmetal, a rather simple naming system is used. Some examples are included in Table 3-6. The rule for these names is to state the name of the metal first, followed by the name of the nonmetal. The ending of the name of the nonmetal is changed to –ide. The systematic names of the first group in Table 3-6 have been assigned on this basis.

3-17 EQUATIONS

Through the use of formulas, it becomes particularly convenient to describe the changes occurring during a chemical reaction. For example, the statement that 1 mole of carbon reacts with 1 mole of oxygen to produce 1 mole of carbon dioxide is written symbolically as

$$C + O_2 \rightarrow CO_2 \qquad (Eq.\ 3\text{-}1)$$

Equation 3-1 is actually much more informative than the longer word statement. Chemists have agreed that the symbols in an equation have all the following meanings.

1. The identity of each reactant and product
2. The number of atoms of each element in each structure unit of reactant and each structure unit of product

3. The number of atoms or molecules or structure units of each substance produced during the reaction of a given number of atoms or molecules or structure units of the reactants.

4. The number of moles of each reactant and product.

It is often helpful to indicate the proper phase for each substance in the equation. This can be done by using the symbols (s), (l), and (g), for solid, liquid, and gas, respectively. Equation 3-1 could then be written in symbols,

$$C \ (s) + O_2 \ (g) \rightarrow CO_2 \ (g) \qquad (Eq. \ 3\text{-}2)$$

which can be translated as: Solid carbon reacts with oxygen gas to produce carbon dioxide gas.

Notice that, in the two equations that have been presented, the number of atoms of each element on the left of the arrow is identical with the number on the right. This is in accord with the earlier finding that the total masses of reactants and products are experimentally the same. When the conservation of atoms is shown, such an expression is called an **equation.** For the reaction of hydrogen with oxygen to form water, however, simply writing the formulas does not result in an equation.

$$H_2 + O_2 \rightarrow H_2O \qquad (Exp. \ 3\text{-}3)$$

The equation is therefore established by multiplying each formula by a suitable coefficient; thus

$$2H_2 + O_2 \rightarrow 2H_2O \qquad (Eq. \ 3\text{-}4)$$

The first assembly of formulas will be called an **expression** (abbreviated Exp. 3-3) and the second an equation (Eq. 3-4). An important rule to remember is that a coefficient multiplies each of the subscripts in the one formula immediately following the coefficient. Another rule is that the set of coefficients in an equation is usually chosen to be the smallest possible set of integers, although there will be occasions when fractions may be suitable. Another example is the equation for the reaction of ammonia with oxygen.

$$4NH_3 \ (g) + 3O_2 \ (g) \rightarrow 6H_2O \ (l) + 2N_2 \ (g) \qquad (Eq. \ 3\text{-}5)$$

Equation 3-5 can be read as: 4 moles of ammonia gas reacts with 3 moles of oxygen gas to produce 6 moles of liquid water and 2 moles of nitrogen gas. In interpreting chemical equations, the word molecule (s) may often replace the word mole (s) with equal validity.

It is possible to write symbols for elements and compounds in the form of a chemical equation so that all the rules described here are obeyed. In fact, any miscellaneous collection of letters can be put into such a form. However, the writing of chemical symbols in the form of an equation does not give any assurance that the reaction shown will actually occur. At this point only written equations which correspond to experimental observations will be considered. In later stages, however, we shall develop ideas which may let you predict a chemical equation for a reaction without first establishing the reaction in the laboratory.

3-18 REACTION OF COPPER AND SULFUR

In the discussion of chemical change in Section 2-10, the copper–sulfur system was explored. A chemical reaction that occurs between copper and sulfur can be written in words as

$$\text{Copper} + \text{sulfur} \rightarrow \text{copper sulfide}$$

Experimental investigation of this reaction indicated the following mass ratios.

$$\frac{\text{Mass of copper}}{\text{Mass of sulfur}} = \frac{3.48 \text{ g of copper}}{1 \text{ g of sulfur}}$$

The atomic mass scale shows the following values for copper and sulfur.

$$\text{Copper atom mass} = 63.5 \text{ amu}$$
$$\text{Sulfur atom mass} = 32.0 \text{ amu}$$

Therefore, 1 mole of Cu would have a mass of 63.5 g, and 1 mole of S would have a mass of 32.0 g.

These relationships permit the experimentally measured mass ratio (3.48 : 1) to be converted to a ratio of moles and finally to a ratio of atoms. The arithmetical operation to do this is

$$\frac{3.48 \text{ g of Cu}}{1 \text{ g of S}} \times \frac{32.0 \text{ g of S}}{1 \text{ mole of S}} \times \frac{1 \text{ mole of Cu}}{63.5 \text{ g of Cu}} = \frac{\text{moles of Cu}}{\text{mole of S}}$$

Notice that the numbers and their labels have been assembled so that g of Cu and g of S appear in both numerator and denominator. These can hence be canceled to leave

$$\frac{3.48}{1} \times \frac{32.0 \text{ moles of Cu}}{63.5 \text{ moles of S}} = \frac{1.76 \text{ moles of Cu}}{1 \text{ mole of S}}$$

This relationship can be used to write a chemical expression for the system, assuming that the data are accurate to at least two significant figures,

$$1.8\text{Cu } (s) + \text{S } (s) \rightarrow \text{Cu}_{1.8}\text{S } (s)$$

If a single substance is the sole result of the reaction, the formula of this substance must itself represent the atomic ratios. The nonintegral numbers can be changed to integers by writing

$$9\text{Cu } (s) + 5\text{S } (s) \rightarrow \text{Cu}_9\text{S}_5 (s)$$

Neither choice is quite as appealing as the small whole numbers found for the other systems discussed so far. Actually, small whole numbers are a characteristic feature of the formulas of most chemical substances in chemistry. The copper–sulfur system serves as a reminder, however, that Nature may not be limited to small whole-number relations when atoms combine. Indeed, nineteenth-century chemists were sometimes blinded by heeding the appeal of small whole numbers.

Recent experimental studies confirm that there is a compound of sulfur with the composition indicated by the formula Cu_9S_5.

3-19 REACTION OF ZINC AND COPPER SULFATE

A study of chemical reactions in another system will show how experimental information about the quantities of material reacting in a system can be used to establish a chemical equation. We choose the reaction between powdered zinc metal and copper sulfate dissolved in water.

Zinc is a metallic element available for laboratory use in sheet form, in granular form, and in fine powder form. Industrially, zinc is widely used for protective coatings for sheet iron. The product is called galvanized iron. Zinc is also mixed and melted with other metals to form materials called alloys (for example, brass).

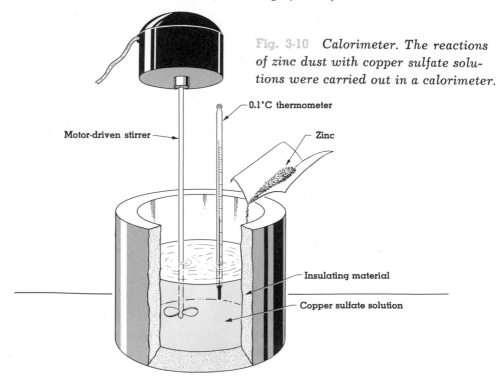

Fig. 3-10 *Calorimeter. The reactions of zinc dust with copper sulfate solutions were carried out in a calorimeter.*

0.1°C thermometer

Motor-driven stirrer

Zinc

Insulating material

Copper sulfate solution

Copper sulfate can be formed when copper and sulfuric acid are heated. Copper sulfate can exist as a white solid with the formula $CuSO_4$. More commonly, copper sulfate combines with water to give a bright blue solid with the formula $CuSO_4 \cdot 5H_2O$, which is an example of a group of substances called hydrates. Either form of copper sulfate dissolves readily in water to give a blue solution.

When zinc metal is added to a blue solution of copper sulfate, the zinc dissolves and, if enough zinc is used, the solution changes from blue to colorless. As the zinc dissolves, a dark-colored powder is formed. The powder can be identified as copper. As the copper separates from the solution, a small amount of gas is produced. If this gas is collected and tested, it is found to be hydrogen.

It appears, then, that a chemical reaction results when zinc is placed in a copper sulfate solution. To write the appropriate chemical equation requires knowledge of the ratios of the moles of components in the system. This knowledge can be obtained by applying the method of continuous variation used in studying the copper–sulfur reaction. The most direct approach is possible when the masses of the reactants and products are expressed in moles.

A mole of Zn weighs 65.4 g, while a mole of $CuSO_4 \cdot 5H_2O$ weighs 250 g. Several samples of copper sulfate can be weighed and dissolved in water to give a series of solutions of varying composition. Each solution in the series should be prepared to contain the same amount of water but a different amount of copper sulfate.

The continuous variation method depends upon the observation of some property of the system which changes by a measurable amount during the process. What is a suitable property for measurement in the study of this system? Preliminary observations suggested that volume changes are less than 0.1 ml for a solution containing 1 mole of copper sulfate and are therefore not well adapted to precise measurements. The copper powder formed during the reaction might be separated from any zinc present and weighed, but this is fairly time-consuming. The addition of powdered zinc to solutions of copper sulfate does produce a quite noticeable increase in temperature. This change in temperature can be determined rather easily. Study of the **temperature-changing capacity** of a system may give still further insight into the behavior of elements and compounds. So far in this study of the amounts of materials involved in chemical change, the only changes in properties that have been measured have been mass or volume. The temperature-changing capacity of a system can be used as a possible means of identification and characterization of a chemical reaction.

In Table 3-7, the data for such an experiment on systems of zinc and copper sulfate are compiled. The arrangement of laboratory equipment is shown in Fig. 3-10, and the data are plotted in Fig. 3-11.

**TABLE 3-7   CONTINUOUS VARIATION STUDY OF SYSTEMS OF
ZINC AND COPPER SULFATE**

Mass of Zinc,[a] g	Mass of Copper Sulfate,[a] g	Zinc, mole	Copper Sulfate, mole	Final Temperature, °C	ΔT,[b] °C
0.00	25.0	0.000	0.100	20.0	0.0
0.65	22.5	0.010	0.090	20.9	0.9
1.29	20.0	0.020	0.080	22.2	2.2
1.93	17.5	0.030	0.070	22.9	2.9
2.58	15.0	0.040	0.060	23.8	3.8
3.22	12.5	0.050	0.050	24.8	4.8
3.87	10.0	0.060	0.040	24.2	4.2
4.51	7.5	0.070	0.030	22.8	2.8
5.15	5.0	0.080	0.020	22.0	2.0
5.80	2.5	0.090	0.010	21.1	1.1
6.54	0.0	0.100	0.000	20.0	0.0

[a] Each reaction was run in 500 ml of water at an initial temperature of 20°C.
[b] ΔT = final temperature − initial temperature.

If more water had been used, the temperature change would have been smaller. Alterations in either the amount of water used or the initial temperature, however, do not affect the mole ratio at which the lines intersect in Fig. 3-11. The magnitude of the change in temperature is determined only by the mass ratio of the reactants in the system.

In Fig. 3-11 the mole ratio for zinc to copper sulfate at the intersection of the two straight lines is 0.051/0.049 or 1.04:1. On page

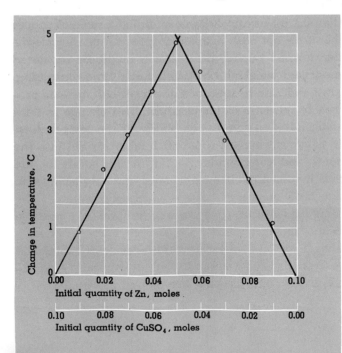

Fig. 3-11   *Temperature changes in systems of zinc and copper sulfate solution. There was 500 ml of water present in each system.*

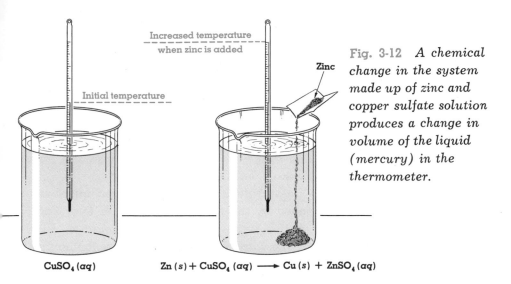

Fig. 3-12 *A chemical change in the system made up of zinc and copper sulfate solution produces a change in volume of the liquid (mercury) in the thermometer.*

Increased temperature when zinc is added

Initial temperature

Zinc

CuSO₄ (aq)

$Zn\,(s) + CuSO_4\,(aq) \longrightarrow Cu\,(s) + ZnSO_4\,(aq)$

105 it was noted that some hydrogen was liberated as the zinc dissolved. Part of the zinc produces hydrogen instead of copper. Careful analysis of the system shows also that a small amount of the zinc does not react with the copper sulfate because the copper produced forms a surface layer on the zinc particles. This layer prevents the copper sulfate from coming in contact with the zinc.

Determination of the quantities of all the products of the reaction shows that

Moles of copper + moles of hydrogen
        + moles of unreacted zinc = moles of zinc initially present

Studies of the reaction of zinc with sulfuric acid solution indicate that 1 mole of hydrogen is produced when 1 mole of zinc reacts. On the basis of this relationship, experimental data indicate that only a small fraction of the zinc in the zinc–copper sulfate systems is involved in the production of hydrogen. For each mole of copper precipitated, 1 mole of zinc dissolves. These observations make it logical to conclude that the mole ratio of zinc to copper sulfate is 1:1. How can this ratio be incorporated into a statement about the reaction?

Knowledge that the mole ratio of Zn/CuSO₄ is 1:1 and that Cu is produced in the reaction permits us to write this expression.

$$Zn + CuSO_4 \cdot 5H_2O \rightarrow Cu + ?$$

In this form, the expression indicates that 1 mole of zinc reacts with 1 mole of copper sulfate. The expression as written is incomplete (it is not an equation) since no product containing zinc is included. More experimental evidence is needed to change the expression into an equation.

If sufficient zinc is added to the copper sulfate solution, the solution becomes colorless. This would indicate that there is no more $CuSO_4$ in solution. When the solution is heated in an open container, water evaporates and a white solid is left as a residue. Analysis of this white solid indicates that its composition and other properties agree with those found for zinc sulfate, a compound with the formula $ZnSO_4$. Like copper sulfate, zinc sulfate can combine with water to form a hydrate but with the formula $ZnSO_4 \cdot 7H_2O$.

In a solution that is unsaturated, there is a large amount of water, much more than demanded by the formulas $CuSO_4 \cdot 5H_2O$ or $ZnSO_4 \cdot 7H_2O$. The presence of this large and variable amount of H_2O is customarily indicated by the word aqueous (aq). The equation for the reaction between Zn and $CuSO_4$ now reads

$$Zn\ (s) + CuSO_4\ (aq) \rightarrow Cu\ (s) + ZnSO_4\ (aq) \quad (Eq.\ 3\text{-}6)$$

This chemical equation represents the experimentally found data for both the identities and masses of the components of the system.

Ex. 3-10　From Table 3-7, plot ΔT against grams of copper sulfate. Are the results the same as those shown in Fig. 3-11?

3-20　REACTION OF SILVER NITRATE AND POTASSIUM CHROMATE

Can properties other than temperature change, volume change, or mass ratios be used to establish chemical equations for reactions? Can an experimentally established and verified chemical equation be used for calculating masses of the components of chemical systems? What is the further significance of temperature change in relation to chemical changes?

The temperature change observed when different quantities of zinc and copper sulfate reacted was used to establish a chemical equation for the change that occurred in the zinc–copper sulfate system. A basic criterion of the property being investigated is that it be possible to measure changes in the property with precision. The continuous variation method can be used to establish a chemical equation for any system if the property under consideration changes during the reaction. For a system in which a precipitate is formed during change, the continuous variation method could be based on the masses of precipitate formed when different relative quantities of the reactants are used.

To determine whether a chemical equation can be established on the basis of the moles of precipitate formed, the reaction of silver nitrate solution with potassium chromate solution is investigated in the laboratory in Experiment 7 of *Investigating Chemical Systems.* When a clear, colorless solution of silver nitrate is added to a clear, yellow solution of potassium chromate, a dark-red precipitate of silver chromate is formed. Solutions containing known concentrations of the reactants are used so that the masses of the reactants can be calculated from the volumes of the solutions used. A series of determinations is made in which the volumes of solutions are varied. By determining the quantity of precipitate formed in each case, the mass of precipitate and the masses of the reactants can be directly related. From what is known about the reagents, the mass ratios can be expressed as mole ratios. A graph of the moles of silver chromate formed against the corresponding mole ratios of reactants should indicate the mole ratio at which there would be the least unreacted silver nitrate or potassium chromate left in the system. This particular mole ratio would indicate the composition of the system in which the maximum change in property measured (or maximum interaction) could occur. This mole ratio should be used in writing the chemical equation for the reaction of silver nitrate with potassium chromate.

In work with reagents in solution, one important part of the description of a system is the composition of the solution. The potassium chloride–water system discussed in Section 2-5 was described by a composition given as 26.8 g of potassium chloride per 100 ml of solution. Compositions of systems in which chemical reactions occur are best described by specifying the number of moles of each reagent. Therefore, it is convenient to describe the compositions of solutions in terms of moles of dissolved material (solute) per liter of solution. Since 1 mole of potassium chloride (KCl) has a mass of 74.6 g, the composition of a solution containing 26.8 g of potassium chloride per 100 ml can be expressed in another way.

$$\frac{26.8 \text{ g per } 100 \text{ ml of solution}}{74.6 \text{ g/mole of KCl}} = \frac{0.36 \text{ mole of KCl}}{100 \text{ ml of solution}} = \frac{3.6 \text{ moles of KCl}}{\text{liter of solution}}$$

Any composition expressed in terms of moles per liter of solution is called a **molar composition** or a **molar concentration.** The phrase molar concentration is often shortened to **molarity.** The abbreviation for molarity is M. Thus the concentration of the potassium chloride solution can be stated as 3.6 M.

Can a chemical equation once established be used for calculations of mass? What is the further significance of temperature changes in relation to chemical changes?

Ex. 3-11 Compare the conclusions resulting from the discussion in the text of the zinc–copper sulfate system and the conclusions based on the data obtained from the investigation of the silver nitrate–potassium chromate system in Experiment 7 of *Investigating Chemical Systems.*

3-21 CALCULATION OF MASSES FROM MASS RATIOS

Experimental evidence for chemical changes that can be represented by chemical equations usually points to the conclusion that the mole ratios are fixed for the various components of a system as they participate in a chemical change. Since they are fixed, calculations are easily made in terms of masses. As an example, consider Equation 3-6.

$$Zn \ (s) + CuSO_4 \ (aq) \rightarrow Cu \ (s) + ZnSO_4 \ (aq) \quad (Eq. \ 3\text{-}6)$$

In a chemical equation, mole ratios are represented by the coefficients preceding the various formulas. Where no numerical coefficient is written, it is understood that the number 1 is intended. So the mole ratio for Cu/Zn or for $Cu/ZnSO_4$ is 1:1, and similarly for every other pair of substances shown in the equation.

But mole has been defined in such a way that replacement of the formula symbols by atomic mass numbers gives a mass in grams. So for Cu/Zn, it is possible to write either

$$\frac{1 \text{ mole of Cu}}{1 \text{ mole of Zn}} \quad \text{or} \quad \frac{63.5 \text{ g of Cu}}{65.4 \text{ g of Zn}}$$

Whatever mass of zinc reacts with copper sulfate to produce copper, the mass of zinc reacting and the mass of copper produced will be in the ratio as stated. Thus if 0.1 mole of zinc reacts, 0.1 mole of copper is produced; or if 1.234 moles of copper is produced, 1.234 moles of zinc must have reacted.

Suppose that you wish to know how much copper can be produced by the reaction of 15.0 g of zinc. The first step in the calculation converts the mass of zinc in grams to a mass in moles.

$$\frac{15.0 \text{ g of Zn}}{65.4 \text{ g of Zn per mole of zinc}} = 0.229 \text{ mole of Zn}$$

The mole ratio for copper to zinc as represented by the chemical equation is a 1:1 ratio. On this basis, 0.229 mole of zinc must, therefore, produce 0.229 mole of copper. The calculation of the mass of copper in grams is

$$\frac{63.5 \text{ g of Cu}}{\text{mole of Cu}} \times 0.229 \text{ mole of Cu} = 14.5 \text{ g of Cu}$$

Another example might be considered from an earlier section.

$$2H_2 \ (g) + O_2 \ (g) \rightarrow 2H_2O \ (l)$$

This equation is based on experimental data. From it, you can conclude that the ratio of oxygen reacting to water formed is

$$\frac{1 \text{ mole of } O_2}{2 \text{ moles of } H_2O}$$

From this ratio, it is possible to compute the mass of oxygen needed to produce a given mass of water. For example, the problem might be that of calculating the amount of oxygen required to produce 54 g of water. If the mass of water is first expressed in moles, it is then possible to calculate the required number of moles of oxygen. Water, with the formula H_2O, has a mass of 18.0 g/mole. So 54 g of water is 3.0 moles of H_2O.

$$\frac{54 \text{ g of water}}{18.0 \text{ g of water per mole of } H_2O} = 3.0 \text{ moles of } H_2O$$

From the chemical equation only 1 mole of oxygen is needed to produce 2 moles of water. Therefore, 3.0 moles of water requires $3.0 \times \frac{1}{2} = 1.50$ moles of oxygen. In grams the oxygen must weigh 48 g.

$$1.50 \text{ moles of } O_2 \times \frac{32 \text{ g of oxygen}}{\text{mole of } O_2} = 48 \text{ g of oxygen}$$

Calculations of masses from mass ratios are conveniently done in several steps.

Problem 1: How many grams of copper are produced when 15.0 g of zinc reacts with copper sulfate?

Solution:
   Step. 1. Chemical equation.

$$Zn \text{ (s)} + CuSO_4 \text{ (aq)} \rightarrow Cu \text{ (s)} + ZnSO_4 \text{ (aq)}$$

   Step 2. Express the mole ratio of desired reaction substances.

$$\frac{Zn}{Cu} = \frac{1 \text{ mole of Zn}}{1 \text{ mole of Cu}}$$

   Step 3. Calculate the amount of zinc in moles. 15.0 g of zinc in moles will be

$$\frac{15.0 \text{ g of zinc}}{65.4 \text{ g of zinc per mole of Zn}} = 0.229 \text{ mole of Zn}$$

   Step 4. Calculate the mass of copper in grams. Since 1 mole of Zn reacts with 1 mole of Cu (Step 2), 0.229 mole of Zn will produce 0.229 mole of Cu. Then

$$0.229 \text{ mole of Cu} \times \frac{63.5 \text{ g of copper}}{\text{mole of Cu}} = 14.5 \text{ g of copper}$$

Answer: When 15.0 g of zinc reacts with copper sulfate, 14.5 g of copper is produced.

Problem 2: How many grams of oxygen are required to produce 54 g of water?

Solution:

Step 1. Chemical equation:

$$2H_2 + O_2 \rightarrow 2H_2O$$

Step 2. Express the mole ratio of desired reacting substances.

$$\frac{O_2}{2H_2O} = \frac{1 \text{ mole of } O_2}{2 \text{ moles of } H_2O}$$

Step 3. Calculate the amount of water in moles. 54 g of water in moles will be

$$\frac{54 \text{ g of water}}{18.0 \text{ g of water per mole of } H_2O} = 3.0 \text{ moles of } H_2O$$

Step 4. Express the amount of oxygen required in moles. From Step 2, for each mole of H_2O, $\frac{1}{2}$ mole of O_2 is required. Therefore $3.0 \times \frac{1}{2} = 1.50$ moles of O_2 is required.

Step 5. Calculate the mass of oxygen in grams.

$$1.50 \text{ moles of } O_2 \times \frac{32.0 \text{ g of oxygen}}{\text{mole of } O_2} = 48 \text{ g of oxygen}$$

Answer: To produce 54 g of water, 48 g of oxygen is required.

3-22 TEMPERATURE-CHANGING CAPACITY

In Section 3-19 a change in the chemical system of zinc and copper sulfate was observed to be accompanied by a temperature change. Nearly every chemical change is accompanied by some temperature change. During some changes, the temperature rises; in others it falls.

Commonly, temperature is measured in the laboratory with a thermometer. A **thermometer** is a tube filled with a liquid or a gas which can change in volume. When the volume of the liquid or gas increases, the temperature is said to rise, whereas a decrease in volume indicates a fall in temperature. The liquid commonly used in laboratory thermometers is mercury.

An electric heater can be used to change the temperature of water. Figure 3-11 shows the effect of a chemical change on the temperature of the water in which the copper sulfate was dissolved. In each case, the system in its initial state is said to have a temperature-changing capacity.

To understand how two such seemingly different agencies as an electric heater system and a chemical reaction in a chemical system can each produce the same effect on a thermometer requires a new idea. Scientists have developed the idea of thermal energy or heat as a major aid to the understanding of the relationship between the two

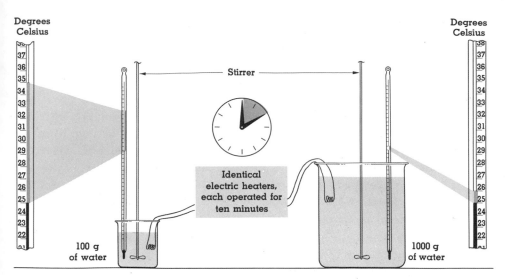

Fig. 3-13 *The same amount of heat is transferred to the water in each beaker by the identical heaters during a ten-minute time interval. The magnitude of the temperature increase depends on the mass of water in the beaker.*

kinds of systems. Quite commonly the term heat is used to mean the same thing as thermal energy. According to this idea, an electric heater transfers heat to any object colder than the heater, a chemical reaction transfers heat to any object colder than the chemical system, and the temperature of water rises when heat is transferred to it. **Heat** or **thermal energy** is defined as energy transferred between two systems that differ in temperature.

To provide a quantitative basis for describing heat, scientists make use of a unit of measurement called the **kilocalorie.** When one kilogram of water absorbs one kilocalorie (kcal) of heat, the temperature of the water increases by one degree Celsius. The calorie (cal) is one-thousandth of a kilocalorie. In other words, one calorie of heat will increase the temperature of one gram of water one degree Celsius. For a known change in temperature, the heat absorbed or evolved is given by the following equations.

$$\text{Number of calories} = \text{grams of water} \times \frac{1 \text{ cal} \times \Delta T}{1 \text{ g of water} \times {}^{\circ}\text{C}}$$

$$\text{Number of kilocalories} = \text{kilograms of water} \times \frac{1 \text{ kcal} \times \Delta T}{1 \text{ kg of water} \times {}^{\circ}\text{C}}$$

It is assumed that no matter what kind of a system furnishes the thermal energy, a single definition is always precisely applicable. Furthermore, it is assumed that if a given mass of water undergoes a given temperature decrease, precisely the same quantity of energy must be removed from the water as would be absorbed in a temperature rise of the same magnitude. These assumptions are usually stated as the *law of conservation of energy.*

In the concept of thermal energy, a change or difference in temperature has been related to thermal energy. Nothing has yet been said about how a particular temperature is related to thermal energy. Another peculiar feature of temperature can be noted in passing. Numbers are assigned to temperature readings. The difference between two temperature readings has a relationship to heat, but the sum of two temperature readings has no interpretable meaning. Throughout this course, much use will be made of temperature differences; no use will be made of temperature sums.

When the same quantities of heat are added to equal masses of different substances, the temperatures of the substances change by different amounts. The characteristic property describing the response of a substance to the addition of heat is called the *heat capacity* of the substance. Heat capacities of substances are expressed in units of calories per gram per degree (cal/g-deg) or calories per mole per degree (cal/mole-deg).

The amount of heat produced or absorbed by chemical systems can be estimated by observing temperature changes. Investigations carried out in an insulated container so that the temperature changes observed can be precisely and reproducibly related to amounts of heat are called *calorimetry.*

Throughout the course, considerable use will be made of calorimetric data. The first laboratory investigation involving the measurement of temperature changes is Experiment 8 in *Investigating Chemical Systems*. The addition of dilute hydrochloric acid to water results in a temperature change. The hydrochloric acid–water system can be used to determine what effect the quantities of reagents present in the system will have on the temperature-changing capacity of the system.

Ex. 3-12   Will addition of more water to one of the zinc–copper sulfate systems described in Table 3-7 change the quantity of heat evolved? You may want to try this in the laboratory as an extension to Experiment 8.

Ex. 3-13   If 1 kcal of heat is transferred to each of the following systems, which system will show the greater temperature change?

a. 100 ml of 2.27 *M* (molar) hydrochloric acid

b. 100 ml of 0.227 *M* copper sulfate solution

The heat capacity of the hydrochloric acid is 0.866 cal/g-deg and the density is 1.0376 g/ml. The heat capacity of the copper sulfate solution is 0.999 cal/g-deg and the density is 1.0349 g/ml.

Avogadro proposed his idea about the relation of gas volumes to numbers of molecules in 1811. Most of the chemists at the time refused to accept his proposal. One telling argument his opponents raised against him was based on Avogadro's conclusion that some of the gaseous elements have diatomic molecules.

The argument against diatomic molecules of hydrogen or oxygen was simple. Diatomic molecules of an element did not make sense. It is fairly easy to believe that two different kinds of atoms could join together. Two different kinds of atoms might be imagined, for instance, to be electrically charged much as a piece of paper and a plastic comb can be charged and made to cling together. But for two identical atoms to stick together—nonsense! So argued Avogadro's critics.

It took fifty years for Avogadro's proposal to be finally accepted. At first it was ignored as contrary to common sense. Then other facts equally incomprehensible according to the earlier views came to light and led a number of chemists to accept his hypothesis, but only in the area of organic chemistry, that is, the chemistry of carbon compounds. Some even went so far as to assume that all elements exist in the diatomic state. Finally another Italian, Stanislao Cannizzaro, wrote an article in 1858 to show how Avogadro's idea could be applied systematically. His article was distributed at the first International Chemical Congress which had been called specifically for the purpose of finding a uniform basis for the determination of atomic and molecular masses. This was held in Karlsruhe, Germany, in 1860. Cannizzaro was able to bring together such an extensive collection of data that the argument was most impressive. Avogadro's proposal was then finally accepted.

In addition to the impressive way that Cannizzaro presented the argument to show that an assignment of formulas could be made straightaway for a great many different compounds, there were probably two other factors responsible for his success. (1) Most of Avogadro's opponents had died or retired by the time Cannizzaro wrote his article. (2) No other convincing way of solving the problems of gas reactions had appeared.

Even so, the problem of how two identical atoms could be joined was still not solved; diatomic molecules were simply accepted as facts. This problem was not to be solved until 1925. In the nineteenth century only two possibilities were recognized as ways of holding atoms together. One way was by gravitational forces. Isaac Newton had proposed this possibility in the seventeenth century. Experiments have shown, however, that gravitational forces are far too small to account for the behavior of atoms. The other way was by electrical forces which are large enough but do imply the need for two different kinds of atoms in any molecule.

So far as the nineteenth-century chemist was concerned, Cannizzaro won the argument for Avogadro. His logic was compelling when applied to experimental data. But no one in the nineteenth century could provide any good explanation of why Avogadro's hypothesis worked.

3-24 ATOMIC THEORY

In addition to the problem of diatomic molecules, there are other problems raised by some of the ideas considered thus far. **Atomic theory** implies that matter consists of discrete particles. If atoms are assumed to be round balls, then matter is made up of spheres packed together. If atoms are spheres, there must be empty spaces among the atoms. Even if atoms are some shape other than spherical, there must still be some point between any two atoms which is considered to be in neither atom. If this were not the case, it would not be reasonable to think about each atom as if it had an identity.

A theory in which matter is viewed as atomic implies that matter contains some empty spaces or gaps between the atoms. The idea that matter consists of particles and gaps is old. Democritus talked about it in Greece more than two thousand years ago. Plato developed the idea and assigned various geometrical shapes to atoms. Aristotle rejected the whole notion of discrete particles and defended the rival idea that matter must be continuous.

Just consider one puzzle if you try to believe that matter is atomic. You are made up of atoms. Yet if the atoms in one of your hands are really disconnected from those in your other hand, how can your right hand know what your left hand is doing? But if you argue that in some way your right and left hands are connected, can you maintain the idea that they are really made up of atoms?

By and large, chemists find that the atomic theory provides so many answers to their problems that they have little reason to seek another theory. Modern physicists, however, are finding some experiments which raise questions about the extent to which matter is atomic. In this book, it is assumed that the atomic theory is satisfactory. The immediate problem to be solved, then, is that of how separate atoms can be connected without losing their identity.

3-25 SUMMARY

The conversion of mass ratios into atomic ratios has been accomplished through the study of the volumes of reacting gases. Central to the discussion was Avogadro's hypothesis—that equal volumes of gases at the same temperature and pressure contain equal numbers of molecules.

Through this idea of Avogadro's, it became possible to establish a scale of atomic masses and develop the notion of molecular mass as a characteristic property of gases. From laboratory observations of alpha particles, a count of the molecules in a gas was obtained first by Rutherford. A mole of material is defined as an amount containing 6.0×10^{23} particles or units—the Avogadro number.

With a way available for establishing atomic ratios for elements involved in chemical change, formulas and chemical equations were given precise meaning. Laboratory data from a chemical system can be presented in the form of a chemical equation. The chemical equation provides a basis for calculations concerned with the amounts of substances which react in the system described by the equation.

Chemical reactions are usually accompanied by temperature changes. Preliminary inspection suggests that these temperature changes bear a precise relation to the amount of chemical change. This possibility will be explored further.

As neatly as the argument for atoms and molecules appears to proceed, it poses at least one serious difficulty. For example, how can two identical hydrogen atoms be held together in a molecule whose formula is claimed to be H_2? The next several chapters will partially develop the evidence and ideas necessary to answer this question.

Ex. 3-14 Experiments show that 1 volume of nitrogen reacts with 3 volumes of hydrogen to produce 2 volumes of ammonia. How can this experimental evidence be used to postulate whether nitrogen gas is composed of diatomic molecules?

Ex. 3-15 What experimental evidence other than that presented in Table 3-2 can be outlined to support the idea that 2 volumes of hydrogen reacts with 1 volume of oxygen to produce water?

Ex. 3-16 Calculate the atomic masses of the underlined gases, using the information given.

   Atomic mass of hydrogen = 1.008   Atomic mass of oxygen = 16.00

Reactants	Volume Ratio	Mass Ratio
Hydrogen-chlorine	1:1	1:35.2
Hydrogen-nitrogen	3:1	1:4.63
Oxygen-nitrogen	2:1	1:0.437
Hydrogen-fluorine	1:1	1:18.9
Fluorine-bromine	3:1	1:1.40

Ex. 3-17 *a.* Determine the molecular masses of the following gases, from their densities at 0°C and 1 atmosphere pressure (molecular mass of oxygen = 32.00; density of oxygen = 1.429 g/liter).

117

$$\begin{array}{ccc} & & Density \\ \text{Diborane} & & 1.241 \text{ g/liter} \\ \text{Propane} & & 2.01 \ \ \text{g/liter} \end{array}$$

b. Determine the molecular masses of the following gases, from the ratio of the density of the gas to the density of oxygen at the same temperature and pressure (molecular mass of oxygen = 32.00; density of oxygen = 1.429 g/liter at 0°C).

	Density of Gas/Density of Oxygen
Hydrogen fluoride	0.63
Phosphine	1.06

Ex. 3-18 Defend or refute each of the following statements.

a. An empirical formula of a compound represents mass ratios and atomic ratios of elements even when the compound is not composed of molecules.

b. The subscripts in molecular formulas are without real meaning. For example, the molecular formula for ethane can be written C_2H_6 or CH_3, whichever is more convenient.

Ex. 3-19 Convert each of the following statements into the appropriate chemical equation.

a. When heated, mercury oxide (HgO) yields mercury and oxygen gas.

b. Ammonia decomposes upon heating to give hydrogen and nitrogen.

c. Lithium hydride and water react to give lithium hydroxide (LiOH) and hydrogen gas.

d. Magnesium oxide reacts with hydrogen chloride to give water and magnesium chloride.

Ex. 3-20 Change the following expressions where necessary so that they become chemical equations. Assume that the formulas of the reactants and products are correct as written.

a. $Sb + O_2 \rightarrow Sb_4O_6$

b. $H_2 + Br_2 \rightarrow HBr$

c. $C_3H_8 + O_2 \rightarrow CO_2 + H_2O$

d. $CO \rightarrow C + CO_2$

e. $Fe_2O_3 + CO \rightarrow Fe + CO_2$

f. $O_2 + SO_2 \rightarrow SO_3$

g. $H_2SO_4 + Ca \rightarrow CaSO_4 + H_2$

h. $P_4O_{10} + H_2O \rightarrow H_3PO_4$

i. $PCl_5 + H_2O \rightarrow HCl + H_3PO_4$

j. $H_2S + Cl_2 \rightarrow S_8 + HCl$

k. $Fe + H_2O \rightarrow Fe_3O_4 + H_2$

l. $H_2O_2 \rightarrow H_2O + O_2$

m. $CaC_2 + H_2O \rightarrow C_2H_2 + Ca(OH)_2$

n. $Fe(OH)_3 \rightarrow Fe_2O_3 + H_2O$

o. $Pb(NO_3)_2 \rightarrow PbO + NO_2 + O_2$

p. $H_3BO_3 \rightarrow H_4B_6O_{11} + H_2O$

q. $CaCN_2 + H_2O \rightarrow CaCO_3 + NH_3$

r. $KClO_3 \rightarrow KClO_4 + KCl$

s. $KClO_3 \rightarrow KCl + O_2$

t. $H_3PO_3 \rightarrow H_3PO_4 + PH_3$

u. $Al_4C_3 + H_2O \rightarrow CH_4 + Al(OH)_3$

Ex. 3-21 Compute the formula mass of each of the following substances: Water, methane, $MgCl_2$, AlF_3, Fe_2O_3, C_2H_5OH, NH_4Br, $(NH_4)_2SO_4$, P_4O_{10}, and H_3PO_4.

Ex. 3-22 The following equation represents the reaction which occurs when sucrose $(C_{12}H_{22}O_{11})$ combines with oxygen.

$$C_{12}H_{22}O_{11} \ (s) + 12O_2 \ (g) \rightarrow 12CO_2 \ (g) + 11H_2O \ (l)$$

Defend or refute each of these statements.

a. The set of coefficient numbers 1, 12, 12, and 11 apply to the reaction of sucrose with oxygen.

b. All reactants and products are gaseous.

c. In an equation the total number of molecules of reactants is equal to the total number of molecules of products.

d. In an equation each formula or symbol is multiplied by a suitable co-efficient.

Ex. 3-23 Refer to the table of data. Plot the volume of oxygen used on the abscissa and the corresponding temperature increase of the calorimeter on the ordinate. The data were obtained when a series of experiments was carried out to determine what happens when 1.20-g samples of magnesium burn in different amounts of oxygen. These reactions were carried out in a calorimeter.

Mass of Mg Used, g	Volume of O_2 Used, liter	Mass of MgO Produced, g	Increase in Water Temperature, °C	Mass of Mg Remaining, g
1.20	0.10	0.36	0.65	0.98
1.20	0.20	0.72	1.30	0.76
1.20	0.30	1.08	1.97	0.55
1.20	0.40	1.44	2.62	0.33
1.20	0.50	1.81	3.28	0.12
1.20	0.60	2.01	3.66	0.00
1.20	0.70	2.02	3.67	0.00
1.20	0.80	2.00	3.65	0.00
1.20	0.90	2.02	3.66	0.00

After you have completed the graph, defend or refute the following statements.

a. The amount of oxygen used does not affect the change in temperature of the system.

b. The greatest temperature increase occurs when all the magnesium present in the system reacts with all the oxygen present in the system.

c. If the calorimeter system is equivalent to 2,000 g of water, the maximum energy released is 7320 cal.

Ex. 3-24 Magnesium metal reacts with sulfuric acid according to the equation

$$Mg \ (s) + H_2SO_4 \ (aq) \rightarrow H_2 \ (g) + MgSO_4 \ (aq)$$

a. How many grams of hydrogen will be produced when 4.05 g of magnesium reacts completely with sulfuric acid?

b. What mass of Mg is required to produce 1.2 g of magnesium sulfate (MgSO$_4$)?

Ex. 3-25 The graph shows a continuous variation plot for the magnesium metal–sulfuric acid system. The procedure used for each system was to mix powdered magnesium metal with sulfuric acid solution at 23°C. In each case the highest temperature reached was recorded. The equation for the reaction is

$$Mg\ (s) + H_2SO_4\ (aq) \rightarrow H_2\ (g) + MgSO_4\ (aq)$$

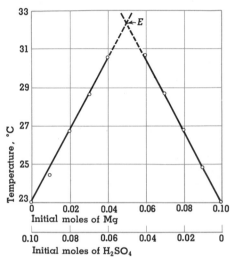

Defend or refute the statements below.

a. The graph indicates that 1 mole of magnesium metal reacts with 1 mole of sulfuric acid.

b. Approximately 98 g of sulfuric acid is required to react completely with 24.3 g of magnesium metal.

c. The greatest temperature increase is coincident with the least amount of magnesium reacting.

Ex. 3-26 Refer to the graph in Exercise 3-25.

a. If the system represented at point E contains the equivalent of 75 g of water, what is the approximate quantity of heat (in kilocalories) transferred as the state of the system changes from the initial state to the final state?

b. Would the graph have the same general form if the heat transferred were plotted against the moles of magnesium?

Ex. 3-27 Assume that an atomic reactor produces 3.00×10^{-7} g of helium per hour and that the total alpha–particle production is estimated to be 1.26×10^{13} alpha particles per second. Use this information to estimate the number of helium atoms in 1 mole (4.003 g) of helium.

Ex. 3-28 Show the relation between the formulas and the compositions (percent by mass) of the following compounds.

a. Water is 11.1 percent hydrogen by mass.

b. Sucrose (C$_{12}$H$_{22}$O$_{11}$) is 42.1 percent carbon, 6.4 percent hydrogen, and 51.5 percent oxygen by mass.

c. For a compound composed of 14.18 percent carbon, 2.36 percent hydrogen, and 83.46 percent chlorine, the formula is CH$_2$Cl$_2$.

120

PART ONE: THE NATURE OF CHEMICAL CHANGE

Chapters 1, 2, and 3

Operational and conceptual	**Solution and mixture**
Homogeneous and heterogeneous	**Order and disorder**
System and environment	**Mass and volume**
Initial and final states	**Gram and mole**
Analysis and synthesis	**Atom and molecule**
Reagent and product	**Experimental and mental**

OUR INVESTIGATION of chemical change began with the isolation of a system for study. Experimental or conceptual isolation of the materials to be studied provides the only assurance that the observations made are directly related to something that can be identified. Since the chemist works with systems in which changes occur, he has to be able to be certain that, both before and after a system undergoes a change in state, he is still dealing with the same system.

A system can be described in terms of its properties. The description of the properties of the individual components assembled for the system makes up the initial state of the system.

If the components are mixed, the system may undergo a change in state. The initial and final states are related in one of two ways. In one case the initial and final states are identical. In the other case the final state differs from the initial state. When initial and final states do not differ, the components of the system are said not to interact. For systems in which initial and final states differ, the components of the system are said to interact.

Another type of result is also found when the initial components of a system are mixed. In its final state, the system will be a mixture, a solution, or a substance different from the initial components. Mixtures or solutions may be formed in systems in which the initial components do or do not interact. The formation of a new substance is always associated with interaction of the initial components.

Our conclusions about mixtures, solutions, and compounds can be put in chart form. The diagram shows how fineness of subdivision and variability of composition are related to mixtures, solutions, and compounds. The extent of interaction can also be interpreted in terms of structure. For systems in which the components do not interact, the arrangement of structural units is believed to be random. Interaction in a system indicates that the final components have a higher degree of order than the initial components.

Interaction among the components initially present in some systems leads to the formation of one or more new substances. These are the systems whose changes in state are characterized as chemical reactions. For each chemical reaction there is one system in which the initial mass ratio of elements is identical with the mass ratio of elements in the products. Further than this, the composition of the products does not change even for considerable change in the initial mass ratio of components. In these cases, there is an excess of one or more of the initial components. That the compositions of the products of a particular chemical reaction do not change for a considerable change in the initial composition of the system is the distinctive characteristic of all chemical reactions. This is the basis for describing a compound as having a fixed, or characteristic, composition.

The characteristic mass ratios of the components of copper sulfide, lead iodide, or silver chromate, and, in fact, of all compounds, suggest some kind of structure that is determined by the way the parts fit together. We assume, as did Higgins and then Dalton, that the parts or structural units of compounds are atoms. The atoms of each element are different from those of other elements. All atoms of one element have the same mass, whereas atoms of different elements have different masses. To develop quantitative relationships for changes involving the combination of atoms, it is necessary to find the relative masses of the atoms of each of the elements. A relationship between the masses assigned to the atoms of different elements makes it possible to express

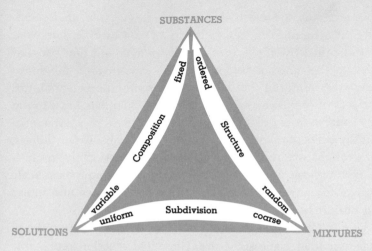

SUBSTANCES

fixed / ordered

Composition / Structure

variable / random

uniform   Subdivision   coarse

SOLUTIONS   MIXTURES

the mass ratios of elements present in compounds in terms of relative numbers of atoms of the elements which comprise compounds.

The study of reactions in gaseous systems provides a way to assign masses to atoms. The basic principle in the development is the assumption first proposed by Avogadro. Avogadro assumed that, at any given temperature and pressure, the volume occupied by a sample of gas is directly proportional to the number of molecules in the sample. No other characteristic of a gas has been found to be involved in the relation between number of molecules and volume when changes in temperature and pressure in the system are not involved. On the basis of Avogadro's assumption, experimental investigations of the nature of reacting gases suggests that a molecule of a compound is composed of atoms of different elements.

Chemists have developed procedures by which the atomic ratios in any compound can be determined either by analysis or by synthesis. At least four million compounds have thus been investigated by chemists. The composition of each compound is expressed as an atomic ratio and hence by a formula. For many, but not all, compounds, the atomic ratios can be represented by small whole numbers. These small whole-number ratios strongly imply that chemical compounds have an internal structure.

To be able to establish the relative numbers of atoms in a compound is a considerable step beyond merely identifying a compound. Beyond this point is the question of the absolute numbers of atoms in a particular sample of material. It is possible to count the number of helium atoms formed as a result of the radioactivity of some substances. The application of Avogadro's hypothesis gives a way to determine the number of molecules in a sample of any other gas through knowledge of the number of helium atoms in a known quantity of helium gas.

The number of atoms or molecules is large in any system that chemists can study. The number of molecules in 32 g of oxygen has been chosen as a unit called the mole. It is equally convenient and conventional to refer to the mass of this amount of oxygen as a mole. An amount of any other material that contains the same number of atoms, molecules, or sets of atoms is also called a mole. Chemists have found that the use of moles to express the relative quantities of components is essential in the conceptual models of chemical systems. Nevertheless, laboratory operations are usually described by indicating the quantities of substances present in grams or milliliters. The atomic mass scale enables chemists to convert grams and milliliters to moles and moles to grams and milliliters.

The discussion in Chapters 1, 2, and 3 suggests that each element and compound has a characteristic structure. Chemical reaction represents a change in structure. In thinking about the structures of substances, the idea of atoms and molecules is found to be very useful. At this point in our study, the only properties assigned to the atom are mass, the ability to be a unit of structure, and the fact that all the atoms for any one element are identical. Just how atoms can be part of a structure and yet maintain their identity will have to be the subject of further exploration.

ELECTRICITY AND MATTER

THE STUDY OF THE properties of materials and the changes in properties which take place under certain conditions is a central theme of this book. One of the first results of this study was a classification scheme in which the categories of matter were organized to show the relation of pure substances (compounds and elements) to other materials. The chemical elements were recognized as the minimum group of substances of which all other materials are composed. Consequently, the composition of any material may be expressed in terms of the relative masses of elements present in that material.

When the quantitative data regarding the compositions of a number of compounds were examined, a pattern was discovered. The composition of a pure compound is constant. These data were interpreted on the basis of the assumption that each element is composed of atoms which are identical with respect to mass and to their abilities to combine with the atoms of other elements. Each compound is composed of atoms of two or more elements. In any given compound, the relative numbers of atoms of the elements present are assumed to be constant in order to account for the constant composition.

The next step in the study of properties of matter was to discover the relative numbers of atoms of the elements present in a compound. It is significant that the data regarding masses alone do not provide a solution to this problem. The information needed for a solution was provided by data concerning the relative volumes of gases involved in chemical reactions. Avogadro's hypothesis proposed that equal volumes of gas samples, compared at a given temperature and pressure, contain equal numbers of molecules. This can be restated to propose that a fixed relationship exists between the number of molecules in a sample of a gas and the volume of that sample for any given temperature and pressure. This hypothesis, based upon a different type of information, permitted the simplest ratios of atoms in the gaseous molecules to be deduced from combining volumes of gases (Gay-Lussac). Hence formulas for gaseous compounds could be written.

The combination of formulas for gases with data on composition expressed in terms of mass permits the assignment of relative masses to the atoms of different elements. The atomic masses so developed proved to be just as relevant to the compositions of solid and liquid compounds as to the compositions of gases. Consequently, it is possible to assign a formula to any compound, providing that its composition is known.

Experimental data for the composition of compounds can be interpreted satisfactorily in terms of presently held concepts of the nature of atoms and their behavior in chemical systems. Determination of the compositions of many additional compounds confirms the usefulness of the ideas developed in Chapters 1, 2, and 3. No new and significant problems are encountered.

4-1 ELECTRIC ENERGY AND CHANGE

Just as it was necessary to turn to a new type of experimental information to arrive at molecular formulas, it is now necessary to consider information other than composition data in order to raise and answer new questions about the nature of matter. Observations made in two specific experiments already encountered will serve to change the direction of the investigation. These observations are similar in that they both involve electricity and water, but are markedly different in terms of the changes produced by the interaction of the electricity and water. Detailed comparisons of the similarities and differences between these two observations may provide an insight into the relationship between electricity and matter.

In one of these experiments, the two terminals of a battery were connected to a heating coil which was immersed in a beaker of water (Fig. 4-1a). The proper combination of the battery and the heating coil supplies energy to the water. Without the battery, the heater does not affect the water. However, the combination of the battery and heating coil causes the temperature of the water to increase until the water finally boils. The heater is a device for transferring energy from the battery to the water. The energy absorbed by the water is used to con-

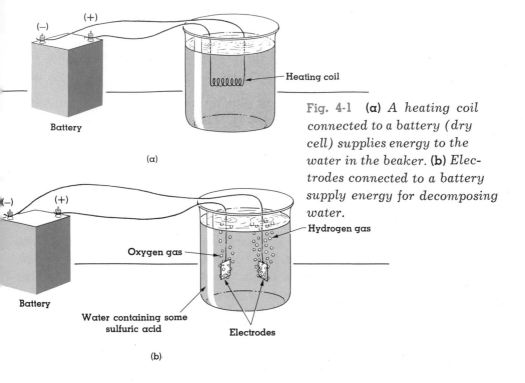

Fig. 4-1 **(a)** *A heating coil connected to a battery (dry cell) supplies energy to the water in the beaker.* **(b)** *Electrodes connected to a battery supply energy for decomposing water.*

vert part of the water from the liquid phase to the gaseous or vapor phase. When the water vapor is cooled (that is, some of the energy is removed from the water vapor), it is converted back into liquid water (see also Fig. 1-2).

In the second experiment, each of the two terminals of the battery was connected to a metal plate which is called an electrode. Both electrodes were then immersed in a beaker of water in such a way that they did not touch each other (Fig. 4-1b). A small amount of sulfuric acid was added to the water. Under these conditions, some of the water was converted into oxygen gas and hydrogen gas. The process was referred to as the electrolysis of water (see also Fig. 3-5).

In the first experiment, the water underwent a change of phase,

$$H_2O \ (l) \rightarrow H_2O \ (g)$$

but in the second experiment, the water underwent a chemical change, that is,

$$2H_2O \ (l) \rightarrow 2H_2 \ (g) + O_2 \ (g)$$

The results of the two experiments are distinctly different.

There are, however, recognizable similarities between the two experiments. For instance, a battery was used to produce both changes. A second similarity is detected most easily by what happens when liquid water is re-formed from the products of each of the changes induced by the battery.

$$H_2O \ (g) \rightarrow H_2O \ (l) \hspace{3cm} (Eq.\ 4\text{-}1)$$

$$2H_2 \ (g) + O_2 \ (g) \rightarrow 2H_2O \ (l) \hspace{2cm} (Eq.\ 4\text{-}2)$$

Water in the vapor phase must give up some of its energy in order to form liquid water (Equation 4-1). Likewise, a system made up of hydrogen and oxygen must give up energy in order to form liquid water. The recombination of hydrogen and oxygen to form water frequently releases so much energy in such a short time interval that the reaction is referred to as an explosion. Any reaction that releases a large amount of energy in a short time interval is an **explosion.**

It is common experience that some systems can undergo changes which release energy. Energy must be supplied to restore these systems to their original conditions. For instance, if a book falls from the desk to the floor, someone must lift it to restore it to the desk. To lift the book requires that energy be supplied to it. Based on the idea that energy must be provided to bring about the reverse of a change which evolves energy, it is logical to conclude that the battery supplies energy to the water during both the heating and the electrolysis.

These conclusions pose a problem. Here are two cases in which a battery is supplying energy to a beaker of water. Yet, the effects of this added energy are observed to be markedly different in the two cases. When the terminals of the battery are connected by a continuous piece of metal (the heater), the water accepts the energy in the form of heat and as a result undergoes a change in phase. A bunsen burner flame could have been used just as well as a source of heat to produce the same change in phase. When there is not a continuous piece of metal in the water (that is, when two electrodes are connected to the battery terminals), the water accepts the energy by undergoing a chemical change. This chemical change cannot be brought about simply by heating a beaker of water with a flame. What relationships between the electric energy supplied by the battery and the nature of chemical substances can be discovered by more detailed study of these phenomena?

4-2 FROM ELECTRICITY TO MATTER

In industrial societies, electric energy is widely used. In general, any use of electric energy can be classified into one of two categories. On the one hand, electric energy is used to start automobiles, operate radio transmitters and receivers, produce light, and drive motors. Most of these cases are similar to the heating of water in that they make use of systems having continuous metallic connections between the termi-nals of the source of electric energy.

On the other hand, electric energy is used on a large scale to bring about chemical changes. Aluminum metal is produced by electrolysis. Protective and decorative layers of silver, copper, or chromium are frequently applied to metallic objects by electrolysis (sometimes called electrodeposition). Millions of tons of chlorine and sodium hydroxide are produced each year by the electrolysis of sodium chloride solutions. All these processes are similar to the electrolysis of water in that the metallic connections between the terminals of the source of electric energy are not continuous and that the chemical reaction occurs at the discontinuities in this metallic connection, that is, at the surfaces of the electrodes.

4-3   FROM MATTER TO ELECTRICITY

The variety of chemical changes which may be induced through the use of electric energy suggests that there is a close relationship between electricity and matter. This relationship is more firmly established by an examination of a source of electric energy. Figure 4-2 is a diagram of a simply constructed source of electric energy known as a Daniell gravity cell. The container, pieces of zinc and copper, and wires are assembled as shown. A solution of sodium chloride is added until the zinc at the top of the container is covered. Crystals of $CuSO_4 \cdot 5H_2O$, called copper sulfate five hydrate or simply copper sulfate, are then poured to the bottom of the container. Some of the copper sulfate dissolves in the region of the piece of copper. After the parts have been assembled properly, energy is available from the cell. For example, a light bulb may be lighted or a door bell may be rung

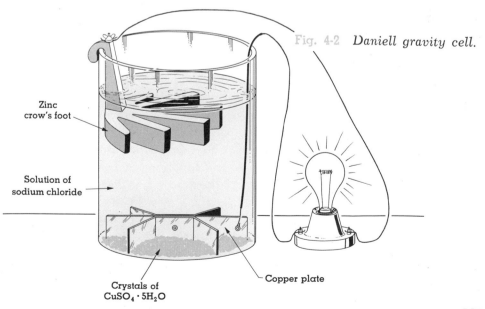

Fig. 4-2 *Daniell gravity cell.*

Zinc
crow's foot

Solution of
sodium chloride

Crystals of
$CuSO_4 \cdot 5H_2O$

Copper plate

when either is connected to the wires leading from the zinc metal and the copper metal. The Daniell cell which produces electric energy is simply an appropriate arrangement of chemicals. In other words it is a system. Dry cells and storage batteries are also appropriate arrangements of chemicals. A battery is made up of two or more cells.

4-4 THE DANIELL CELL

The chemical components of the Daniell cell (that is, the reagents present in the system in its initial state) include a solution of copper sulfate and zinc metal. The chemical reaction occurring when zinc metal is dipped into the copper sulfate solution has been discussed previously (Section 3-19) and can be represented by

$$Zn\ (s) + CuSO_4\ (aq) \rightarrow Cu\ (s) + ZnSO_4\ (aq)$$

In the cell, the copper sulfate is in the bottom part of the solution, whereas the zinc metal is in the top part. Consequently, there is no direct physical contact between the zinc metal and the copper sulfate solution. However, when the cell is used to supply electric energy, the mass of the piece of zinc metal decreases while the mass of the piece of copper increases. This suggests that the chemical reaction occurring in the cell is the same as the reaction occurring when zinc is immersed in a copper sulfate solution. Yet in the cell, these two substances are not in direct physical contact. How, then, can the reaction occur?

Apparently, the wires outside the container and the solution within the container provide sufficient connection between the zinc and the copper sulfate solution to permit this chemical reaction to take place. As the reaction occurs, electric energy is made available in the wires connected to the zinc and copper. If this is the case, the reaction is different from the chemical reactions studied so far in that the reactants, zinc and copper sulfate solution, are not in direct physical contact with one another. The changes occurring in the Daniell cell can be observed and measured in the laboratory.

The chemical reaction between zinc and copper sulfate has now been examined in two different ways. In the first instance, the reactants were mixed directly and the temperature rose. The reactants therefore have a temperature-changing capacity. In Section 3-22, temperature-changing capacity was related to the supplying of heat by a chemical reaction. The temperature rise of the water is a measure of the heat made available to and absorbed by the water. In the second instance, the reactants were not in direct contact but were connected through a solution and by copper wires. Energy was available as electric energy. Is the quantity of energy available in the two cases the same, or does the way in which energy is transferred from a chemical system influence the quantity of energy available?

a. What would happen in the cell described in Section 4-3 if the piece of zinc fell into the copper sulfate solution?

b. Suppose that a student assembles a Daniell cell (Fig. 4-2), but reverses the positions of the zinc and copper electrodes. Does this make any difference in the operation of the cell?

4-5 ELECTRICITY: CHEMICAL PRODUCERS AND CONSUMERS

The Daniell cell is one of a number of systems used as sources of electric energy. Examination of other electrochemical cells shows that what is observed in the case of the Daniell cell is always observed. An *electrochemical cell* is a system of chemicals arranged in such a way that two things occur.

1. The production of electric energy in the cell is always associated with a chemical reaction.

2. The reaction must be carried out in such a way that it is impossible for the necessary reactants to come into direct contact. This condition is sometimes met by surrounding one electrode with a porous cup to prevent the mixing of the solutions that surround each electrode.

There is, then, some similarity between the electrolysis apparatus and the electrochemical cell as a source of electric energy. In the electrolysis apparatus, the wires leading from the two battery terminals must not be in direct contact with one another if electrolysis is to occur. In electrochemical cells, the essential components for the chemical reaction producing the electric energy must be arranged so that they are not in direct contact with one another. In both cases, the chemical reaction occurs at the electrode surfaces.

Sometimes, a cell can undergo electrolysis when a source of electric energy is connected to the electrodes and can also produce electric energy upon demand after the source of electric energy has been disconnected. The chemical reaction occurring during the electrolysis is the reverse of the chemical reaction by which the cell provides electric energy. It is possible to use a cell of this type as a storage place for electric energy. The conventional automobile battery, which is made up of reversible cells, is called a *storage battery.*

Electrochemical cells are only one source of electric energy. Most of the electric energy used in the United States is produced by the conversion of chemical energy to heat (burning coal or oil), of heat to motion (steam turbine), and of motion to electricity in a generator. Chemists are more interested in studying electrochemical cells than generators because electrochemical cells provide a simpler way to study the relationship between electric energy and matter.

The ideas developed so far about the nature of electrochemical cells and electrolysis reactions provide a new way of considering an electrolysis reaction in which a battery is used as a source of electric energy. The electric energy is produced by one set of substances undergoing a chemical reaction in the battery of electrochemical cells. The energy is used to cause a second set of substances to undergo a chemical reaction in the electrolysis apparatus. In essence, then, the entire assembly of the battery and the electrolysis apparatus simply provides a means by which one chemical reaction supplies the energy needed for a second chemical reaction. In this situation, which includes two systems, the coupling between the systems is provided solely by wires.

A wide variety of chemical reactions is used in the cells of the different types of batteries available. There is an equally large number of electrolysis reactions used. The fact that so many chemical reactions can be used either to produce or to consume electricity implies once more that a close relationship exists between electricity and matter. Moreover, this relationship can be expressed in a quantitative way.

4-6 QUANTITATIVE PROPERTIES OF ELECTRICAL SYSTEMS

The quantitative study of electrical systems requires instruments which permit the measurement of properties characteristic of these systems. The voltmeter and the ammeter are two such devices that can be used to define and measure two properties of electrical systems. The property measured by the **voltmeter** is called **electric potential difference,** sometimes called simply **potential difference.** The unit of measurement for electric potential difference is called a **volt.** The property

Fig. 4-3 (a) *The voltmeter is used to measure electric potential difference.* (b) *The ammeter is used to measure electric current.*

(a)

(b)

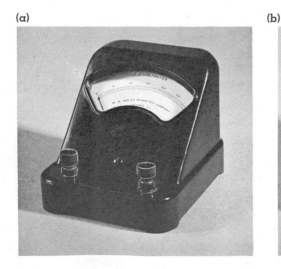
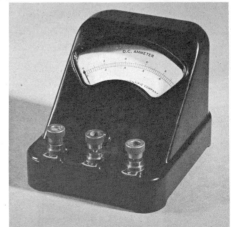

measured by the **ammeter** is called **electric current.** The unit of measurement of electric current is called an **ampere.**

Both the voltmeter and the ammeter are frequently thought of as black boxes, each of which has a scale and pointer and terminals for attaching it by wires to an electrical system. When either instrument is connected properly to an electrical system, the position of the pointer on the scale indicates the numerical value of the appropriate property of that electrical system.

The term black box is used in a way slightly different from that in Section 1-4. The difference is really only a difference in emphasis. In Experiment 2 of *Investigating Chemical Systems,* certain manipulations of a sealed box gave rise to reproducible observations which were recorded. The emphasis there was an attempt to design a model whose properties would provide a basis for explaining the responses of the object in the box to the manipulations. In the present case, the ammeter and voltmeter provide reproducible observations when they are connected to electrical systems. The emphasis here is on the fact that the observations, that is, the scale readings, are reproducible. They can, therefore, be a basis for measurement even though the internal working of the instruments may be unknown to the operator.

It may be pointed out that many of the instruments used to define and measure properties of matter are black boxes in this same sense. For instance, mass was defined as the property measured by an equal-arm balance, volume was defined in terms of calibrated glassware, and temperature in terms of changes in a mercury thermometer. In none of these cases were the details of the construction and mechanism of the measuring instrument explained. They are all black boxes which respond in a reproducible way when they are properly employed. The description of the instrument and the way it is to be used constitutes an operational definition of the property measured by the instrument.

The techniques necessary to obtain reproducible and significant measurements using ammeters and voltmeters have not yet been presented, so the operational definitions of electric current and electric potential difference are incomplete. However, the significance of the techniques of measurement will be more understandable if the implications of electric current and electric potential difference are discussed briefly.

4-7   THE AMMETER AND ELECTRIC CURRENT

In ordinary usage, the word current means rate of flow. For instance, the current of a river is the speed at which a floating object passes a given point on the river bank. The speed is commonly expressed in miles per hour. In the case of electric current, it is assumed that what flows is **electric charge.** Electric current is a statement of the amount of electric charge passing a given point in the electrical system per unit of time. A current of one ampere is defined as the passage of one unit of charge per second. This unit of charge is known as a **coulomb.**

It is important to recognize, however, that although the ammeter measures the current directly, it does not operate by counting coulombs and measuring time intervals. In this respect, an ammeter is similar to the speedometer of a car. At any given time, the scale reading on the speedometer shows the speed of the car, usually in miles per hour. Similarly, at any given time, the scale reading on the ammeter shows the current in an electrical system. The reading on a speedometer does not represent the average speed, a quantity arrived at by dividing the number of miles traveled by the time taken to travel them. The calculation of average speed of a car involves the use of two scale readings, that of the odometer (on the dashboard), which records the number of miles traveled, and that of a clock. An average current is measured by employing information about coulombs and time, the first obtained from a **coulometer,** which counts units of electric charge passing through an electrical system, and the second obtained from a clock. An ammeter gives a value for the current at the instant of the reading.

There is another significant similarity between the ammeter and the speedometer. In both cases a scale reading indicates the magnitude of a property and implies a direction of motion as well. The speedometer provides a scale reading only when the car is moving forward. An ammeter provides a scale reading only when it is connected into an electrical system so that the positive (+) terminal of the ammeter is connected to the positive (+) terminal of the battery and the two negative (−) terminals are similarly connected by materials which permit the flow of charge. Materials which permit the flow of electric charge are called **electric conductors.** By convention the direction of the current is from the positive terminal to the negative terminal of the ammeter.

4-8 THE VOLTMETER AND ELECTRIC
POTENTIAL DIFFERENCE

The voltmeter provides a way of measuring the difference in electric potential between any two points in an electrical system. Specifically, it measures the difference in electric potential between the two points in the system which are immediately connected to the two terminals of the voltmeter. The direction of the current is the same as the direction in which the electric potential decreases. In other words, the direction of the current is from high potential to low potential. Voltmeters are constructed so that, when their positive (+) terminals are connected to the point of higher potential and their negative (−)

Fig. 4-4 **(a)** *An electric heater circuit. When the switch is closed, the electric current can be read from the ammeter scale. The potential difference between the ends of the heater coil is indicated on the scale of the voltmeter.* **(b)** *Schematic diagram of the electric heater circuit shown in* **(a).**

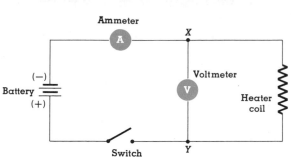

(b)

terminals are connected to the point of lower potential in electrical systems, they will provide scale readings.

4-9   ELECTRIC HEATING CIRCUIT

The use of the voltmeter and the ammeter may be clarified by describing a specific case. Figure 4-4a is a picture of a simple electrical system representative of those in which electric energy is employed for generating heat. The voltmeter and the ammeter are placed in the system in a proper fashion to make measurements. Figure 4-4b is a conventional way of representing the same system on paper. It is frequently referred to as a **schematic diagram** of the system or as a **circuit diagram.** The expression circuit diagram reflects the use of the term circuit to refer to an arrangement of wires and apparatus through which electric charge can flow.

When the switch is open as shown in Fig. 4-4b, the readings on the voltmeter and the ammeter are both zero, no charge flows, and there is no current in the circuit. When the switch is closed, the needles of both the voltmeter and the ammeter swing to new positions and remain steady. Closing the switch, then, establishes both a potential difference between points x and y and a current in the circuit.

Placing the ammeter and voltmeter at different locations in the circuit to map it in terms of potential differences and current yields the following information. As long as the positive terminal of the voltmeter is connected to the copper wire between the positive battery terminal and the heater coil and as long as the negative terminal of the voltmeter is connected to the wire between the negative terminal of the battery and the heater coil, the electric potential difference reading on the voltmeter is essentially constant. This means that the electric potential at all points on each of these wires is essentially the same. In fact, the potential on each of the wires is very nearly the same as that of the terminal of the battery to which the wire is attached. In other words, the electric potential is uniformly high between the positive terminal of the battery and the heater and is uniformly low between the negative terminal of the battery and the heater. This indicates that the major change in electric potential in the circuit occurs in the heating coil. Direct measurement of electric potential difference between various points on the coil and one of the battery terminals confirms this conclusion.

4-10 CONSERVATION OF ELECTRIC CHARGE

The readings obtained when the ammeter is placed at different points in the circuit represented in Fig. 4-4 are all the same. In other words, the current has the same value wherever it is measured in the circuit. What significance does this fact have when it is considered in terms of electric charge? Consider an arbitrarily chosen length of wire, the ends of which are designated by A and B and through which electric charge is flowing.

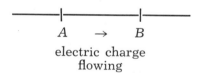

electric charge
flowing

Measurement indicates that the current (defined in Section 4-6) at A is equal to the current at B. Let this constant value of the current be I. During any time interval Δt, the quantity of charge entering the section of wire is equal to $I \Delta t$. When I is expressed in coulombs per second passing point A and when Δt is expressed in the number of seconds that charge flows past point A, $I \Delta t$ is expressed as the number of coulombs flowing past A in Δt seconds. The quantity of charge leaving the wire at B is also equal to $I \Delta t$ so that no charge is lost as it passes through the segment of the circuit between A and B. More broadly, no charge is lost at any point in the entire circuit while charge flows.

4-11 POTENTIAL DIFFERENCE AND ENERGY

Considering the idea of a battery as a source of energy will provide further qualitative understanding of the circuit represented in Fig. 4-4. The energy is apparent in this case as heat generated in the heating coil. The change in electric potential in the circuit was also found to occur in the heating coil. These observations would indicate that the generation of heat is associated with a decrease in the electric potential in the coil. Therefore, potential difference can be associated with energy. How this relationship may be established in more detail is the subject of the next investigation which considers the changes occurring when the same type of circuit is used with the heater coil immersed in a known quantity of water. The potential difference across the coil, the rate of charge flow (current) in the circuit, the length of time that charge flows, and the temperature of the water sample can be measured. The change in temperature of a known mass of water has already been used as a measure of the quantity of heat energy supplied to the water (Section 3-22). Thus, experimental data relating values for potential difference, current, and the change in temperature of a sample of water heated by an electric heater may be used to relate the electrical properties of a heating circuit to the energy produced.

Figure 4-5 is a schematic diagram of the apparatus employed in this investigation. The electric potential difference between the two ends of the heater (frequently phrased "the potential drop across the heater") is measured by means of the voltmeter. The current in the circuit is measured on the ammeter. When the switch is closed, steady readings

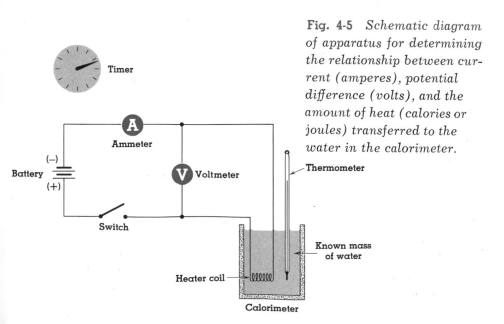

Fig. 4-5 *Schematic diagram of apparatus for determining the relationship between current (amperes), potential difference (volts), and the amount of heat (calories or joules) transferred to the water in the calorimeter.*

are observed on both instruments. If a second battery is added in an appropriate way or if the battery is replaced by a different type and the switch is closed, two new values are obtained for the potential drop and the current.

4-12 ELECTRIC CONDUCTANCE

Before the changes occurring in the completely assembled electrical system when charge passes through the circuit are considered, it will be helpful to study the characteristics of the heater by itself. Table 4-1 lists values for the potential difference across the heater and for the current in the circuit. Figure 4-6 is a graph of the data in Table 4-1 with the current in the circuit plotted against the potential drop across the heater. Figure 4-6 may be interpreted by saying that the ratio of the current in the heater to the potential difference across the heater is equal to a constant, the slope of the straight line.

$$\frac{\text{Current}}{\text{Potential difference}} = \text{constant}$$

Symbolically this equation is frequently written

$$\frac{I}{\Delta V} = K \qquad (Eq.\ 4\text{-}3)$$

where I is the current in the circuit expressed in amperes, ΔV is the potential difference across the heater expressed in volts, and K is the constant value of the ratio $I/\Delta V$ which has the units amperes/volts. The value of K is the slope of the straight line in Fig. 4-6.

These data imply that the heating coil has a characteristic property

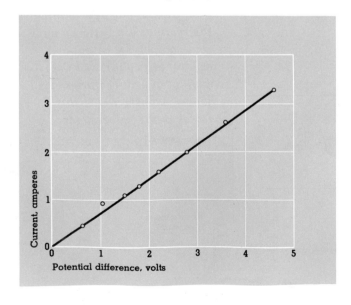

Fig. 4-6 *Current through a heater coil measured at several potential differences.*

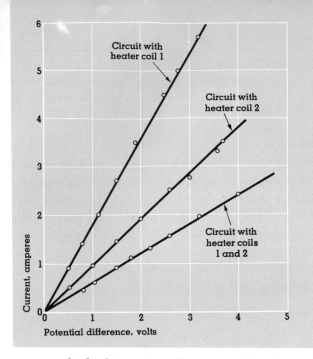

which determines the current in the coil at any particular potential difference across the coil. This relationship may be seen more clearly if it is expressed in the following form,

$$I = K \, \Delta V \qquad \qquad (Eq.\ 4\text{-}4)$$

which states that the current in the circuit is proportional to the potential difference across the heater. The characteristic property of the coil is then measured by K and is called the **conductance** of the coil.

Similar experiments with other heating coils or other metallic circuits reveal that for each of these the graph of current in the circuit against potential difference across the circuit is a straight line. Each circuit, then, has a characteristic conductance which may be calculated from the slope of a straight-line graph. For example, in Fig. 4-7, the slope of the graph for Circuit 1 is 1.8 amperes/volts. Therefore, the conductance K of Circuit 1 is 1.8 amperes/volts.

TABLE 4-1 CHARACTERISTICS OF A HEATER COIL

Electric Potential Difference, volts	Current, amperes
0.63	0.46
1.02	0.93
1.5	1.1
1.8	1.3
2.2	1.6
2.8	2.0
3.6	2.6
4.6	3.3

Calculate the conductance for Circuits 2 and 3 in Fig. 4-7. Circuit 3 is a combination of Circuits 1 and 2 connected in series so that the charge must flow through both heating coils. Establish the relationship between the conductances of Circuits 1 and 2 and the conductance of Circuit 3.

4-13 ELECTRIC RESISTANCE

If a circuit had infinite conductance, the current would be infinite for any potential difference other than zero. In a circuit with zero conductance, charge would not flow and the current would be zero. Under normal conditions, air has nearly zero conductance since charge does not flow through it. However, all the circuits considered so far permit charge to flow only at a particular measurable rate for a given potential difference. Conductance can be considered to be the current in a circuit per unit of potential difference,

$$K = \frac{I}{\Delta V}$$

It is customary also to describe the circuit by the potential difference per unit current. This is given by dividing the identity $1 = 1$ by the above equation.

$$\frac{1}{K} = \frac{\Delta V}{I}$$

The potential difference per unit current is then called the resistance of the circuit and is frequently indicated by R so that

$$R = \frac{1}{K} = \frac{\Delta V}{I} \qquad (Eq.\ 4\text{-}5)$$

The relationship between I and ΔV for the circuit is also expressed by

$$IR = \Delta V \qquad (Eq.\ 4\text{-}6)$$

The resistance of a circuit has the units volts/amperes which are called **ohms.** This name is given in honor of Georg Simon Ohm (1787–1854), who established the relationship between I, ΔV, and R. It is amusing to note that a conductance unit is called a **mho** (pronounced mo) where mho is ohm spelled backward.

Ex. 4-3 Calculate the resistances of Circuits 1, 2, and 3 from the graphs shown in Fig. 4-7. Establish the relationship between the resistances of Circuits 1 and 2 and the resistance of Circuit 3, a combination of Circuits 1 and 2. Does this suggest a reason for the common use of the resistances of circuits instead of their conductances?

4-14 ELECTRICITY AND CALORIMETRY

The relationship between $I, \Delta V$, and R for electric heating circuits can be used to establish further relationships between these properties

TABLE 4-2 COMPARISON OF TEMPERATURE RISE IN UNINSULATED
AND INSULATED BEAKERS[a]

Time of Heating, minutes	Temperature, °C	
	Uninsulated Beaker, A	Insulated Beaker, B
0	21.70	21.70
1	22.70	22.80
2	23.65	23.80
3	24.60	24.80
4	25.50	25.75
5	26.45	26.70
6	27.35	27.65
7	28.25	28.60
8	29.10	29.60
9	29.95	30.50
10	31.40	30.70
11	31.60	32.45
12	32.50	33.35
13	33.25	34.05
14	34.00	34.70
15	34.70	35.40

[a] Current, potential difference, and amount of water are kept fixed.

and the amount of energy transferred by a given circuit as heat. Figure 4-5 shows an apparatus that can be used for investigating this relationship. The heater coil is made of a wire whose temperature rises as charge flows through the wire. Heat transferred from the hot wire in turn raises the temperature of the water in the calorimeter. The flowing charge represents electric energy within the wire. Heat or thermal energy is transferred from the hot wire to the colder water. For this reason the hot wire is spoken of as an electric heater.

The apparatus in Fig. 4-5 includes a calorimeter in which the change in temperature of the water (ΔT) is proportional to the quantity of heat transferred from heater to water. If current in the heater, potential difference, time interval, and quantity of water are kept fixed, is a given temperature rise always a reliable indication that the same quantity of heat has been transferred? Data for one investigation of this question, collected in Table 4-2, shows two different temperature rises which indicate that insulation of the system is an important factor.

4-15 HEAT AND CHARGE FLOW

The quantities ΔV and I remained essentially constant throughout the time the data were obtained for Table 4-2. The temperature of the

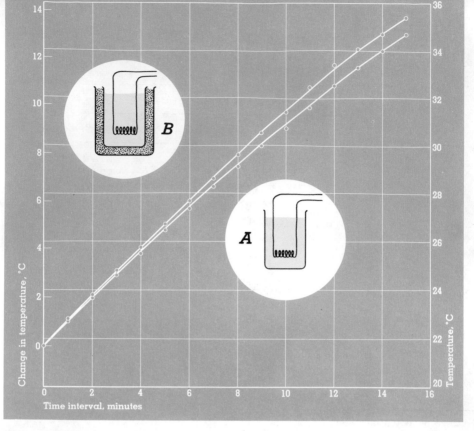

Fig. 4-8 *Change in temperature of two systems while they are being heated. Curve A applies to a case where a heater was placed in 250 g of water in an uninsulated beaker. Curve B was found for a case where a heater was placed in 250 g of water in the same beaker insulated with crumpled paper inside a larger beaker.*

water increases during the time interval that charge flows through the heater. The relationship between these two quantities is shown in Fig. 4-8. The change in the temperature of the water (ΔT) is plotted against the time interval (Δt). The curve representing changes in temperature occurring during small time intervals is nearly a straight line.

The experiment was repeated, using a beaker insulated with crumpled paper inside a larger beaker (B) as a container for the water instead of an uninsulated beaker (A). The data obtained are plotted in Fig. 4-8. For the insulated beaker, the graph is more nearly a straight line. On the basis of this trend, one may imagine an ideal apparatus and experiment in which the plot is indeed a straight line. In such an ideal case, the change in the temperature of the water would be directly proportional to the time interval during which there was a constant current in the circuit.

Change in temperature of water $=$ constant $\times$ time interval
$$\Delta T = K_1 \times \Delta t$$

For a current of given magnitude, the number of units of electric charge (number of coulombs) flowing through the circuit is directly proportional to the time interval during which charge flows.

$$\text{Number of coulombs} = I \times \Delta t \qquad (Eq.\ 4\text{-}7)$$

During any particular time interval, then, a certain number of coulombs flows through the heater and the temperature of the water changes by a definite amount. When the same time interval is used in the two preceding equations, they may be rearranged and combined to obtain

$$\frac{\Delta T}{K_1} = \Delta t = \frac{\text{number of coulombs}}{I}$$

Therefore
$$\frac{\Delta T}{K_1} = \frac{\text{number of coulombs}}{I}$$

Multiplying both sides of this equation by K_1 gives

$$\Delta T = \frac{K_1}{I} \times \text{number of coulombs}$$

For a current of given magnitude the temperature change is proportional to the number of coulombs flowing through the heater. In Section 3-22, a temperature change in water was defined as a measure of heat. This definition can be used to interpret the temperature change ΔT of the known mass of water in the calorimeter in terms of the quantity of heat absorbed by the water from the heater. The quantity of heat absorbed by the water from the heater is proportional to the number of coulombs flowing through the heater.

4-16   HEAT AND POTENTIAL DIFFERENCE

The battery is the source of potential difference in the heating circuit. In any of the experiments discussed so far, the heater has operated with a constant potential difference so that the effect of difference in potential cannot be identified. In what way is the potential difference related to the energy released to the water and the calorimeter? It is possible to carry out a series of experiments in which the current is measured for other potential differences. It is then possible to compare, for the same quantity of water in each case, the changes in temperature occurring when the same number of coulombs have passed through the heater at other potential differences. A development similar to that in Section 4-15 shows that

$$\text{Energy released as heat} = K\,\Delta V$$

when the number of coulombs is constant. Experimentally, then, the energy released as heat by an electric heater is proportional to the number of coulombs flowing through the heater and to the electric potential difference across the heater. This may be expressed algebraically.

$$\text{Energy released as heat} = K \times \Delta V \times I \times \Delta t \qquad (Eq.\ 4\text{-}8)$$

where $I \Delta t$ is the number of coulombs (Equation 4-7).

The relationship may also be viewed in a different manner, and this becomes evident when both sides of Equation 4-8 are divided by $I \Delta t$.

$$\frac{\text{Energy released as heat}}{I \Delta t} = K \times \Delta V \qquad (Eq.\ 4\text{-}9)$$

This equation says that the electric potential difference ΔV across a heater is proportional to the energy released per unit of charge $I \Delta t$ flowing through the heater. Here, then, is a new understanding of the meaning of potential difference. The potential difference tells how much energy can be obtained from an electrical system per unit of charge flowing through the circuit.

The calorie was defined in Section 3-22 as the amount of heat required to raise the temperature of one gram of water one degree Celsius. The defined value of the calorie can be used to calculate from experimental data the value of the proportionality constant K in Equation 4-8. The presently accepted value of K is 0.2391 calorie per volt-coulomb (cal/volt-coulomb). In other words, the passage of 1 coulomb of charge through a circuit in which there is a potential difference of 1 volt releases 0.2391 calorie of heat energy.

$$K = 0.2391 \ \frac{\text{cal}}{\text{volt-coulomb}}$$

In work with electrical systems, the calorie is an inconvenient unit of energy because the proportionality constant 0.2391 must be used to convert energy values from volt-coulombs into calories. Consequently, a different unit of energy called the joule is used. One joule is equivalent to the amount of energy available when one coulomb of charge passes through a potential difference of one volt; that is, 1 **joule** is equal to 1 volt-coulomb or to 0.2391 calorie.

$$1 \text{ joule} = 1 \text{ volt} \times 1 \text{ coulomb} = 0.2391 \text{ calorie}$$

This relationship between potential difference and energy may be expressed in a different way. If each of two points is maintained at a constant electric potential, the potential difference between these two points (in volts) is numerically equal to the change in energy (in joules) per unit of charge (in coulombs) moving from one point to the other. In the case of the heating circuits discussed, the electric charge flows through the circuit and the system transfers energy in the form of heat.

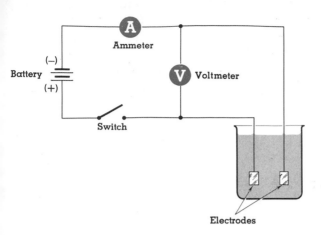

Fig. 4-9 *Schematic diagram of apparatus for determining the relationship between current (amperes), potential difference (volts), and the products of the electrolysis of water or of aqueous solutions.*

4-17 CONDUCTION IN SOLUTION: IONS

This new understanding of the significance of I, ΔV, and R, which are all measurable properties of an electric circuit, permits the establishment of the relationship between these properties and the electrolysis of water. An apparatus which permits a study of this problem is shown schematically in Fig. 4-9.

If the container into which the electrodes are inserted is filled with pure water and the switch closed, the ammeter indicates no current in the circuit. Increasing the potential difference between the electrodes by connecting more batteries in the circuit does not produce any significant flow of charge.

If the experiment is repeated, starting with low values for ΔV and using water containing sulfuric acid instead of pure water in the electrode container, the system is observed to behave differently. At very low values of ΔV, the ammeter reading is still essentially zero. Increasing the potential difference between the electrodes will cause a flow of charge, and hydrogen and oxygen gases are separately produced at the two electrodes. The detection of the current and the evolution of gases occur simultaneously for potential differences at which no charge flow was detected in the pure water. In other words, at the same potential differences, no flow of charge is observed in pure water whereas flow of charge is detected in water containing sulfuric acid. Apparently, then, the pure water does not provide a mechanism for charge flow, whereas the water containing sulfuric acid does. (See Section 3-2 and Fig. 3-5.)

Sulfuric acid is only one of a large number of substances whose solutions in water permit the flow of charge, that is, whose aqueous

145

solutions are conductors. On the other hand, solutions of many substances, for example, sugar or methanol, are not conductors. It would
be reasonable to assume that a particular type of chemical species is
present in the solutions that conduct charge, whereas this type of
species is not present in solutions that do not conduct charge. Solutions that conduct charge are called *ionic solutions.* The chemical
species responsible for the flow of charge through the solutions are
called *ions.*

Ex. 4-4   How could you proceed in the laboratory to answer these questions about
the electrolysis of an aqueous solution of sulfuric acid.

a. Is heat produced during electrolysis?

b. Do all substances which permit charge flow in an aqueous solution behave
like sulfuric acid?

c. Of what significance is the finding that the ratio of the volume of oxygen
produced to the volume of hydrogen produced is 1:2?

4-18   CONDUCTION AT ELECTRODE SURFACES: CHEMICAL REACTION

However, the presence of ions alone does not seem to account for
the transfer of electric charge between the electrodes and the solution.
During the electrolysis of water, the transfer of electric charge at the
electrodes is associated with the chemical reaction producing hydrogen
and oxygen. Moreover, this transfer takes place only at potential differences ΔV above a certain minimum. In Equation 4-9, the energy transferred as heat from an electric circuit indicated that the potential difference was proportional to the energy per unit of charge transferred.
Requirement of a minimum potential difference then indicates the
need of a minimum energy for a unit of charge to flow. A qualitative
explanation of these observations is suggested by the intuitive understanding that a change which releases energy can be reversed only by
the absorption of energy. Hence, the energy released when hydrogen
and oxygen react to form water must be added to the water to convert
it back into hydrogen and oxygen. This interpretation associates the
chemical reactions occurring at the electrodes with the transfer of
charge between the solution and the electrodes. This interpretation
also requires that there be sufficient energy available to bring about
these chemical reactions before the transfer of charge can take place.
In other words, if the energy is not available, no reaction occurs. If no
reaction occurs, no charge is transferred.

The electrolysis circuit has already proved to be more complicated
than the simple heater circuit. Explanation of the observations made
during electrolysis requires the consideration of three types of *electric
conduction* or flow of charge.

1. Conduction in metals: The flow of charge through metallic conductors. In general, metallic conductors have low resistances. The flow of charge through metals is associated with heating effects and the operation of motors but is not accompanied by chemical change. Any potential difference across a metallic conductor will induce a flow of charge.

2. Conduction in water solutions: The flow of charge through a solution. This may occur whenever certain substances are added to water. To account for this flow of charge the existence of ions in these solutions is postulated. Any potential difference across a solution containing ions will start a flow of charge.

3. Conduction across the boundary between electrodes and solution in an electrolysis cell: This type of conduction is always accompanied by a chemical change. A specific energy per unit of charge transferred is required (Equation 4-9). The energy requirement is dependent upon the nature of the substance in the solution and in the electrodes.

The explanation of what happens in the electrolysis of water is far from complete even though the flow of charge in the circuit can be explained. The following questions suggest areas in which new experimental information may be helpful.

1. If the sulfuric acid provides ions permitting the transport of charge through the solution, why is only the water decomposed at the electrodes?

2. Do all substances which permit conduction in aqueous solution behave as does sulfuric acid, or do some of these substances contribute to the products formed?

3. Are the transport of charge in solution and the changes at the electrodes accompanied by the evolution of heat as is metallic conduction?

4. Why is hydrogen produced only at the electrode connected to the negative battery terminal while oxygen is produced only at the electrode connected to the positive battery terminal?

5. Why is the ratio of the mass of oxygen produced to the mass of hydrogen produced or the ratio of the moles of oxygen produced to the moles of hydrogen produced constant?

Answers to questions 2 and 3 may be obtained in the laboratory. Answers to questions 1 and 4 will have to wait until a more thorough understanding of the relationship between electricity and matter has been presented. Some answers to question 5 can be proposed from the laboratory work in Experiment 10 in *Investigating Chemical Systems*. In Experiment 10, the effect of electric energy on a chemical system is investigated. A Daniell cell is constructed, and its ability to produce electric energy is studied. The effects of electric energy on several chemical systems are observed, and some conclusions are developed.

4-19   MASS RELATIONSHIPS IN ELECTROLYSIS REACTIONS

One possible explanation of the constant ratio of the mass of oxygen to the mass of hydrogen produced by the electrolysis of water is that electric energy can be used only to break up molecules and that both parts of any molecule must appear as reaction products. Since hydrogen and oxygen are present in a constant mass ratio in water molecules, they would then be produced during electrolysis in a constant mass ratio. If this explanation is generally true, the ratio of the masses of the elements in the products of any electrolysis reaction must correspond to the ratio of masses of the elements in a substance which is present in the material being electrolyzed. A study of different electrolysis reactions will reveal whether the above generalization is useful or whether it must be modified.

4-20   ELECTROLYSIS OF SILVER SULFATE

Instead of a solution of sulfuric acid in water, a solution of silver sulfate, Ag_2SO_4, in water can be electrolyzed. Figure 4-9 is a schematic representation of an appropriate apparatus for this experiment. When a sufficiently high potential difference is established between the two electrodes, oxygen gas is evolved at the positive electrode and silver metal is deposited at the negative electrode. These two products could result from the decomposition of silver sulfate if there were left in solution a third product which contained sulfur but differed from the silver sulfate by containing less oxygen. This is not the case. All the sulfate groups (SO_4) originally added to the water in the preparation of the silver sulfate solution may be recovered from the solution which has been electrolyzed. To recover the sulfate groups, barium nitrate solution can be added. Barium sulfate, which is insoluble in water, precipitates readily. The other logical source of the oxygen evolved is the water. However, if the oxygen evolved at the positive electrode comes from the water, what happens to the hydrogen? It is significant that as the electrolysis proceeds, the solution develops characteristics of a solution of an acid in water. For instance, it turns blue litmus pink. The equation representing the electrolysis is

$$2Ag_2SO_4 \ (aq) + 2H_2O \ (l) \xrightarrow{\text{electrolysis}} 4Ag \ (s) + O_2 \ (g) + 2H_2SO_4 \ (aq)$$

$$(Eq. \ 4\text{-}10)$$

Thus the hydrogen originally present in the water that was decomposed to produce oxygen stays in solution in a new chemical combination, specifically the form characteristic of sulfuric acid (H_2SO_4) solutions.

This means that we cannot apply the hypothesis that, in the electrolysis of all water solutions, the ratio of atomic masses of hydrogen and oxygen in the products will correspond to the ratio of atomic masses of these elements in water. Moreover, if Equation 4-10 is correct, water may react at one electrode but not at the other, and the hydrogen from the water is not evolved as a gas. So the hypothesis by which we attempted to predict the ratio of masses of electrode products has failed.

However, experimental data show that in the electrolysis of silver sulfate solutions, as in the electrolysis of water, the ratio of the masses of products produced at the two electrodes is constant. Specifically, the ratio of the mass of silver to the mass of oxygen is 13.49:1. This is precisely the ratio of the mass of silver to the mass of oxygen in the compound silver oxide (Ag_2O). So, in spite of the fact that the silver is produced from silver sulfate and that oxygen is produced from water, the ratio of the masses produced during electrolysis is the same as the ratio of masses that would be obtained if the compound silver oxide is decomposed. For every mole of oxygen gas evolved, 4 moles of silver metal is deposited.

$$\frac{32.00 \text{ g of } O_2}{\text{mole of } O_2} \times \frac{13.49 \text{ g of Ag}}{1 \text{ g of } O_2} \times \frac{\text{mole of Ag}}{107.88 \text{ g of Ag}} = \frac{4 \text{ moles of Ag}}{\text{mole of } O_2}$$
$$(Eq. \text{ 4-11})$$

Similar experiments have been carried out using different solutions in which different reactions take place at the electrodes. It has been observed that, whenever a single reaction occurs at each electrode, the ratio of the masses of the products at the electrodes is a constant. Moreover, these mass ratios may be converted to ratios of moles of products formed. The mole ratios are the ratios of small whole numbers which are the same as the whole-number mole ratios obtained from the analysis of chemical compounds. How can this be interpreted in terms of the flow of charge through the electrolysis circuit?

4-21 **MASSES OF ELECTRODE PRODUCTS AND ELECTRIC CHARGE**

The quantities of products formed at the two electrodes may be related by assuming once more that electric charge is conserved (Section 4-10) and that the same number of units of charge (x units) must be transferred between the solution and each electrode during the electrolysis. For the deposition of 4 moles of silver metal,

> x units of charge at one electrode
>   passing through the solution yields   431.6 g of Ag
>
> x units of charge at the other electrode
>   passing through the solution yields   32.00 g of O_2

Since the silver is deposited at the negative electrode, it is reasonable to conclude that the solution at that electrode either accepts x units of negative charge from the electrode or transfers x units of positive charge to the electrode.

The most revealing part of this interpretation emerges when the idea of conservation of charge is combined with the assumption that matter is atomic. In terms of the atomic theory, the silver must be deposited atom by atom. It is logical to assume that the deposition of each atom of silver requires the exchange of the same quantity of electric charge between the solution and the negative electrode. This would account for the fact that the mass of silver deposited in an electrolysis is directly proportional to the number of units of charge (coulombs) passing through the solution. Furthermore, if you assume that, on the average, the evolution of one oxygen molecule at the other electrode requires the transfer of just four times the quantity of charge as does the deposition of one atom of silver, you can account for the fact that the electrolysis produces silver atoms and oxygen molecules in a ratio of 4:1.

Do all atoms of silver exchange the same quantity of charge with the electrode during deposition, or do they exchange variable amounts of charge, the average of which is constant? The large numbers of atoms involved in any sample that can be weighed make it necessary to consider the second possibility. Certainly the simpler of the two explanations is that every silver atom exchanges the same quantity of charge with the electrode. If the quantity of charge which must be exchanged to deposit one atom of silver is accepted as an atomic unit of charge, then the evolution of one molecule of oxygen requires an exchange of four atomic units of charge. These atomic units of charge are called *electrons.*

Further consideration of electrolysis reactions in view of this assumption about the nature of charge transfer processes leads to the question of why the transfer of one unit of charge (one electron) per atom should change the properties of a substance so drastically. The silver in a silver sulfate solution displays properties that are different from those of the silver metal. Some of the properties of the oxygen in the compound water are markedly different from those of the oxygen in oxygen gas. Yet in both cases, interpretation of the electrolysis data suggests that the change in properties is brought about when the species existing in solution gives up or accepts small units of charge at the electrode surface. Are these small units of charge related to all physical and chemical properties of matter? Are these units of charge natural constituents of atoms and molecules which influence the reactions between substances during all chemical changes as well as electrolytic reactions? Affirmative answers to both of these questions are consistent with the data that have been considered.

4-22 ATOMIC UNITS OF CHARGE: ELECTRONS

The name electron can carry with it just the significance that the experimental evidence will support. Do electrons flow from the positive to the negative terminal of a battery or vice versa? The experimental evidence for this point does not provide a definite answer. Perhaps charge flows in both directions. Is there mass associated with electrons? Again the experimental evidence is inconclusive at this point. But the hypothesis of electrons does explain the constant ratio of the masses of the products of an electrolysis reaction.

4-23   **CHARGE/MASS RATIOS**

The discussion has led to the conclusion that the production of one atom or molecule of a substance at an electrode will require an integral number (1, 2, 3, . . .) of electrons. From this conclusion, the production of a mole of the same substance would require the transfer of the same integral number of moles of electrons. Determination of the number of coulombs of charge required to produce 1 mole of hydrogen, oxygen, or silver provides data that can be used to calculate multiple values for the total charge of 1 mole of electrons. Since 1 mole of electrons would be one Avogadro number of electrons, a knowledge of the total charge of 1 mole of electrons would permit us to calculate the charge of one electron.

The electrodeposition of silver is a convenient electrolysis reaction to employ in such an investigation. An apparatus in which the electrodeposition of silver is accomplished using a constant current I can be used to calculate the number of coulombs flowing through the circuit in any time interval Δt.

$$\text{Number of coulombs} = I \times \Delta t$$

Measurement of the mass of silver deposited during the same time interval by determining the mass of the negative electrode before and after deposition will allow calculation of the number of coulombs of charge which must be transferred at the electrode to deposit 1 g of silver metal.

$$\frac{\text{Number of coulombs transferred during } \Delta t}{\text{Grams of silver deposited during } \Delta t}$$

This is called the charge/mass ratio for the electrodeposition of silver. The accepted experimentally determined value for this ratio is 894.5 coulombs/g of Ag.

Scientists have in fact based the definition of the coulomb on the mass of silver deposited during electrolysis. One coulomb of charge will cause 0.0011180 g of silver to be deposited during electrolysis.

4-24   **CHEMICAL UNIT OF CHARGE: THE FARADAY**

To calculate the number of coulombs required to deposit 1 mole of silver, the charge/mass ratio for silver is multiplied by the mass of 1 mole of silver. The charge/mass ratios and the number of coulombs

TABLE 4-3 COULOMBS REQUIRED TO PRODUCE A MOLE OF SEVERAL SUBSTANCES

Substance Produced	Grams / Mole	Coulombs / Gram	Coulombs / Mole
H_2	2.016	95,700.	193,000
O_2	32.00	12,070.	386,000
Mg	24.32	7,940.	193,000
Na	22.99	4,200.	96,500
Cu	63.54	3,040.	193,000
Cl_2	70.91	2,720.	193,000
Ag	107.9	894.5	96,500

required to produce 1 mole of other products by electrolysis are recorded in Table 4-3.

$$894.5 \text{ coulombs/g} \times 107.9 \text{ g/mole} = 96{,}500 \text{ coulombs/mole}$$

In every case the number of coulombs required to produce a mole of product is an integral multiple of 96,500. This can most easily be explained by assuming that 96,500 coulombs/mole represents the same thing as the transfer of one electron per atom. The charge of 96,500 coulombs can be regarded as a mole of unit charges or electrons. A mole of electrons is a significant unit of electric charge, especially to chemists, and is called a *faraday* after Michael Faraday, who established the mass relationships associated with electrolysis.

The electrolysis of silver sulfate provides information that was used to establish the relationship between the masses of electrode products formed during a change and the quantity of electric charge passing through a system. The quantitative aspects of the relationship between chemical change and the electric energy passed through a system is studied in the laboratory in Experiment 11 in *Investigating Chemical Systems*. A Daniell cell is used as a source of electric energy for the quantitative study of the changes which occur when a specific quantity of electric charge is passed through a chemical system. The chemical system that is studied includes two lead electrodes immersed in a solution of lead nitrate.

Ex. 4-5 Some conclusions have been reached regarding the relationship between quantity of electric charge and the mass of the electrode products in an electrolysis of silver sulfate. In Experiment 11, a set of conclusions is based on the study of the electrolysis of lead nitrate solution, using lead electrodes. Compare these conclusions.

MICHAEL FARADAY *1791–1867*

An English scientist born near London. Faraday was one of the towering speculative and experimental geniuses of the nineteenth century. The son of a blacksmith, Faraday received a rudimentary education to age thirteen when he became errand boy and later apprentice to a bookbinder. He read voraciously and became interested in science. After performing some experiments and listening to lectures by Humphry Davy, the director of the Royal Institution, he wrote to Davy, asking for a job. Faraday became Davy's assistant in 1813, director of the Institution's laboratories in 1825, and its professor of chemistry for life in 1833. He was elected a Fellow of the Royal Society in 1824.

Faraday created a complete descriptive theory of electricity; he discovered how electricity can be produced by means of magnetism and utilized this discovery to develop the dynamo; he invented the transformer, discovered benzene, and was the first to liquefy chlorine and carbon dioxide. He originated the concept of a field to explain the effects of magnets and electric charges and conceived of atoms as centers of force fields rather than as particles. He also discovered the quantitative laws of electrolysis, relating quantities of electric charge to changes in composition in chemical systems.

Faraday had no students or assistants. He gave brilliant lectures but otherwise engaged in practically no activities outside of his scientific research and his participation in the small Protestant sect, the Sandemanians. His voluminous publications contain not a single algebraic or chemical formula. Even in Faraday's time a problem existed with regard to the growing volume of scientific literature. He is reported to have said that it would be quite impossible to read it all if one wanted to do any experimental work.

4-25 CHARGE OF AN ELECTRON

If the charge representing 1 mole of electrons is 96,500 coulombs, the charge on each electron must be equal to this total charge divided by the number of electrons in a mole, the Avogadro number.

$$\frac{\dfrac{96,500 \text{ coulombs}}{\text{mole of electrons}}}{\dfrac{6.02 \times 10^{23} \text{ electrons}}{\text{mole of electrons}}} = 1.60 \times 10^{-19} \text{ coulomb/electron}$$

$$(Eq.\ 4\text{-}12)$$

Thus, a quantitative study of the mass of silver deposited for a given transfer of charge between an electrode and a solution permits the calculation of the charge of an electron as 1.60×10^{-19} coulomb. The calculation involved the use of the atomic mass of silver and a numerical value for the Avogadro number. The value of 1.60×10^{-19} coulomb/electron is, therefore, as reliable as the numerical values representing these two quantities.

4-26 QUANTITATIVE LINK BETWEEN ATOMS AND ELECTRIC CHARGE

Perhaps the most significant point to be made about Equation 4-12 is not that it permits calculation of the charge of an electron but that it quantitatively relates the charge of an electron, the faraday, and the Avogadro number. To the extent that the concept of the relationship between electrons and atoms is correct, the form of this relationship is also correct. Experimental determination of values for any two of these quantities permits calculation of a value for the third.

4-27 INTERRELATIONS OF CONCEPTS AND NUMBERS

The mental model of the nature of matter has grown from its beginnings in Dalton's postulates about the nature of atoms. Avogadro clearly extended the idea of atoms by postulating molecules to relate gas density measurements to combining masses. Because of Avogadro's ideas, atomic and molecular masses could be assigned to provide an internally consistent system. To relate this internal system of atomic masses to the standard kilogram scale of mass requires a knowledge of how many atoms are in a known mass of material. This relationship is expressed in the Avogadro number. Examination of the quantitative relationship between charge transfer and chemical reaction led to the faraday as a unit of electric charge which was related to the Avogadro number. Building a model to explain the relationship between the faraday and the Avogadro number involved postulating the existence of fundamental units of charge called electrons. Through the expansion of the original Dalton model, relationships have been established among combining ratios, gas densities, and charge/mass ratios during electrolysis reactions. No longer can consistency of measurements within only one of these areas act as an indication of the reliability of a physical constant such as an atomic mass or the Avogadro number. Such physical constants must now satisfy the data provided by two or more different types of experimental measurement. Values for these physical constants must be chosen to provide the maximum consistency among all the interconnected fields of study that make use of these constants.

This chapter has developed concepts about the relationships between electricity and matter. It has been demonstrated that electric energy can be transferred to a substance as heat simply by flow of electric charge through a metal in contact with the substance or by causing a chemical change. If a chemical change takes place, the chemical system in its final state contains more energy than in its initial state. The quantity of energy added is that required to cause the chemical change. The energy added is now stored in the chemical system as chemical energy. It was also established that chemical systems which release energy in going from the initial state to the final state will release electric energy if the initial components are arranged in the form of an electric cell. These discussions established a definite connection between chemical change and electricity.

A study of the nature of electricity revealed its atomicity, and charge flow is ultimately described in terms of elementary units of charge called electrons. Investigation of the relationship between the atoms of matter and the atoms of electricity (electrons) disclosed that in electrochemical changes a small integral number (1, 2, 3, . . .) of electrons were associated with the changes in atoms of matter. Implicit in these investigations was the idea that the electric charge in solutions of electrolysis cells was moved by charged species, called ions, carrying these same integral units of electrons.

A definite link has been established between matter and electricity. However, very little is known about electric charges. Are electric charges matter? Do they have mass and occupy space? These questions still need to be answered.

Ex. 4-6 Defend or refute the following statements concerning the systems in the diagram.

a. System I transfers electric energy; System II transfers chemical energy.

b. The electric energy produces a thermal energy change in System I and a chemical change in System II.

c. These two systems are different because of the difference in arrangement of the components of the system.

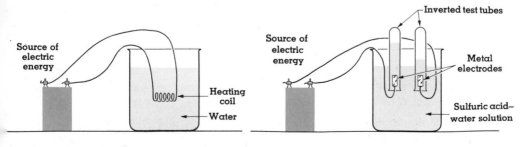

SYSTEM I   SYSTEM II

d. The thermal energy absorbed by the water in System I can never be liberated. In other words, this energy is lost.

e. The energy absorbed to produce a chemical change in System II can be regained by mixing the hydrogen gas and the oxygen gas.

Ex. 4-7 The text describes the Daniell cell as a system made up of chemicals arranged in a certain way. Defend or refute these statements regarding the Daniell cell.

a. When electric energy is produced by the cell, the copper electrode decreases in mass.

b. The copper and zinc electrodes are arranged in such a way that there is no direct contact between them.

c. Electric energy is not supplied by the cell unless an external circuit is connected between the copper and zinc electrodes.

d. The overall chemical reaction within the Daniell cell is the same reaction that takes place when zinc metal is dipped into a copper sulfate solution.

Ex. 4-8 Examine the schematic drawing of the apparatus.

a. Which part of the apparatus is arranged to produce electric energy?

b. Which part of the apparatus is arranged to use electric energy?

c. Compare the function of part (a) in the accompanying illustration with the function of part (b).

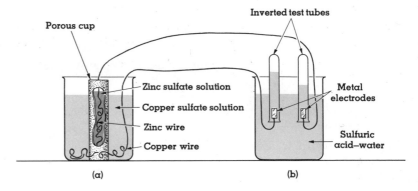

Ex. 4-9 *a.* What instrument is used to measure electric potential difference?

b. In what units is electric potential difference expressed?

c. What instrument is used to measure electric current?

d. In what units is electric current expressed?

Ex. 4-10 Refer to the schematic diagram at the top of page 157.

a. What electric measurement is read on Instrument 1? on Instrument 2?

b. By convention, is the electric potential, with respect to point *G*, higher at point *C* or at point *D*? higher at point *F* or at point *B*?

c. If the ammeter is placed between points *A* and *B*, instead of between points *E* and *D*, would it indicate the same current?

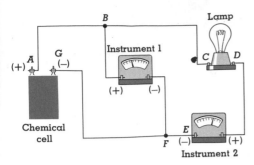

B
Lamp
Instrument 1
G
(+) A (−)
(+) (−)
C D
Chemical
cell
E
F (−) (+)
Instrument 2

d. What would happen if the positions of the ammeter and the voltmeter were exchanged in the circuit?

e. Would the lamp light if the wire between point G and point F were removed? Would the voltmeter indicate electric potential difference between B and F if the wire between points G and F were removed?

f. If the ammeter shows a current of 1 ampere, what quantity of electric charge (in coulombs) passes through the lamp in one minute?

g. If the voltmeter indicates an electric potential difference equal to 1.5 volts and the ammeter an electric current of 1.0 ampere, what is the total resistance (R) of the circuit in ohms? What is the total conductance (K) of the circuit in mhos?

$$\text{Ohms } (R) = \frac{\text{volts } (\Delta V)}{\text{amperes } (I)} \qquad \text{Mhos } (K) = \frac{\text{amperes } (I)}{\text{volts } (\Delta V)}$$

h. What is the total heat released by the lamp if 1 ampere of current flows for one hour through an electric potential difference of 1.5 volts? Express your answer in calories and in joules.

Ex. 4-11 a. In which circuit(s) represented in the accompanying diagram will electric charge not flow?

b. Three types of electric conduction can be identified in Circuit II. Identify and describe each one.

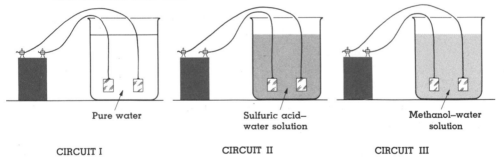

Pure water   Sulfuric acid–   Methanol–water
                          water solution   solution

CIRCUIT I   CIRCUIT II   CIRCUIT III

Ex. 4-12 An aqueous solution of silver sulfate undergoes electrolysis.

a. What is the product formed at each electrode?

b. What is the atom ratio of the products?

c. What is the mole ratio of the products?

d. What is the mass ratio of the products?

e. What compound would be formed by the combination of the electrode products in the ratios expressed above?

Ex. 4-13 If you assume that the transfer of one unit of charge is required to deposit one atom of silver during the electrolysis, how many units of charge are

157

required to release (a) one molecule of oxygen gas (O_2)? (b) one molecule of hydrogen gas (H_2)?

Ex. 4-14 Change the following expressions where necessary so that they become chemical equations.

a. $Al + Fe_2O_3 \rightarrow Al_2O_3 + Fe$

b. $KBr + Cl_2 \rightarrow KCl + Br_2$

c. $SO_3 \rightarrow SO_2 + O_2$

d. $Ca(OH)_2 + CO_2 \rightarrow CaCO_3 + H_2O$

e. $B + F_2 \rightarrow BF_3$

f. $SiO_2 + HF \rightarrow SiF_4 + H_2O$

g. $H_3PO_4 + Ca(OH)_2 \rightarrow HOH + Ca_3(PO_4)_2$

h. $Ca(HCO_3)_2 \rightarrow CaCO_3 + CO_2 + H_2O$

i. $Al + Br_2 \rightarrow AlBr_3$

j. $C_4H_{10} + O_2 \rightarrow CO_2 + H_2O$

k. $Ba(NO_3)_2 + H_2SO_4 \rightarrow BaSO_4 + HNO_3$

l. $H_2O + KI \xrightarrow{\text{electrolysis}} I_2 + KOH + H_2$

m. $Cu_2I_2 \xrightarrow{\text{electrolysis}} I_2 + Cu$

Ex. 4-15 The chemical reaction in the Daniell cell can be described by

$$Zn\ (s) + CuSO_4\ (aq) \rightarrow Cu\ (s) + ZnSO_4\ (aq)$$

Refer to Fig. 4-2.

a. What mass of copper is deposited on the copper electrode when the zinc electrode loses 0.01 mole of zinc?

b. If the loss of 1 mole of zinc is accompanied by the production of 2 moles of charge, what quantity of charge, in coulombs, has passed through the external circuit?

c. If 0.01 mole of zinc was lost in one hour, what was the rate of charge flow in amperes?

CHARGE SEPARATIONS AND ENERGY

CHANGE IN COMPOSITION is a distinctive feature of chemical systems. These composition changes can sometimes be demonstrated by actual isolation of the substances present after the reaction has run its course. Isolation of components is only one of many kinds of experimental procedures, however, which provide information to a chemist as he tries to understand the chemistry associated with a reaction. In Experiment 6 of *Investigating Chemical Systems*, the effect of the mass of lead nitrate used on the mass of lead iodide formed is determined. In the investigation of reactions in the copper–sulfur systems (Section 2-10), it proved convenient to determine the change in mass of non-volatile material for different mass ratios of copper and sulfur. With the gaseous systems of hydrogen and oxygen (Section 3-1), the reaction produced a decrease in gas volume. The amount of the decrease was different for different volume ratios of the two initial gases. The volume ratios found for reacting gases led to an interpretation of the molecular nature of gases on the basis of Avogadro's hypothesis. The Avogadro number led to the mole as a unit in chemical work. The use of moles to express quantities of substances as an aid to the quantitative interpretation of a change in a chemical system is applied in Experiment 7 of *Investigating Chemical Systems* to the precipitation of silver chromate.

Chemical change has also been found to be accompanied by electrical phenomena. In Chapter 4 experimental evidence was used to show that the application of an electric potential can produce a measurable electric current in such systems as a solution of silver sulfate in water. This current is assumed to imply flow of charge through the system. When, in Experiment 11, quantitative measurements are made of the amount of charge transferred and the moles of substance reacting, a fixed relation is found. In every case an integral multiple of 96,500 coulombs/mole is found to express the ratio of charge transferred at the electrodes to the number of moles of substances (reactants or products) taking part in the reaction. Charge flow through metal wires produces no chemical changes that can be detected and is quite different from charge flow through solutions where there is always an accompanying chemical change.

5-1 CHEMICAL CHANGE, CHARGE FLOW, AND ENERGY

The fact that charge flow through a solution is always accompanied by chemical change suggests a direct connection between the two. Work with coulometers such as the lead coulometer in Experiment 11 shows that the number of moles of substance reacting at an electrode is proportional only to the quantity of charge transferred between solution and electrode and is characteristic of a given substance. Neither temperature nor pressure nor any other feature of the surroundings appears to play any role.

In Section 3-19, reaction systems of zinc with aqueous copper sulfate were examined. It proved convenient to measure initial and final temperatures (temperature changes) for different mole ratios of zinc to copper sulfate. The observed temperature changes proved to be directly related to composition changes. Later, in Section 3-22, the temperature changes were interpreted in terms of heat transfer and hence energy.

Initially Chapter 4 focused attention on the reaction of zinc with copper sulfate and on the fact that this reaction can be not only the source of thermal energy but also the basis of a Daniell cell and the production of electric current. With electric current available, two alternative changes could be accomplished at will. (1) On one hand electric current in heater coil wires produces temperature change and results in transfer of thermal energy. (2) On the other hand electric current in chemical systems produces composition changes.

Figure 5-1 summarizes the developments presented in Chapters 1 to 4. The diagram points out that the connection between charge flow and chemical change is the most intimate connection so far established. This connection runs in both directions. What can be learned by further study of the connection between charge flow and energy? This

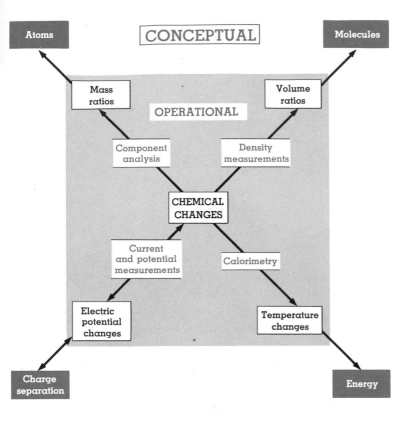

Fig. 5-1 *Four laboratory operations have been used thus far to characterize chemical changes. The operations can be interpreted conceptually.*

question can be looked at by examining several phenomena, the interpretation of which can be made in terms of electric charge.

5-2 CHEMICAL AND FRICTIONAL ELECTRICITY

If a number of chemical cells such as Daniell cells are connected in series, it is quite possible to develop a battery of cells with a potential difference of several hundred volts. In experiments with batteries having a potential of several hundred volts between the terminals, visible effects can be produced even though no charge flows. This can be shown by arranging two wires so that they are separated by a space of about 1 millimeter (mm). When the two wires are connected (Fig. 5-2), one to the positive and the other to the negative terminals of the battery, the wires are observed to move toward each other. When the wires are disconnected from the battery and connected to each other, the wires move apart. This cycle of movement can be observed every time the experiment is repeated. One explana-

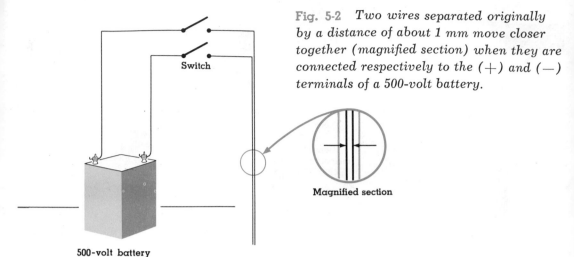

Fig. 5-2 *Two wires separated originally by a distance of about 1 mm move closer together (magnified section) when they are connected respectively to the (+) and (−) terminals of a 500-volt battery.*

Magnified section

Switch

500-volt battery

tion of the movement of the wires is that some attraction is produced when they are connected to the battery.

So it appears that a system which can produce charge flow can also produce motion in objects such as wires attached to the terminals of the battery, that is, to the electrodes of the battery. In everyday language either a push or a pull is developed between the wires. Even with a battery of 500 volts the effect on wires is quite small, however. Fortunately the same result can be accomplished and can be more easily observed by rubbing materials together.

The ancient Greeks knew that after an amber rod had been rubbed with fur or cloth, the amber attracted other objects. Amber was called Elektron by the Greeks. Electron, electricity, and related terms have been derived from Elektron. An object which attracts other objects after having been rubbed with fur or cloth is said to be **charged.**

The phenomena which the Greeks observed with amber can be repeated, using a piece of plastic such as a rubber or nylon comb or a piece of glass rod. After a glass rod has been rubbed with a silk cloth, the glass rod will attract bits of paper to it. The bits of paper will even jump through an air gap of several millimeters to reach the glass rod. Study of the effect of charged objects on other charged or uncharged objects is known as **electrostatics.**

Ex. 5-1 Explain why a toy rubber balloon sometimes can be made to cling to the ceiling or walls of a room after it has been rubbed against your sweater.

5-3 SOME PROPERTIES OF CHARGED OBJECTS

For an investigation of the behavior of objects bearing an electric charge, the primary requirement is a mechanical system which will move in response to a relatively small force. A force may be considered as a push or pull for present purposes. One suitable mechanical system involves a small light object hanging on a nylon thread a foot or so in length. A plastic ball or a pith ball coated with metal is quite satisfactory to use as the light object. Any force pushing or pulling horizontally on such a ball moves it away from its initial position (Fig. 5-3).

The following discussion will deal primarily with the behavior of the ball when objects charged in different ways are brought near the ball. One object to be used is a glass rod charged by rubbing it with a silk cloth. The second object is a hard rubber rod charged by rubbing it with a piece of cat fur. When these two charged objects are used in experiments with the pith ball, at least eight observations can be made. The experimental procedures and the observations are shown in schematic form on pages 164 and 165.

The nature of the charge on any object may be classified on the basis of the effect of the object on a hanging ball which is uncharged or which has been previously charged by touching with a rubbed glass rod or with a rubbed rubber rod. Three cases are defined.

1. An object is uncharged if it does not cause motion when it is close to the uncharged ball.

2. An object has the same charge as a rubbed glass rod if it repels the ball which was charged by the rubbed glass rod.

3. An object which attracts the charged ball has the same charge as the rubbed rubber rod.

These effects have been observed in systems in which air filled the space between the objects. The same observations have been made using evacuated space, that is, systems in which the air has been removed from the space between the objects. It is also observed that there is no measurable difference between the mass of an object when it is charged and the mass of the same object when it is uncharged.

The eight observations describe what happens to various objects which have been treated in certain ways. The behavior of the objects which are charged implies that there is some relationship between

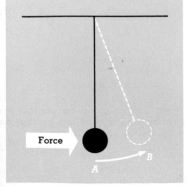

Fig. 5-3 *Any horizontal force acting on an object (for example, a plastic ball) hanging by a thread moves the object away from its initial position.*

1.

An uncharged glass rod or an uncharged rubber rod held close to but not touching the ball has no effect on the hanging ball. Under the same conditions, either rod when charged attracts the hanging ball.

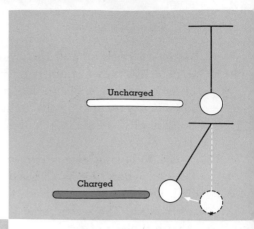

Uncharged

Charged

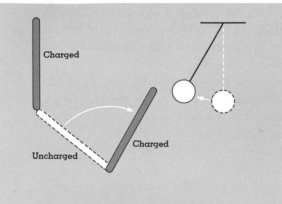

Charged

Charged

Uncharged

2.

When uncharged objects are touched by the charged glass rod or the charged rubber they acquire the ability to attract the hanging In other words, a second initially uncharged can be charged by contact with a charged Charge is assumed to be transferred by c from the charged object to the uncharged

3.

If the hanging ball is allowed to touch the charged glass rod, charge is transferred to the ball. If the charged glass rod is brought close to the charged ball, the ball is then repelled (pushed away) by that rod. A charged ball which is repelled by a charged glass rod is attracted by a charged rubber rod.

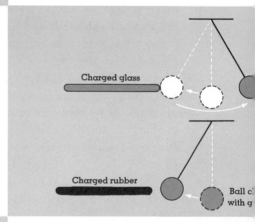

Charged glass

Charged rubber

Ball c
with g

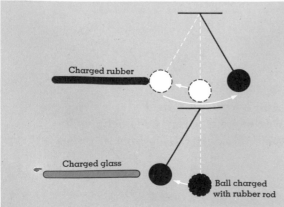

Charged rubber

Charged glass

Ball charged
with rubber rod

4.

A hanging ball charged by contact wit charged rubber rod is repelled by that rod attracted by the charged glass rod.

5.

Two plastic balls are charged, one by contact with the glass rod and the other by contact with the rubber rod. These two balls will attract one another.

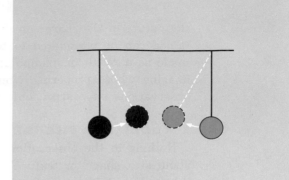

6.

If two balls, one charged from glass and the other from rubber, touch one another, the attraction between them decreases noticeably and may disappear entirely.

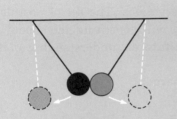

7.

When either charged rod is held close to but not touching some initially uncharged objects, the initially uncharged objects acquire the ability to attract the hanging plastic ball. When the charged rod is removed, this ability disappears and the initially uncharged objects are not finally charged.

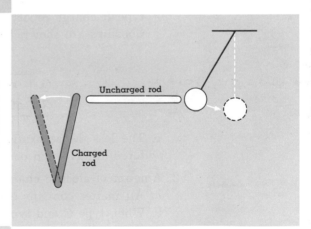

Uncharged rod

Charged rod

8.

All the observed movements of the ball are larger when the charged objects are moved closer together.

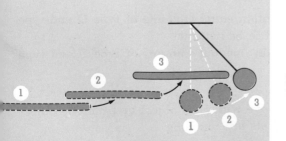

the nature of the charge on the object and its behavior. The data obtained can be considered to be comparable to a set of observations made as a result of manipulating a black box. What model can you imagine whose properties would provide logical explanations of the observations on charged objects?

5-4 A MODEL FOR CHARGE

Nothing in the observations on charged objects indicates anything about size, shape, or texture of the charges. This seems to imply that the model cannot be a physical object. However, the model-building process involved is still much the same as that encountered in Experiment 2 of *Investigating Chemical Systems*. The aim is to assemble the simplest set of postulates which, when subjected to logical reasoning, will account for the experimental observations. The set of postulates and the conclusions drawn from them will constitute the model for charge. The postulates will also constitute an understanding of the meaning of charge.

Postulates for a Model of Electric Charge:

1. Type of electric charge:
   a. There are two types of electric charge which may be designated as type G (glass) and type R (rubber).
   b. Type G charge repels type G and attracts type R. Similarly type R charge repels type R and attracts type G. These relationships are shown by diagram.

	G	R
G	repels	attracts
R	attracts	repels

   c. The less the separation between the charges, the greater the force of attraction or repulsion.

2. Amount of electric charge:
   a. All matter contains electric charge.
   b. When type G and type R charges are both placed on the same object, they **neutralize** each other either partially or completely.
   c. Uncharged objects contain equal amounts of type G and type R charge and are said to be neutral.
   d. Charged objects contain unequal amounts of type G and type R charge.

3. Motion of electric charge:
   a. Electric charge can move within an object or from one object to another when objects are touching.

b. Charges move more freely through some substances (conductors) than through others. For example, charge moves readily through metal but not readily through air.

Does the set of postulates account for all the observations listed in Section 5-3? In some cases, the postulate is closely connected with the observation. In other cases, some thought may be required to see the connection between the postulate and the observation. For instance, how can the observation that a neutral object is attracted to an object charged with either type of electric charge be explained? The answer to this question will serve to illustrate the way in which the postulates may be applied to the explanation of an experimental observation.

According to postulate 2c, a neutral object contains within it equal amounts of type G charge and type R charge. According to postulate 2d, a glass rod which has been charged by rubbing with silk contains more charge of type G than of type R. According to postulate 1b, when a charged glass rod is brought close to the neutral ball, the type G charge in the ball tends to be repelled by the charge on the glass rod while the type R charge tends to be attracted to the charge on the glass rod. If the two types of charge are initially distributed evenly in the ball and if the repulsion and attraction have the same dependence on the distance of separation of charge (postulate 1c), then the repulsion of type G charge would be equal to the attraction for type R charge and there would be no observable motion of the ball toward the rod or away from it. This, however, is not what happens. The ball is attracted to the charged rod.

Therefore, the attraction between the ball and the rod can be explained if it is assumed (postulate 3a) that one or both types of charge within the ball are able to move. It is possible that type R charge moves to that side of the ball nearer the glass rod because of the attraction of type G charge on the glass rod or that type G charge moves to the side of the ball farther from the glass rod owing to repulsion by the type G charge on the rod. For that matter, both of these effects might be operating, but the net result in any case is that the type R charge in the ball is closer to the glass rod than is the type G charge in the ball (Fig. 5-4a). Consequently, on the basis of postulates 1c and 3a, it is quite reasonable to find that the charged rod attracts the neutral plastic ball.

Although only one observation (the attraction of ball and rod) of the behavior of charged objects has been explained here in terms of the postulates for a model of electric charge, this model has been found to be generally useful in describing the behavior of charged objects.

An **electrostatic system** is a collection of charged objects isolated for study. The study of such systems will provide information that will

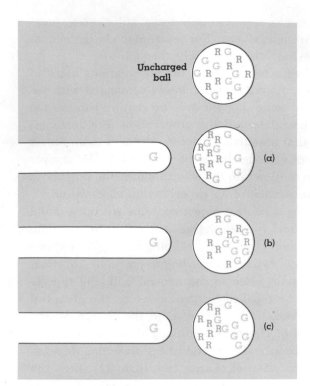

Fig. 5-4 *Attraction of an uncharged ball to a charged glass rod can be explained by* (a) *movement of type* R *charge toward the glass rod,* (b) *movement of type* G *charge away from the glass rod, or* (c) *movement of both type* G *charge and type* R *charge.*

be useful in understanding the extent to which matter itself can be thought of as an electrostatic system. The creation of the model introduces the idea of electric charge and permits the use of the idea of a flow of electric charge from one object to another, as must be done in explaining the charging of an object by contacting a charged object. The same terms and ideas have been used in discussing the electrostatic systems as were employed in dealing with electric circuits. What is the experimental evidence which justifies such use? What is the relationship between the *G* and *R* types of charge and the positive and negative terminals on electric batteries?

5-5 CHARGED OBJECTS AND CURRENT ELECTRICITY

One piece of evidence relating electrostatic systems and electric circuits is the fact that substances which transfer or distribute charge readily in electrostatic systems are those which are good conductors in electric circuits. In neither case does air permit a ready transfer of charge, whereas copper is an excellent conductor of charge in both cases.

On the theoretical side, it can be pointed out that a current in an electric circuit can be explained in terms of the model developed to explain electrostatics. Assume that the battery transports charge internally from one of its terminals to the other so that there is an excess of type G charge on one terminal and an excess of type R charge on the other terminal. If a conductor permitting the ready flow of charge is connected to both terminals, electric charge would be expected to flow between the terminals since the two types of charge attract each other. When a battery is connected in this way, an electric current may be observed. Therefore, according to the model of electric charge, a flow of charge constitutes an electric current. If this explanation is valid, then the terminals of the battery must be charged in the electrostatic sense and it should be possible to charge a metal ball from a battery terminal.

If a single electric cell and a metal ball are used to test this hypothesis, the operations described are not sensitive enough to detect charge on the metal ball after contact with the terminal. However, if a battery of many cells having a potential difference of hundreds of volts between the terminals is used, then sensitive methods of detecting electrostatic charge do show that objects may be charged from the battery terminals. The positive (+) and negative (−) notation for terminals is generally accepted, and the conclusion based on experimental evidence is that type G charge is positive and that type R charge is negative. When it is used to denote charge type, the term positive will be indicated by $\oplus$; the term negative will be indicated by $\ominus$.

In the discussion of electric circuits, it was assumed that electric charge flowed from the positive terminals of the battery to the negative terminal. The analysis of electrostatic systems led to the conclusion that the observations could be explained equally well by assuming that either type of charge, or both, was free to move. What, then, is the basis for the assumption that it is the positive charge, $\oplus$, which moves in an electric circuit?

Actually, the basis for this assumption is a desire for simplicity. When faced with the problem of describing electrical systems, Benjamin Franklin decided that the simplest description was one involving the assumptions that one type of charge moved while the other did not. He decided that the type of charge produced on a glass rod rubbed with silk should be called positive charge. He also decided that it was this positive charge which moved from one object to another in elec-

An electroscope. A thin metal foil hangs over the bent wire attached to the top knob. When the system—made up of the metal knob, wire, and foil— is charged with electricity of either type, the charge is distributed throughout the system since the metal is a conductor. The two halves of the foil, having the same type of charge, repel each other.

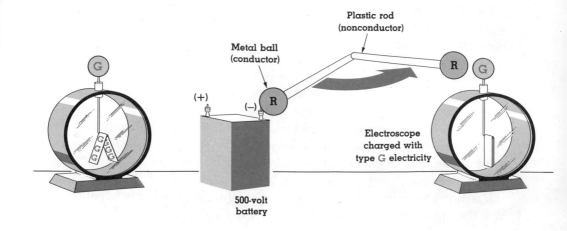

Metal ball
(conductor)

Plastic rod
(nonconductor)

(+)

(−)

R

R   G

G

Electroscope
charged with
type G electricity

500-volt
battery

Fig. 5-5 *When a ball charged at the* (−) *terminal of a battery is
brought near the knob of an electroscope with type* G *charge, the
metal foil leaves no longer repel each other. This implies that type* G
*charge becomes concentrated in the electroscope knob. The charge
initially transferred to the metal ball from the* (−) *terminal of a
battery must be type* R *charge.*

trostatic systems. These were arbitrary decisions on his part, but they
simplified the discussions of electrostatic phenomena and were generally adopted by other scientists. Benjamin Franklin's notion that it
is positive charge which moves is still widely used and is convenient.
Note, however, that these conventions are not based on any experimental evidence. You will see that the experimental evidence now
available indicates that either positive or negative charge or both may
move, depending upon the system under investigation. In each case,
a decision regarding the type of charge moving should be made on the
basis of the experimental evidence.

The adoption of positive and negative signs for charges implies that
the charges present on plastic rods and metal balls are in some way
the same as the charges flowing through a wire connected to a battery.
There is some experimental evidence for such a claim. This means, of
course, that either arranging chemicals in the form of a cell or rubbing
a glass rod with silk can produce charge separation. **Charge separation** is the result of a process that produces unequal amounts of positive and negative charge on one or more objects. In the chemical cell,
an excess of positive charge (type G) is present on the (+) terminal
and an excess of negative charge (type R) is present on the (−)
terminal. When a glass rod is rubbed with silk, an excess of positive
charge (type G) is present on the glass rod and an excess of negative

charge (type R) is present on the silk. Both of these phenomena are examples of charge separation. Experimental work indicates that charge separation can be produced in any material. It is therefore a general phenomenon. The generality makes it worthy of considerable study. Ideas that are developed about the behavior of charged objects should be applicable to every material.

Each of the experiments described thus far began with materials that were initially uncharged. Friction or chemical change produced charge. In the case of friction between two objects (for example, a glass rod and a cloth), one object became positively charged and the other became negatively charged. In the electrochemical cell, one terminal became positively charged and the other negatively charged. In every case, it seems that the production of charge is a process in which the two types of charge become separated by a large or small distance. In Section 4-10 the conservation of charge was discussed as a property of electric circuits. This conservation of charge must be generally true. Charges on objects are not created, but rather they are separated. The electrostatic effects and the electrochemical effects can be regarded, therefore, as the effects produced by separated charges.

Ex. 5-2 What differences would there be in thinking about electrical phenomena if Benjamin Franklin had arbitrarily suggested that both negative and positive charges were free to move?

5-6   IONS IN CHEMICAL SYSTEMS

Charge flow in chemical cells was described in Section 4-18. It was suggested that solutions through which charge was flowing contained ions that in some way made the charge flow possible. The behavior of both electrostatic systems and chemical cells indicates that two kinds of charge are present in the solution. In a chemical cell it was also found that substances were separated. For example, the electrolysis of water led to the separation of hydrogen and oxygen. In other words, the electric charge on the ions is intimately associated with substances present in the solution.

Suppose that ions are charged chemical species. Since solutions as a whole are always found to be uncharged, a solution containing charged ions must contain an equal quantity of charge of both types uniformly distributed throughout the solution. But charged ions in solution would tend to move toward charged electrodes. Thus charge and substance should flow together through any solution in an electric circuit whenever ions are present.

Whether ions are produced during the solution process or whether ions are present in the undissolved substance or whether ions are pro-

171

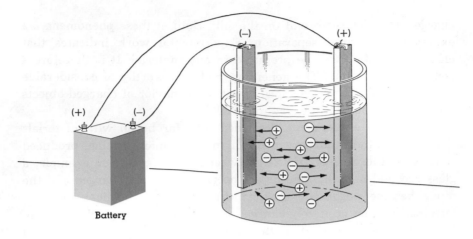

Fig. 5-6 *Conduction of electric current by ionic solutions can be explained by the assumption that charged ions move toward oppositely charged electrodes.*

duced during the conduction process cannot be decided from the evidence presented up to this point. Nonetheless the hypothesis that conducting solutions contain electrically charged ions does fit the phenomena discussed in Chapter 4 and makes the phenomena more understandable.

Understanding chemical systems now is a problem with a form somewhat different from its earlier aspects of composition changes and energy transfer discussed in Chapters 3 and 4. Chemical systems can produce charge separation, a flow of charge, and the release of energy. Between separated charges, forces of either attraction or repulsion operate. Is there any relation between these forces and the energy which is transferred between a system and its surroundings? Can the relation be described quantitatively?

5-7 SYSTEMS OF MOVING OBJECTS

Interest in the relationship between force and energy is by no means restricted to the field of electrostatics. In fact, the very ideas of force and energy were generated by people who were attempting to understand the observed behavior of moving objects that were being pushed or pulled.

When an object is pushed, one of two things must happen; either the object moves or it does not. The interest here is with cases in which the object moves. Many objects which do not move readily when they are resting on the ground or the floor can be moved with ease if they are on wheels or on a smooth surface such as ice. In addition, the ease with which an object is moved is affected by whether the surface upon which it rests is level or slopes uphill or downhill.

These simple observations contain the essential ingredients of the models which have been developed to interpret the response of objects to forces.

If an object is pushed horizontally on a smooth or slippery surface, only a slight push is needed to set the object moving. The smoother the surface is made, the less the initial push that is required. On a perfectly smooth surface, then, there is no minimum push required to move an object. Also, the harder the push, the faster the object moves. If the pushing stops, the object moves along at constant velocity.

Upward motion of an object seems to proceed in a manner somewhat different from horizontal motion. A slight push upward does not move the object, but as the strength of the pushing is increased, there is a point at which the object starts to move. This push that is just enough to begin motion can be called a minimum force. With only the minimum force applied, the object moves, not faster and faster, but at a constant velocity. Whenever pushing stops, the object stops its upward motion.

Ex. 5-3   If the level floor of a room had a perfectly frictionless surface, would you be able to walk or crawl from the middle of the room?

5-8   HORIZONTAL AND VERTICAL MOTION AND KINETIC ENERGY

Experience with vertical motions and horizontal motions on slippery surfaces can be summarized as follows. See also Table 5-1.

Horizontal motion on a perfectly frictionless surface:
1. There is no minimum push necessary to produce motion.
2. So long as the push is continued, velocity increases.
3. When the push stops, motion continues at constant velocity.
4. The longer the push continues, the faster the object moves.
5. The more massive the object, the lower the velocity produced by a given push.
Vertical motion upward:
6. A slight push produces no motion, but a minimum force upward is required to start the object in motion.
7. The more massive the object, the greater the minimum force required to produce motion.
8. A push of minimum force produces constant velocity upward.
9. When the push stops, the upward motion stops.
10. The longer the push acts, the higher the object rises.

When measurements of mass m, velocity v, and time t are made in quantitative terms, the conclusions about horizontal and vertical mo-

TABLE 5-1 COMPARISON OF THE EFFECTS OF HORIZONTAL AND VERTICAL FORCES ON AN OBJECT

	Horizontal	Vertical
Minimum push necessary to produce motion	No minimum.	Minimum force upward is required.
Effect of push on velocity	If push is continued, velocity increases.	Push of minimum force produces constant velocity.
Action when push is discontinued	Motion continues at constant velocity.	Upward motion stops.
Effect of length of time push continues	Velocity increases as long as the push continues.	The object rises higher.
Effect of mass	The greater the mass, the less the velocity.	The minimum force required to produce motion is greater.

tions can be concisely stated in mathematical language. For horizontal motion the relations can be stated as

$$m \, \Delta v = KF \, \Delta t$$

Dividing by $K \, \Delta t$,

$$F = \frac{m \, \Delta v}{K \, \Delta t} \qquad \text{(Eq. 5-1)}$$

where F is the push or, as it is usually called, the **force.** The equation says that a given force F on an object is proportional to the product of the mass of the object and the change in velocity $m \, \Delta v$ divided by the time Δt the force acts on the object times proportionality constant K. It has also been found that the velocity achieved for a force continuing to act over a distance d is related by the kinetic energy equation.

$$\tfrac{1}{2}mv^2 = KFd$$

Dividing by K,

$$Fd = \frac{mv^2}{2K} \qquad \text{(Eq. 5-2)}$$

It is customary to call the product of mass and velocity, mv, by the name **momentum** (so that $m \, \Delta v$ is the change in momentum) and the product, $\tfrac{1}{2}mv^2$, **kinetic energy.** A force F producing horizontal motion can now be measured by either of two procedures. A measurement of mass, change in velocity, and the time interval gives a measure of the force acting (Equation 5-1). A measurement of mass, velocity, and distance gives a measure of the force acting.

For vertical motion, quantitative experiments can be summarized by the mathematical equation

$$F_{\min}d = gmd \qquad\qquad (Eq.\ 5\text{-}3)$$

where g is a proportionality constant. The other symbols have the same meaning as in Equations 5-1 and 5-2—although, of course, d refers to vertical distance upward and the force $F_{\min}$ is a minimum force, just large enough to produce vertical motion of the object (Equation 5-2).

5-9   WORK

The product of a force and the distance through which it acts has appeared in the equations for kinetic energy (Equation 5-2) and vertical motion (Equation 5-3). This product is found repeatedly in discussions of motion. It is commonly called **work,** a word used in the following sense. The object lifted vertically has had work done on it, or the object given kinetic energy $\frac{1}{2}mv^2$ has had work done on it. But is it reasonable to apply the same term, work, to these two rather different cases of motion?

Experiments can help answer this question. For example, consider an object which has been lifted a distance d to a shelf by a minimum force $F_{\min}$. If this object is now allowed to fall back down through the distance d, it will have a velocity v at the end of the fall. This velocity

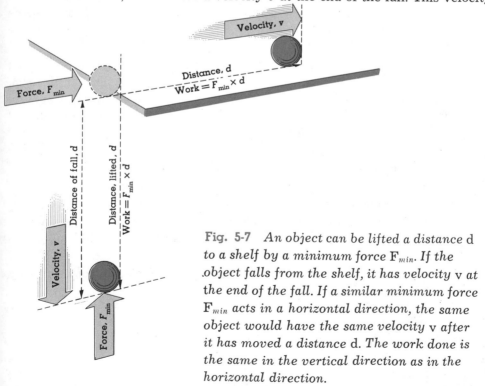

Fig. 5-7   *An object can be lifted a distance* d *to a shelf by a minimum force* F$_{min}$. *If the* .*object falls from the shelf, it has velocity* v *at the end of the fall. If a similar minimum force* F$_{min}$ *acts in a horizontal direction, the same object would have the same velocity* v *after it has moved a distance* d. *The work done is the same in the vertical direction as in the horizontal direction.*

at the end of its fall is equal to the velocity the object would have had if it had been moved horizontally through distance d by a force of the same magnitude F_{min}. Work can therefore produce either kinetic energy or vertical lift. Conversely, a fall from a height d will produce a certain kinetic energy. Even further, it is found that an object moving horizontally with this same kinetic energy will just rise to the same height d when its velocity and hence kinetic energy are allowed to come to zero in a suitable system. A suitable system for this last conversion is one that is able to change horizontal motion to vertical motion. This can be done fairly well by some kind of guide rails or by an inclined plane.

5-10 POTENTIAL ENERGY

To explain further the relationships among kinetic energy, motion, work, velocity, force, mass, and distance, let us imagine that when an object is pushed upward, it gains **gravitational potential energy.** Let us also imagine that work is a commodity in which energy is transferred so as to change the motion of an object. How can the commodity of energy be used to describe the action of a force on an object?

The question can be answered in this way. A force acting on an object over a distance transfers energy to the object in the form of work. The energy is taken up by the object and stored either as kinetic energy which is evidenced by how fast the object travels through space or as potential energy which is determined by how high above the earth the object rises.

No matter what the nature of energy is, the assumption is that the total energy remains unaltered in quantity but may change in form. This is usually stated as the principle of the conservation of energy. Energy is never increased or decreased in quantity but only altered in form as it is transferred from one system to another.

But practical experience raises questions. An object moving along with kinetic energy sooner or later comes to a halt. This happens even though there is no push or pull on the object. If the object comes to a halt, its kinetic energy is gone but it has seemingly neither acquired potential energy nor performed work. The general term used to explain this stopping process is **frictional resistance.** Does this imply that there is some other form of energy possible in addition to work, kinetic energy, and potential energy? Is energy transferred in some form by the action of frictional resistance?

5-11 ENERGY AND HEAT

When a moving object is stopped because of friction on a surface, experiments show that the temperature of the object and of the surface increases. In every case, the final temperature of the object and the surface is higher than the initial temperature. In Section 3-22 the observed rise in temperature of a system was described as a temperature-changing capacity for the system in its initial state. A system containing one object moving across the surface of another object is observed to have a temperature-changing capacity. As the moving object comes to a halt, its kinetic energy drops to zero, but to restore the system to its initial temperature, energy must be removed from the hot system.

The common way to remove energy from a hot system is to place it in contact with an environment at a lower temperature. The energy transferred from the hot system to the cold environment because of the temperature difference is defined as heat. Note that heat is an energy being transferred because of temperature difference and is not, therefore, like kinetic energy which is stored in a moving system. Friction generally results in the transfer of kinetic energy as heat. The quantity of heat transferred can be measured in a calorimeter.

All objects moving with the same amount of kinetic energy transfer the same amount of heat when they are stopped. An elevated object allowed to fall a distance d into a calorimeter transfers heat when it strikes and is stopped by a calorimeter. All objects with the same gravitational potential energy can transfer the same quantity of heat when they are allowed to fall.

The scheme in which work, potential energy, and kinetic energy are all regarded as forms of energy must be broadened to include heat. According to this broader scheme, frictional resistance to motion results not in the destruction of energy but in the transfer of kinetic energy as heat (or thermal energy) to the surroundings.

Thermal energy is peculiar in its relation to work, potential energy, and kinetic energy. Experiments have shown that work, potential energy, and kinetic energy are interconvertible. Thus all the kinetic energy stored in a moving object can be converted into potential energy without any other energy changes necessarily taking place. The same is true of converting potential energy into kinetic energy. It is possible to go another step to say that work, potential energy, or kinetic energy can be converted to thermal energy. Here again no other energy change need be involved. Can heat transfer produce kinetic energy?

A steam turbine is a device which accepts thermal energy and transfers work out to some machine. The thermal energy that is converted to work is exactly equivalent to the work produced by the turbine. But there are always other energy changes that take place simultaneously. In other words, not all the thermal energy transferred from the hot steam can be converted to work.

Consider a diagram, Fig. 5-9, of a steam turbine. A necessary part of the steam turbine system for converting heat into work is a con-

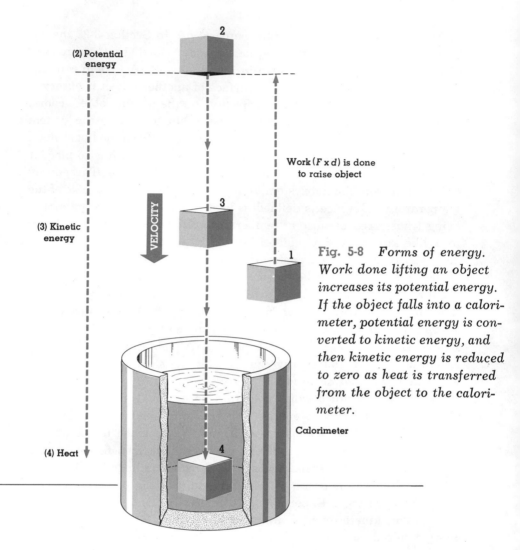

(2) Potential energy

2

Work (F x d) is done to raise object

VELOCITY

(3) Kinetic energy

3

1

Fig. 5-8 *Forms of energy. Work done lifting an object increases its potential energy. If the object falls into a calorimeter, potential energy is converted to kinetic energy, and then kinetic energy is reduced to zero as heat is transferred from the object to the calorimeter.*

Calorimeter

(4) Heat

4

denser for changing steam to water. In the condenser, cold water becomes warm as the steam condenses. Every attempt to build a turbine without a condenser has resulted in a turbine that would not produce work from heat. Experience indicates that the condenser and its temperature changes are an essential part of a successful turbine.

Although many people have tried to avoid the temperature change in the condenser, no one has ever succeeded. The conclusion is inescapable for this case that whenever thermal energy is converted into kinetic energy or work, other energy changes outside the turbine necessarily occur simultaneously and unavoidably.

No one using any sort of machine has ever been successful in converting all of a given quantity of thermal energy into an equivalent quantity of work, potential energy, or kinetic energy without any other unavoidable energy effects. Although heat has an equivalent of energy in these three forms, the conversion of heat to a single different form of energy has never been done. In the steam turbine, a fraction of the heat is always used to warm up the condenser while the remainder is changed to work.

With elevated objects, the potential energy was completely transferred as heat when the object fell. The motion of the object (kinetic energy) was essential. This observation, coupled with the fact that all motion in everyday experience is resisted by the system within which motion takes place and generates heat, suggests that heat itself may be related to some form of motion. If heat were related to undirected motion, that is, to a random motion in all directions, then the failure to be able to transfer it completely to create motion in one direction, as in raising objects or pushing them horizontally, might be explained. Whatever is set in motion within a system if heat is transferred into the system is too small to see. Random motion of atoms and molecules would be consistent with these requirements. In fact, the conceptual model for the nature of temperature is based upon the random motion of atoms and molecules. This concept of the nature of temperature is then related to the fact that heat is defined as energy transferred because of a temperature difference.

The discussion of kinetic and potential energy raises a problem when changes in systems that include electric charges are considered. When a charged plastic rod lifts a piece of paper, the gravitational potential energy of the paper increases. When a charged plastic rod causes an object to move, kinetic energy is involved. Where does the energy come from? A chemical cell can cause a wire to transfer heat or a motor to transfer work. Where does this energy come from?

Fig. 5-9 *Schematic diagram of a steam turbine.*

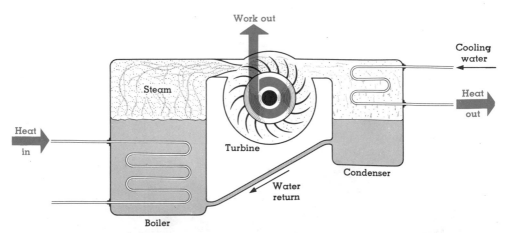

The model for a charged object and the model for an electrochemical cell have the common feature of charge separation. A model has been described in which work, heat, elevated position, and motion are thought of in terms of energy, with the energy conserved in all its transfers from one system to another. The energy model must be expanded then if it is to be used to explain the motions and heat produced by charged objects. To explain these observations, it is possible to assume that, when unlike charges are separated in a system, energy is available for transfer. This assumption has two advantages. On one hand it preserves the idea that energy is never created or destroyed but merely transferred. On the other hand it provides a way of studying the nature of the energy in systems of separated charges by looking at the conversion of electric energy into motion or elevated position by the transfer of heat or work.

It has already been concluded that separation of charge is something that can occur in an electrochemical system, for example, in a Daniell cell. Whatever can be learned about the nature of charges and their energies in other systems should give a better insight into the nature of substances. Hopefully it will furnish a path to an understanding of chemical systems.

What are the factors in a system of charges that govern the amount of energy present? Think of a unit of charge on one terminal of a battery as being analogous to an object pulled away from the earth (which attracts it) to an elevated position. If the charge is permitted to do so, it will move toward the other terminal which carries the opposite and attractive charge. So, in this sense the terminals have potential energy. When the switch is closed in an electric circuit, charge is permitted to move through the circuit, but, as was explained in Section 4-12, charge cannot move freely. The rate of flow of charge (current) in a particular circuit reaches a fixed maximum value. The

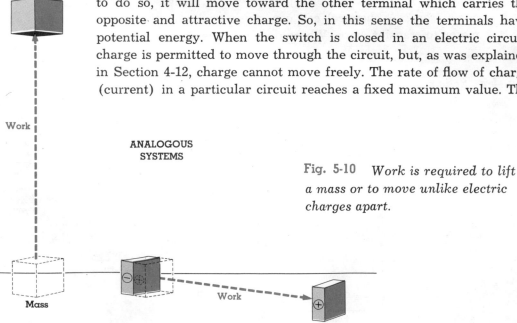

Work

ANALOGOUS
SYSTEMS

Fig. 5-10 *Work is required to lift a mass or to move unlike electric charges apart.*

Mass

Work

electric resistance of the circuit, then, is analogous to the frictional resistance to the motion of an object on a plane. Suppose that the unit of charge flowing through the wire collides with an atom or a molecule or some other small part of matter, causing them to move. If the resulting motion of the small parts of matter were a random motion and if the earlier suggestion that temperature was related to the random motion of atoms or molecules is accepted, it is possible to explain the increase in temperature of the wire as charge flows through it. As the temperature rises in the wire, the wire can transfer heat to other objects around it. One might say that the potential energy of the unit charge on the battery terminal is converted into kinetic energy of the unit charge. This kinetic energy which can be transferred to the atoms of the wire by collisions then becomes apparent as heat flowing out of the wire to warm something else.

It is impossible to carry out experiments directly on a system such as the one described in developing the hypothesis in the preceding paragraph to explain how heat can be produced by an electric current. The atomic unit of charge was merely a mental model devised to explain the constant relationships between chemical change and quantity of electricity observed in electrolysis reactions. To determine experimentally the force operating on an electric charge and to relate this force to the position of the charge relative to another electric charge is the next job. This requires that electric charges of some considerable magnitude be present on objects whose motion in response to the electric forces can be observed. A study of electrostatic systems is necessary to obtain quantitative data.

Imagine the case in which a small sphere has been fixed in one position, so that it cannot move, and charged with positive charge. If a second small sphere carrying a negative charge is brought close to the fixed positively charged sphere, the negative charge will be attracted. If it is free to move, the negative charge will move toward the fixed positive charge. This case is quite analogous, then, to the case in which an object falls toward the earth because of gravitational attraction. On the other hand, if a small positively charged object is brought into the vicinity of the fixed positive charge, it will be repelled and will move away from the fixed charge if it is released. This case has some similarity to the case of an object in the gravitational field of the earth, but the direction of the force on the movable positive charge is away from the fixed charge instead of toward it. Both attractive and repulsive electric forces are present in electrostatic systems and result in the movement of charges either away from or toward each other. Gravitational force is known only as a force of attraction.

To proceed further in relating electrostatic forces and electric energies, it is necessary to know more about the magnitudes of the forces operating between two charges. In particular, the way in which this force depends upon the distance of separation is important because force and distance are the two quantities involved in Equation 5-2 which relates force and energy transfer.

5-13 COULOMB'S LAW

The way in which the force acting between charges depends upon the distance separating them was firmly established by Charles Augustin Coulomb in 1785. What Coulomb determined experimentally was the force that had to be exerted on a charged object, which was otherwise free to move, in order to hold it at various distances from a rigidly held object carrying a known quantity of the same type of charge. Coulomb's experiment is represented schematically in Fig. 5-11.

A and B are spheres carrying electric charges of the same type. The force F_1 exerted on the movable charged sphere B by the charge on A is represented by the arrow. The force F_2 exerted on B holds sphere B in one position at a distance r from A. The apparatus employed permits the measurement of force F_2, which must be equal to force F_1, when B is held stationary. An excess of force in one direction would cause B to move in that direction. Therefore, a measurement of force F_2 is equivalent to a measurement of force F_1, which is the force exerted on B by A. Any influence of gravity was ruled out by the apparatus design, and the measured force F_2 is the force of repulsion between the charged spheres. Table 5-2 presents the data reported by Coulomb in announcing his work. Force F_1 is equal to force F_2 and is designated by F in Table 5-2.

Figure 5-12 shows the curve obtained when the values of the force F between the charges in Table 5-2 are plotted against the corresponding values of the distance r by which the charges are separated. The values of F on the curve increase very sharply as the value of r decreases, and F becomes smaller more gradually as r increases.

TABLE 5-2 COULOMB'S DATA[a]

Distance of Separation of Charged Objects, r	Force Required to Hold Mobile Object in Position, F
36 units of length	36 units of force
18 units of length	144 units of force
8.5 units of length	576 units of force

[a] Relating the force acting between two charged objects to the distance separating the objects.

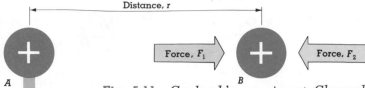

Fig. 5-11 *Coulomb's experiment. Charged sphere A exerts a force* F_1 *on a similarly charged sphere B. Coulomb determined the force* F_2 *needed to keep sphere B at a distance* r *from sphere A.*

The curve in Fig. 5-12 indicates that the mathematical expression of the relationship between F and r involves F in the numerator on one side of the equation and r in the denominator on the other side. Any one of the following expressions might satisfy this requirement.

$$F = \frac{K}{r} \qquad F = \frac{K}{r^2} \qquad F = \frac{K}{r^3}$$

If a graph of F against $1/r$ will yield a straight line, then the mathematical expression $F = K \times 1/r$ describes Coulomb's data. If the graph of F against $1/r^2$ yields a straight line with slope K, then the

Fig. 5-12 *Graphical representation of Coulomb's data from Table 5-2.*

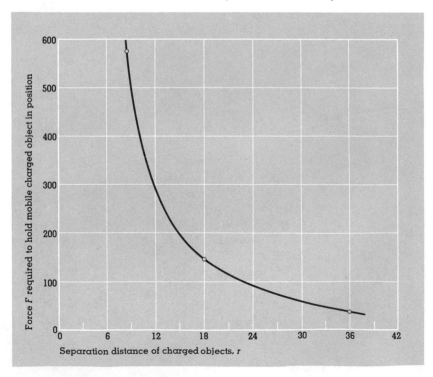

Force F required to hold mobile charged object in position

Separation distance of charged objects, r

F	r	$\dfrac{1}{r}$	r^2	$\dfrac{1}{r^2}$
36	36	2.78×10^{-2}	13.0×10^2	0.722×10^{-3}
144	18	5.56×10^{-2}	3.24×10^2	3.085×10^{-3}
576	8.5	11.8×10^{-2}	0.722×10^2	13.9×10^{-3}

^{a} Calculated from Coulomb's data (Table 5-2) relating F and r.

data are described by the equation $F = K/r^2$. Table 5-3 contains values for $1/r$, r^2, and $1/r^2$ calculated from Coulomb's data. These values are used in plotting F against $1/r$ and $1/r^2$ as in Fig. 5-13.

In Fig. 5-13, the plot of F against $1/r$ is a curve, whereas the plot of F against $1/r^2$ is nearly a straight line through the origin of the graph. Coulomb's data indicated that the force between two charged objects

Fig. 5-13   *Graphical representation of Coulomb's data from Table 5-3.*

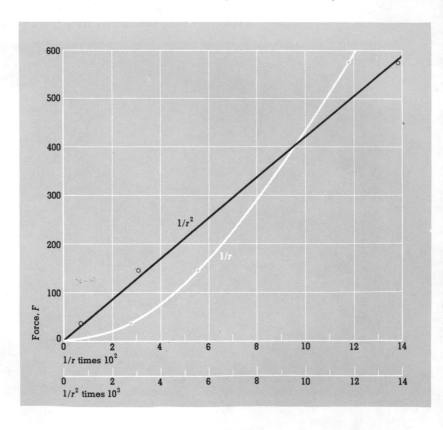

CHARLES AUGUSTIN COULOMB *1736–1806*

A French scientist and engineer. Coulomb was educated for a military career in Paris and spent nine years in the West Indies as a military engineer supervising the construction of fortifications in Martinique. At the time of the French Revolution in 1789, he resigned his military and academic positions and retired to the country, returning in 1799 to Paris. Coulomb discovered laws describing the friction between sliding objects and the dependence of torsion (that is, the amount of twist) in a wire on its length and thickness. Utilizing the torsion balance which he developed, he placed the laws of electrostatic and magnetic attraction and repulsion on a firm experimental basis.

decreased as the square of the distance separating the two charges increased (Equation 5-4).

$$F = \frac{K}{r^2}$$ (Eq. 5-4)

Equation 5-4 was established for the case in which the fixed charge and the movable charge were of equal magnitude throughout the experiment. If part of the charge is removed from the movable object by touching it with a neutral object, the force on the movable object owing to the fixed charge decreases. Removal of part of the fixed charge also results in a decrease in the force. The qualitative observation of the change in force resulting from a change in charge may be expressed in a quantitative relationship. The quantitative relationship provides a definition for the magnitude of electric charges in terms of the forces acting between these charges. If q_1 is the magnitude of the fixed charge and if q_2 is the magnitude of the movable charge, the relationship can be expressed as

$$F = \frac{K'q_1q_2}{r^2}$$ (Eq. 5-5)

where K' is a proportionality constant which is different from K. With his experimental techniques, Coulomb was able to demonstrate the validity of Equation 5-5 within about 3 percent.

Coulomb established in separate experiments that Equation 5-5 described the force between unlike charges as well as between like charges. Numerous subsequent applications to many different experimental situations involving the interactions of electric charges have established the widespread utility of Equation 5-5 which has become known as Coulomb's law. The law has now been verified with a precision of about one part in 1,000,000,000.

Ex. 5-4   According to Coulomb's law, if the distance between charged objects is increased by a factor of 2, by what factor does the force change? If the distance between charged objects is decreased by a factor of 3, by what factor does the force change?

Ex. 5-5   According to Coulomb's law, what would happen to the force between two charged objects if the magnitude of either charge is doubled? If the magnitude of both charges is decreased by a factor of 2, what happens to the force?

5-14   DIELECTRIC PROPERTIES OF MATTER

So far the discussion has considered electrical systems in which the charges were separated only by empty space. Experimentally it has been found that placing a piece of paper, cloth, or any material between the separated charges reduces the magnitude of the force. The amount of reduction of the force is governed primarily by the nature of the material. Gases such as air cause only a small change in the force, whereas solids and liquids cause a comparatively large change.

This experimental observation is included in Coulomb's law by introducing another factor. The factor by which the force between two separated charges is changed is customarily represented by the fraction $1/D$, so that

$$F = \frac{K'q_1q_2}{r^2} \times \frac{1}{D} \qquad (Eq.\ 5\text{-}6)$$

where D is a property of the material between the charges. The quantity D is a measure of the effect of the material on the force between the charges. To determine a value for D for any given substance, an electrical system can be assembled with two charged spheres or plates separated by a fixed distance. The force between the charges can be measured when the plates are separated by a vacuum. This has a value F_v. When some material is placed between the charges, then a new value of the force F_m is obtained. The relationship between force F and the quantity D is found to be

$$\frac{F_m}{F_v} = \frac{D_v}{D_m}$$

It is customary to assign the value of 1 to D_v. The value calculated for D_m is then called the **dielectric constant** of the material. The dielectric constant of a material is a ratio of the forces between two charged objects with a vacuum and a material, respectively, between them. Dielectric constant data are included in Table 5-4.

All values in Table 5-4 are greater than unity. No substance has ever been found to have a dielectric constant less than 1, the value assigned to a vacuum.

TABLE 5-4 DIELECTRIC CONSTANTS OF SOME COMMON SUBSTANCES

Substance	Form	Formula	Dielectric Constant	Temperature, °C
Ice	Solid	H_2O	4.8	−12
Sulfur	Solid	S_8	4.0	20
(Vulcanized rubber)	Solid		2.94	25
Water	Liquid	H_2O	80.37	20
Methanol	Liquid	CH_3OH	33.62	20
Ethanol	Liquid	C_2H_5OH	24.30	25
Ammonia	Liquid	NH_3	22.4	−33.4
Benzene	Liquid	C_6H_6	2.284	20
Carbon tetrachloride	Liquid	CCl_4	2.238	20
n-Octane	Liquid	C_8H_{18}	1.948	20
(Air)	Gas		1.00059	0
Carbon dioxide	Gas	CO_2	1.000985	0
Helium	Gas	He	1.0000684	0
Ammonia	Gas	NH_3	1.0072	0

5-15 ELECTROSTATIC FORCE AND ELECTRIC POTENTIAL ENERGY

Coulomb's law establishes the connection between force and the distance separating charges. Do electrostatic charges q_1 and q_2 possess potential energy by virtue of their being separated from each other by a distance r?

One general description of energy (work in this case) is given by the product of force and distance $(F \times d)$. In this description the distance referred to is that through which the system moves while the force acts. In Coulomb's law, however, the force is described in terms of the distance by which the charges are separated, not the distance through which the force moves the charges.

The graph of electric force against separation distance of unlike charges given in Fig. 5-14 illustrates the problem. Increasing the distance of separation of unlike charges requires energy.

Figure 5-14 shows that the force between the charges varies considerably as the distance of separation changes. To calculate the energy required to separate two charges involves the product of force and distance, both of which change as the distance increases.

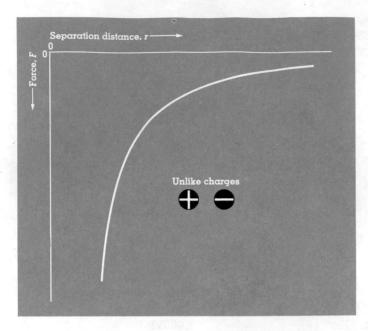

Fig. 5-14 *The force between unlike charges varies considerably as the separation distance changes.*

A calculation strategy for the case in which the force is changing is suggested by first considering the situation of a constant force operating over a distance. A graph of a constant force is given in Fig. 5-15. In this graph the product $(F \times d)$ is equal to work (energy) and is represented on the graph by the area of the rectangle enclosed by the four lines. This relation between energy and an area can be applied to graphs of forces that are either constant or changing. Whenever force is plotted against distance, the area, whether regular or irregular, between the axes and the plotted curve represents the energy.

Consider an electrical system with two like charges, which will repel each other. Figure 5-16 is a plot of the force exerted between them. For a change from separation distance r_1 to r_2, the energy is represented by the irregular area of the shaded portion of the figure.

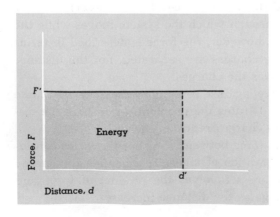

Fig. 5-15 *A graph of constant force and distance. The shaded area $(F' \times d')$ is the energy involved when a constant force F' moves through a distance d'.*

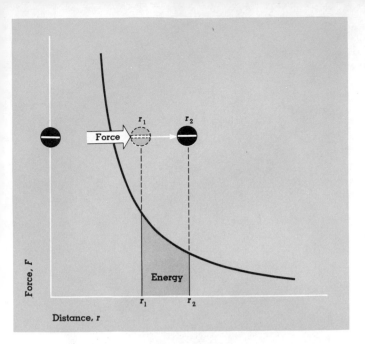

Fig. 5-16 *Force
between two like
charges plotted
against distance of
separation. The
energy change for
the movement of
one charge from
distance r_1 to r_2 is
represented by the
shaded area under
the curve.*

The distance d through which the charge moves, for purposes of calculating energy, is $r_2 - r_1$.

On the other hand, as the distance of separation gets larger, the
force between like charges gets smaller in magnitude. This implies that
the energy also decreases as the force gets smaller. It is possible to
assume that as the separation distance gets larger and larger, the force
gets so close to zero that it is impractical to distinguish the value of the
force from zero. Whatever this large distance may be, it is convenient
to refer to it simply as infinite separation of charges.

In the system shown in Fig. 5-16, the energy required to move
the charges closer together (decrease the separation distance) must
be supplied to the system. The system possesses high energy when the
charges are close together. If the separation distance between the
charges is increased, energy is given up by the system to the environment. At infinite separation the force will be zero, and the energy will
also be zero.

Now it is possible to ask a question about the electric potential
energy of separated charges in a slightly different fashion. How much
energy is involved when two like charges are brought from infinite
separation to some relatively small separation of r? Experiment and
theory have shown that for this question the energy E required is

$$E = \frac{K'q_1q_2}{r} \qquad (Eq.\ 5\text{-}7)$$

when the charges are separated by a vacuum. But

$$E = \frac{K'q_1q_2}{Dr}$$

when a material with dielectric constant D separates the charges.

189

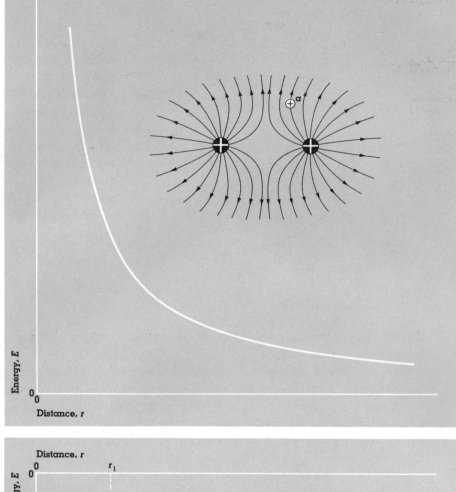

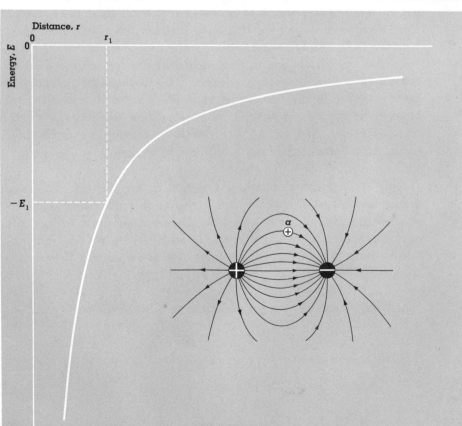

The relationship between energy and the separation of two like charges (Equation 5-7) is shown graphically in Fig. 5-17. In the graph zero energy has been chosen as the energy for which the charges are so far apart that no effect of one on the other can be detected. Whatever this large distance may be, it is called **infinite separation.** As the distance of separation becomes smaller and smaller, the system acquires more and more energy (E increases). This fits observations that pushing objects of like charge together requires that work be done on the objects.

Two objects with unlike charges also exert a force on each other. To separate the charges, work must be done on the system. As a result of the work done, unlike charges will have a maximum amount of energy stored in the system when the unlike charges are at infinite separation. For like charges, the energy at infinite separation is found to be zero. It is therefore convenient to assign zero energy arbitrarily to the systems of unlike charges at infinite separation. This choice leaves no alternative but to say that for unlike charges close together the energy of the system must be below zero. Negative energy for a system of unlike charges is consistent with the discussion; zero energy is always higher than any negative value of energy. On a graph of energy and distance the relation is described in Fig. 5-18.

Figure 5-18 represents the conclusion that to separate unlike charges means that work has to be done on the system. For example, for objects at a distance r_1 the energy is $-E_1$. To separate these objects to infinite distance means that enough energy has to be added to take the system from $-E_1$ to 0, a gain in energy equal to E_1. Conversely, if unlike charges are attracted to each other from infinite separation to distance r_1, work equal to energy E_1 is done by the system (transferred out of the system).

The energy relations of like charge and of unlike charge are combined into one graph in Fig. 5-19. In general, it is possible to conclude

Fig. 5-17   (Top) *Relationship between energy and the distance separating two like charges. Arrows indicate directions a small positive test charge a would move if placed in the system of two large positive charges.*

Fig. 5-18   (Bottom) *Relationship between energy and distance of separation for two unlike charges. Arrows indicate directions a small positive test charge a would move if placed in a system of two large unlike charges.*

191

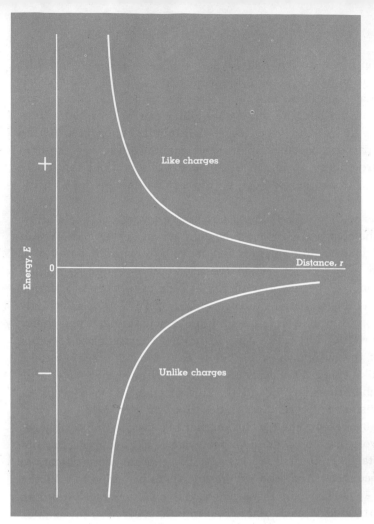

Fig. 5-19 *Relation-
ship between energy
and distance for like
and unlike charges.*

that like charges starting close together lose energy (upper curve in
Fig. 5-19) by separation almost as if they slid downhill to zero energy
at infinite separation. By the same token, unlike charges lose energy
(lower curve) by coming together. The shorter the separation distance
between unlike charges, the lower the energy of the system.

Tracing the curves in Fig. 5-19 in the opposite direction leads to the
following statements. As unlike charges are separated, energy has to
be transferred into the system. It is as if the unlike charges were
pushed uphill toward zero energy (the maximum) at infinite separation. Also with the like charges, pushing them together can be accomplished only by transferring energy into the system.

Ex. 5-6   In a system consisting of two oppositely charged spheres, is the potential
energy of the system highest or lowest when the force between the spheres
is at a maximum? Answer the same question for a system consisting of
spheres of like charge. Refer to Figs. 5-17 and 5-18.

5-16 ENERGY IN DIELECTRIC MATERIALS

The energy changes observed in many chemical systems are associated with the separation of electric charge. It is easier to pull unlike charges apart when some substance is between the charges than when empty space (a vacuum) is between them. A quantitative measure of this effect is given by the dielectric constant of the substance. For liquid water the value of the dielectric constant D listed in Table 5-4 is about 80. This means that to separate a positive and a negative charge in a vacuum requires about eighty times as much energy as would be needed for the same purpose in water.

The ratio of dielectric constants for water to benzene is 35.19; that is, $80.37/2.284 = 35.19:1$. This means that to separate charges in benzene requires about thirty-five times the energy required to carry out the same process in water. What happens in liquids having different dielectric constants if only a fixed and limited amount of energy is available to separate two unlike charges?

Whenever the energy available to separate charges is limited, the charges are separated by a shorter distance. The distance of separation is also affected by the dielectric constant of the liquid. For the same quantity of energy, charges cannot be separated by as great a distance in a liquid of low dielectric constant as they can be in a liquid of high dielectric constant. It is this type of situation which is encountered in chemical systems that contain charged ions.

In Chapter 2 a solution system of potassium chloride and water was discussed. A substance that dissolves in a liquid spreads out and eventually becomes uniformly distributed through the liquid. If the substance contains or produces charged parts, these may become separated. The higher the dielectric constant of the liquid, the more readily such a separation can occur.

The discussion of the dielectric constant D leaves unanswered the question of why some substances, such as sodium chloride, dissolve in water whereas others, such as naphthalene, do not. But Equation 5-6 and data in Table 5-4 do tell why the force required to keep charged particles apart is smaller in water than in benzene. Why the dissolving process ever starts must be left an open question until Chapter 13 when the structure of substances is studied more fully.

5-17 ELECTRICAL SYSTEMS AS ENERGY SOURCES

The discussion of systems containing separated charges has uncovered a new type of energy, electric potential energy (Equation 5-7). This energy is considered to be on the same footing with kinetic energy for moving objects (Equation 5-2) and gravitational potential energy for elevated objects (Section 5-10). From electrical systems, energy can be transferred as heat (Section 5-11) or as work (Section 5-12). When this transfer occurs, the electric potential energy must be lowered by an amount exactly equal in energy units to the heat or work transferred. Systems in which charge separation has occurred, that is, systems possessing electric potential energy, can therefore be energy sources.

Chemical cells are examples of systems which can produce charge separation. The chemical evidence discussed in Chapter 4 indicates that a chemical reaction is an essential accompaniment of the separation of charge. Thus the flow of charge from a cell can be interpreted as a process in which separated charges with high potential energy move together and acquire a low potential energy. The difference between the final low and the initial high potential energy represents energy that can be evolved from the system. So long as the system can continue to react chemically, more separated charges are produced and the process of energy evolution continues.

It has also been found experimentally that in some cases the cell reaction can be reversed so that a flow of charge through the cell produces a chemical change. In this case the existence of electrically charged ions in the chemical system has been postulated. As these ions move in response to the charge flowing through the system, chemical changes take place. It must be that in some way these chemical changes are accompanied by conversion of the electric energy into energy stored within the chemical system. Thus, when charge flows through water, hydrogen and oxygen gases are produced at the electrodes. In some way the separated gases have stored energy which can again be transferred whenever the gases react to form water. The two separated gases have the potential (possibility) of reacting to form water and evolving the energy that is stored in them. The exploration of electrical systems and their significance for chemical systems suggests that the relation between electricity and chemical change is intimate.

Electric potential energy has a heat equivalent just as gravitational potential energy has a heat equivalent. In both cases, the idea of potential energy is developed through consideration of the movement of an object in a field of force and the action of a force on that object through the distance moved. Consequently, it would be expected that the heat equivalents of the two types of potential energy would be the same (Fig. 5-10).

5-18 SUMMARY

Chemical systems have electrical properties. These properties can be studied through electrochemical cell systems and electrolysis systems. In both types of systems, the electrical features are accounted for by a mental model of separated charges.

In this chapter, major attention was given to systems in which separated charges could be produced by friction rather than by chemical change. With charges produced by friction, it became possible to explore what is called electrostatics, the properties of charged objects.

In the exploration of electrostatics, it was found that like charges repel each other whereas unlike charges attract. This led to the introduction of Coulomb's law for the force acting between charges, $F = Kq_1q_2/r^2$.

A study of the forces produced by an electrostatic system was then interpreted in terms of the energy of an electrostatic system. The energy of such a system is given by the relation $E = K'q_1q_2/r$. In a system of electric charges the appropriate value for the electrostatic potential energy E depends upon the distance between the charges r, upon the size of the charges q_1 and q_2, and upon whether the charges are of the same or unlike type. Like charges have a high potential energy when they are close together (Fig. 5-19). As the like charges separate, the system loses energy and the potential energy drops toward zero. On the other hand, a system of unlike charges has a low potential energy when the separation distance is small. With increase in separation, the unlike charge system rises in potential energy toward a value of zero.

Energy stored in a system is described by terms identified with the method of storage.

Energy Term	Storage Mechanism
Kinetic	Motion
Gravitational potential	Separation of masses
Electric potential	Separation of charges
Chemical	Separation of reactants

A change in the quantity of energy stored in a system is produced by transfer of energy into or out of the system. Energy transfer is commonly identified by the conditions under which the transfer occurs.

Energy Term	Transfer Conditions
Work (mechanical energy)	Change in motion
Heat (thermal energy)	Objects at different temperatures and in contact
Light (radiant energy)	Objects at different temperatures but not in contact

Relating electric energy to the energy of charged objects can satisfactorily unify different areas of information, but the relationships raise troublesome questions. For instance, how do the chemicals in an electric cell produce the potential difference between the terminals of the cell? This potential difference implies that the chemicals in the cell are capable of separating positive and negative charge, a process which requires energy. What is the source of the energy? Is it the same energy that is available as heat when the reaction of the chemicals in the cell is carried out in a calorimeter? If so, can the energy be related to the motion of small objects in the chemical substances or can it be interpreted in terms of electric energy?

According to Sections 3-2 and 4-18, certain chemical systems, such as a solution of lead nitrate in water (Experiment 11 in *Investigating Chemical Systems*), can conduct electricity. As the conduction process occurs, chemical reaction at the electrodes occurs as well. The amount of charge that flows and the amount of reaction that occurs are quantitatively related in a constant way. It seems reasonable to suppose that some chemical species are involved in the conduction process. On the basis of the observed behavior of electrical systems studied in this chapter, it also seems reasonable to assume that the chemical species are electrically charged. Such electrically charged species present in conducting solutions are called ions.

The characteristics of moving charges in solution are hidden by the properties of the substances used in studying the phenomena. This suggests the possibility of investigating the separation of electric charges from matter so that the properties of charge alone can be observed. Space which is entirely free of matter is known as a perfect vacuum. Such a space should be the ideal place to attempt the separation of electric charge from matter since matter itself would not be present to interfere with the interpretation of data. Since charged objects do exert forces on one another in a vacuum, an electric potential may be established in an evacuated space. This offers the opportunity to impart energy to any charge which is separated from matter.

Ex. 5-7   Each of the following diagrams represents a simple system. Examine each diagram, then defend or criticize each statement which accompanies the illustration.

In System I:

a. Both spheres are charged with the same kind of charge.

In System II:

b. Both spheres are charged with either type *G* or type *R* charge.

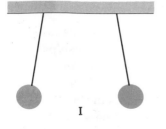

I

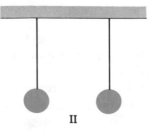

II

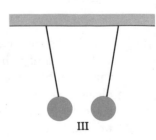

III

c. One sphere is charged with type G charge, and the other sphere with type R charge.

In System III:

d. The spheres are charged so that either both have type G charge or both have type R charge.

e. One sphere is charged with either type G or type R charge, and the other sphere is uncharged.

Ex. 5-8 The following experiment was performed by a group of students. A large sphere similar to the one shown in views (a) and (b) of the figure was charged by an electrostatic generator.

Observation A: A small sphere represented by R and charged with type R charge is attracted to the large sphere; a small sphere represented by G and charged with type G charge is repelled by the large sphere.

Observation B: When one terminal of a very sensitive microammeter was connected to a water pipe and the other terminal was touched to the charged sphere, the needle of the meter moved in the same direction as if it were connected across a portion of the external circuit of a Daniell cell, as indicated in view (c).

a. Is the large sphere charged with type G or type R charge?

b. What is the sign of the charge on the large sphere?

c. What is the sign of the type R charge? of the type G charge?

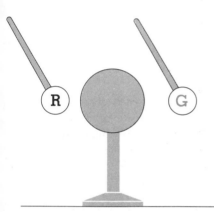

(a)

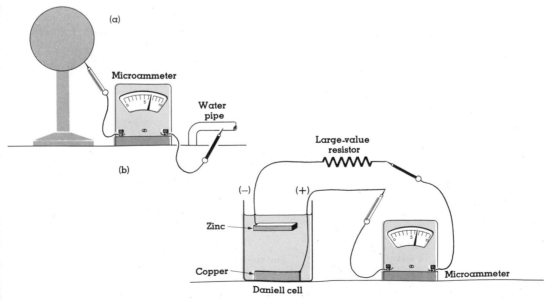

(b)

(c)

Ex. 5-9   Describe how you can use an electroscope to determine the signs of type G and type R charges.

Ex. 5-10   Two platinum electrodes are placed in a solution containing positive ⊕ ions and negative ⊖ ions. These electrodes are connected to the zinc and copper electrodes of a Daniell cell, as shown in the accompanying diagram. Will the positive ions in the solution tend to move toward the platinum electrode connected to the copper electrode of the Daniell cell or toward the platinum electrode connected to the zinc electrode of the Daniell cell? In which direction will the negative ions in the solution tend to move?

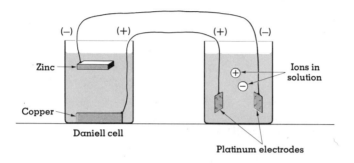

Ex. 5-11   Two metal plates are mounted at a distance r from each other. The charge transferred from one plate to the other plate is q. By what factor will the force between the plates change (a) if the plates are immersed in pure water instead of in air? (b) if vulcanized rubber is placed between the plates instead of air? Refer to Table 5-4.

Ex. 5-12   The drawing below represents the deflection of a single positively charged alpha particle by a positively charged nucleus of a metal atom with large atomic mass.

a. At what position(s) is the kinetic energy of the alpha particle at a maximum?

b. At what position(s) is the potential energy of the alpha particle at a maximum?

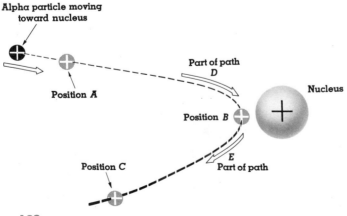

c. Along what part of the path is the kinetic energy of the alpha particle being converted into potential energy?

d. Along what part of the path is the potential energy of the alpha particle being converted to kinetic energy?

Ex. 5-13 After artificial satellites have orbited the earth for some time they drop back to the earth.

a. What causes the satellite to fall back to the earth?

b. Why do satellites usually burn up before they reach the earth's surface?

Ex. 5-14 Experiments indicate that any quantity of kinetic energy can be completely converted into potential energy and that any quantity of potential energy can be completely converted into kinetic energy. However, the conversion of a quantity of thermal energy entirely to potential energy or of a quantity of thermal energy entirely to kinetic energy is experimentally impossible. Explain.

Ex. 5-15 *a.* What is the name assigned to an atomic unit of negative charge?

b. How many electrons must be transferred to deposit one atom of silver? one mole of silver? (Hint: One mole of silver equals one Avogadro number of silver atoms.)

c. Experimentally, 894.5 coulombs of charge is required to deposit 1 g of silver. What number of coulombs is required to deposit 1 mole of silver atoms? (Hint: One mole of silver has a mass of 107.9 g.)

d. What is the charge, in coulombs, of a single electron?

6

ELECTRICAL NATURE OF MATTER

CHEMICAL CHANGE and electricity are related experimentally in two ways. (1) The flow of charge through a solution (for example, the electrolysis of solutions of silver sulfate, sulfuric acid, or lead nitrate in water) leads to chemical changes. (2) A reaction in a chemical system can produce charge separation (for example, the Daniell cell or the storage battery). Chemical changes are ordinarily accompanied by the transfer of energy between the system and its surroundings. The flow of charge through a solution and the production of charge separation in a chemical system are accompanied by the transfer of energy. In other words, electrical systems as well as chemical systems have the capacity to transfer energy between the system and its surroundings.

To provide information that would explain these connections between chemical changes and the behavior of charges, energy stored in a system of separated charges was discussed in Chapter 5. A quantitative expression, $E = K'q_1q_2/r$, is used to describe how electric potential energy E, charge q, and charge separation r are related. The fact that chemical systems can produce separated charges while the flow of electric charge can lead to chemical change suggests that there is some relation between chemical systems and electrical systems which remains to be explored.

Since charge is so intimately associated with chemical change, more information about the nature of charges themselves should be helpful in studying the central problem—the nature of chemical change. To get more information, systems of electric charges, isolated from matter as completely as is possible, will be studied. Electric energy can be stored in an electrostatic system even when the space between the charges is free of matter. Is it possible to produce a flow of charge through empty space?

6-1 ELECTRIC CURRENT IN GASES

On the basis of the discussion of electrostatics (Section 5-3), air did not seem to be a conductor. Under some circumstances, however, air and other gases do conduct electricity.

If you walk across a wool or nylon rug on a day when the air is dry, your whole body becomes charged as a result of friction between your shoes and the rug. The charge that you acquire is produced by friction. One type of charge accumulates on the rug, and the other type on your shoes. The charge separation produced here is of the same nature as that produced by rubbing a glass rod with a piece of silk cloth.

The charge acquired by your body as a result of friction between your shoes and the rug can become quite large. If you bring your finger close to a metal object (for example, a light fixture, a radiator, or a water faucet), you can see a small flash of light. This light is not bright but can sometimes be seen if the room is dark. A simple way to observe the flash after you are charged is to bring your finger to within 1 or 2 mm of a metal electric light fixture or metal radiator in a dark room. The light is accompanied by a crackling noise and by the loss of charge from the body. The light associated with the transfer of charge is called a spark.

When an electric potential difference exists, sparks can be produced in both electrostatic and electric current systems. When a wire, connected to one terminal of an automobile battery and touching a wire connected to the other terminal is moved, a spark occurs when the contact between the wires is broken. Sparks can be observed in this case until the battery is dead, that is, until there is no longer a potential difference (or charge separation) between the terminals. A spark, then, is the visible evidence that charge flows through air from one object to another. Air serves as the conductor (although a poor conductor) for the charge in the examples that have been described. The experimental conditions for conduction require only that the potential difference be sufficiently high. In dry air, a potential difference of 10,000 volts will produce a spark about 1 cm in length.

About 1750 William Watson, in England, showed that the flow of charge through a gas in a sealed container increases as the pressure is lowered. As the pressure in the container is reduced below that of the atmosphere, conductivity increases until, at a pressure of about 0.001 atmosphere, gases become fairly good conductors.

Two things can be observed about electric conduction in a gas at low pressure. (1) A considerable potential difference (voltage) has to be applied to the gas before any current can be detected. The exact value of the minimum voltage depends upon both the gas used and the design of the apparatus. (2) As charge flows through the gas, the gas glows with a light whose color depends on the gas used. This process is often called *gas discharge,* and the apparatus used is referred to as a *gas discharge tube.*

A neon sign is a glass tube containing neon at low pressure. Metallic electrodes are placed at either end of the tube. When a potential difference of several thousand volts is applied to the electrodes, electricity flows through the gas and a red glow is produced in the gas throughout the length of the tube.

This indicates then that gases at low pressure conduct electricity. When gas pressure is lowered still further, charge will still flow. In addition to gas discharge, there are three other ways in which charge flow through gases occurs.

6-2 THERMIONIC EMISSION

In 1883 Thomas Edison observed that charge would flow through a gas at low pressure if a hot electrode and a cold electrode were present in an enclosed gas. The process by which charge is transferred between a hot and a cold electrode is called **thermionic emission.** Sir John Ambrose Fleming used the principle in 1904 to construct the forerunner of the present-day radio tubes. A sketch of an apparatus similar to Edison's is shown in Fig. 6-1.

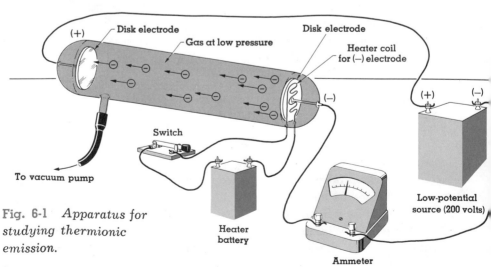

Fig. 6-1 *Apparatus for studying thermionic emission.*

The essential parts of the thermionic emission apparatus are two metal electrodes in an evacuated tube. When the apparatus in Fig. 6-1 is arranged as shown, charge flows through the ammeter. However, if the switch controlling the heater is opened so that the negatively charged electrode in the evacuated tube is not heated, no current is indicated by the ammeter. The current suggests that charge crosses the space between the heated electrode and the other metal plate. However, when the connections to the low potential source are reversed, thus charging the heated electrode positively and the plate negatively, no charge flows through the circuit. No current is conducted when the switch controlling the heater circuit is open. Evidently charge can only flow from the hot negative electrode to the cold positive electrode.

Unlike the conduction of electricity through a gas by the gas discharge process described in Section 6-1, thermionic emission does not depend upon the nature of the gas in the tube so long as the gas pressure is low enough. No matter how much the pressure is reduced, the flow of charge continues so long as the hot electrode is negatively charged. Although it is not possible, for practical reasons, to remove all traces of gas from the evacuated tube, the conduction process in thermionic tubes seems to be independent of the presence of small amounts of gas.

In gas discharge, a minimum voltage is required for charge to flow. This is not the case for thermionic emission if the negative electrode is hot enough. If the negative electrode is heated to a temperature above 500°C, charge flow takes place no matter how small the voltage. The results of the thermionic emission experiments can be interpreted to mean that charge can flow through an evacuated space when a potential difference exists between electrodes. Since a hot negative electrode is essential to the thermionic emission process, it can be concluded that the high temperature loosens up the charge so that it is released from the negative electrode. Once separated from the electrode, this negative charge will move toward the positive electrode because of the attractive forces between opposite charges.

No matter how long thermionic emission continues, neither electrode is found to change in mass. There is no experimental evidence to indicate that any part of the electrode material is carried between the electrodes. Furthermore, the presence of residual gas in the tube does not contribute to the charge flow. Whatever the negative charge may be, it appears not to be associated with an element or a compound within the electrodes or within the space between the electrodes.

6-3 PHOTOELECTRIC EMISSION

There is one set of circumstances in which charge can flow through the apparatus used for thermionic emission even though the negative electrode is not at high temperature. To demonstrate this phenomenon,

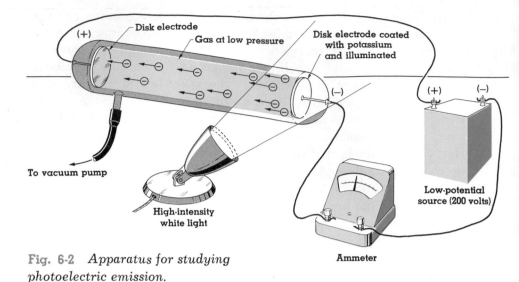

Fig. 6-2 *Apparatus for studying photoelectric emission.*

the negative electrode must first be coated with one of a small group of substances. Lithium, sodium, and potassium are examples of substances that can be used. When an intense white light shines on the coated negative electrode, a current can be produced. An apparatus for exploring this type of conduction is shown in Fig. 6-2. Since light is essential to the charge flow, the process is called **photoelectric emission.** As the light is increased in intensity, the current increases in magnitude. If the illuminated electrode is positively charged, however, no charge flows.

The pressure of gas in the apparatus has no effect on the photoelectric emission so long as the pressure is low. Thus, as in the thermionic emission apparatus, the photoelectric emission apparatus can be considered to produce charge flow through empty space.

From these observations, you may conclude that the current produced by illumination of a negative electrode in a photoelectric emission apparatus is a negative charge just as was observed in thermionic emission. Charge must travel from the negative electrode to the positive electrode. The electrodes in the photoelectric tube are not altered in mass or composition by the emission or absorption of the negative charge.

6-4 HIGH-VACUUM DISCHARGE

In Section 6-1 it was pointed out that a gas at low pressure in a sealed tube conducts electricity. The only requirement for the gas discharge process is that there be a sufficiently large potential difference between two electrodes in the gas.

When a gas discharge tube with a gas pressure of about 0.001 atmosphere conducts electricity, the gas glows. If the pressure of the gas is reduced still further, the glow in the gas disappears. Even though a glow is no longer visible at low pressure, charge continues to flow between the electrodes. At sufficiently low pressures, the nature of the residual gas has little or no effect on the flow of charge. Almost any metal can be used for the electrode, and charge will flow in the presence or absence of light. This type of charge flow is called **high-vacuum discharge.**

An apparatus for studying the process of high-vacuum discharge is shown in Fig. 6-3. It consists of a glass tube and two electrodes. When the electrode at the small end of the tube is negatively charged to a potential difference of several thousand volts with respect to the positive electrode, a glow appears in the glass at the large end of the tube opposite the negative electrode. If the negative and positive electrodes are interchanged, the glow appears in the glass directly above what would then be the negative electrode.

When the electrodes are charged as indicated in Fig. 6-3, not only does the glass at the large end of the tube glow, but various other materials placed on the inside surface of the glass at the large end of the tube will glow brightly whenever there is a large potential difference between the electrodes.

The direction of the charge movement in the high-vacuum discharge tube can be determined with the apparatus shown in Fig. 6-4. A metal disk with a small hole is placed close to the negative electrode, between the negative electrode and the positive electrode. When the perforated disk is in place, a small glowing spot appears at the opposite end of the tube. No spot is produced anywhere in the tube when the disk is placed

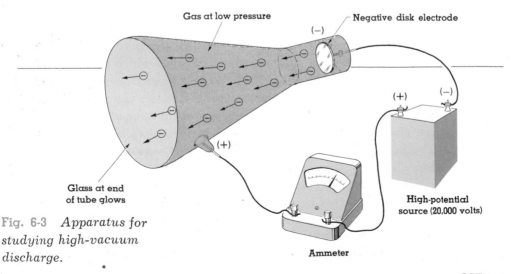

Gas at low pressure

Negative disk electrode

(−)

(+)

(+)   (−)

Glass at end
of tube glows

High-potential
source (20,000 volts)

Fig. 6-3 *Apparatus for studying high-vacuum discharge.*

Ammeter

near the positive electrode. This must mean that negative charge travels from the negative electrode in a straight line through the hole in the disk to the large end of the tube.

Electricity can pass through empty space as a result of thermionic emission, photoelectric emission, and high-vacuum discharge, all of which result in the flow of a beam of negative charge. Whether or not the negative charge is identical in all these cases cannot be decided on the basis of the information that has been presented. The high-vacuum discharge apparatus provided the starting point for J. J. Thomson to investigate the nature of the negative charge.

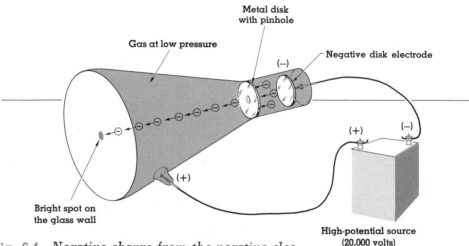

Fig. 6-4 *Negative charge from the negative electrode travels through a hole in the positively charged metal disk and produces a glowing spot when it strikes the end of the tube.*

6-5 NEGATIVE CHARGE

In 1897 Thomson modified the apparatus shown in Fig. 6-4 by placing in the tube two parallel metal plates between which he could establish a potential difference (Fig. 6-5a). When a beam of negative charge was produced without having the two parallel plates charged, a bright spot with a sharp edge appeared on the end of the tube at position A. When the plates were charged, the spot shifted from position A to position B. The beam producing the spot moves as if it were attracted by the positive charge on the plate. This shift in position of the spot confirms the conclusion that the beam consists of negative charge.

Thomson further modified the apparatus shown in Fig. 6-5a by placing the north pole of a magnet directly above the beam and the south pole directly below the beam, as in Fig. 6-5b. With the parallel plates uncharged, he examined the effect of the magnet on the beam. The spot

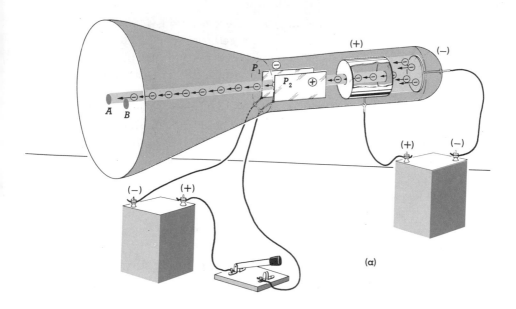

Fig. 6-5   (a) *The beam of negative charge produces a glowing spot on the end of the tube at* A *if the switch that controls the charge on the deflecting plates* P₁ *and* P₂ *is open and at* B *if the switch is closed.* (b) *With the magnet poles in place, the spot appears at* C *when the switch is open and at* A *when the switch is closed.*

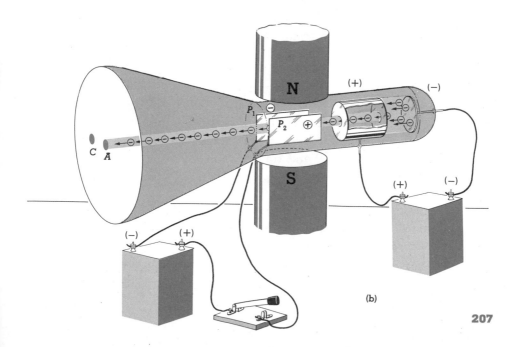

on the end of the tube appeared at a position C. Here, as in the case when the parallel plates were charged, the spot had a fairly bright and well-defined boundary. If he charged the parallel plates and used the magnets, he found it possible to adjust the potential difference on the plates and the positions of the magnet poles so that the center of the spot again appeared at position A. In other words, the effect of the magnet on the position of the spot could just counterbalance the effect of the charged deflecting plates on the position of the spot.

In Thomson's experiments the following observations were recorded.

1. The beam was deflected toward the positively charged plate; and the larger the charge on the plate, the greater the deflection.

2. The deflection of the beam away from the magnet poles was increased when the potential difference used to produce the beam was increased.

3. The deflection of the beam toward the positively charged plate was decreased when the potential difference used to produce the beam was increased.

From the first observation, Thomson deduced that the beam consisted of negative charge. To account for the other two observations, Thomson assumed that the beam had both mass and velocity. His reasoning can be summarized in two points.

First, a wire carrying a current is acted upon by a magnet so as to push the wire away from the magnet. The force acting on the wire is proportional to the charge flow per second in the wire. The deflection produced by the magnet acting upon the beam in Thomson's apparatus indicates that the time required for a given amount of charge to travel along the beam is decreased when the potential difference producing the beam is increased. Thomson decided that the beam travels with greater velocity as a result of the increased potential difference.

Secondly, the increase in beam velocity produces a decreased deflection when the beam goes past the deflecting plates. But if the velocity of the beam is greater, this reduces the time that the force produced by the deflecting plates can act upon the beam. In Section 5-8, force and time were shown to be related by the equation $F \, \Delta t = m \, \Delta v$, where Δt is the time the force F acts, m is mass, and Δv is change in velocity. Since velocity, force, and time are known from observations 1 and 2, Thomson was able to calculate the ratio of charge to mass from the deflection.

Although neither the observations nor the ideas give any direct suggestions about whether the beam is a continuous fluid or a collection of separate particles, it is customary to assume that the beam is a collection of charged particles in motion. Each particle has a mass, a velocity, and a negative charge. The problem is that of determining the mass, velocity, and charge on the particles.

6-6 THE ELECTRON

Thomson found that the glowing spot remained reasonably well defined when either the magnet poles or the charged plates shifted it from its undeflected position. In other words, according to Thomson's hypothesis, each of the particles is diverted from its normal path to the same extent as all the others. If this were not so, the spot would not remain round but would spread out along a line joining A, D, and C in Fig. 6-5b. A uniform deflection of all particles is accounted for by assuming that all the particles are the same in mass, in velocity, and in charge. If this assumption is not made, it is necessary to conclude that any one or two of the three properties of the different particles must change in such a way that the changes always compensate each other. Since no evidence is available to indicate that the particles have variable mass or charge, it is simpler to assume that negative charge in the high-vacuum discharge tube consists of identical particles than to assume that there are many different kinds of negative charges. Is it possible to determine any of the three properties which Thomson used to account for the deflection of the beam of particles from its path?

Thomson's mathematical analysis of his experimental results gave the velocity of the negative particles. Thomson was then able to reconstruct the path of the charge when either the magnet poles were present or the plates were charged, and to calculate the ratio of the charge of each negative particle to its mass. The ratio of charge to mass which Thomson determined for the negative particle was about 2×10^8 coulombs/g. To the particle having this charge/mass ratio and displaying the ability to move, Thomson assigned the name *electron.*

Thomson carried out identical experiments in which he varied both the material of which the negatively charged plate was made and the nature of any small amount of gas in the tube. In every case, the ratio of charge to mass which he calculated for electrons was the same within experimental error. This result suggests that electrons are common to all matter.

Thomson was in fact able to show that thermionic emission, photoelectric emission, and high-vacuum discharge were each examples of electrons traveling through space to produce a flow of negative charge. The fundamental similarity of the three phenomena is indicated by the nature of the properties that he and others observed for the three different processes.

1. The charge travels away from the negative electrode and toward the positive electrode.

2. The mass and other properties of the electrodes are not altered by the flow of charge.

3. The path along which negative charge flows in each of the three cases is changed by charged plates placed near the negative charge.

4. The path along which charge flows is changed by a magnet.

5. For thermionic emission, the negative electrode must be hot. For photoelectric emission, the negative electrode must be illuminated. For high-vacuum discharge, there must be a large potential difference between the positive and negative electrodes.

6. In each of the three cases, the pressure of any gas in the system must be well below 0.001 atmosphere.

In Section 4-21 the term electron was given to the unit of charge indicated by electrolysis experiments. If the electrons involved in electrolysis are assumed to be the same as the electrons with which Thomson worked, a value for the mass of the electron can be computed.

On the basis that hydrogen is the element whose atoms have the smallest atomic mass, it is reasonable to assume that one electron is required to produce one atom of hydrogen in the electrolysis of water. The quantity of charge required for the formation of 1 mole of hydrogen atoms is 96,500 coulombs. The mass of this quantity of negative charge (the mass of 1 mole of electrons), according to Thomson's charge/mass ratio, would be

$$\frac{\dfrac{96,500 \text{ coulombs}}{\text{mole of electrons}}}{\dfrac{2 \times 10^8 \text{ coulombs}}{\text{g of electrons}}} \cong 1/2,000 \text{ g/mole of electrons}$$

In other words, the mass of the electron must be approximately 1/2,000 the mass of a hydrogen atom, if the assumption that one electron is required to form one hydrogen atom is correct. Because no chemical element that has been isolated has an atomic mass less than hydrogen, it is not possible to identify the electron as an element. If an electron, which has relatively little mass, can be separated from a hydrogen atom, the remaining part of the hydrogen atom must be positively charged and must have a mass of the same magnitude as that of the hydrogen atom. This would be expected because separating a negative charge from a neutral atom would form a positive charge and because 1 amu −1/2,000 amu is still very nearly 1 amu. Or is the mass of the hydrogen atom not associated directly with the positive charge at all?

6-7 POSITIVE CHARGE

One answer to this question may be found by considering data obtained with a high-vacuum discharge tube similar to that used by Thomson. The fundamental new feature added to the tube is that the negatively charged metal electrode in the tube has holes in it as indicated in Fig. 6-6. In 1886, Eugen Goldstein observed that with such an apparatus, containing somewhat more gas than the high-vacuum discharge tube, a glowing spot was produced on the side of the tube behind the negative electrode as shown in Fig. 6-6. At the same time

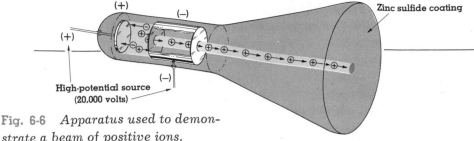

Fig. 6-6 *Apparatus used to demonstrate a beam of positive ions.*

there was an increase in the number of electrons that were traveling toward the positive electrode. The glowing spot was accounted for on the basis that positively charged particles and more electrons were produced in the gas in the tube by collisions between gas molecules and electrons. These positively charged particles were attracted to the negatively charged electrode. Some of the positively charged particles passed through the hole in the electrode and struck the wall of the tube.

If the wall of the tube was coated with zinc sulfide, a glowing green spot could be detected where the beam of positive particles struck the wall. The similarity between the beam of positive charge and negative charge was recognized by numerous investigators, but it was J. J. Thomson who used the technique of deflecting the beam with magnets and charged plates to obtain quantitative data about the properties of the positively charged particles.

It proved much more difficult to deflect and analyze the beam of positive charge than to deflect and analyze the electron beam. The positively charged beam required stronger forces to deflect it, and when it was deflected, the beam spread out to give a large diffuse spot on the zinc sulfide screen. Just as the beams of negative charge were assumed to be made up of negatively charged particles, so the beams of positive charge are assumed to be made up of positively charged particles. Because the positively charged beam is deflected diffusely, it cannot be considered to be composed of particles all having the same charge, mass, and velocity—which is the reverse of the case with the beam of electrons. To explain the observations, there are three possibilities. (1) The velocities of the particles must be variable and higher than those of the electrons. (2) The masses of the positive particles must be variable and greater than those of the electrons. (3) The magnitudes of the positive charges must be variable and less than those of the electrons. The third possibility is contrary to the basic assumption that there is no unit of either positive or negative charge smaller than that of the electron (Section 6-6). Thus, the first two possibilities can be used as working hypotheses.

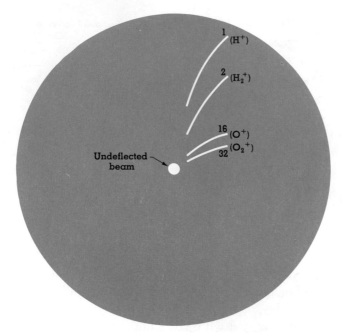

Fig. 6-7 *Curves produced on zinc sulfide coating at the end of the tube when beams of positive ions are deflected by charged plates and a magnet. The numbers are the relative masses of the positive ions calculated from their deflections. The identities of the ions and their charges are shown in parentheses.*

By arranging the charged deflecting plates and magnet poles appropriately, Thomson was able to demonstrate that the beam of positive charge was, in fact, made up of positively charged particles of different velocities and with different ratios of charge to mass. He also showed that each different gas placed in the apparatus gave a different assortment of charge/mass ratios for the particles. Figure 6-7 is a schematic representation of the types of patterns produced on the end of the tube when the beam of positive charge was produced first with hydrogen gas and then with oxygen gas.

Analysis of the patterns was made by assuming that each of the particles had a positive charge of one unit and that the one deflected to the greatest extent had a mass of 1 amu. On the basis of these assumptions, the four tracks in the pattern represented particles of masses 1, 2, 16, and 32. All four tracks in the pattern can be accounted for by assuming that the positive charges are positively charged atoms or molecules. The mass ratio of 1:16 for the H^+ and O^+ ions (1:16) and the H_2^+ and O_2^+ ions (2:32) corresponds to the mass ratio of hydrogen to oxygen obtained by chemical analysis (Section 3-8).

The question of the relation between the mass of a hydrogen atom and the positive charge produced when an electron is removed from a hydrogen atom is answered by the conclusion that the positive charge from a hydrogen atom has practically the same mass as that of the hydrogen atom. In Fig. 6-7 four different particles are represented. These can be indicated by a chemical symbol and a positive charge as H^+, H_2^+, O^+, and O_2^+.

.The particle represented by the symbol H$^+$ is sometimes called a *hydrogen ion* but more often is called a *proton.* The names of the other three ions are hydrogen molecule ion, oxygen ion, and oxygen molecule ion, respectively.

6-8 POSITIVE IONS

Experimental evidence obtained in working with beams of positive charge produced from different gases leads to these conclusions.

1. The charge/mass ratio of beams of positive charge is never greater than 1/2,000 that of electron beams.

2. The charge/mass ratios of beams of positive charge are found to have many different values instead of the single value found for electron beams.

3. If the unit of positive charge is no smaller in magnitude than the unit of negative charge on an electron, the masses of positive charges are nearly identical with the masses of corresponding neutral atoms of the substances used to produce the beams of positive charge.

The overall conclusion is that the positive charges produced by Thomson are atoms from which one or more electrons have been removed to give positively charged atoms called *positive ions.* The beam of positive charges represents ions in the same sense as in Section 5-6 where an ion was defined as a charged chemical species.

Refinements in the experimental apparatus for the study of positive ions since the time that Thomson designed it give measurements of high precision. The equipment used is usually referred to as a *mass spectrometer.* It is possible to determine the mass of one positive ion relative to another with a precision of at least one part in 1,000,000. One result of improved precision has been the identification of many ions from each element. Are these different ions to be interpreted as being the result of variations in charge or in mass? Might it be possible that the charge on an ion could change by any amount, or does the charge vary by increments of uniform magnitude?

6-9 ELECTRON CHARGE

Several people attacked the problem of whether electric charge could have any magnitude or could change only in regular steps or increments. Robert Andrews Millikan and his coworkers produced the experimental evidence which solved the problem.

Millikan found that if fine oil droplets were sprayed into a small chamber, it was possible to observe the motion of a single droplet with a microscope. Because of gravitational force, a droplet falls through air with a uniform velocity which is determined by the size of the droplet and by the temperature and pressure in the apparatus. The apparatus is shown in schematic form in Fig. 6-8.

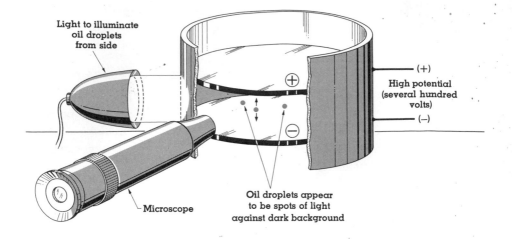

Light to illuminate
oil droplets
from side

(+)
High potential
(several hundred
volts)
(−)

Microscope

Oil droplets appear
to be spots of light
against dark background

Fig. 6-8 *Diagram of the apparatus for Millikan's oil-drop experiment to determine the charge/mass ratio for an electron.*

When Millikan performed the experiments, most droplets became electrically charged because of friction during the spraying process or through other causes. By applying an electric potential to metal plates placed at the top and bottom of the chamber, it was possible to alter the velocity with which the droplets fell. Indeed, by the action of the electric force produced by the electric potential difference, the rate of fall of any particular charged droplet could be increased or decreased, or the droplet could be made to stand still or even made to travel up instead of down.

When the electric potential difference between the plates was just sufficient to stop the droplet, gravitational force and electric force were balanced. A separate measurement of the mass of the droplet made it possible to calculate the electric force necessary to hold the drop stationary. Coulomb's law relating charges and distance to force and the data from the oil-drop experiments were used by Millikan to calculate the magnitude of the charge on the droplet. Millikan's apparatus can be looked upon as a delicate balance for comparing gravitational and electric forces.

Millikan described his conclusions about electric charge in these words. "Indeed, I have observed, all told, the capture of many thousands of ions in this way, and in no case have I ever found one the charge of which, when tested as above, did not have either exactly the value of the smallest charge ever captured or else a very small multiple of that value. Here then, is a direct, unimpeachable proof that the electron is not a statistical mean, but that rather the electrical charges found on ions all have either exactly the same value or else small exact multiples of that value."*

From his data, Millikan calculated the charge on the electron to be 1.591×10^{-19} coulomb. More important than the quantitative result, however, is the qualitative conclusion. Every negative charge is based on multiples of the charge on the electron unit. To this day no one has succeeded in producing evidence for any negative charge smaller in magnitude than 1.591×10^{-19} coulomb.

Actually the most precise measure of the charge of an electron is now given by calculation from the faraday and the Avogadro number. These two quantities can be determined with more precision than is possible with Millikan's oil-drop experiment. Experiments of great precision give the faraday as 96,493 coulombs/mole of electrons and the Avogadro number as 6.0238×10^{23} electrons/mole. These two values can be used to compute the charge on the electron as

$$\frac{\dfrac{96{,}493 \text{ coulombs}}{\text{mole of electrons}}}{\dfrac{6.0238 \times 10^{23} \text{ electrons}}{\text{mole of electrons}}} = 1.60186 \times 10^{-19} \text{ coulomb/electron}$$

In Section 6-6 it was concluded either that the charges on the ions must differ by small amounts or that the masses of the ions must differ to explain the experimental observations. From Millikan's work, it appears that negative charge, at least, comes in discrete units. But Millikan worked with oil droplets that contained both positive and negative charges initially. Yet all the positive and negative charges he observed were always some multiple of a unit charge whose magnitude was the same as the charge he measured for one electron. If electrons are the units of negative charge in matter which neutralize units of positive charge, it must be that positive and negative charges come in packages of identical magnitude. If this were not so, then the negative and positive charges in an object would not always match to give charges of either exactly zero or some whole-number multiple of the electron charge unit. How can the experimental data which showed variations in the charge/mass ratios of positive ions be interpreted?

The only way to answer this question seems to require that the atoms of a single element differ in mass. But such an answer is at odds with the assumptions about atoms which Dalton made—assumptions which have proved to be very useful in interpreting observations made on chemical systems.

*R. A. Millikan, *Electrons (+ and —), Protons, Photons, Neutrons, and Cosmic Rays,* The University of Chicago Press, Chicago, 1935, p. 72.

A major clue to the nature of atoms was provided by the work and the ideas of Ernest Rutherford and his students, work mentioned briefly in Section 1-1.

Rutherford described his work in the following words. "I would like to use this example to show how you often stumble upon facts by accident. In the early days I had observed the scattering of α-particles [alpha particles], and Dr. Geiger in my laboratory had examined it in detail. He found, in thin pieces of heavy metal, that the scattering was usually small, of the order of one degree. One day Geiger came to me and said, 'Don't you think that young Marsden, whom I am training in radioactive methods, ought to begin a small research?' Now I had thought that, too, so I said, 'Why not let him see if any α-particles can be scattered through a large angle?' I may tell you in confidence that I did not believe that they would be, since we knew that the α-particle was a very fast, massive particle, with a great deal of energy, and you could show that if the scattering was due to the accumulated effect of a number of small scatterings the chance of an α-particle's being scattered backwards was very small. Then I remember two or three days later Geiger coming to me in great excitement and saying, 'We have been able to get some of the α-particles coming backwards. . . .' It was quite the most incredible event that has ever happened to me in my life. It was almost as incredible as if you fired a 15-inch shell at a piece of tissue paper and it came back and hit you. On consideration, I realized that this scattering backwards must be the result of a single collision, and when I made calculations I saw that it was impossible to get anything of that order of magnitude unless you took a system in which the greater part of the mass of the atom was concentrated in a minute nucleus. It was then that I had the idea of an atom with a minute massive center carrying a charge. I worked out mathematically what laws the scattering should obey, and I found that the number of particles scattered through a given angle should be proportional to the thickness of the scattering foil, the square of the nuclear charge, and inversely proportional to the fourth power of the velocity. These deductions were later verified by Geiger and Marsden in a series of beautiful experiments."*

Rutherford and his associates made their observations by a procedure indicated in Fig. 1-1. The results were accounted for by assuming that an atom contains within itself a center or nucleus of very small cross section (Fig. 6-9). In the nucleus is concentrated an elec-

*From the 1936 essay by Ernest Rutherford, "The Development of the Theory of Atomic Structure," in J. Needham and W. Pagel (eds.), *Background to Modern Science,* The Macmillan Company, New York, 1938.

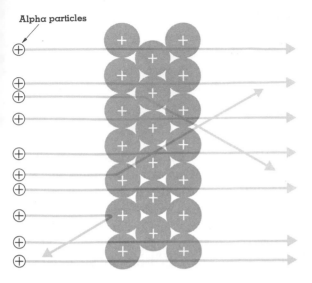

Alpha particles

Fig. 6-9 *Deflection of alpha particles in a metal foil is explained by the assumption that metal atoms have positively charged nuclei with radii less than 1/10,000 the radii of the whole atoms.*

tric charge of a single type. This charged nucleus either is very massive or is held fixed by forces within the solid, or it is both massive and fixed, since some of the alpha particles are deflected so greatly from their original path. Since electrons are not massive and are negatively charged, it is necessary to conclude that this central massive nucleus is positively charged and that the deflection of the positively charged alpha particles is the result of electrostatic repulsion. According to Rutherford's calculations, the radius of the nucleus was of the order of 1/10,000 that of an atom or smaller.

Since the volume of a sphere is proportional to the cube of the radius of the sphere, an atom must have a volume that is more than 10^{12} times the volume of the nucleus within the atom. With most of the mass of an atom in the nucleus, the density of the nucleus will have to be at least 10^{12} times the density of the entire atom.

But, if this is so, then the electrons must occupy a much larger volume than the nucleus because the density of an element is much smaller than the estimated density of the nucleus of an atom.

If, indeed, a positively charged nucleus is responsible for the deflection of the positively charged alpha particles by coulombic repulsion in the Rutherford experiment, then the number of alpha particles deflected through a given angle from a straight-line path through the metal foil will depend upon the magnitude of the charge on the nucleus. Nuclei of high charge will deflect more alpha particles through a given angle than will nuclei of lower charge.

Rutherford worked out the mathematical relationship which describes how the relative numbers of alpha particles deflected through any given angle should depend on the nuclear charge. H. Geiger and

E. Marsden found it possible to assign to carbon and to aluminum, gold, and other metals a numerical value for nuclear charge. They discovered, moreover, that this nuclear charge was approximately equal to one-half of the magnitude of atomic mass, if the positive nuclear charge was expressed in units whose magnitude was the same as the charge on the electron.

6-11 ATOMIC NUMBER

The known chemical elements can be listed in order of increasing atomic mass, starting with the element of lowest mass, hydrogen. Such a listing is given in Fig. 3-8. When Fig. 3-8 is compared with a listing of elements made on the basis of the numbers obtained by Rutherford for the number of units of nuclear charge, the order of elements appears to be almost identical. The number of units of positive charge in the nucleus of an atom of an element is called the **atomic number** of the element.

From his data Rutherford was able to make only a rough estimate of the atomic numbers of the elements. Other methods have since given more precise data and have completely confirmed Rutherford's conclusion. Each chemical element does indeed appear to possess a number which puts it in a numerical order with hydrogen at 1, helium at 2, lithium at 3, and so on through the list. In every case this number for an element is the same as the number of positive unit charges on the nucleus of an atom of the element.

A chemical element now can be defined in a way different from the operational procedure used in Section 1-16. The new definition is essentially a conceptual definition and states that a chemical element is a substance composed of atoms all of which have the same atomic number (nuclear charge). A list of the elements and their atomic numbers is included in Chapter 10.

The theory of atoms has developed in such a way that atomic numbers must be integers. This means that, when elements are listed in order of increasing atomic number, no element can ever be found that should logically fit between hydrogen and helium, for example, an element with atomic number $1\frac{1}{2}$. If such an element is ever found, our present ideas about atoms, about electricity, and about chemical systems will have to be modified drastically.

6-12 ATOMIC MASSES AND ISOTOPES

How is it possible to explain the fact that the analysis of beams of positive ions as described in Section 6-8 gives results which indicate that the same element can produce a number of different ions, each of which has a different charge/mass ratio?

A chemical element is now defined as a substance all of whose atoms

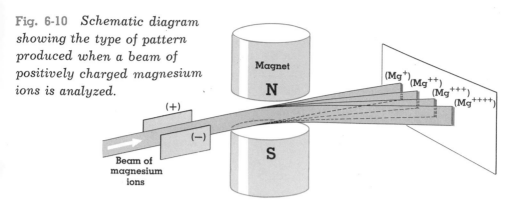

Fig. 6-10 *Schematic diagram showing the type of pattern produced when a beam of positively charged magnesium ions is analyzed.*

have the same atomic number. In a neutral hydrogen atom there is one proton and one electron with charges equal in magnitude but opposite in type. The atoms of all other elements are also neutral so that there will be as many electrons present in each atom as there are positive units of charge in each nucleus. Thus magnesium with atomic number 12 must have 12 protons in the nucleus and 12 electrons per atom. The formation of positive ions, as described in Section 6-7, must then be a process in which electrons are removed from individual atoms. Since electrons cannot be subdivided, the atoms of a single element, such as magnesium, should produce only positive ions with whole-number units of positive charge. The positive ions that can be produced from magnesium atoms make a sequence Mg^+, Mg^{++}, Mg^{+++}, and Mg^{++++} (Mg^+, Mg^{++}, Mg^{3+}, Mg^{4+}), where each positive sign represents one unit of positive charge. The charge/mass ratio of the second is twice the first, while the third is three times the first, and so on for the others in the sequence. But closer inspection of the data for the charge/mass ratio of the first ion (Mg^+) shows that instead of a single ratio of 3.99 $\times$ 10^3 coulombs/g of Mg, three ratios are found. These are 3.99 $\times$ 10^3, 3.83 $\times$ 10^3, and 3.69 $\times$ 10^3 coulombs/g of magnesium. Each of the other magnesium ions gives three ratios. The three ratios are much too close together to be accounted for by differences in the number of charge units (Fig. 6-10).

The data obtained from the analysis of positive-ion beams for most elements indicate some other charge/mass ratios in addition to the ones identified with unit increase in positive charge. This must mean that a single sample of most elements does not consist of atoms all of whose masses are identical. Dalton had assumed that all atoms of a single element are identical in mass. Experimental evidence from analysis of the magnesium ion sequence and other ion sequences contradicts Dalton's assumption. To account for mass spectrometric data, it is necessary to conclude that a single element with atoms all having the same nuclear charge can have atoms of more than one mass. Two samples of an element which are identical in atomic number but which differ in atomic mass are called *isotopes.*

Most of the elements that occur on the earth are actually mixtures of isotopes. The processes of separation and analysis that are described in Chapter 1 do not ordinarily separate isotopes. Only in work with an apparatus sensitive enough to detect differences of at least one part in 100,000 is it possible to separate the isotopes of a single element from one another. The atomic masses that chemists measure by analyzing compounds are, in fact, average masses for the naturally occurring mixtures of the isotopes of each element. Thus for magnesium the analysis of the ion sequence indicates that magnesium obtained from natural deposits of magnesium compounds contains three isotopes. These isotopes have atomic masses of 24, 25, and 26. The isotopes of atomic mass 24 makes up about three-quarters of the magnesium in the natural mixture. On the scale of atomic masses, the chemist assigns magnesium a mass of 24.3 amu.

A survey of all the known elements shows that the atomic mass of each isotope is nearly but not quite a whole number. The atomic mass of an isotope rounded off to the nearest whole number is called the *mass number* of an isotope. In Table 6-1 the mass number is given as a superscript to the left of the symbol of the element. In this description the isotope of carbon with mass number 12 is represented by ^{12}C and referred to as carbon-12. Table 6-1 also lists in the fourth column the percentage by which each isotope contributes to the mass of any sample of the naturally occurring element.

TABLE 6-1   ATOMIC MASSES AND ABUNDANCES FOR THE
            ISOTOPES OF SOME ELEMENTS

Element	Symbol	Mass	Abundance, %
Hydrogen	^1H	1.01	99.985
	^2H	2.01	0.015
Helium	^3He	3.02	0.00013
	^4He	4.00	100.
Lithium	^6Li	6.02	7.5
	^7Li	7.02	92.5
Beryllium	^9Be	9.02	100.
Carbon	^{12}C	12.00	98.9
	^{13}C	13.01	1.1
Oxygen	^{16}O	16.00	99.76
	^{17}O	17.00	0.04
	^{18}O	18.00	0.20

6-13 NEUTRONS AND PROTONS

James Chadwick, in England, obtained experimental evidence in 1932 to indicate that all but one of the atomic nuclei consist of two different parts. One part is made up of identical units without charge but with a mass essentially the same as the mass of a hydrogen atom. The unit is called a **neutron.** The other part consists of units each with about the same mass as a hydrogen atom but with a positive charge. Each of these units is called a **proton.** The nucleus of a hydrogen atom ($^1H^+$) is the only nucleus of any of the elements or isotopes which does not contain at least one neutron. In Section 6-7 the name proton was given to the nucleus of a hydrogen atom. Information about these particles is summarized below.

Particle	Charge	Mass, amu
Electron	$\ominus 1$	0.00054
Proton	$\oplus 1$	1.01
Neutron	0	1.01

The masses and charges of the nuclei of all atoms are determined by the number of protons and neutrons each nucleus contains.

The nuclear atom is an arrangement made up of a nucleus surrounded by electrons. The number of protons present in the nucleus of an atom is equal to the atomic number of the corresponding element. The sum of the number of neutrons and the number of protons in the nucleus is equal to the mass number of the element. The sum of proton masses and neutron masses equals the atomic mass to within about 0.1 percent.

When the atomic mass scale was established toward the end of the nineteenth century (Section 3-9), the standard chosen was oxygen as it is found in nature. Mass spectrometer studies have shown that the element oxygen found in nature (as the free element in air, or combined in water, clay, or ores) is a mixture of three isotopes with mass numbers 16, 17, and 18. Oxygen of mass number 16 makes up more than 99.76 percent of the mixture as indicated in Table 6-1. In work of high precision, particularly in the mass spectrometer, the existence of these isotopes must be recognized. Until recently, chemists defined a scale of atomic masses in terms of the average mass of all three isotopes of oxygen as it is found in nature. Physicists, until recently, defined an atomic mass scale in terms of the mass of the isotope ^{16}O as the standard. The physicist's definition and the chemist's definition led to atomic masses for each element which differed slightly from one another.

Chemists and physicists worked out an international agreement in 1961 to define a new atomic mass unit with a mass one-twelfth the mass of an atom of the isotope ^{12}C. The difference between the oxygen scale and the new carbon-12 scale is less than one part in 10,000. Work of high precision will, however, in the future be reported on the basis of the carbon-12 scale of atomic masses, and the values listed in the International Atomic Mass Table, Chapter 10, are based on the carbon-12 scale for the atomic mass unit.

6-14 THE ATOM: A MENTAL MODEL

Thomson showed by experiment that negative charge could be separated from every element that he examined. Both the mass and the magnitude of the unit of negative charge (the electron) are entirely independent of its source. He also showed that the positive charge present in an element cannot be separated from the massive part of an element but appears in the form of a charged atom whose properties are identified as an ion of the element.

Rutherford and his associates carried out experiments to show that a beam of charged particles could pass through thin metal foils. A small fraction of the beam was deflected from its original path, and an even smaller fraction was reflected back toward the source of the alpha particles.

On the basis of essentially this information about electrons, ions, and metal foils, Rutherford proposed a set of assumptions concerning the atom as a basis for interrelating the data.

1. Matter is made up of atoms which have both mass and volume.

2. Atoms have a central nucleus surrounded by electrons.

3. The central nucleus has a positive charge which is different in magnitude for each element.

4. In a neutral atom the number of electrons outside the nucleus equals the number of units of positive charge in the nucleus.

5. The mass of an atom is almost entirely in the nucleus.

6. The volume of the nucleus is smaller than the volume of the atom by a ratio of about $1:10^{12}$ or less.

7. The volume of the atom is provided in some way by the electrons.

8. All electrons have the same electric charge and cannot be subdivided.

Subsequent work by Rutherford, Chadwick, and others has led to three more assumptions.

9. Every nucleus is an assembly of protons and neutrons.

10. All protons are identical and have a charge equal to but opposite in type to that of the electron. The mass of a proton is essentially equal to that of a hydrogen atom.

11. A neutron has no charge but has a mass approximately equal to the mass of the proton.

Such a set of assumptions and the conclusions which can be drawn from them are sometimes referred to as a conceptual model or sometimes a **mental model.**

The nuclear atom model has one rather curious implication. Matter was defined in Section 1-8 as stuff which has mass and volume. In the nuclear atom the mass of a material has become a property assigned almost completely to the atomic nucleus, while the volume of a material is almost entirely associated with the electrons in each atom.

If Rutherford's mental model of an atom is a truly useful one, it should lead to deductions in agreement with conclusions based on the experimentally determined properties of chemical systems.

6-15 SUMMARY

In earlier chapters, evidence was discussed for two types of electric charge which were labeled positive and negative. Work with electrochemical cells suggested that electric charge could exist in unit quantities. In this chapter negative electric charge has been demonstrated to occur in units called electrons which are never subdivided. Measurements by Thomson, Millikan, and others have shown the charge on each electron to be 1.602×10^{-19} coulomb and its mass to be $1/1,836$ that of the proton.

Experiments with electric charge in gases, in thermionic emission (Section 6-2), in photoelectric emission (Section 6-3), and in high-vacuum discharge (Section 6-4) all point to the presence of electrons in every substance. The electrons always have the same charge and mass no matter what substance is the source.

In every case for which measurements have been made, the magnitude of charge, whether positive or negative, on any object is always some multiple of the charge on one electron. Positive charge must therefore occur in units of the same magnitude as electrons but of opposite charge type.

Beams of positive charge can be produced when electrons travel through a gas (Section 6-7). The evidence indicates that the positive charges are multiples of a unit charge with the same magnitude as the charge of the electron. But the mass associated with positive charge is determined by the substance which is the source. The conclusion is that beams of positive charge are made up of ions produced from atoms or molecules by loss of electrons.

Analysis of positive ions gives atomic mass data of high precision. All the atoms of a single element have the same nuclear charge, but they may differ in mass. Such different atoms are called isotopes. The naturally occurring elements with which the chemist works are, in most cases, mixtures of isotopes. Since 1961 the atomic mass scale has been based on a mass unit which is one-twelfth the mass of an atom of the carbon-12 isotope.

Central to the further study of chemistry is the work of Rutherford. He showed that the scattering of alpha particles by metal foils can be most simply interpreted in terms of a nuclear atom model. In this model, the atom is imagined to consist of a nucleus surrounded by electrons. The nucleus is positively charged, includes nearly all the mass of the atom, and has almost no volume. The positive charge and about half of the mass of the nucleus is associated with protons. The remainder of the mass of the nucleus is associated with neutrons. In a neutral atom the number of electrons equals the positive charge on the nucleus.

Ex. 6-1   On the basis of the experimental results he obtained, why did Rutherford not assume that the entire atom is of uniform density throughout? Why did Rutherford not assume that in a piece of solid matter uniformly dense atoms are separated by large empty spaces through which the alpha particles passed?

Ex. 6-2   What would be the mass of an atom if the nucleus consisted of two protons and one neutron? What characteristics would be predicted for the atom?

Ex. 6-3   Compare thermionic emission, photoelectric emission, and high-vacuum discharge with respect to (a) the nature of charge transfer through evacuated space, (b) the relation of charge transfer to minimum voltage required for charge flow, (c) the process of charge separation, and (d) the direction of negative charge flow.

Ex. 6-4   a. What properties are characteristic of a beam of negative charge that moves between and parallel to charged parallel plates in a vacuum tube? that moves between the poles of a magnet?

b. By analogy with the answer to question a, answer the same two questions for a beam of positive charge.

Ex. 6-5   a. Outline the reasoning which may have led Thomson to the conclusion that the ratio of charge to mass for all the particles making up the beam of negative charge had a fixed magnitude.

b. One electron is required to produce one atom of silver in the electrolysis of a silver sulfate solution, and 96,500 coulombs of charge is required to deposit 1 mole of silver atoms on the negative electrode of an electrolysis apparatus. From this information, calculate the mass of 1 mole of electrons. The charge/mass ratio of the electron is 1.76×10^8 coulombs/g.

c. One mole of electrons is equal to one Avogadro number of electrons. What is the mass of one electron?

d. One mole of electrons represents a charge of 96,500 coulombs. What is the charge represented by one electron?

e. How many electrons are represented by 1 coulomb of negative charge?

Ex. 6-6 How can the following aspects of Millikan's oil-drop experiment be explained?

a. Oil droplets become positively or negatively charged by friction with air when they are sprayed out of an atomizer.

b. The vertical motion of the charged oil droplets between the parallel plates was controlled by altering the type and magnitude of the charges on the plates.

c. Any charged body possesses a charge whose magnitude is a multiple of the charge of the electron.

Ex. 6-7 What would happen to a system consisting of helium atoms if the unit of the positive charge on the nucleus differed slightly in magnitude from the unit of negative charge on the electrons?

Ex. 6-8 How are the following assumptions consistent with the observations made from the Rutherford-Geiger-Marsden alpha-particle scattering experiments?

a. Atoms contain a nucleus of extremely small cross section and large mass.

b. The space between the nuclei is filled by electrons which have negative charge.

c. The extent of alpha-particle scattering is a function of the magnitude of the positive charge on the nuclei.

Ex. 6-9 The atomic number is the number of charge units on an atomic nucleus. Upon what basis, then, is each sodium atom assigned eleven electrons, each nitrogen atom seven electrons, and each helium atom two electrons?

Ex. 6-10 What is the magnitude and type of electric charge on a lithium atom which has lost one electron? on a beryllium atom which has lost two electrons?

Ex. 6-11 What evidence can you use to support or criticize the following statement? Dalton assumed that all atoms of a single element are identical in mass.

Ex. 6-12 Mass spectrometric analysis of positive-ion beams created by ionization of naturally occurring mercury vapor reveals at least seven different charge/mass ratios for the particles in the beam. From detailed measurements the largest ratio is found to be 494 coulombs/g of mercury, and the smallest ratio 474 coulombs/g of mercury. Explain.

Ex. 6-13 Consider the following observations and make a generalization about the neutrons and protons in atomic nuclei.

a. The four isotopes ^{16}O, ^{28}Si, ^{40}Ca, and ^{56}Fe make up more than 85 percent of the atoms in the earth's crust. These four atoms have even atomic numbers.

b. Of all the naturally occurring elements only five isotopes, ^2H, ^6Li, ^{10}B, ^{14}N, and ^{50}V, have atoms with both an odd number of protons and an odd number of neutrons in the nucleus. These five elements contribute less than 1 percent of all the atoms in the earth's crust.

PART TWO: THE ELECTRICAL NATURE OF CHEMICAL SYSTEMS

Chapters 4, 5, and 6

THE PROBLEM we faced at the end of Chapter 3 was to provide some rules or a fundamental theory which could be used to account for the interaction of all kinds of atoms to form compounds. In Chapter 3 we found that identical atoms of certain elements such as oxygen, nitrogen, and hydrogen join together to form diatomic molecules. Atoms of some other elements do not join together and, like helium, form only monatomic molecules. Furthermore, unlike atoms join together in a great variety of arrangements.

Two types of phenomena are common to all forms of matter. One type is gravitational attraction of one mass for another. Attempts have been made in the past to use gravitational attraction as the basis of a theory of compound formation; all attempts have failed to produce useful results. A second type of general phenomenon is the production of electrically charged objects. In Chapter 4 our exploration turned to the relation of electricity to chemical systems.

Electricity passed through a solution produces a chemical reaction. Conversely, a chemical reaction can be used to generate electricity. Electricity passing through a system is interpreted as a flow of charge. Whenever charge flows through a material, thermal energy is transferred. For a solution, charge flow between solution and an electrode is accompanied by chemical change. Charge flow can result in thermal energy transfer or in chemical change. On the other hand, chemical reactions can result in the transfer of thermal energy or in charge flow. There seems to be an intimate relation among chemical change, energy, and electric charge.

The further study of the nature of electric charge is based in part on the processes for producing charge outside of chemical systems. In Chapter 5 it was found that charged objects can be produced by friction between two surfaces. In systems where charge is produced by friction, attractive and repulsive forces are found between the charges. To account for two oppositely directed forces, two types of charge have to be imagined. Further study of chemical systems indicates that the same types of forces can be produced in chemical systems and that the same two types of charge are adequate to interpret both frictional and chemical electricity.

Experimental data for the interaction of charges are summarized by Coulomb's law—the force between a pair of charges is proportional to the product of the quantity of charge and inversely proportional to the square of the distance of separation. In chemical systems, forces between charges are less apparent than are energy changes. Coulomb's law governing the behavior of interacting charges can also be stated in terms of the energy stored in a system of charges. This energy is proportional to the product of the quantity of charge divided by the distance of separation.

The fact that electricity will flow through certain solutions leads to the idea of ions as carriers of charge. Substances move in a solution which is part of a circuit that is conducting current. The next step is to assume that ions are charged chemical species. Chemical changes in conducting solutions must therefore represent either the separation or the coming together of ions.

The fact that electrical effects can be produced in space, even with no substances present, leads to the conclusion that negative charges can travel through a vacuum without transporting any substance. The negative charge has mass as well as charge, and experimentally the ratio of charge to mass is a constant quantity. It is also found that all observed quantities of negative charge are always integral multiples of a fundamental unit of charge. It is convenient then to consider that a quantity of negative charge is made up of identical particles called electrons.

This identification of an electron as the unit of electric charge can be linked with the chemical changes produced at electrodes. It was found that the quantity of charge and the number of atoms reacting are related in a fixed way. This implied that if matter is atomic, electric charge must be atomic also. The electron is then the atomic unit of negative charge. The electron is not, however, an atom of a substance.

Since materials are ordinarily neutral, the production of negative charge implies the simultaneous production of positive charge somewhere in the system. For a gas the positive charge can be produced and studied as a beam of positive ions. Positive ions are associated with units of matter having much greater mass than is characteristic of electrons. A study of the masses of positive ions provides a method for obtaining atomic mass data of high precision.

Radium and certain other elements give off streams of positive helium ions ($_2\text{He}^{++}$) called alpha particles. When a beam of alpha particles is directed at a thin metal film, most of the beam passes through without being deflected. A small fraction of the beam, however, is scattered through a large angle.

The Rutherford scattering experiment, together with Thomson's earlier work on electrons, gives rise to a new idea about the arrangement of positive and negative charge within atoms. Each atom must be composed of a central nucleus that is small in volume compared to the atom. The nucleus contains nearly all the mass of the atom and all of the positive charge. Outside the nucleus the atom is composed entirely of electrons. Electrons have nearly zero mass, but they supply all of the negative charge within each atom.

Dalton identified the atoms of each element by a characteristic mass. It is now known that the atoms of a single element may consist of several isotopes that differ in mass without significant differences in any other properties. Each element is found to have a characteristic atomic number which distinguishes one element from another. Conceptually an atom of an element is therefore defined as a structural unit which has a single nucleus, a characteristic nuclear charge, and a number of electrons equal to the nuclear charge.

The properties of electrical systems not only provide a picture of the way charge might flow through a chemical system, but they also suggest a picture of the nature of all matter. It now remains to be seen how well the idea of a nuclear atom as an electrical system can be applied to the problem of chemical composition.

CHEMICAL AND ELECTRICAL STRUCTURES

EXAMINATION OF CHEMICAL systems has led to the idea that each different compound has a particular set of atoms combined in a fixed ratio. Experimental studies since 1800 have provided data that can be used to calculate the atomic compositions of nearly four million compounds. Each compound can be designated by a unique word name and represented in compact form by a formula which describes the kinds and proportions of atoms present in the compound. There is no room to doubt the great utility of the development and use of formulas in equations describing changes during chemical reactions.

But even a cursory study of known compounds raises questions. The most general question is, "Why are there so few compounds?" If the 103 different elements could form compounds by the combination of each possible pair of two different atoms in a 1:1 ratio, this would provide about 5,000 possibilities. Combinations of each possible set of three different atoms should provide 150,000 additional compounds, whereas each possible set of four different atoms would add another 4,000,000 compounds. In addition, combinations are found in which atoms are present in other than a 1:1 ratio. Predictions based on all imaginable combinations should give an almost unlimited number of compounds.

Although the possible number of compounds seems to be almost unlimited, a relatively small number (four million) has been isolated and identified. Thus combinations of nitrogen and hydrogen give the compounds ammonia, hydrazine, and hydrazoic acid, which have the formulas NH_3, N_2H_4, and N_3H, respectively. However, no compounds of nitrogen and hydrogen which would be represented by formulas such as NH_5 or N_2H or N_3H_2 have been isolated. Does the fact that many imaginable combinations of elements are not known suggest that chemists simply are not clever enough to produce or identify them, or does the fact imply some underlying principle that limits the number of combinations?

Rutherford's development of the idea of the nuclear atom provides a particularly intriguing basis for investigating the nature of chemical substances. Does this idea suggest any reasons for the comparatively few compounds known out of all the imaginable compounds that might be formed from the known elements? Certainly as important as the answer to this first question is the answer to a second question. How can the nuclear atom be helpful in relating the observed properties of known compounds?

7-1 ELECTRONS IN A NUCLEAR ATOM

Rutherford's experiments on the scattering of alpha particles and the work of Thomson and others are interpreted to mean that positive charge at the center of an atom is surrounded by negative charge. The central positively charged part of the atom, the nucleus, must occupy less than $1/10^{12}$ of the total atomic volume since the radius of the nucleus is of the order of $1/10,000$ $(1/10^4)$ of the radius of the atom. However, the mass of the nucleus is nearly as great as the mass of the atom itself. The negatively charged part of the atom, comprised of the electrons, makes up almost all the volume occupied by the atom but contributes only a small part of the mass of the atom. Other experiments indicate that the electrons do not contribute more than $1/1,800$ of the mass of any neutral atom.

How can the electrons provide practically the entire volume exhibited by an atom? Two possibilities have been explored by scientists. One possibility is to consider the electron to be a relatively tiny particle which moves rapidly around the nucleus. As worked out by Niels Bohr in 1913, an atomic model based on this suggestion has been quite fruitful for explaining some of the observed properties of elements. Bohr's theory has not been particularly successful, however, in dealing with the observed properties of combinations of atoms in compounds.

The major difficulty with the Bohr model of the atom was that it attempted to describe the behavior of the electron as if it were simply a small moving particle in the atomic system. Getting the experimental

NIELS BOHR *1885–1962*

*A Danish physicist. From 1920 to 1962, Bohr was head of
the Copenhagen Institute for Theoretical Physics, which
he founded. Following his education in Copenhagen, he
moved to Cambridge, England in 1911 to do postdoctoral
work under J. J. Thomson, the first head of the Cavendish
Laboratory. During 1912 he worked with Rutherford in
Manchester, and from 1914 to 1916, he was the reader
in mathematical physics at Manchester University. His
papers on the Bohr atom appeared in 1913 and 1915. He
was appointed professor of theoretical physics at Copenhagen University in 1916 and was awarded the 1922 Nobel Prize in physics
for his studies of atomic structure. After 1939 he made important contributions to our knowledge of the structure of the atomic nucleus.*

*Bohr escaped to the United States from German-occupied Denmark in
1943 and participated in the atomic bomb project. He was actively concerned for the control and peaceful utilization of atomic energy and, in
1957, was the first recipient of the Atoms for Peace Award. Under Bohr's
leadership, the Copenhagen Institute for Theoretical Physics became one
of the leading intellectual centers of the world.*

---

information necessary to give a valid description of the behavior of
an electron proved impractical. This effort turned out to be even more
difficult than getting enough information in advance to predict the
lifetime of an individual. But just as it is possible to predict the average
lifetime of an individual (insurance companies base their life insurance rates on predictions of average lifetimes), so it is possible to predict the probable behavior of an electron.

In 1926, Erwin Schroedinger developed an atomic model based on
the premise that the electron could be described in mathematical terms
similar to those used in treating wave motion. Known as wave mechanics, Schroedinger's theory has contributed greatly to the understanding of atomic behavior. Unfortunately, a detailed mathematical
analysis of the electron as a wave motion complicated by the presence
of other electrons is difficult even with modern computing machines.
Only four systems of electrons and nuclei—the hydrogen atom (H),
the hydrogen molecule ion (H_2^+), the hydrogen molecule (H_2), and
the helium atom (He)—have been analyzed with high precision.

Many scientists believe, however, that wave mechanics can be used
to calculate complete descriptions of all systems of electrons and nu-

ERWIN SCHROEDINGER   *1887–1961*

*An Austrian physicist and creator of wave mechanics. Born
and educated in Vienna, Schroedinger accepted the pro-
fessorship of physics at Stuttgart (Germany) in 1920,
followed by university appointments in Zurich (1921)
and Berlin (1927). He left Germany in 1933 to take up
a temporary position at Oxford University, then became
professor at Graz (Austria) from 1936 to 1938. In 1940
he was appointed professor at the Institute for Advanced
Studies in Dublin, Ireland, and in 1955 he returned to
Vienna. He shared with P. A. M. Dirac the 1933 Nobel
Prize in physics, awarded for their parallel development of wave mechanics.*

*In his later years, Schroedinger wrote extensively on the wider meaning
of modern developments in science in essays and books such as* Nature
and the Greeks, *and* Science, Theory and Man, *and* What is Life?

*Schroedinger's wave mechanics had its origin in Louis de Broglie's proposal
that if light had both wave and particle properties, as Einstein's explanation of the photoelectric effect had demonstrated, then electrons should
show a similar dual character. Schroedinger, therefore, introduced the
mathematics of classical wave motion into the formulas developed by
de Broglie for the wavelengths of matter waves. The resulting wave
mechanics model of the atom proved fruitful for science beyond all
expectation, clarifying many points left unexplained by Bohr's model of
the atom.*

---

clei. The difficulty arises only because of the elaborate calculations
required to produce complete analyses. Any other theory of atomic
structure proposed to make calculation easier must nonetheless agree
with the wave mechanics description.

When scientists find that a theoretical proposal or mental model is
too complex to deal with logically or mathematically, they may simplify some part of the theory in applying it. Proper choice of the part
of the theory or model to be simplified and of the nature of the simplification can give results which agree in a general way with experimental data. Simplification of the model and comparison with experimental data often suggest further ways of improving the theory or
model so that its use is not so complex.

One possible simplification of the nature of the electron is suggested by the results of the Rutherford experiments. These results suggest that it is reasonable to assume that an electron has a volume much larger than that of the nucleus and comparable to the volume of an atom. Five basic assumptions can be made to establish a mental model for electrons and nuclei. An electron is assumed to be somewhat like a cloud. In other words, an electron varies in size and shape in the model with the circumstances in which it may be found, much as is true of a cloud in the sky. Because Millikan's and Thomson's experiments described in Chapter 6 indicate that it is not possible to produce a charge less than that on one electron, it is assumed that the electron cloud cannot be subdivided.

To assume that a cloud can be of any shape will require a procedure for calculating the shape in a given situation. For all but the simplest cases, calculations of the shape of a cloud have so far proved to be impossible. Nor has any generally satisfactory method been worked out for experimentally determining the shapes of electron clouds. In the face of this difficulty, one might hope that the precise shape of the electron cloud may not be of major importance in determining the behavior of an atom. If this is true, a simple and fixed shape can be arbitrarily chosen to duplicate as nearly as possible the observed electrical properties of a system containing an electron. The simplest of all three-dimensional shapes is the sphere (Fig. 7-1). A sphere is simple because

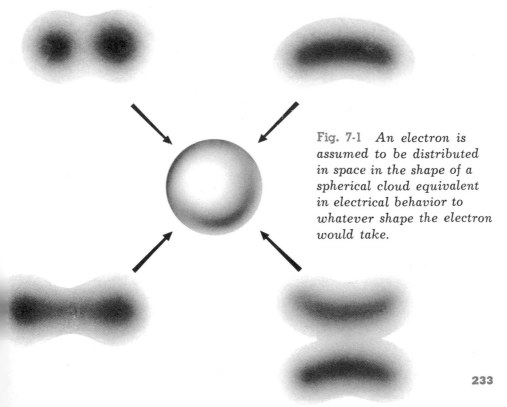

Fig. 7-1 *An electron is assumed to be distributed in space in the shape of a spherical cloud equivalent in electrical behavior to whatever shape the electron would take.*

only the radius of a sphere and coordinates of the center have to be specified in order to describe the sphere completely.

An electron will be assumed to be a sphere with variable radius and with a uniform distribution of negative charge throughout the volume of the sphere. In each model that is prepared, the radius of the sphere will be chosen so that the predicted electrical properties of the spherical model of the electron will be as nearly as possible equivalent to the properties of the real electron.

The nucleus of an atom will be treated as a point with positive charge. The nucleus of each atom has a charge that is an integral multiple of the charge of a proton. In each neutral atom there will be as many electrons outside the nucleus as there are units of positive charge within the nucleus.

Since positive charges and negative charges attract each other, a nucleus and an electron will move toward each other in all cases but one. The only case where motion will not occur is the one in which the nucleus happens to be in the center of a spherical charge cloud. In this position the attractive forces between the nucleus and the cloud are the same in all directions, and the forces must therefore balance each other to give a net force of zero and an arrangement of electron and nucleus as indicated in Fig. 7-2.

7-2 ONE PROTON AND ONE ELECTRON

The simplest model to consider is the one for one electron and one proton. Now if a proton is placed at the center of a spherical electron charge cloud, the proton and electron do not tend to move toward each other. Because they do not tend to move in this arrangement, the proton and electron are said to be stable with respect to position. If the proton and the electron are placed in any other relative positions, they will always move initially to bring the proton and the center of the spherical cloud closer together. Any arrangements in which the

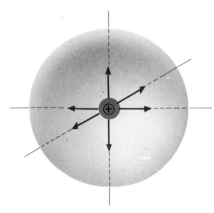

Fig. 7-2 *When a proton is at the center of a spherical charge cloud, the attractive forces in all directions are equal. In this arrangement the proton and electron are stable with respect to position.*

proton is not at the center of the electron charge cloud must therefore be unstable with respect to position.

An electron and a proton have equal and opposite electric charge. This means that a system of one electron and one proton must have a total net charge of zero. So long as the electron cloud surrounds the positively charged nucleus, there is an attractive force which draws each portion of the electron cloud toward the central proton. This implies that the charge cloud should continue to shrink until it has merged with the nucleus to produce an electrically neutral point. If the electron should shrink to the size of the nucleus, the atom would have almost zero volume. The nucleus is so small by comparison with the volume of the atom that if the electrons in all the atoms in the oceans were to shrink into the nuclei of the atom, the remaining volume of the nuclear matter would be about equivalent to that of four swimming pools. Obviously this has not happened because all our experience shows us that matter does have volume. If the atoms were to shrink to zero volume, matter as we know it would no longer exist. The consequences of the four assumptions so far proposed for a mental model of the atom, however, are that atoms and, thus, matter have zero volume. To achieve a model of an atom which will possess volume requires further assumptions.

Mention has been made of the development of an atom model by Niels Bohr. Bohr assumed that the electron was a small particle traveling at high velocity around the nucleus. The attraction of the proton for the moving electron produces a potential energy which decreases as the electron approaches the nucleus. But if the electron approaches the nucleus even slightly, its velocity and hence its kinetic energy must increase just as the velocity of an orbiting satellite increases as it approaches the earth. The increased velocity would result in the electron moving farther from the nucleus. The electron would therefore tend to follow a circular path around the nucleus. Bohr called the path of an electron around a nucleus an *orbit.*

If an atom is to have a size or volume that remains fixed over a long period of time, then some basis is needed to ensure stability. In Chapter 5 it was pointed out that one criterion of stability can be described in energy terms. When a system can change from an initial state to a final state only if energy is added to it from outside, the system in its initial state is said to be stable with respect to change to the final state. So far as electric potential energy (Equation 5-7) is concerned, the model of a proton in an electron cloud appears to be unstable with respect to collapse (loss of volume) because the collapse of the electron onto the nucleus does not require energy but rather it should make energy available.

The Bohr atom model, on the other hand, circumvents the instability by assuming that a kinetic energy contributes to the state of a system so that a stable electron orbit is possible. There is one path around the nucleus in which the electron can travel so that any path either closer to or farther from the nucleus will have more energy. Closer to the nucleus, the kinetic energy of the electron will be greater. On the other hand, in any path farther from the nucleus the electron will have a greater electrostatic potential energy. The electron can shift from the stable path to any other path either closer to or farther from the nucleus only if energy is supplied to the electron from outside the atom. The conclusion is that in the Bohr atom model, electrostatic attraction holds the proton and electron together but that kinetic energy in the system is responsible for the volume of the atom.

In the wave model of electrons in atoms, it is possible to include an energy which opposes the electrostatic energy generated between the nucleus and the surrounding electrons. A wave exhibits an energy of its own. For example, a vibrating violin string possesses a certain amount of energy. If the tension on the string is increased, the vibration frequency increases. At higher frequencies, each portion of the string must move faster than at low frequencies. This means that the kinetic energy of the string increases as the tension on the string is increased. In the wave model of the atom as in the Bohr model, electric attraction holds the electron and proton together, but the kinetic energy of the wave provides for the volume of the system.

7-3 AN ATOMIC MODEL

The nature of wave mechanics and the assumption of kinetic energy in the Bohr model suggest another assumption for an electron cloud. The electron will be assumed to possess an energy which is related to the size of the cloud but which is not an electrostatic potential energy. As the cloud shrinks, this energy will be assumed to increase. This energy, which is assumed to be a characteristic of the cloud, will be referred to as a kinetic energy, even though no part of the cloud is considered to be in motion. The term kinetic energy is intended to emphasize that this particular energy is a property of the cloud itself, a self-energy. A kinetic energy characteristic of the cloud operates in opposition to a potential energy which the system of charges has as the result of the interaction among the various charges. Figure 7-3 suggests in graphical form how the potential energy of a system made up of an electron cloud and a proton goes down as the cloud radius shrinks. The rise in kinetic energy of a cloud as the cloud shrinks is also shown on the same graph.

Another way of looking at the electron cloud is to consider its charge in relation to its volume. The larger the volume of a cloud, the more spread out is its charge, although the total charge itself is fixed in

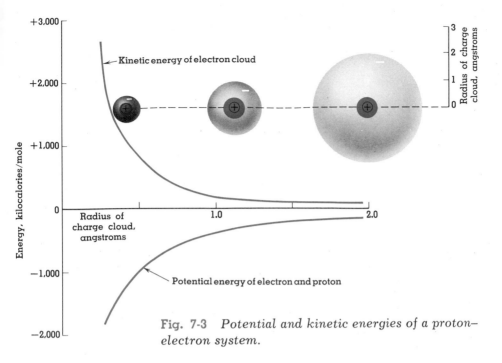

Fig. 7-3 *Potential and kinetic energies of a proton–electron system.*

magnitude. One measure of the extent to which the charge is spread out through the cloud is provided by considering the ratio of charge to volume. This ratio is analogous to the ratio of mass to volume, which is called density, so the ratio of charge to volume is commonly referred to as a **charge density.** As a cloud shrinks, its charge density increases; and as a cloud expands, its charge density decreases (Fig. 7-4).

In an analogous sense, a balloon full of gas has potential energy, kinetic energy, and gas density. Any attempt to make the gas in a sealed balloon more dense without lowering its temperature requires

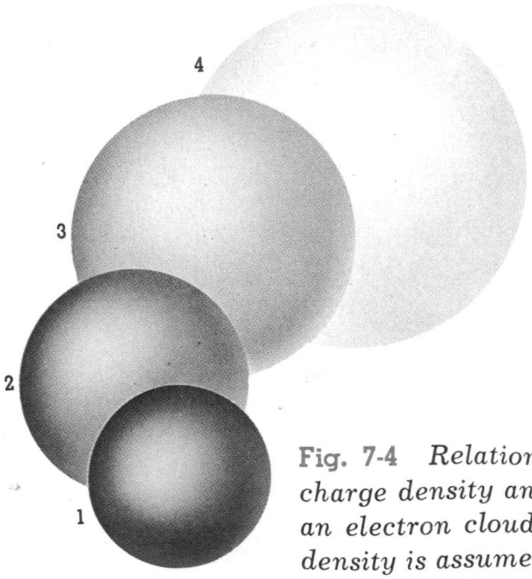

Fig. 7-4 *Relation between charge density and radius of an electron cloud. The charge density is assumed to be uniform throughout the cloud.*

squeezing on the balloon. This process of squeezing puts energy into the gas as the balloon gets smaller and its contents become more dense. Similarly, the assumption that the electron cloud has a kinetic energy means that to make an electron cloud smaller and denser requires that energy must be put into the cloud. The nucleus–electron and balloon-gas systems also are analogous in that both systems possess potential energy which opposes unlimited expansion of either system. When all possible arrangements of a given set of electrons and nuclei are considered, the arrangement which has the lowest energy will be the most stable. The arrangement with lowest energy necessarily can only change to arrangements of higher energy. Such a change will require the transfer of energy from the surroundings. This also means that the appropriate energy of the system to consider will be the total energy or, in other words, the sum of potential energy and kinetic energy.

The assumptions for the model can be listed with full realization that their evaluation hinges upon how well the deductions from the assumptions are consistent with the properties observed for substances.

1. Atomic nuclei are assumed to be points with positive charge. The magnitude of the positive charge will be a whole-number multiple of the charge on an electron.

2. Electrons are assumed to be negatively charged clouds which cannot be subdivided.

3. For simplicity, each cloud will be considered to behave in a way equivalent to the behavior of a sphere of uniform charge density throughout.

4. Each cloud is assumed to possess a kinetic energy (a self-energy) which increases as the radius of the equivalent sphere decreases.

5. The negatively charged clouds and the positively charged nuclei interact according to the laws of electrostatics.

It has been shown that these assumptions lead to a model made up of one electron and one proton which represents a hydrogen atom. According to the model, a one-electron cloud and a proton should give a system which has a spherical shape and a fixed volume. The value of the model will be determined by whether there is a detailed correspondence between the model and the properties of the substance hydrogen. In Chapter 3, hydrogen gas was found to consist of diatomic molecules. Will the model suggest the possibility that hydrogen atoms stick together to give diatomic molecules?

7-4 TWO ELECTRONS AND TWO PROTONS

From the discussions in Sections 7-2 and 7-3, two electrons and two protons would be expected to form two hydrogen atoms. There are several possible ways in which the two resulting hydrogen atoms can be arranged in relation to each other. Which one, of all possible arrangements, is the lowest in total energy (the sum of potential energy and kinetic energy) and hence the most stable with respect to change into some other arrangement?

One possible arrangement is two separated hydrogen atoms as indicated in Fig. 7-5. In Fig. 7-5 the center of the positive sign indicates the location of the nucleus (a proton), while the sphere represents the charge cloud with its charge given by the negative sign placed near one edge of the sphere. Another possibility is provided by two partially merged charge clouds as in Fig. 7-5b. Three other arrangements suggested in Fig. 7-5 allow for the possibility that the two clouds merge completely to form a single spherical cloud with twice the charge of a one-electron cloud. The shading gives an indication of relative charge density in the charge clouds. The models in Fig. 7-5, of course, include only five of the many ways in which two electron clouds and two protons might be arranged. Of all the arrangements, the most stable will be the one with lowest total energy. The lowest-energy arrangement obviously can only change to arrangements of higher energy. This means that the lowest-energy arrangement cannot

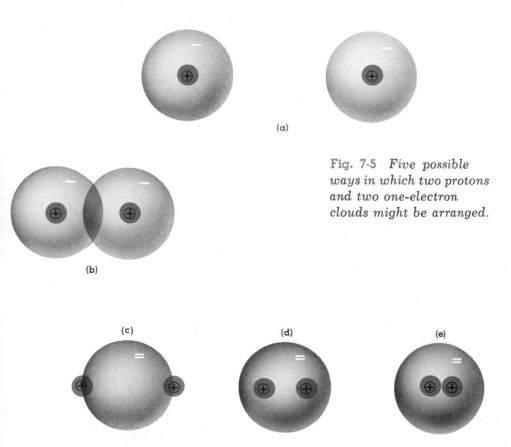

(a)

Fig. 7-5 *Five possible ways in which two protons and two one-electron clouds might be arranged.*

(b)

(c)   (d)   (e)

change by itself and can change only if energy is supplied to it from outside. The arrangement of lowest energy is therefore called the stable arrangement. Which of the five arrangements, then, will have the lowest total energy?

Potential energies can be made low in electrical systems by placing negative charge as close as possible to positive charge. When the negative charge is spread out like a cloud, getting close to a positive charge means not only putting the positive charge at the center of the cloud but also giving the cloud as high a charge density as possible. This leads to a tendency for the electron cloud to collapse onto protons, except for assumption 4 which postulates a kinetic energy that increases as the radius of the cloud decreases. In Fig. 7-5a each hydrogen atom is electrically neutral and therefore has no effect on the other atom. The total energy for two atoms is the same, no matter what the distance of separation of the two atoms may be, at least so long as the electron clouds do not merge.

The effect of merging clouds can be considered in relation to Fig. 7-5b. Merging increases the charge in the cloud and hence increases the charge density near the positive charge, thus lowering the potential energy. Since the size of the cloud does not necessarily have to change, the merger provides a way of lowering potential energy without increasing total kinetic energy. But if a bit of merging is good, why isn't more still better?

Complete merging is represented in Fig. 7-5c, d, and e. Since the only assumption made about kinetic energy is that it increases with a decrease in cloud radius, complete merging provides an alternative way of increasing negative charge density without increasing kinetic energy. Stable atoms can therefore become more stable by the merging of electron charge clouds. There remains, then, the need to consider the best way of arranging the protons.

Three possibilities for proton arrangements are indicated in Fig. 7-5c to 7-5e. Figure 7-5c hardly seems to be the arrangement of lowest energy since the protons are far from the center of the cloud. On the other hand, putting two protons close together, as in Fig. 7-5e, raises the electric potential energy to an enormous value (Fig. 5-19). It would seem that some intermediate position of cloud and nuclei, as in Fig. 7-5d, should be of lowest energy. Calculations based on this model indicate that the configuration of lowest energy is the one with the protons situated so that the distance from each proton to the center of the cloud is half the radius of the cloud. This means that, in the model of the most stable arrangement shown in Fig. 7-5d, the distance between the protons is the same as the radius of the cloud.

The fact that two protons must repel each other is a reminder that two electrons repel each other. The repulsion between electrons should also raise the potential energy and reduce the stability of the electrical system. Separated so that they do not merge, two electrons must repel each other, just as do two protons. The potential energy of a system made up of two separated electrons is inversely proportional to the distance between cloud centers (Coulomb's law).

The shorter the distance between cloud centers, the higher the potential energy. When two clouds approach each other, the potential energy increases. As the clouds merge, the potential energy continues to increase, but more gradually. The potential energy changes are shown in Fig. 7-6, and the leveling off of the increase is evident as one follows the curve from point A to point B. In Fig. 7-6, the charge clouds are treated as if their radii are equal initially and as if they remain equal as the distance between them changes.

With their centers separated by a distance of $2R$, the two charge clouds just touch and are therefore tangent to each other. Complete merging gives a two-electron cloud, and the double negative sign indicates that the charge is twice the charge of a one-electron charge cloud. Complete merging also means that the distance between centers of the original one-electron clouds is zero. When the two centers of the clouds are in coincidence (distance $r = 0$), the potential energy is calculated to be only slightly more than twice the value found for two clouds whose outer edges are just touching at a single point (distance $r = 2R$).

Fig. 7-6 *Change in potential energy for the merging of two one-electron clouds, each of radius* R.

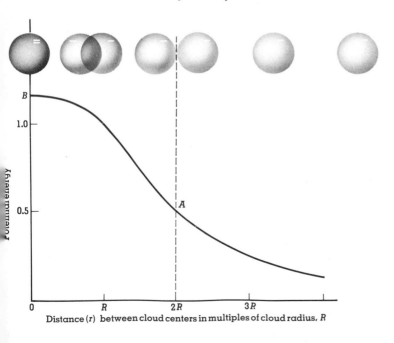

Distance (r) between cloud centers in multiples of cloud radius, R

The model in Fig. 7-5d, with a two-electron cloud and the two protons between the edge and the center, looks as if it might be a satisfactory physical model for a hydrogen molecule, H_2, except for one difficulty. What happens if more than two electrons and two protons are considered? The five assumptions made so far lead to a mental model which permits three electrons in a single cloud surrounding three protons. In fact, any number of electrons and protons could be assembled into a single structure or molecule. Such an assembly of unlimited size would always result in a total energy lower than for the model in which any or all of the charges are kept separated. For the model to produce such a conclusion is most embarrassing because this conclusion is not in accord with the earlier conclusion that hydrogen gas consists of diatomic molecules.

The situation is reminiscent of that described in the story of the sorcerer's apprentice. The young apprentice wanted water to appear without effort on his part. To get it, he used the sorcerer's magic words which started the flow of water. But as the water rushed into the house, the apprentice could not remember the magic that turned it off. He was almost overwhelmed. Finally, the sorcerer saved his assistant by arriving just in time to say the right words which stopped the flood. Just so with the hydrogen model. The assumptions lead nicely to the desired diatomic hydrogen molecules except that they then refuse to stop at two electrons and two protons. Instead the only logical conclusion is that all hydrogen atoms in the universe ought to be in a single giant molecule. The only way out of the difficulty is either to provide another assumption that modifies the model or to find a sorcerer.

7-5 AN EXCLUSION PRINCIPLE

The model of the Rutherford nuclear atom was based on the fact that most alpha particles passed through the atom without interference from the electron. This implies that much of the volume of every atom is more like a tenuous cloud than it is like a solid object. Nonetheless, solids, which are thought to be collections of atoms packed together, can be compressed only with extreme difficulty, and penetration of one solid by another takes place only if material is removed to make a hole. These observations imply that it must be extremely difficult and may even be impossible to cause the electron clouds of adjacent atoms or molecules to penetrate each other. Yet in Fig. 7-6 the interpenetration of two one-electron clouds was described and the results used to develop a model for a hydrogen molecule. These observations and others can be interpreted if two electrons present in the same region of space exclude all other electrons from that region. An exclusion principle can be incorporated in the model of the atom by introducing a sixth assumption, that no more than two one-electron charge clouds can merge. This assumption means that if a two-electron cloud is drawn toward a one-electron cloud by some nearby positive charge, the two spheres can approach no closer than to touch. In this position, the two spheres are then tangent to each other. According to the model including this additional assumption, a collection of equal numbers of electrons and protons could only form a set of H_2 molecules, and never a combination such as H_3 or H_4. In fact, no substances have ever been isolated whose molecular masses and chemical properties correspond to the formulas H_3 or H_4. After the inclusion of assumption 6, the model agrees with the conclusions from experiments that hydrogen gas is made up of diatomic molecules.

Assumption 6 may seem to be more artificial than any of the other assumptions. The justification of assumption 6 comes from observations that models developed for systems containing other than two electrons and two protons agree with experimental observations. If experimental results such as the identification of formulas of known compounds are in agreement with deductions based on the six assumptions, the six assumptions are reasonable. Of course, the purpose of the model is to provide not only interpretation of formulas but also interpretation of chemical reactions among substances.

7-6 TWO ELECTRONS AND ONE NUCLEUS

According to the six assumptions, two electrons merged into a single cloud can enclose a nucleus having any number of positive charges. This arrangement will be one of low potential energy since it gets negative and positive charge close together. For the known elements, the positive nuclear charge can be any whole number from 1 to 103. The examination of the models for a few atoms containing different nuclei can show something of how the electron cloud changes with change in nuclear charge. For a system made up of a nucleus of charge $\oplus 1$ and a two-electron cloud, called the hydride ion (H^-), the model is shown in Fig. 7-7a. Included in Fig. 7-7 is the model of a hydrogen atom for comparison.

The model for an atom with a nucleus which has a double positive charge and a two-electron cloud is shown in Fig. 7-7b. This corresponds to a helium atom, which has a nucleus with a charge twice that of hydrogen. The six assumptions lead to a model in which a single helium atom consists of a spherical two-electron cloud surrounding a doubly charged nucleus.

The exclusion principle, assumption 6, means that no additional electrons can merge with the first two electrons to form a single three-electron cloud. Therefore, neutral helium atoms should not join with one another to form stable molecules in which there is more than one

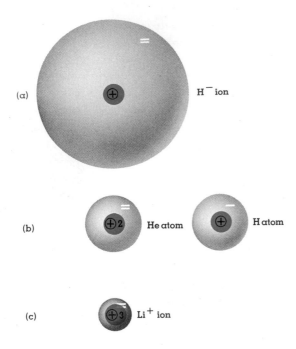

(a)

H⁻ ion

(b)

⊕2 He atom   ⊕ H atom

(c)

⊕3 Li⁺ ion

Fig. 7-7 *Two-electron charge clouds with ⊕1, ⊕2, and ⊕3 charges at center. Compared with hydrogen atom model.*

atom per molecule. This conclusion is in agreement with laboratory evidence which indicates that helium gas consists of molecules that are monatomic.

Lithium with an atomic number 3 has a nucleus with three positive charges. Figure 7-7c shows a model for a two-electron cloud and a lithium nucleus. The increase in positive charge from ⊕1 to ⊕2 to ⊕3 leads to a decrease in the calculated radius for the two-electron cloud. The model in Fig. 7-7c corresponds to a lithium ion, Li⁺. Experimental evidence from mass spectroscopy demonstrates the existence of the lithium ion.

Sizes of two-electron clouds have been calculated for any nuclear charge at the center of the cloud. A graph of calculated radii are presented in Fig. 7-8. The radii are expressed in **angstroms** (A), a unit of length equal to 10^{-10} meter or 10^{-8} cm. Although the graph is shown as a continuous curve, the only points which represent real atomic systems are, of course, those for whole-number positive central charges. The calculated radius of the cloud shrinks by more than a factor of 4 when the nuclear charge changes from ⊕1 to ⊕3. However, increasing the nuclear positive charge above ⊕6 or ⊕7 produces a relatively minor decrease in cloud radius. A two-electron cloud undergoes little further shrinkage when the nuclear charge is increased to charges larger than ⊕10 or ⊕11. The two-electron cloud with a high nuclear

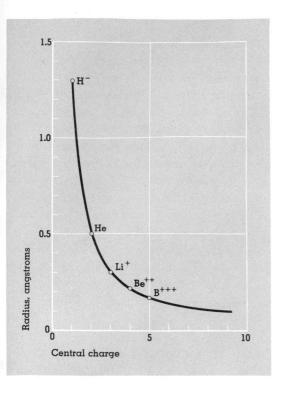

Fig. 7-8 *Radius of a two-electron charge cloud for different central charges.*

charge acts as if it were hard, since increases in nuclear charge have little effect on the size of the cloud. Presumably this means that other changes in electrostatic potential energy produced by nearby electrons or nuclei will also have but little effect upon the size of the two-electron cloud around a nucleus with $\oplus 10$ charge or larger charge.

Whatever the magnitude of the nuclear charge, assumption 6, the exclusion principle, limits the discussion to only one-electron clouds and two-electron clouds. This means that no more than two electrons can enclose a given nucleus. All other electron clouds must remain outside the first two-electron cloud, although they might be just in contact.

Ex. 7-1   Two possible models for electrons surrounding a helium nucleus are below. Which model would you predict to have the lower energy? Give reasons for your choice, and point out any factors that might contribute to a low energy for the model you did not choose.

(a)   (b)

7-7 PROTONS IN NUCLEI

At this point it is useful to contrast the models for the He molecule and the H_2 molecule. Both of these models contain two protons and a two-electron cloud. The difference between the two models is that in the He model the two protons are present in a single nucleus, whereas in the H_2 model the two protons exist as two separated nuclei. In the model for the He molecule there is electrostatic attraction between the doubly charged nucleus and the two-electron cloud, and electrostatic repulsion between the negatively charged electrons. No proton repulsion is involved because the model is based on the assumption that a nucleus is a point charge of magnitude equal to the atomic number. On the other hand, the model for H_2 involves repulsion between the two separate nuclei (protons) as well as between the two electrons. These repulsions have to be overcome by the attractive forces between the two-electron cloud and the two protons if the system is to be stable. In discussions of molecular models, the repulsion between nuclei is an important factor in determining which arrangement of the system has the lowest energy.

7-8 A POSSIBLE STRATEGY FOR MOLECULAR MODELS

The six assumptions are the basis of a scheme for building atomic and molecular models. Assumption 5 includes the basic principles on which the other assumptions can be interpreted to lead to particular conclusions. The electrostatic principles can be summarized as four factors that must be considered in the construction of any model representative of a collection of electrons and nuclei.

The stable arrangement for a set of electrons and nuclei is the one that combines those factors which affect kinetic and potential energies to give the lowest total energy. In the most stable (lowest total energy) arrangement, (a) electrons and nuclei should be as densely packed as possible, (b) electron clouds should be as large as possible, (c) electrons should be as widely separated from each other as possible, (d) a two-electron cloud cannot merge with another electron cloud, and (e) nuclei should be as widely separated from each other as possible. But putting electrons close to nuclei will usually conflict with keeping electrons widely separated and nuclei widely separated. Some compromise among the factors will therefore have to obtain for the final structure. It is the compromise that corresponds best with the observed behavior of real substances to which attention will be directed.

Although the discussion thus far has been largely expressed in terms of the electrical properties of the model, it is possible for several features of the model to be represented by the geometrical properties of a physical model. In particular, the possible arrangements of spherical charge clouds can be simulated with physical spheres made of cork,

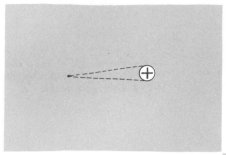

1. Atomic nuclei are assumed to be positive point charges.

2. Electrons are assumed to be indivisible charge clouds.
3. Electron charge clouds are assumed to be represented by spheres of uniform charge density.

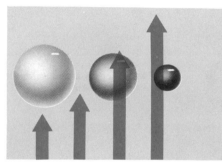

4. It is assumed that the larger the cloud, the lower its kinetic energy.

5. The laws of electrostatics are assumed to be applicable.

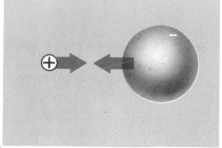

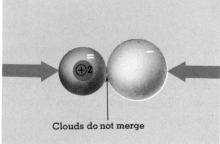

Clouds do not merge

6. It is assumed that no more than two electrons can be merged to form a single cloud.

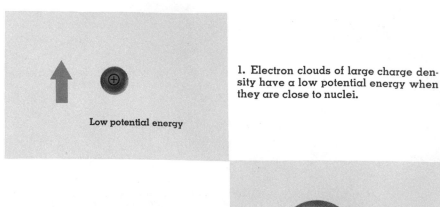

1. Electron clouds of large charge density have a low potential energy when they are close to nuclei.

Low potential energy

2. Electron clouds of small charge density have low kinetic energy.

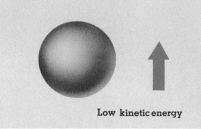

Low kinetic energy

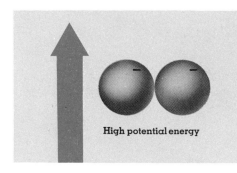

High potential energy

3. Two electron clouds close together have a high potential energy.

4. Two or more nuclei close together have a high potential energy.

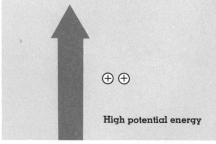

High potential energy

wood, plastic, or other materials. These three-dimensional models may be regarded as geometrical analogies of some of the electrical relationships. Construction of physical models is helpful in understanding the geometrical analogies of the electrical systems which have been discussed thus far in this chapter (see also Experiment 16 in *Investigating Chemical Systems*).

7-9 LITHIUM AND BERYLLIUM

The next element after helium in order of increasing nuclear charge is lithium. In Section 7-6 the combination of a lithium nucleus of charge $\oplus 3$ and a two-electron cloud was discussed. This model represented the lithium ion Li^+. An electrically neutral lithium atom has three electrons, however. Where, then, does the third electron fit in relation to the other two?

In a model with one nucleus and three electrons, one two-electron cloud will enclose the nucleus. This will place a fairly high charge density close to the nucleus. The third electron of a lithium atom is excluded from the two-electron cloud. As a cloud some distance from the center of the lithium ion (that is, the distance between the charges is large), this single electron will have a large volume and therefore will have low charge density. Any description of the arrangement of the three electrons in the lithium atom should make it clear that the charge density is low in the outer portion of a lithium atom and that the presence of low charge density in the atom raises the potential energy of the nucleus–electron system.

The assumptions used in developing a model for an atom having two electrons do not permit one to predict with certainty the structure of a single lithium atom with three electrons. The model can be used to consider the structure assumed by a collection of a large number of lithium atoms. Two lithium atoms can be considered to be a system of two lithium ions and two one-electron clouds. There are several ways in which such a system could be arranged. Figure 7-9 indicates three of the possibilities.

To increase the charge density and thereby lower the potential energy still more, a large number of one-electron clouds and lithium ions can be assembled. Figure 7-10 suggests one possible pattern of arrangement. The sketch is in only two dimensions, whereas a three-dimensional model would extend both above and below the plane of the paper.

The pattern indicated in Fig. 7-10 does not suggest any limitation on the number of ions and electrons that can be included in a piece of lithium metal. Any number may be incorporated, so that a large piece of lithium metal can be formed simply by adding equal numbers of ions and electrons. The regular repetition of the units will produce a crystalline arrangement. The model suggests correctly that lithium would be a solid crystal at moderate temperatures, although the experimentally determined arrangement of lithium atoms in a lithium crystal is different from that implied by the model.

A similar conclusion concerning an extended structure is also reached for the atom with four protons in the nucleus. The model for

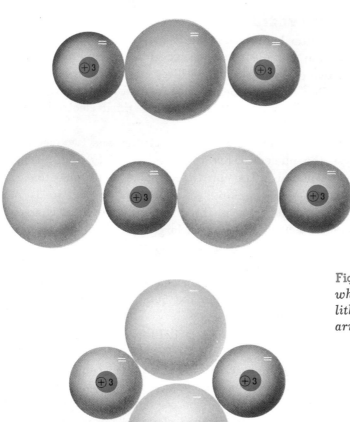

Fig. 7-9 *Three ways in which models for two lithium atoms might be arranged.*

an atom of beryllium (atomic number 4), with four electrons and a nucleus of charge ⊕4, will have two outer one-electron clouds arranged around one inner cloud.

The inner cloud is a two-electron cloud surrounding the nucleus. The outer clouds are one-electron clouds. To avoid repetitious use of the terms outer and inner clouds, the term **kernel** will be used to refer to the nucleus of an atom plus all electrons in the structure except those in the outer clouds. In the models for lithium and beryllium, the kernel is the nucleus plus the inner two-electron cloud.

The outer clouds in the model for beryllium will repel each other so that they will remain separated. Other than this, the arrangement is quite similar to the model of the lithium atom. From the model for the beryllium atom, one would also predict, then, an extended and repeating pattern of nuclei and electrons. Beryllium does form a crystalline solid. On this basis the model agrees with experimentally determined data for both lithium and beryllium.

In the models for collections of lithium and beryllium atoms, each nucleus is surrounded by, and interacting with, not just one or two electrons, but with several more from other atoms which in turn are close to other nuclei. The arrangement is, therefore, not at all the same as the model for H_2 in which the molecule was held together by the attractive forces between just one two-electron cloud and two nuclei. The two nuclei in a hydrogen molecule appear always to be associated with the same two-electron charge cloud. Metals can be pictured by models in which many one-electron charge clouds are attracted by many nuclei. By this attraction each nucleus does get close to several electron clouds to produce a low potential energy. This can lead to a considerable force of attraction between the nuclei of metal atoms and the surrounding electrons. The strong attraction of many nuclei for many electrons leads to a solid structure for metals in contrast to hydrogen molecules which exist as a gas. The model for a metallic

Fig. 7-10 *One possible model for a layer of lithium atoms in a crystal.*

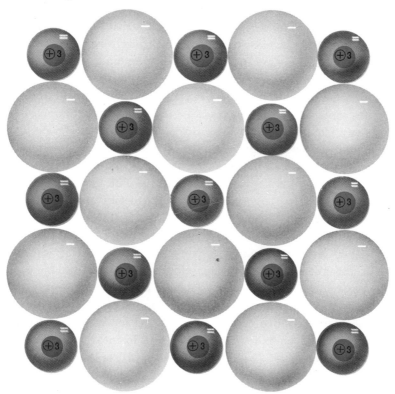

solid is different from the model for H_2 molecules in that it is not possible to assign a particular electron charge cloud to one kernel. Each kernel can be considered to have an equivalent relationship to several electron clouds as shown in Fig. 7-10. In a sense, the nucleus of the metal atom can be said to exert an attractive force on several adjacent charge clouds. The force of attraction between the metal atom and all the electrons under its influence is called the **metallic bond.**

Ex. 7-2   Suppose that the experimental evidence had led to a conclusion that three, but not more than three, one-electron charge clouds can merge.

a. What would be the formula and charge cloud model for a stable molecule made up of hydrogen atoms?

b. Describe the charge cloud model for the molecule of the simplest monatomic gas.

c. Describe the charge cloud model for the arrangement of ions and electrons for the metal of smallest nuclear charge.

7-10   ELECTRONS AROUND A CARBON NUCLEUS

The model for a carbon atom, whose nucleus has a $\oplus 6$ charge, allows a choice among several configurations. Three arrangements of the charge clouds representing the four outer electrons are presented in Fig. 7-11. In each case, the black circle represents the kernel (nucleus plus the surrounding two-electron cloud). The choice of the most stable of these three is made by selecting the arrangement which permits the closest approach between each outer cloud and the kernel. At the same time, a low potential energy requires that charge clouds keep away from each other. The three arrangements can be placed in order based on decreasing distance (reflecting the lowering of potential energy) between the kernel and the centers of the outer electron clouds assumed to be of fixed radius. The arrangement in Fig. 7-11b, which is called trigonal, has the shortest distance between kernel and cloud centers, although (c) and (b) differ only slightly. The order based on potential energy will therefore be (a), (c), and (b), with (b) as the arrangement of lowest potential energy due to interaction of the kernel and the outer clouds. On the other hand, arrangement (a), which is called square planar, provides the greatest separation of electron clouds. On the basis of cloud separations, (b) and (c) differ considerably since two clouds are merged in (b) but not in (c). The order based on potential energy due to interaction of electron clouds will therefore be (b), (c), (a), with (a) as the arrangement of lowest potential energy. Qualitatively the tetrahedral arrangement of Fig. 7-11c seems to offer the better compromise between the opposing tend-

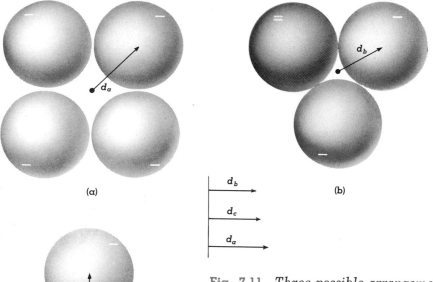

(a)

(b)

(c)

d_b →

d_c →

d_a →

Fig. 7-11 *Three possible arrangements for electron charge clouds associated with a carbon nucleus.* (a) *Square planar.* (b) *Trigonal.* (c) *Tetrahedral. The black dot at the center of each array represents the carbon kernel, that is, the carbon nucleus surrounded by a two-electron charge cloud.*

encies of charge clouds and nuclei to assume arrangements with the least distance between electron charge clouds and kernels but the greatest distance between the outer electron charge clouds. The model predicts that the four outer one-electron charge clouds in the carbon atom are arranged tetrahedrally around the kernel of the carbon atom.

7-11 ELEMENTS OF ATOMIC NUMBERS 7 TO 10

The tetrahedral arrangement associated with a nuclear charge of ⊕6 can be used as a starting point to explore ways of distributing charge clouds around nuclei with charges of ⊕7 to ⊕10. When the nuclear charge increases, but with the number of charge clouds fixed at five, the assembly of nuclei and clouds should only shrink. Will the addition of more charge clouds lead to rearrangement of all the clouds to give some new geometrical pattern which is not tetrahedral?

In an atom with six electron charge clouds available, there appears to be no way of fitting the five spherical clouds around a central kernel which does not result in considerably greater distances between one or more outer clouds and the kernel than in the tetrahedral arrangement. This leaves another alternative to consider. Can additional electron clouds be merged with the four charge clouds already present in the tetrahedral arrangement of Fig. 7-11c to produce two-electron clouds?

Merger of additional charge clouds with any one of the established one-electron charge clouds tends to raise the electric potential energy because of the repulsion between the merged clouds. But merger also brings the two-electron cloud much closer to the nucleus and thereby tends to lower the potential energy. For arrangements in which the kernel charge is $\oplus 5$ or more, detailed calculations suggest that the clouds merge. In other words, the repulsion between clouds has less tendency to raise the potential energy than has the close approach of nucleus and cloud to lower the potential energy.

With electrons merged in pairs wherever this can reduce the separation between clouds and kernels, the models for atoms with nuclei having charges of $\oplus 7$ to $\oplus 10$ are represented in Fig. 7-12. In each of these pictures the diagram is in only two dimensions. The most informative geometrical models, however, are in three dimensions to show a tetrahedral arrangement of the spherical clouds.

The model for the atom with nuclear charge $\oplus 10$ (neon) is a tetrahedral arrangement of four charge clouds around the kernel (Fig. 7-12d). Assumption 6 in Section 7-8 excludes any further merging of clouds with this kernel. Additional charge clouds beyond 10 can be added to the model, either by placing clouds outside the tetrahedral pattern or by moving all the clouds away from the central nucleus. Neither procedure can provide an increase in charge density about the kernel or a smaller separation between the nucleus and the surrounding electrons. The inference to be drawn, then, is that the pattern in Fig. 7-12d must represent a particularly stable arrangement compared to other possibilities, for example, the square planar arrangement in

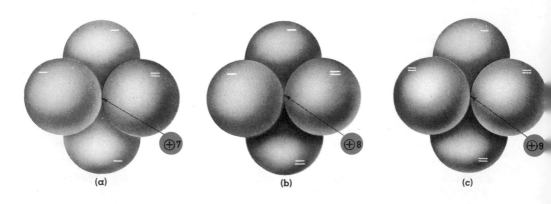

(a)   (b)   (c)

Fig. 7-11a. For the neon atom with 10 electrons around a nucleus of charge $\oplus 10$, the arrangement in Fig. 7-12d gives the greatest possible density of negative charge based on the assumptions of the charge cloud model.

Neon is a gas containing monatomic molecules. It exhibits no tendency to add more electrons, nor does it give up electrons readily. In these respects neon is similar to helium. The model provides deductions which are consistent with what is known experimentally.

Can these mental models for atoms of elements with atomic numbers 1 to 10 now be used to explain experimental observations and to account for the properties of these elements and their compounds? To explore this question, structures containing two or more nuclei will be considered.

Ex. 7-3   Would you expect the inner two–electron cloud surrounding the nucleus to be smaller or larger in the model for the beryllium atom than in the model for the lithium atom?

7-12   MOLECULE FORMATION

If large numbers of nitrogen nuclei and associated electron charge clouds are assembled, what will be the arrangement that will have lowest total energy? First, consider Fig. 7-12a as a possible model for a nitrogen atom. This is a structure with three one-electron clouds and one two-electron cloud arranged around a kernel. The centers of the set of the three one-electron clouds in the nitrogen atom lie in a plane. This means that a set of three one-electron clouds in each of two nitrogen atoms could be joined by merging six electron charge clouds to form three two-electron clouds in a molecule with the formula N_2. Each nitrogen atom also brings one two-electron cloud to the N_2 structure, so the model for the N_2 molecule is a five-cloud structure with two kernels as shown in Fig. 7-13a. Although two nuclei are placed

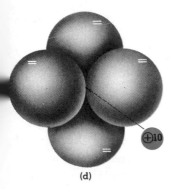

(d)

Fig. 7-12 *Low-energy configurations for charge clouds and kernels with nuclear charges $\oplus 7$ to $\oplus 10$.*

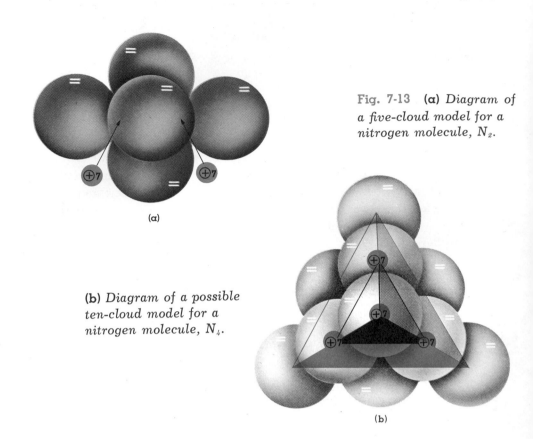

Fig. 7-13 (a) Diagram of a five-cloud model for a nitrogen molecule, N_2.

(a)

(b) Diagram of a possible ten-cloud model for a nitrogen molecule, N_4.

(b)

close together (which raises the potential energy), seven charge clouds are placed close to two nuclei (which lowers the potential energy). Placing seven charge clouds close to two nuclei leads to high charge density and a low total energy compared to the total energy of two separate nitrogen atoms.

Other combinations of nitrogen atoms can be considered. It is not possible, however, to assemble three nitrogen nuclei and the twenty-one electron charge clouds (N_3) into a compact pattern consisting of only two-electron clouds since twenty-one is an odd number. Four nuclei and the twenty-eight electron charge clouds (N_4) can be assembled into a compact structure. The four kernels, consisting of one nucleus and one two-electron charge cloud each, can be most compactly arranged so that the four kernels form a tetrahedron (Fig. 7-13b). Of the remaining twenty charge clouds, twelve (six two-electron clouds) may be pictured as occupying positions at the midpoints of the six edges of the tetrahedron. The last eight charge clouds (four two-electron clouds) are located at the four vertices external to the original tetrahedron. This compact structure puts four nuclei close together, however, and thereby gives the assembly a high potential energy. The repulsion among the four nuclei is not adequately compensated by the lowering of potential energy due to the presence of the twenty-eight charge clouds. The model for the diatomic nitrogen molecule with two nuclei (Fig. 7-13a) has the formula N_2. Phosphorus, an element closely related to nitrogen, has the formula P_4 and the charge cloud structure which was discussed but rejected for N_4 (Fig. 7-13b).

There are two differences which distinguish a nitrogen atom from a phosphorus atom: the nuclear charge and the radius of the kernel. The nuclear charge is $\oplus 7$ for nitrogen, but $\oplus 15$ for phosphorus. On the other hand, the kernel in a nitrogen atom consists of a nucleus and one two-electron charge cloud, whereas the kernel for a phosphorus atom consists of a nucleus and five two-electron charge clouds. In each atom the net charge on the kernel will be $\oplus 5$, but the radius of the nitrogen kernel will be smaller than the radius of the phosphorus kernel. The number of charge clouds outside the kernel will be the same—five.

Because of the difference in the sizes of the kernels, the four nuclei in P_4 are therefore farther apart than would be possible in a molecule with the formula N_4. The potential energy contributed by repulsion of the four phosphorus kernels in the tetrahedral structure is adequately compensated by the 20 outer charge clouds to give P_4 a lower total energy than P_2. Nitrogen atoms are better fitted together, however, in N_2 to give a total energy that is lower for N_2 than for N_4.

Avogadro's assumption about molecules provides an interpretation of experimental data for nitrogen gas. The conclusion based on Avogadro's assumption is that nitrogen gas contains diatomic molecules. The charge cloud structure model comes to the same conclusion. A photograph of a three-dimensional model of a nitrogen molecule is shown in Fig. 7-14. Phosphorus in the gas phase is found to have a molecular mass consistent with the molecular formula P_4.

Fig. 7-14 *A five-cloud model for a nitrogen molecule,* N_2.

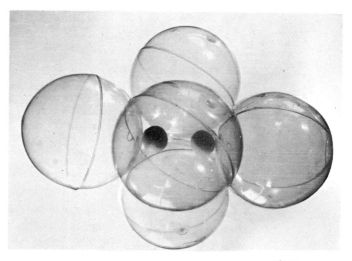

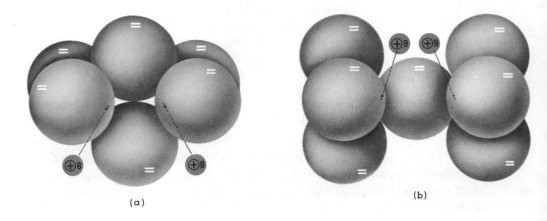

(a)   (b)

Fig. 7-15   *Possible models for molecules of* (a) *oxygen,* O₂, *and*
(b) *fluorine,* F₂.

Arguments similar to those developed for nitrogen can be applied
to the models for oxygen and fluorine. Figure 7-15 represents the results in schematic form. The models suggest that molecules of oxygen
and fluorine are represented by the formulas O_2 and F_2, respectively.
As in the case of nitrogen, these formulas are in agreement with experimental evidence based on Avogadro's hypothesis.

7-13   ELECTRON PAIRING AND MAGNETISM

Substances containing an odd number of electrons and hence at least
one one-electron cloud are attracted to a magnet. If the charge cloud
model is to be consistent with the magnetic properties of a substance, the
model should indicate the number of one-electron clouds. It has been
found that solid, liquid, and gaseous oxygen are each attracted by a
magnet. Only a few other molecular substances, (for example, ClO_2
with 33 electrons) show this magnetic property strongly. The six-cloud
and two-kernel oxygen molecule (Figure 7-15a) does not fit the observed magnetic behavior of oxygen.

The magnetic behavior of oxygen indicates that, in the model for
the oxygen molecule, two of the clouds should be one-electron clouds.
The model for oxygen in Fig. 7-15a is therefore inadequate to account
for this magnetic property since it shows six two-electron clouds.

An alternative model of the oxygen molecule with two kernels and
seven clouds is given in Fig. 7-16. This structure, in comparison with
the model in Fig. 7-15a, separates the nuclei by a greater distance. Internuclear repulsion is thereby reduced and potential energy is lowered.
At the same time, the nuclei and charge clouds are nearly the same
distance apart in each model so this part of the potential energy remains nearly the same. The model in Fig. 7-16 represents a molecule

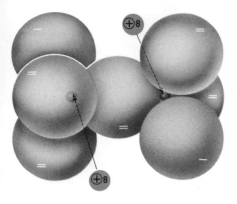

Fig. 7-16 *A seven-cloud model for an oxygen molecule, O_2.*

of lower total energy than the six-cloud model in Fig. 7-15a and also is in accord with the magnetic behavior of oxygen.

For oxygen you can conclude, then, that complete merging of all charge clouds into two-electron clouds to give a molecule with six clouds does permit electrons to pack closely around the nuclei. At the same time, the six-cloud arrangement brings the nuclei themselves rather close together so that a considerable repulsion is introduced. With two of the charge clouds in one-electron clouds (Fig. 7-16), however, the nuclei can be more widely spaced while the electron charge density around each nucleus is not much reduced. The seven-cloud model is the more satisfactory for O_2.

Ex. 7-4   Which of the following substances have molecules whose models contain an odd number of electrons and hence would be attracted by a magnet: N_2, N_2O, NO, N_2O_3, NO_2, N_2O_4, N_2O_5?

7-14   COVALENT BONDS

Both experiments and models indicate that the most stable forms of hydrogen, nitrogen, oxygen, and fluorine are diatomic molecules. In the models there is one common feature. Between each pair of nuclei in a molecule are found the centers of the clouds for one or more two-electron clouds. Thus in a hydrogen molecule the center of the two-electron cloud lies between the nuclei. It is the mutual attraction between the two protons and the electron cloud which holds the molecule together. Similarly, in the nitrogen molecule the centers of three two-electron clouds are between the two nuclei.

Although in the nitrogen molecule, as in other molecules, all the electron clouds participate in the interaction with the two nuclei, it is customary to consider that those electron clouds between the nuclei are of particular importance. The electron cloud (or clouds) between the nuclei forms a **bond** with the nuclei. Where centers of one or more

TABLE 7-1   CLASSIFICATION OF COVALENT BONDS

Number of Electrons Involved	Name
Two in one cloud	Single bond
Four in two clouds	Double bond
Six in three clouds	Triple bond

electron clouds lie between two nuclei, and the electrons are strongly attracted to both nuclei, the nuclei are said to be joined by a **covalent bond.**

Covalent bonds are classified into three types based on the number of electron charge clouds between the nuclei. The classification scheme is given in Table 7-1.

The listing in Table 7-2 shows that not all the elements of atomic numbers 1 to 10 are gases at room temperature. Indeed, there is a striking difference in properties between one group made up of lithium, beryllium, boron, and carbon, which are solids at room temperature, and the group made up of hydrogen, helium, nitrogen, oxygen, fluorine, and neon, which are gases at room temperature. The models indicate that for single atoms of helium and neon as well as for diatomic molecules of hydrogen, oxygen, nitrogen, and fluorine, the outside coating consists entirely of negative charge clouds arranged so that the center of negative charge is near the center of the model. The positive nuclear charge is buried near the center of the model so that the center of positive charge is also near the center of the model. When the center of positive charge and the center of negative charge are both at the same point, the model is said to be **electrically symmetrical** or to possess **symmetry.** This implies that there will be little attraction between small molecules. When models for atoms of lithium, boron, beryllium, and carbon are assembled, electrically symmetrical distributions of charge can be formed with two atoms. However, each positively charged kernel is only partially surrounded by electron clouds. Still lower potential energies can be realized by bringing large numbers of atoms together so that each kernel is surrounded by electron clouds from several atoms. In this way large aggregates of molecules are built up, producing an assemblage which is solid at room temperature. Structurally small molecules correlate with gases at room temperature, whereas extended structures correlate with solids.

In general it seems that the models imply that the differences among the elements with atomic numbers 1 to 10 are geometrical in nature. These geometrical differences result from the way spherical charge clouds can be fitted together.

7-15 COMPOUNDS WITH UNLIKE ATOMS

The discussion of the arrangement of charge clouds and nuclei has been based largely on systems in which all nuclei are identical. In other words, the center of attention has been on arrangements for atoms of single elements. Of equal interest to chemists are systems made up of two or more different elements. A major question of this chapter is why many imaginable combinations of elements are not represented among the known compounds. What types of structures can be built from two different nuclei and electron charge clouds?

In one systematic approach to the question, the elements can be considered in order of increasing atomic number beginning with hydrogen. The nucleus of a hydrogen atom (a proton) has a charge of $\oplus 1$. In this approach, models in which a proton is assembled with charge clouds and a second nucleus of charge $\oplus 2$ or more will be examined.

A helium nucleus and a hydrogen nucleus together require three charge clouds for electric neutrality. When two electron clouds are merged around a helium nucleus, the result is an electrically neutral structure. The charge density around the nucleus of a helium atom cannot be increased by merging additional electrons. This restriction

TABLE 7-2   MELTING AND BOILING POINTS FOR ELEMENTS OF ATOMIC NUMBERS 1–10

Element	Atomic Number	Melting Point, °C	Boiling Point, °C
Hydrogen	1	−259.2	−252.8
Helium	2	−269.7[a]	−268.9
Lithium	3	180.	1326.
Beryllium	4	1283.	(2500.)
Boron	5	2040.	(2550.)
Carbon	6		4347.[b]
Nitrogen	7	−210.0	−195.8
Oxygen	8	−218.8	−183.0
Fluorine	9	−218.0	−187.9
Neon	10	−248.6	(−245.9)

[a] Measured at 100 atmospheres pressure.
[b] Carbon sublimes at this temperature.
SOURCE: Values in parentheses are taken from N. A. Lange, *Handbook of Chemistry*, 10th ed., McGraw-Hill Book Company, Inc., New York, 1961. All other values are from *National Bureau of Standards Bulletin* 500.

is a consequence of the exclusion principle. Because the atoms are neutral and because of the exclusion principle, hydrogen and helium are not expected to form stable compounds with each other. Compounds containing helium and any other element have in fact not been isolated.

In a model for a possible compound between lithium (atomic number 3) (Fig. 7-9) and hydrogen, there are four charge clouds to be distributed. Figure 7-17 is a possible arrangement. In this arrangement the lithium nucleus is surrounded by a two-electron cloud to form a kernel with a net charge of $\oplus 1$ which can be regarded as a lithium ion, Li^+. At the same time, the hydrogen nucleus is surrounded by a two-electron cloud to give an arrangement with a net charge of $\ominus 1$ which is called a hydride ion, H^-. But this means that the complete structure for a compound containing lithium and hydrogen atoms is a positively charged ion at one end and a negatively charged ion at the other end. Other ions of opposite charge will be attracted toward each end. According to the model, a collection of many lithium and hydride ions will form a structure similar to that shown in Fig. 7-18.

In the model for lithium metal discussed in Section 7-9 (Fig. 7-9), the limitation on the size of the metal crystal was found to be determined primarily by the number of atoms available for inclusion in the assembly and not by any internal geometrical consideration of charge cloud assumptions. In a structure made up of two or more different ions repeated endlessly, the ions are said to be joined by **ionic bonds.** The endless repetition of the ions produces a structure with a pattern in three dimensions. Ionic bonds are characteristic of many solid crystals.

In an ionically bonded system, the forces are electrostatic as they are in a covalently bonded system. In this sense, ionic bonds are not different in principle from the covalent and metallic bonds. The nuclei are distributed among electron clouds in a pattern that produces as high a negative charge density as possible. Since the spherical nature of any one negative ion prevents it from completely surrounding the positive ion, the alternative possibility is to arrange several negative

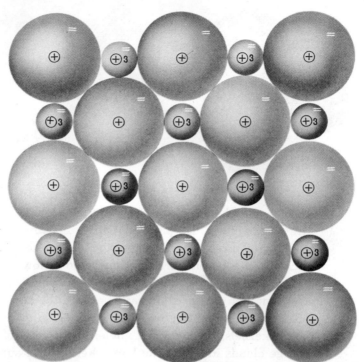

Fig. 7-18 A
model for an
assembly of lith-
ium and hydrogen
atoms.

ions around each positive ion. In turn, positive ions become arranged around negative ions. The ratio of positive ions to negative ions in the structure must be such that the whole system is electrically neutral.

The formula found by experimental analysis of the compound lithium hydride is LiH. For beryllium hydride, experimental analysis indicates a formula of BeH_2, and the charge cloud model predicts the same formula.

A model for boron hydride is suggested in Fig. 7-19. This model differs from that developed for the structure of lithium hydride. As drawn, the boron kernel with charge $\oplus 3$ is located at the center of a

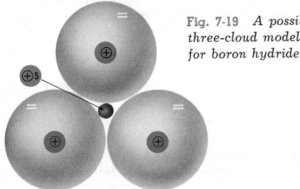

Fig. 7-19 A possible
three-cloud model
for boron hydride.

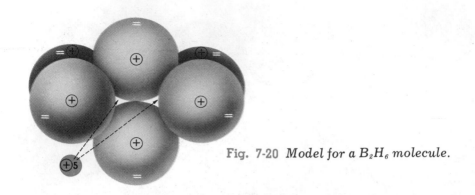

Fig. 7-20 *Model for a B_2H_6 molecule.*

triangle of charge clouds. You must remember, however, that the drawing is on a flat piece of paper. In three dimensions the model consists of three spheres whose centers all lie in a single plane which includes the boron kernel. Above and below the plane through the kernel are holes of considerable size where the charge density is low. Another charge cloud can approach the kernel closely by entering one of these holes. Figure 7-20 is a six-cloud model for assembling two boron kernels, six hydrogen nuclei, and a total of twelve one-electron charge clouds in which the boron kernels are surrounded more effectively by charge clouds than they are in the three-cloud model of BH_3. The provision of sufficient negative charge density around boron nuclei leads, then, not to BH_3 but to B_2H_6 as the most stable arrangement. Several compounds of boron and hydrogen have been prepared. The compound with the smallest number of boron and hydrogen atoms per molecule is called diborane, is a gas at room temperature, and is composed of B_2H_6 molecules. More complex molecules of boron and hydrogen (for example, B_4H_{10}, B_5H_{11}, and $B_{10}H_{14}$) are also known, but BH_3 has not been isolated.

7-16 COMPOUNDS OF CARBON AND HYDROGEN

When a carbon nucleus (charge $\oplus6$) and six charge clouds are assembled, one possible arrangement of the four charge clouds around the kernel is a tetrahedral configuration with four one-electron clouds. This was sketched in Fig. 7-12. Greater density of negative charge about the nucleus can be secured by adding other charge clouds. To do so will produce a negative ion, however, whose charge tends to repel charge clouds.

Greater charge density around the carbon nucleus can be attained if each added charge cloud includes a proton. In this case, the tetrahedral structure which is electrically neutral will include ten charge clouds, four protons, and the carbon nucleus. A picture of such a model is given in Fig. 7-21.

In the model in Fig. 7-21, the space around the carbon nucleus is well filled with electron charge clouds. This means that an eleventh electron charge cloud cannot approach at all closely in such a way as to increase the charge density. Addition of a fifth proton would require that it enter a cloud already containing one proton. This would be difficult owing to the repulsive forces between the two protons and between each proton and the carbon nucleus. The structure in Fig. 7-21, for ten electrons, four protons, and a carbon nucleus, then, corresponds to a compound with the formula CH_4.

A compound called methane, which has the formula CH_4, has been isolated. Methane, a gas at room temperature, is the chief constituent of natural gas. Methane is of prime importance both as a fuel and as a reagent for preparing other chemicals.

No experiments have ever resulted in isolating a compound corresponding to the formula CH_5. The assumptions used to develop the model for CH_4 suggest that the model for CH_5 would be difficult to form for electrical and geometrical reasons. To fit a fifth cloud in among the four outer two-electron clouds of methane requires that all five clouds be moved farther away from the carbon nucleus if all are to remain equally distant from the nucleus. Such a move would raise the potential energy of the system since negative charge clouds are being moved away from the positive nucleus. This conclusion indicates that, on the basis of the six assumptions proposed for the charge cloud model, formation of the compound CH_5 is very improbable.

If fewer than four protons per carbon atom are available for compound formation, could the molecule CH_3 be formed? The model does not rule out this possibility. It does require, however, that one of the four charge clouds be a one-electron cloud, giving that one a lower negative charge density than the other three. High charge density was one of the factors favoring compound formation (Section 7-8). If two CH_3 units are present, they could produce an arrangement of higher charge density and lower energy (than in two CH_3 molecules) by merging two one-electron clouds to give C_2H_6. The model of the C_2H_6 molecule would consist of seven two-electron charge clouds effectively

4 protons

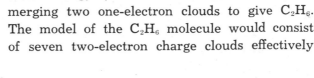

Fig. 7-21   *Model for a methane molecule, CH_4.*

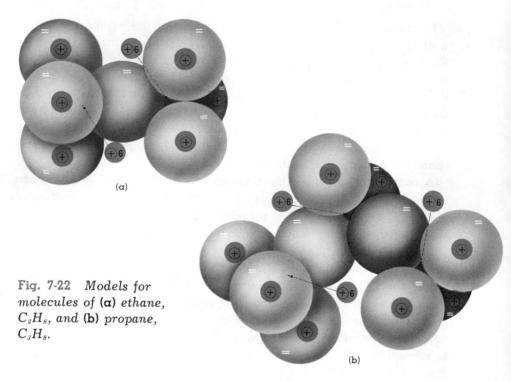

Fig. 7-22 *Models for molecules of (a) ethane, C_2H_6, and (b) propane, C_3H_8.*

(a)

(b)

filling the space around the two kernels. One of the seven charge clouds has its center on a line between the two kernels (Fig. 7-22a).

In petroleum and natural gas a substance called ethane is found. Ethane is a gas with the molecular formula C_2H_6. A molecular formula gives the number of atoms of each element present in a molecule. No compound with the molecular formula C_2H_7 has been isolated, but compounds with formulas such as C_3H_8 are known (Fig. 7-22b).

7-17 A SET OF ISOELECTRONIC MOLECULES

A methane molecule contains ten charge clouds and a total of ten positive charges in five nuclei. The positive charges are distributed so that six are present in a carbon nucleus while the remaining four are found singly in each of four nuclei. The same total positive charge can be provided equally well in other ways. Thus, a nitrogen nucleus with a positive charge of $\oplus 7$ and three hydrogen nuclei each with charge $\oplus 1$ would make a total of ten positive charges. In a model containing a nitrogen nucleus and three hydrogen nuclei, a neutral molecule will again result when ten charge clouds are present.

Molecules that have the same number of electrons but have a different number of nuclei are said to be **isoelectronic.** To get a view of the effect of differing arrangements of positive charge, the comparison of a number of isoelectronic molecules is most helpful.

One set of isoelectronic molecules is made up of those containing

TABLE 7-3   A SET OF FIVE SUBSTANCES WITH
ISOELECTRONIC MOLECULES

Substance	Molecular Formula	Molecular Mass	Boiling Point, °C
Methane	CH_4	16.03	−161.5
Ammonia	NH_3	17.03	−33.4
Water	H_2O	18.02	100.0
Hydrogen fluoride	HF	20.01	19.9
Neon	Ne	20.18	−245.9

ten positive charges and ten charge clouds in each molecule. Table 7-3 lists the members of this set together with their molecular masses and boiling points. This set can form a convenient basis for studying four compounds of hydrogen. From experiment, it is also known that at least two of the substances, ammonia and hydrogen fluoride, react with each other. The product of the chemical reaction is a white solid called ammonium fluoride. Are models of the isoelectronic molecules consistent with the observed properties?

Charge cloud models have already been discussed for both neon and methane. In each of these models, the four outer clouds were placed in a tetrahedral arrangement. If neon is used to provide an initial model, a purely imaginary operation can be used to produce models for each of the other substances listed in Table 7-3.

If a proton is imagined to be withdrawn from the nucleus of a neon molecule, the remaining nucleus has a charge of ⊕9 and corresponds to a fluorine nucleus. If the withdrawn proton could now be released near the outside of the molecule, where would it enter the arrangement to give the greatest stability? It will be drawn into one of the charge clouds by electrostatic attraction, but it will be repelled by the positive nucleus. Detailed calculations show that the arrangement of lowest total energy for the system will have the proton somewhere between the outside of the molecule and the center of one of the charge clouds. Figure 7-23 is a drawing of a model made to represent the

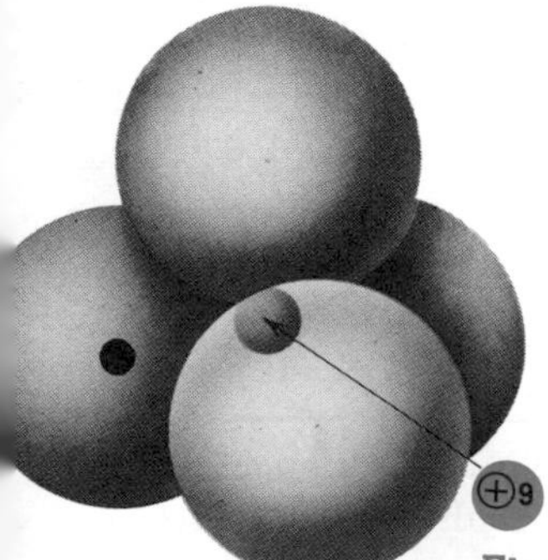

1 proton

Fig. 7-23   *Model for a molecule of hydrogen fluoride, HF.*

267

Fig. 7-24 *Model for a molecule of water, H₂O.*

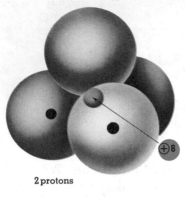

2 protons

3 protons

Fig. 7-25 *Model for a molecule of ammonia, NH₃.*

arrangement corresponding to hydrogen fluoride. The model indicates a molecule with the formula HF.

The model for hydrogen fluoride implies that a two-electron charge cloud is holding the hydrogen and fluorine nuclei together. The two-electron cloud is a covalent bond.

Two hydrogen nuclei (protons), an oxygen nucleus, and ten charge clouds can be arranged to produce a model of a molecule that corresponds to the formula H_2O. Figure 7-24 shows a model for the water molecule. Three protons, a nitrogen nucleus, and ten charge clouds can be arranged to produce a model for the molecule of NH_3, an ammonia molecule (Fig. 7-25). Four protons, a carbon nucleus, and ten charge clouds can be arranged to form a model for CH_4, a methane molecule.

The models of hydrogen fluoride, water, and ammonia differ markedly from the models for both neon and methane. In the neon model each outer electron cloud is related to every other cloud in precisely the same way. This is also true for methane. Such molecules are said to possess high symmetry. In contrast, the models for hydrogen fluoride, water, and ammonia are less symmetrical. Some of their outer clouds hold protons, whereas others do not.

Ex. 7-5 On the basis of charge cloud models, what is likely to be the success of a research project intended to prepare substances with formulas NH_4 and H_3O? Why?

7-18 GEOMETRY OF MOLECULES

In the models built so far, the charge clouds and nuclei of various atoms are arranged to give molecular structures in which nuclei of high mass are surrounded by charge clouds of low mass. This situation results from the two fundamental assumptions that the mass is concentrated in the nuclei of atoms and that most of the volume of atoms is due to electrons. Sometimes the volume (space-filling property) of the atoms and molecules is of interest. Other times the shape of the geometrical figure obtained by connecting the nuclei in a model with straight lines is of interest.

The models of the substances described in Section 7-17 can be expressed in the form of the geometric figures in Fig. 7-26 if the nuclei

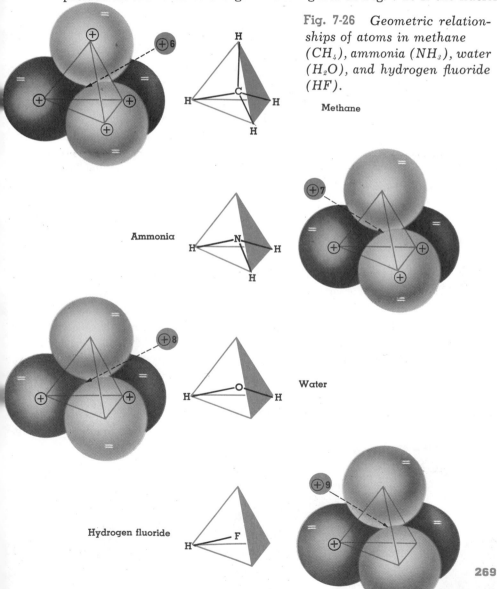

Fig. 7-26 *Geometric relationships of atoms in methane* (CH_4), *ammonia* (NH_3), *water* (H_2O), *and hydrogen fluoride* (HF).

Methane

Ammonia

Water

Hydrogen fluoride

are imagined to be joined by straight lines. Methane, CH_4, will have a tetrahedral skeleton as shown by the heavy lines joining nuclei. Ammonia, NH_3, will have a trigonal pyramid shape because the fourth charge cloud in the model contains no nucleus. Water, H_2O, is a V-shaped molecule since there are only three nuclei, while two of the four charge clouds are not occupied by protons in the skeletal model. Hydrogen fluoride, HF, will be a linear molecule since there are only two nuclei, and two points determine a straight line.

Ex. 7-6   Describe the geometric shape of the molecules OF_2 and CH_2F_2.

7-19   LEWIS STRUCTURES

Charge cloud models of molecules can be cumbersome to handle on paper because they are made in three dimensions. For speed in writing it is often convenient to represent three dimensions in a two-dimensional sketch by use of a suitable shorthand notation. Two shorthand methods are available which can be used interchangeably. One method uses a dot to represent a one-electron charge cloud, and a pair of dots to represent a two-electron charge cloud. Electronic arrangements in models of CH_4, NH_3, and H_2O can be represented in this fashion (Fig. 7-27). These diagrams are known as Lewis structures. Professor G. N. Lewis was the first person to suggest that a covalent bond was a pair of electrons shared by two nuclei.

In Lewis structures the kernel of the atom and not the nucleus is represented by the symbol for the element. Thus for methane, represented as in Fig. 7-27, C will represent the kernel (six protons plus two electrons) of the carbon atom.

The second shorthand notation is a further simplification of the Lewis system. A single bond is represented by a single dash, a double bond by a double dash, and a triple bond by a triple dash. Hence a single dash represents two electrons, a double dash four electrons, and a triple dash six electrons between two nuclei. This notation using dashes was first proposed by William Higgins in the eighteenth century and developed further by A. S. Couper in 1858. Several molecules are represented in Fig. 7-27 by the Couper notations. The Couper structures indicate charge clouds involved in covalent bonds between nuclei only, whereas Lewis structures emphasize all the outer charge clouds whether between nuclei or not.

Ex. 7-7   Write a Lewis structure for hydrogen fluoride.

7-20   OTHER ISOELECTRONIC MOLECULES

In the set of isoelectronic molecules discussed in Section 7-17, each molecule contained 10 electrons, but the term isoelectronic is

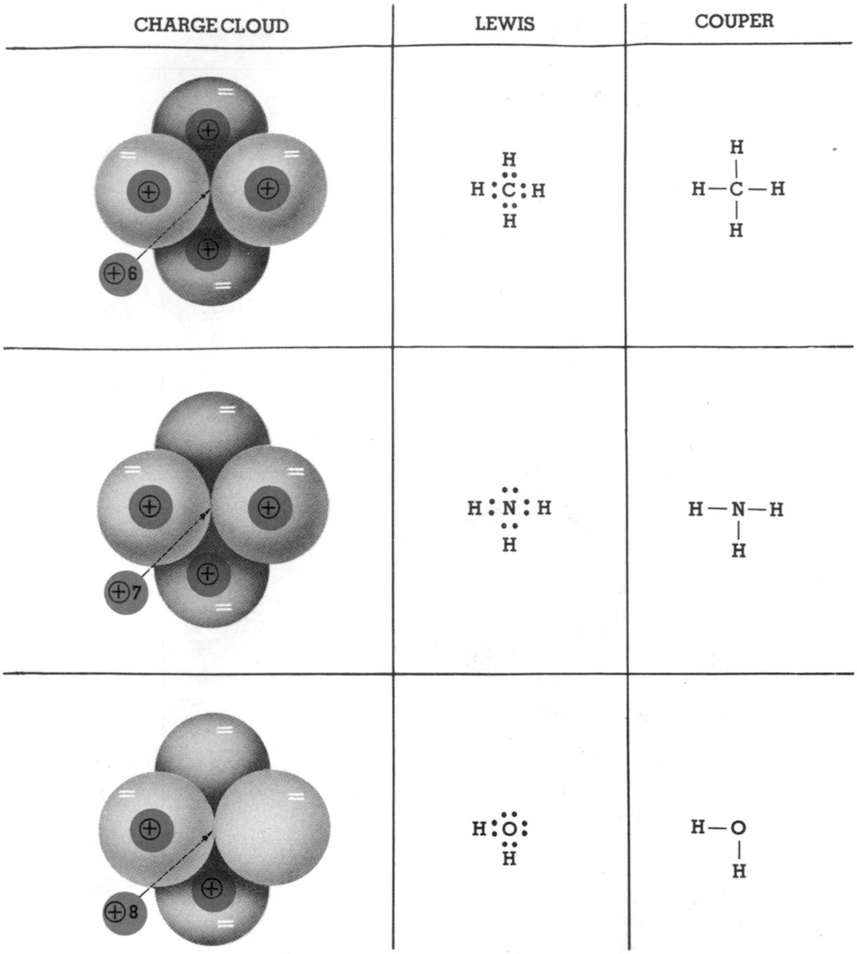

CHARGE CLOUD	LEWIS	COUPER
	H $\overset{\cdot\cdot}{H:C:H}$ $\overset{\cdot\cdot}{}$ H	H | H—C—H | H
	$\overset{\cdot\cdot}{H:N:H}$ $\overset{\cdot\cdot}{}$ H	H—N—H | H
	$\overset{\cdot\cdot}{H:O:}$ $\overset{\cdot\cdot}{}$ H	H—O | H

Fig. 7-27 *Various ways of depicting bonds in* CH_4, NH_3,
and H_2O.

not limited to the number 10. Table 7-4 lists sets of isoelectronic molecules containing 14, 16, 18, and 22 electrons where each set is arranged in order of increasing boiling point. Charge cloud models of these molecules, Lewis structures, and Couper structures are shown in Fig. 7-28. These structures may be obtained from the charge cloud models in a manner analogous to that described for the first set of isoelectronic molecules (Section 7-19).

The fourth set of isoelectronic molecules (Table 7-4) includes the compounds called nitrous oxide and carbon dioxide.

Nitrous oxide, a substance commonly called laughing gas, was once used by dentists as a mild anesthetic. Nitrous oxide contains three nuclei of high charge, two of $\oplus7$ and one of $\oplus8$. The charge cloud

ELECTRONS PER MOLECULE	CHARGE CLOUD		LEWIS	COUPER
14		Nitrogen, N_2	$:N::N:$	$N\equiv N$
		Carbon monoxide, CO	$:C::O:$	$C\equiv O$
		Acetylene, C_2H_2	$H:C::C:H$	$H-C\equiv C-H$
16		Oxygen, O_2	$:O:O:$	$O-O$
		Ethylene, C_2H_4	$\begin{matrix} H & H \\ C &::& C \\ H & H \end{matrix}$	$\begin{matrix} H & H \\ \| & \| \\ C &=& C \\ \| & \| \\ H & H \end{matrix}$
18		Fluorine, F_2	$:F:F:$	$F-F$
		Ethane, C_2H_6	$\begin{matrix} H & H \\ H:C:&C:H \\ H & H \end{matrix}$	$\begin{matrix} H & H \\ \| & \| \\ H-C&-C-H \\ \| & \| \\ H & H \end{matrix}$
22		Nitrous oxide, N_2O	$\ddot{N}::N::\ddot{O}$	$N=N=O$
		Carbon dioxide, CO_2	$\ddot{O}::C::\ddot{O}$	$O=C=O$

272

TABLE 7-4 FOUR SETS OF SUBSTANCES MADE UP OF ISOELECTRONIC MOLECULES

Substance	Molecular Formula	Electrons per Molecule	Molecular Mass	Boiling Point, °C[a]
Nitrogen	N_2	14	28	−195.8
Carbon monoxide	CO	14	28	−191.5
Acetylene	C_2H_2	14	26	−84.0[b]
Oxygen	O_2	16	32	−183.0
Ethylene	C_2H_4	16	28	−103.7
Fluorine	F_2	18	38	−187.9
Ethane	C_2H_6	18	30	−88.6
Nitrous oxide	N_2O	22	44	−88.5
Carbon dioxide	CO_2	22	44	−78.5[b]

[a] Boiling points are from *National Bureau of Standards Bulletin 500*.
[b] Sublimes at the temperature indicated.

model of nitrous oxide can be used to help solve the problem of the order of arrangement of these nuclei in the molecule. Are the nuclei arranged in the order NNO or NON? If nuclei of high charge tend to stay away from other nuclei, the NNO arrangement best accomplishes this by putting an oxygen next to only one other nitrogen nucleus and not between two. When the same argument is applied to a carbon dioxide model, the decision will be against the arrangement of nuclei in the order COO and in favor of the order OCO. Experimental studies of nitrous oxide and of carbon dioxide show that the molecules each have three nuclei in a straight line with the arrangements NNO and OCO, respectively (Table 7-5).

Ex. 7-8   *a.* How many electrons are there in each of the following molecules: CO, H_2S, OF_2, N_2H_4, F_2, N_2, O_2, and H_2O_2?

b. Arrange these substances in isoelectronic groups.

7-21 BOND ANGLES AND MOLECULAR SHAPES

The geometric shape of a molecule (Section 7-18) can be described from the charge cloud model by connecting the central nucleus with

Fig. 7-28 *Various ways of depicting bonds in four sets of isoelectronic substances.*

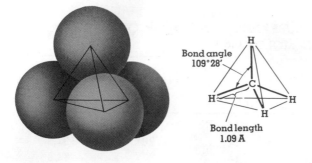

Fig. 7-29 *Bond angle and bond length for methane. All four bond angles are 109°28′ and all four bond lengths are 1.09 A.*

the other nuclei that share electron charge clouds in covalent bonds. The shapes of the isoelectronic molecules in Section 7-17 are shown in Fig. 7-27. The straight-line distance between two nuclei is called the **bond length** for that pair of atoms. The angle between any pair of intersecting lines in such a geometric figure (Fig. 7-29) is called a **bond angle.** The bond angles between hydrogen nuclei and the central nucleus (H—C—H, H—N—H, and H—O—H) in the three molecules CH_4, NH_3, and H_2O should be 109°28′, based on the geometry of a tetrahedron. Bond angles and bond lengths can be determined by x-ray diffraction measurements. Experimentally determined bond lengths in angstroms and bond angles in degrees and minutes are given in Table 7-5.

The experimental data are satisfactorily represented by the charge cloud model for each of the molecules. It does appear that, in ammonia and in water, the bond angles are distorted somewhat from the tetrahedral angle of 109°28′, but even here the agreement is considered to be reasonably satisfactory.

TABLE 7-5 BOND ANGLES AND BOND LENGTHS FOR SIX MOLECULES

Molecular Formula	Bond Angle		Bond Length, A^a	
CH_4	H—C—H	109°28′	C—H	1.09
NH_3	H—N—H	107°20′	N—H	1.01
H_2O	H—O—H	104°28′	O—H	0.99
HF			F—H	0.92
CO_2	O—C—O	180°	C—O	1.16
			O—O	2.31
N_2O	N—N—O	180°	N—N	1.13
			N—O	1.19
				2.32

^{a} The angstrom A is a unit of length equal to 10^{-10} meter or 10^{-8} cm.

In Section 7-20, the order of bonding for nitrous oxide was suggested as NNO rather than NON from consideration of nuclear repulsion in the charge cloud model. The two bond lengths (1.19 A and 2.32 A) for the N—O bond given in Table 7-5 substantiate the argument. The longer N to O distance of 2.32 A (equal to 1.19 A plus 1.13 A) could be obtained by measurement only if the molecule is linear. A triangular arrangement would give a shorter distance than 2.32 A since the sum of two sides of a triangle is greater than the third. What conclusion about the shape of CO_2 would you reach from the bond lengths given in Table 7-5?

Ex. 7-9 Write Couper structures and sketch charge cloud models for hydrazine (N_2H_4) and hydrogen peroxide (H_2O_2).

Ex. 7-10 Sketch charge cloud models of NF_3, CH_3F, and CH_2O.

Ex. 7-11 Describe the geometric shapes of the three molecules in Exercise 7-10. What bond angles would be expected between the covalent bonds in these molecules?

Ex. 7-12 From the electron charge cloud model for CH_3F, predict which of the bonds, C—H or C—F, is probably longer. Give your reasons.

7-22 PROTON-TRANSFER REACTION

The isoelectronic molecules, ammonia and hydrogen fluoride, are each a gas at room temperature. When the two gases are mixed in the presence of a trace of moisture, a white solid called ammonium fluoride is produced. The chemical equation which fits the experimental results is

$$NH_3 + HF \rightarrow NH_4F$$

There is evidence that solid ammonium fluoride is composed of two ions, NH_4^+ and F^-. The reaction, called a **proton-transfer reaction,** should, therefore, be written as

$$NH_3 + HF \rightarrow NH_4^+ + F^-$$

Each of these ions will have 10 electrons, and the reaction can be interpreted to proceed by the transfer of a proton from hydrogen fluoride to ammonia. Why does this transfer take place? Why are the products not NH_2^- and H_2F^+?

The models discussed in Section 7-16 contained protons held in electron clouds by the mutual attraction of the positive proton and the negative electron cloud. At the same time, each proton was repelled by the central nucleus. The greater the charge on this central nucleus, the greater the repulsion.

In hydrogen fluoride the single proton must be repelled by a central

275

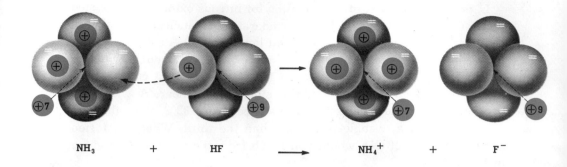

NH₃ + HF ⟶ NH₄⁺ + F⁻

Fig. 7-30 *Proton transfer in the reaction of hydrogen fluoride with ammonia.*

charge of ⊕9, whereas in ammonia the repulsion of three protons is controlled by a nuclear charge of only ⊕7. The chemical reaction can be viewed as a process in which a proton moves away from a nucleus of high charge into a system where the central nuclear charge is lower. Since the number and arrangement of electrons are about the same in the two systems, differences in nuclear charge tend to control what happens. As a proton enters a charge cloud in the ammonia molecule, it is repelled mainly by the central nitrogen nucleus since the three protons already present are farther away from the entering proton than the nucleus would be in a model containing one nitrogen atom and four protons.

A reaction in which a proton or a hydrogen ion is transferred from one charge cloud to another is an example of a major type of chemical reaction. This type of reaction is an example of an **acid-base reaction.** In the chemical system in which a proton-transfer reaction occurs, the substance that loses the proton is called an **acid** and the substance that gains a proton is called a **base.** These conceptual definitions of acids and bases are based on the charge cloud theory of molecular models.

Both ammonia and hydrogen fluoride are substances which can be thought of as having molecules made up of atoms joined by bonds. When they react, the product, ammonium fluoride, is also a substance in which atoms are joined by bonds. The initial substances have a set of bonds different from that found in the product. A **chemical reaction** can in general be thought of as a change in the state of a system conceptually defined by the breaking of an initial set of bonds followed by the making of a final set of bonds.

In Experiment 17 in *Investigating Chemical Systems,* the changes occurring during an acid-base reaction are measured. Although this reaction does not involve isoelectronic molecules, charge cloud models of the reactants can be used to predict the possible products of the reaction.

Ex. 7-13 In terms of the charge cloud model, what prediction can be made about the possibility of a reaction between hydrogen fluoride and neon?

Ex. 7-14 What are the charge cloud models for the products of the reaction between hydrogen fluoride and water and between ammonia and water?

7-23 SUMMARY

Molecular and crystal models have been developed from a set of assumptions consistent with the Rutherford experiment (Section 6-9), the electrostatic nature of matter (Section 6-13), and the total numbers of electrons and positive charges in an atom. From these assumptions structural arrangements of electrons and nuclei can be deduced. The set of assumptions is given in Section 7-8.

At first sight, electrons and nuclei are simply electric charges. In an atom the negative electric charge in a collection of charge clouds is neutralized by the corresponding number of positive charges on one nucleus. A nucleus is so small that it is almost a point, while electrons are comparatively large and cloudlike. The differences between a compact ⊕ charge and a voluminous ⊖ charge must be taken into account in postulating the models of compounds made from atoms. The energy of a system of electron clouds and nuclei will be lowered not only by bringing the centers of electron clouds and nuclei closer together but also by allowing the electron clouds to shrink and thus develop a high charge density. It is found therefore that a smeared-out voluminous negative charge cannot develop as low a potential energy for an electrical system as can a compact charge.

The question with which the chapter began—Why are there so few different compounds?—has its answer, then, in terms of electrical and geometrical restrictions. Since electron clouds are negatively charged, they tend to repel each other. Similarly, nuclei with large positive charges tend to stay apart. More important, however, electron clouds resist compression and maintain space around nuclei.

The model developed here for atoms and molecules is more appropriate for collections of atoms than it is for isolated atoms. Thus, the model does not deal effectively with a single lithium atom, but does predict qualitatively that a collection of lithium atoms should form a crystal (Section 7-9). Likewise, although the model for the neon atom had a tetrahedral shape, the actual neon atom may have another shape. No experimental evidence has been given to indicate whether or not the neon atom is tetrahedral in shape. A tetrahedral model for neon has been assumed because it is a convenient starting point for dealing with models of molecules of HF, H_2O, NH_3, and CH_4, all of whose structures are determined experimentally to be based on a tetrahedral model (Section 7-17).

Compounds are described by models in which atoms are joined by bonds. Three major bond types are found—metallic, covalent, and ionic. In each case the forces of attraction are electrostatic. Metallic and ionic bonds generally produce systems in which atoms are arranged in a repeating pattern that extends throughout a large aggregate and which often result in the formation of a crystalline solid. Many systems containing covalent bonds are found to consist of molecules each of which contains a small number of atoms.

In discussing structures for atoms and molecules, the treatment of the behavior of chemical systems in which reactions occur must answer the question of why the reaction occurs and why the observed new products are formed rather than others. The classification of substances by bond type leads to a conceptual definition of a chemical reaction as the breaking of old bonds and the making of new bonds.

In the reactions between acids and bases (viewed as proton-transfer processes), the assumptions about the behavior of electrons and nuclei in the charge cloud model provide some help in understanding why reactions occur. When the number of electrons was kept constant at 10 (forming isoelectronic systems), the arrangement of electron clouds was tetrahedral and the direction of proton transfer was governed by the factor of nuclear repulsion (Section 7-22). The proton was transferred from a molecule with a nucleus of higher positive charge to a molecule with a nucleus of lower positive charge.

The five factors which have been proposed for describing how to build models for arrangements of atoms in molecules or crystals that have a chance of existing in nature are the following.

1. Electrons and nuclei should be as closely packed as possible.
2. Nuclei should be as widely separated from each other as possible.
3. Electron clouds should be as large as possible.
4. Electron clouds should be as widely separated from each other as possible.
5. A two-electron cloud cannot merge with any other electron cloud.

Ex. 7-15   *a.* Lewis structures for hydrogen peroxide (H_2O_2) and ethane (C_2H_6) can be written

$$
\begin{array}{cc}
\text{H} & \quad\quad \text{H H} \\
\ddot{\text{O}}\!:\!\ddot{\text{O}} & \quad\quad \text{H}\!:\!\text{C}\!:\!\text{C}\!:\!\text{H} \\
\text{H} & \quad\quad \text{H H}
\end{array}
$$

What common feature do these molecules share?

b. Hydrogen peroxide decomposes at room temperatures to form water and oxygen gas. Ethane is considered to be quite stable and decomposes to form carbon and hydrogen only at high temperatures. Are the relative stabilities observed for ethane and hydrogen peroxide reasonable in terms of predictions based on the charge cloud model?

Ex. 7-16 The two compounds NO and NO_2 are attracted by a magnet.

a. Draw a charge cloud model for the molecule of NO.

b. Write a Lewis structure for NO_2.

Ex. 7-17 On the basis of the assumptions for the charge cloud model, defend or refute the following statements.

a. The total charge of a system consisting of one proton and one electron is zero.

b. If the total charge of a system consisting of one proton and one electron is zero, then all arrangements of the electron and the proton are equally stable.

Ex. 7-18 Assumptions based only on electrostatic forces between the electron cloud and the proton lead to a model which implies that an atom has no volume. What additional assumption must be made to account for the fact that the electron does not collapse into the proton?

Ex. 7-19 The assumptions made for the charge cloud model can be applied to the hydrogen molecule (Section 7-4). Defend or refute the following statements.

a. The hydrogen molecule system consists of two one-electron clouds and two singly charged pointlike protons.

b. The components of the model for the hydrogen molecule can be imagined to be arranged in many ways. However, the most stable arrangement must be the one with the lowest total energy.

c. High negative charge density is always necessary for low total energy of a system.

d. The total energy of a hydrogen molecule system is lower for arrangements in which the two electrons are merged into a single cloud around the two positive point charges than when they are not merged.

e. Placing two protons close together tends to raise the total energy of the system.

Ex. 7-20 With regard to charge cloud models for molecules and their use in predicting properties, what are some of the consequences of an exclusion principle which allows two, and only two, electron charge clouds to merge?

Ex. 7-21 Each of the following phrases describes a factor which contributes to the total energy of a system made up of an electron charge cloud and a positively charged nucleus. In each case decide whether the phrase describes a condition which tends to lower the potential energy of this system or to raise the potential energy of the system.

a. High negative charge density close to the positive nucleus as in the Li$^+$ ion

b. Two positively charged nuclei close together

c. Two merged one-electron clouds

Ex. 7-22   a. Why does the size of the two-electron cloud surrounding a positively charged nucleus decrease as the magnitude of the positive charge of the nucleus increases?

b. Arrange these ions in order of decreasing ionic radius: C^{4+}, Li$^+$, N^{5+}, Be^{++}, F^{7+}, B^{3+}, Ne^{8+}, and O^{6+}.

Ex. 7-23   Examine each of the three series of diagrams shown, and make the most appropriate choice for each set of diagrams in accordance with the charge cloud model.

a. The lowest-energy arrangement of three one-electron clouds and a single nucleus with a net charge of ⊕3

b. The lowest-energy arrangement of four one-electron charge clouds and a single ⊕4 nucleus

c. The lowest-energy arrangement of five one-electron charge clouds and a single ⊕5 nucleus

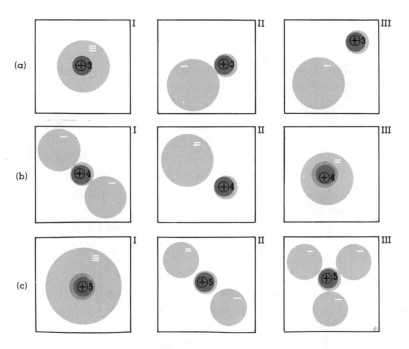

Ex. 7-24   According to the electron charge cloud model, molecular fluorine (F$_2$) may be represented by the model shown in Fig. 7-15. Defend or refute the following statements regarding the diatomic molecule.

a. Merging the two one-electron clouds of two fluorine atoms results in a structure of lower potential energy.

b. In a system of seven two-electron charge clouds, bringing the clouds closer together raises the electron-electron potential energy of the system.

c. Bringing two positively charged kernels closer together lowers the nucleus-nucleus potential energy of the system.

d. Bringing electrons closer to two positively charged kernels lowers the electron-nucleus potential energy of the system.

e. The total energy of the diatomic fluorine molecule is lower than the total energy for the two separated atoms. Thus the diatomic molecule is more stable than two separate atoms.

Ex. 7-25   *a.* Group the charge cloud models of H_2, He, CH_4, NH_3, H_2O, HF, and Ne according to a scale of decreasing symmetry. Use the following scale of decreasing symmetry in answering this question: (1) sphere with all centers of charge in center of sphere, (2) sphere with some charge centers not in center of sphere, (3) tetrahedron with the same charge pattern in each charge cloud, (4) tetrahedron with charge pattern not the same in each charge cloud.

  b. Do the data in Tables 7-2 and 7-3 show that there is any correlation between symmetry and boiling point of the seven substances?

Ex. 7-26   Write Lewis structures and Couper structures for hydroxylamine (H_2NOH), hydrazine (N_2H_4), methylamine (CH_3NH_2), and methanol (CH_3OH).

Ex. 7-27   *a.* Refer to Table 7-4. Give the formulas of two molecules that are isoelectronic with a molecule of formaldehyde, CH_2O.

  b. Write Lewis structures for the three molecules.

  c. The boiling point of formaldehyde is $-19.3°C$. Is the boiling point of formaldehyde reasonable in the light of charge cloud models and boiling points of the two substances in Table 7-4 whose molecules are isoelectronic with molecules of formaldehyde?

Ex. 7-28   Change the following expressions where necessary so that they are chemical equations.

a. $H_2 + F_2 \rightarrow HF$

b. $H_3PO_4 + KOH \rightarrow K_3PO_4 + HOH$

c. $SbCl_3 + H_2S \rightarrow Sb_2S_3 + HCl$

d. $HClO_2 \rightarrow ClO_2 + Cl_2 + H_2O$

e. $C_2H_6 + Cl_2 \rightarrow C_2Cl_6 + HCl$

f. $Ca(OH)_2 + H_3PO_4 \rightarrow Ca_3(PO_4)_2 + H_2O$

Ex. 7-29   Compute the formula masses of each of the following substances from Exercise 7-28: antimony sulfide, Sb_2S_3; phosphoric acid, H_3PO_4; calcium phosphate, $Ca_3(PO_4)_2$; and hexachloroethane, C_2Cl_6.

KINETIC-MOLECULAR THEORY

THE CHARGE CLOUD MODEL provides deductions about the nature of substances. These deductions are found to be in qualitative agreement with the experimentally determined properties of a number of elements and compounds. In Chapter 7, the fact that at room temperature the elements lithium, beryllium, boron, and carbon are crystalline solids consisting of large numbers of atoms joined together was contrasted with the fact that at room temperature the elements hydrogen, nitrogen, oxygen, and fluorine are gases consisting of diatomic molecules. Knowledge of the ways in which electron clouds can be arranged around nuclei provides an interpretation of why crystals exist in one case and diatomic molecules in another. The interpretation is based on electrical attractive forces between positively charged nuclei and negatively charged electron charge clouds. Each of the chemical elements can be a solid, a liquid, or a gas, depending upon the temperature. At room temperature, some elements and compounds are solids, others are liquids, and still others are gases. Can deductions based on the charge cloud model be used to establish any relationships between the atomic or molecular structure of a substance and the existence of the substance as a solid, liquid, or gas at room temperature?

Equal masses of the solid and liquid phases of most substances differ only slightly in volume, whereas equal masses of the gas and liquid phases of most substances differ in volume by factors of about 1,000.

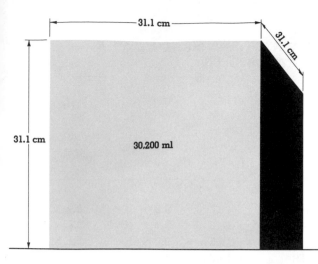

Fig. 8-1 *Comparison of the volumes occupied by 1 mole of liquid water and 1 mole of gaseous water at 100°C and 1 atmosphere pressure.*

In addition, densities of gases are generally only about one-thousandth of the densities of solids and liquids. Figure 8-1 is a diagram comparing the relative volumes of equal masses of liquid water and water vapor at 100°C and 1 atmosphere pressure.

8-1 DENSITY AND PHASE CHANGES

Many substances change from rigid compact solids to the fluid liquid phase and finally to the fluid gas phase as their temperatures are raised. Among the variety of physical properties that can be determined for a substance, density is often the most easily studied property. Table 8-1 presents the densities and volumes occupied by 1 mole of water and by 1 mole of methane in the solid and liquid phases at their melting points and in the liquid and vapor phases at their boiling points. The explanation of the change in volume as a substance changes from a liquid or solid to a gas must relate temperature change to a change in some feature in the charge cloud model.

The densities of both water and methane in a given phase decrease as the temperature increases. Moreover, of the four phase changes associated with the substances whose properties are listed in Table 8-1, all but one are accompanied by a decrease in density and hence an increase in volume of a given sample as water or methane changes from the solid to the liquid or from the liquid to the gas. The melting of ice is the only exception. An increase in density accompanying a change from solid to liquid is characteristic of only a few substances. The decrease in density shown by methane when it melts is characteristic of most substances.

The most striking feature of the data in Table 8-1, however, is that the difference between the densities of the liquid and solid phases of a substance is relatively small in comparison with the difference be-

	Temper-ature, °C	Density, g/cm³	Apparent Volume per Mole, cm³	Apparent Volume per Molecule, cm³	Average Distance Between Centers of Molecules, cm
Water, H_2O:					
Solid	0	0.915	19.7	3.3×10^{-23}	3.2×10^{-8}
Liquid	0	1.000	18.0	3.0×10^{-23}	3.1×10^{-8}
Liquid	25	0.997	18.1	3.0×10^{-23}	3.1×10^{-8}
Liquid	100	0.958	18.8	3.1×10^{-23}	3.1×10^{-8}
Gas	100	5.974×10^{-4}	30,200.	$5,000. \times 10^{-23}$	36.9×10^{-8}
Methane, CH_4:					
Solid	−183	0.518	30.9	5.1×10^{-23}	3.7×10^{-8}
Liquid	−183	0.477	33.6	5.6×10^{-23}	3.8×10^{-8}
Liquid	−161	0.422	38.0	6.3×10^{-23}	4.0×10^{-8}
Gas	−161	1.830×10^{-3}	8,770.	$1,460. \times 10^{-23}$	24.4×10^{-8}

tween the densities of either the solid or liquid phase and the gas phase. This situation is found to be true of substances generally. The densities of liquid methane and liquid water and of solid methane and solid water can be used to calculate an apparent volume per molecule.

The molecular volumes listed in Table 8-1 are consistent with values that would be predicted on the basis of experimentally determined bond lengths. This consistency is more apparent if the molecules in a given mass of a substance are arbitrarily assumed to be cubes arranged to fill completely the space occupied by the liquid or solid. The cube root of the volume of the molecule will be the length of one side of the molecule and also the distance between centers of adjacent molecules in the liquids and solids. The calculated average distances between centers of molecules are listed in the sixth column of Table 8-1. For liquids and solids, the distances between centers of molecules are generally a few angstroms in length (1 A $= 10^{-8}$ cm or 10^{-10} meter).

Bond lengths of about 1 or 2 A were found for the bonds within molecules discussed in Section 7-21 (Table 7-5). A bond length is a distance between nuclei within a molecule and is a measure of molecular size somewhat different, but hardly totally different, from the distance between the centers of adjacent molecules. That the distances between centers of molecules listed in Table 8-1 are about the same in magnitude as the bond lengths listed in Table 7-5 lends support to the suggestion that the size of a molecule is the main factor which determines the volume of a mole of a substance in the liquid or solid state. There is no corresponding relationship between the size of a molecule and the volume occupied by a mole of a substance in the gaseous state. The volume occupied by a mole of structural units of any substance is called the **molar volume.** Molar volumes for water and for methane are listed in Table 8-1. For liquid and for solid, the molar volumes represent the volume of an Avogadro number of molecules.

Ex. 8-1   Compare the molar volumes of nitrogen in the gas, liquid, and solid phases. The densities are 1.25 g/liter for the gas at 0°C, 0.808 g/ml for the liquid at −195.8°C, and 1.026 g/ml for the solid at −252.5°C. What conclusions can be drawn about the structure of the nitrogen in the three different phases?

Ex. 8-2   When a system undergoes a change in phase from a liquid to a gas, what is the nature of the energy transfer which accompanies the change? What experimental evidence can you obtain from the laboratory which would support this conclusion? From this information what conclusion might be drawn concerning the structure of the system in the two phases?

8-2   HEAT AND PHASE CHANGES

The molar volumes of substances in liquid and solid phases indicate that the molecules are packed closely together in each of these phases. By comparison, the molar volumes of gases are much greater, in fact, about a thousand times greater. This means that the volume available to a molecule of a substance in the gas phase is about a thousand times the volume occupied by a molecule of the same substance in the liquid or solid phase. A satisfactory mental model for the structure of matter should include deductions that will explain the differences in observed properties of solids, liquids, and gases, and especially the large difference between the molar volumes of the solid or liquid phases and the gas phase of a substance. Can the observed changes in volume accompanying changes in phase be related to features of the electron charge cloud model?

Whenever a solid changes to a liquid or a liquid to a gas at constant temperature, heat is absorbed by the system. The amount of material that changes phase in any given system is always found to be proportional to the quantity of heat transferred to the system. This implies that a given quantity of gas must store more energy than the liquid from which the gas is vaporized. Along with the usual increase in volume, then, there is always a rise in energy when solid changes to liquid or liquid changes to gas.

In the electron charge cloud model, the volume (space-filling property) of matter is determined by the counteraction of two features of the model. A low kinetic energy of the electron cloud favors electron clouds of large volume. On the other hand, low electrostatic potential energy favors electron clouds of small volume tightly packed around nuclei. The assertion and application of an exclusion principle means that only one-electron and two-electron clouds can be considered. When more than two electrons are involved, there will have to be a number of clouds fitted around each nucleus. A system of molecules will, of necessity, occupy space because electron charge clouds have kinetic energy and because two-electron clouds exclude other electron clouds. The charge cloud model then accounts for the fact that matter has volume.

In the electron charge cloud model, there was just one arrangement of the nuclei and electrons which gave a stable structure, with low energy, for each substance considered. On this basis, it is not reasonable to suppose that molecules themselves suddenly expand to a marked degree when a substance changes from liquid to gas, although this possibility has been proposed in the past by reputable scientists, including Dalton. In the seventeenth century, Robert Boyle suggested that gas molecules fill space not by molecular expansion but by molecular motion. An analogy is provided by the way the blade of an electric fan fills more space when it is twirling rapidly than when it is standing still. Although Boyle's suggestion was little more than a guess at the time, there are several properties of gases which support his suggestion.

8-3 MOTION OF GAS MOLECULES

Observations show that gases uniformly fill containers of any size and shape in which they are placed. This implies that the molecules of a gas have a tendency to move away from one another if the individual molecules do not expand. Not only do gases fill their containers, but gases push on the walls and resist any attempt to reduce their volume or to pack more gas into the same volume. Experience with the inflation and use of air-filled tires, basketballs, and footballs provides opportunities to observe the properties of gases. How can the charge cloud model for molecules, which are electrically neutral and which have fixed bond

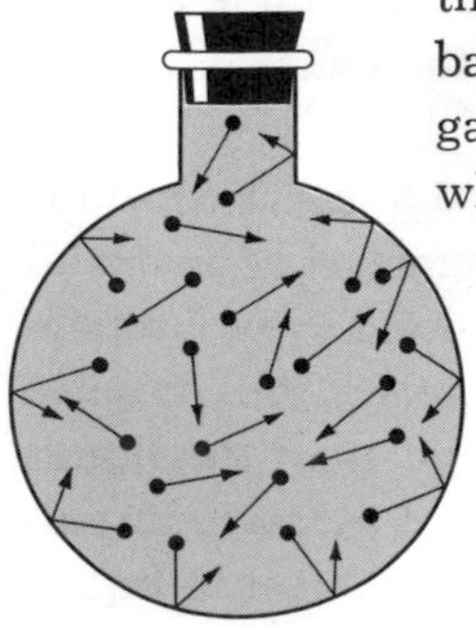

Fig. 8-2 *Rapid random motion of gas molecules can account for the fact that a gas fills any container and exerts pressure on its walls.*

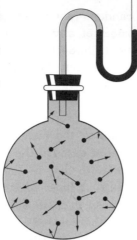
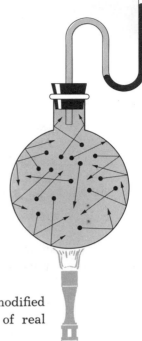

Fig. 8-3 *Increase in pressure as a flask is heated can be explained on the basis of a rise in the kinetic energies of the molecules of the gas inside the flask.*

lengths and fixed bond angles between nuclei, be modified to account for the observations on the properties of real gases?

A gas fills a container uniformly whether it is released near the bottom or near the top of the container. This behavior of a gas is quite different from that of either a solid or a liquid.

A solid released in a container moves only downward until it rests on the bottom of the container. A liquid released in a container moves downward to the bottom and also moves sideward and spreads out along the bottom. Neither solids nor liquids move upward in a container unless something pushes them upward.

Both gases and liquids can flow when pushed by a stirrer or a paddle. With liquids, such a flow is called a current, as it is found, for instance, in a river. Currents also can be produced in gases. Large currents in the earth's atmospheric gases are called winds.

When a substance has nothing pushing on it to make it move, any motion that is observed is called **diffusion.** At home when dinner is being prepared, pleasant-smelling gases emerge from the food on the stove. You are usually quickly aware of these pleasant smells anywhere in the house. There may be air currents that help to move the gases in some one direction but hardly in every direction. So the pleasant-smelling gases that you detect in an upstairs corner are quite likely carried by diffusion from the food to your nose.

If rapidly moving gas molecules were to strike the walls of a container, would the molecules not, in striking the walls and rebounding, exert a force on that wall? And could this not be the basis for an explanation of the pressure of a gas on the walls of its container? And would not rapid random motion of gas molecules account for their seeking out all corners of any container, thereby filling it regardless of its size and shape (Fig. 8-2)? In addition, could not the transfer of thermal energy into a system be explained by assuming that at least some of the absorbed energy goes into raising the average kinetic energy of the gas molecules and hence the pressure exerted by the gas (Fig. 8-3)? All these proposals are reasonable. A hypothesis that relates these proposals to the observed behavior of gases should be useful. The movement of gases in the absence of stirring can be shown in an apparatus similar to that in Fig. 8-4. The colorless and colored gases originally separated from one another (Fig. 8-4a) intermingle once a pathway is opened to them (Fig. 8-4b). The colorless gas is said to have diffused into the colored gas and vice versa. Gases mix by diffusion whenever the opportunity for diffusion exists. The reverse of diffusion, that is, the separation of a mixture of gases into its constituent gases, is never observed so long as the mixture is isolated from outside interference.

Qualitatively, the suggestion that gases consist of rapidly moving molecules seems necessary in explaining diffusion. Can the hypothesis that gases consist of rapidly moving molecules account for quantitative experimental data?

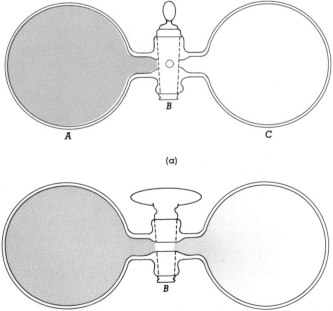

Fig. 8-4 *Reddish-brown nitrogen dioxide, NO₂, originally in flask* A *diffuses into the air in flask* C *when stopcock* B *is opened.*

PRESSURE AND GAS VOLUME

Records of quantitative experimentation on gas systems begin with the reports by Robert Boyle in 1662. Using an apparatus similar to the one given in Fig. 8-5a, Boyle measured simultaneously the volume V of an air sample and the height h of the mercury column that the sample of air was supporting. By adding more mercury to the open end of the J-shaped tube, he could increase the height of the mercury column in the open arm of the tube. This resulted in a decrease in the volume of the gas sample. He recorded each volume and height of the mercury column.

Boyle's data are presented in Table 8-2. You may wonder about the third column where pressure is equal to $h + 29.1$ in. As part of his experiment, Boyle constructed an apparatus similar to that shown in Fig. 8-5b. After he had removed as much air as was possible with a vacuum pump, he found that the vertical distance between mercury levels in the two arms of the tube was 29.1 in. While one arm was connected to the vacuum pump, the other arm of the tube was open to the atmosphere. From the observation that the mercury levels were different, he inferred, as Torricelli had before him, that the gas in the atmosphere pressed on the surface of the mercury in the arm of the tube open to the atmosphere. The air of the atmosphere was also pressing on

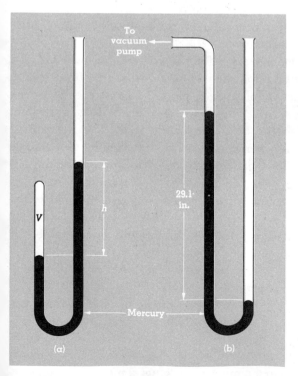

the mercury in the open arm of the tube of Fig. 8-5a, hence the gas in the closed arm of the J-tube was supporting the mercury column h plus the air in the atmosphere. This accounts for the notation $h + 29.1$ in. in Table 8-2. The mercury in either the J- or the U-tube is being used in much the same way as the arms of a balance.

Fig. 8-5 *Boyle's apparatus for the investigation of the relationship between pressure and volume of a gas.* (**a**) *J-tube.* (**b**) *U-tube.*

TABLE 8-2 COMPRESSION OF AIR[a] (DATA FROM ROBERT BOYLE)

Volume	Pressure	
Number of Spaces in Short Leg of J-tube	Difference Between Mercury Levels, h, in.	h + 29.1, in.
48	0.0	29.1
44	2.8	31.9
40	6.2	35.3
36	10.1	39.2
32	15.1	44.2
28	21.2	50.3
24	29.7	58.8
22	35.0	64.1
20	41.6	70.7
18	48.8	77.9
16	58.2	87.3
14	71.3	100.4
12	88.5	117.6

[a] Atmospheric pressure = 29.1 in. of mercury.

Wherever the pressures are equal on the two arms, the mercury levels are also the same. Any difference between the mercury levels is interpreted as a difference in pressure.

In Fig. 8-6a, the data Boyle found for the volume and pressure of a sample of air in his J-tube apparatus (Fig. 8-5a) are plotted. In Fig. 8-6b, the volume of the sample of air is plotted against the reciprocal of the pressure (1/pressure). The graph in Fig. 8-5b is a straight line which passes through the origin and close to each of the plotted points. The relationship between the pressure and volume of a sample of air, known as **Boyle's law,** can be expressed in any one of the following ways.

1. The volume V of a sample of air is inversely proportional to the pressure P on it.

2. $V = K/P$, where K is the slope of the straight line obtained by plotting V against $1/P$.

3. $PV = K$. The product of the pressure P on the sample of air and its volume V is equal to a constant.

In Boyle's experiment, the mass of the sample of air remained unchanged and the temperature was essentially constant, being the temperature of the laboratory. Boyle's law is applicable, then, only in cases where mass of sample and temperature remain constant. Experiments show that all gases behave in a similar way. Thus, a more general state-

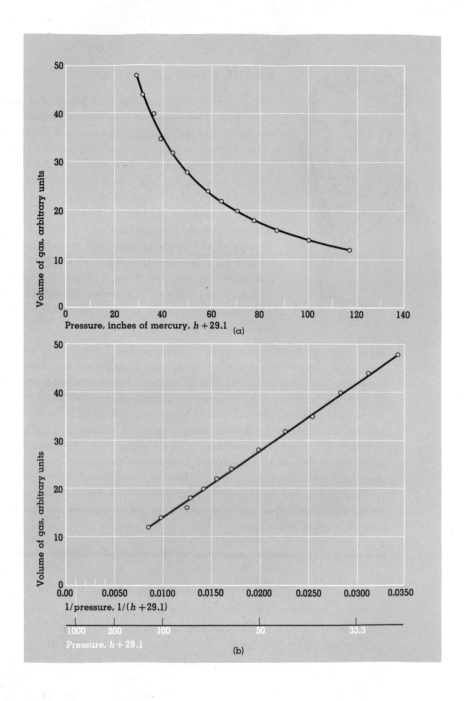

Fig. 8-6 *Boyle's data plotted in two ways.* (**a**) *Volume against pressure.* (**b**) *Volume against 1/pressure.*

ROBERT BOYLE *1627–1691*

British natural philosopher and pioneer of modern chemistry. Robert Boyle was born at Lismore Castle, Munster, Ireland, the fourteenth child of the Earl of Cork. He was educated mainly by private tutors and as a consequence was less dominated by the classical Aristotelian views than if he had studied at a university. He lived in Oxford from 1654 until 1668 and then moved to London. As one of the founders of the Royal Society "for the improvement of natural knowledge," he was in the circle of scientists including Newton (who admitted his indebtedness to Boyle) and the architect Christopher Wren. The Royal Society has become one of the most eminent scientific organizations, and election to it is an honor second only to receiving the Nobel Prize.

As a believer in the possibility of creating a vacuum, he studied and improved the air pump. Using the air pump to create a vacuum, he demonstrated that light can travel through a vacuum whereas sound cannot. In the process of refuting an Aristotelian critic, he chanced on the reciprocal relation between gas volume and pressure (Boyle's law). He clearly distinguished between compounds and mixtures, was an early believer in the atomic constitution of all matter, and developed procedures for the identification of substances, including flame tests and the use of acid-base indicators. He learned Hebrew, Greek, and Syriac for his biblical studies and wrote extensively on theology, chemistry, and medicine. His social standing helped the new scientific philosophy to become established and to receive royal favor.

ment of Boyle's law $(PV = K)$ can be made. When the temperature remains constant and the mass of any gas sample is kept fixed, the product of pressure and volume is a constant.

Numerous experiments of a similar type, but with apparatus that permits the use of gas samples of different masses, have shown that the value of K, a proportionality constant, is directly dependent upon the mass of gas in the sample. The relationship of the pressure, volume, and mass of any sample of gas are found to be

$$PV = mK_1 \qquad \text{(temperature constant)}$$

For each different gas, a different numerical value for K_1 is found.

Volumes and pressure are today not expressed in the units employed by Boyle. However, Boyle's law is independent of the units in which pressure and volume are expressed. Hence, there is no need to convert his measurements into other units.

A variety of units can be used to express measurements of volume and of pressure. Volumes can be expressed in quarts, gallons, cubic feet, and many other ways, but for the most part, liters and milliliters are used in scientific work. Pressures can be expressed in atmospheres, pounds per square foot, or ergs per cubic centimeter, but in scientific work the unit of pressure most frequently used is the vertical distance between two mercury levels in a tube similar to the one Boyle used. One instrument for measuring pressure is called a **manometer,** an example of which is shown in Fig. 8-5b. Without any gas pressure above the mercury in one arm of the U-shaped tube and with the other arm connected to the container holding the gas whose pressure is to be measured, there will be a difference between the mercury levels in the two arms of the manometer tube. The vertical distance between the mercury levels, expressed in units of millimeters of mercury, can be used as a measure of the pressure on the gas.

In the remainder of the course, volumes of gases will be expressed in liters or milliliters, and pressures in millimeters of mercury. The measured atmospheric pressure (called barometric pressure) varies from day to day and from place to place. For this reason, atmospheric pressure cannot be reliably described by a fixed number of millimeters of mercury. However, in order to standardize their notations and to permit ease of communication, scientists have defined a standard **atmosphere of pressure** as 760 mm of mercury. It is frequently desirable to express large pressures in units of larger size than millimeters of mercury. This is sometimes done by expressing pressure in at-

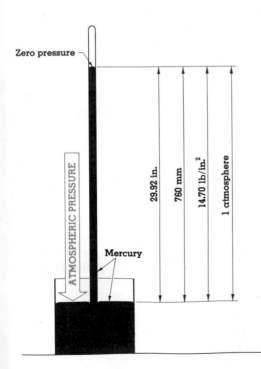

Fig. 8-7 *Standard atmosphere of pressure.*

mospheres. Whenever the atmosphere is used as a pressure unit, **one atmosphere** is equivalent to 760 mm of mercury.

Ex. 8-3   A gas sample weighs 50.0 g and has a volume of 20.0 liters at a pressure of 2.0 atmospheres.

a. What is the density of the gas at 2.0 atmospheres pressure?

b. What is the density of the gas at 1.0 atmosphere pressure if the temperature remains constant?

Ex. 8-4   A sample of gas occupies 1.0 liter at 27°C and 1.0 atmosphere pressure. What volume will the gas sample occupy at the same temperature and at 2.0 atmospheres pressure? at the same temperature and at 0.50 atmosphere pressure?

8-5   TEMPERATURE AND GAS VOLUME

Pressure is one factor that is related to the volume of a gas. Boyle recognized that changes in temperature affected the volume of a gas sample. When he warmed or cooled his apparatus, however, he concluded that the changes in volume were too small to alter his conclusions about the relation between gas pressure and volume. More than one hundred years after Boyle did his work, Jacques Charles (about 1790) investigated the effect of temperature on the volumes of gas samples. Joseph Gay-Lussac (1802) made the first definitive report on this subject, including a report of the work done by Charles. Gay-Lussac confined separate samples of various gases (nitrogen, air, hydrogen, and carbon dioxide) in containers where he could measure the volumes of each sample at various temperatures while he kept the pressure constant at 1 atmosphere. His results may be summarized as follows.

1. For each gas, the change in volume of the sample was directly proportional to the change in temperature at constant pressure (*Charles's law*).

2. Gay-Lussac reported his data as the ratio of 2 volumes of a gas sample at two different temperatures. The ratio 1.375:1 was obtained for all gases when the volume of the gas sample at the temperature of boiling water was divided by the volume at the freezing point of water (*Gay-Lussac's law*).

Charles's law says that for a constant mass of any gas, studied at constant pressure, the change in volume ΔV of the sample is proportional to the change in temperature ΔT. In mathematical terms this is

$$\Delta V = K_2 \, \Delta T \qquad (P \text{ constant})$$

For all gases the proportionality constant K_2 always has the same value if the initial volumes and the initial temperatures are the same for all samples and if the pressure remains constant.

Experimentation since the time of Gay-Lussac has established that the more accurate value for the ratio of volumes is 1.366:1 instead of 1.375:1. The value 1.366:1 can be used to make a graph showing the volume of a sample of gas plotted against the temperature. The data for all gases are represented by the two points in Fig. 8-8. If the proportional relationship between volume change and temperature change which Charles's law describes applies at all temperatures, a straight line can be drawn through the points and this straight line can be extrapolated, that is, extended indefinitely in either direction. If the line is extended toward the region of lower temperatures, the line crosses the base line of the graph. The graph must be interpreted to mean that all samples of all gases would occupy zero volume at the temperature represented by the intersection of the extrapolation of the line and the temperature axis. What significance does this temperature have?

So far in this chapter, no mention has been made of the units for measuring temperature. Three different temperatures have been used in Fig. 8-8: that of melting ice ($P = 1$ atmosphere), that of boiling

Fig. 8-8   *Temperature scales. The numbers shown in color are used to define the size of a degree on the respective scales.*

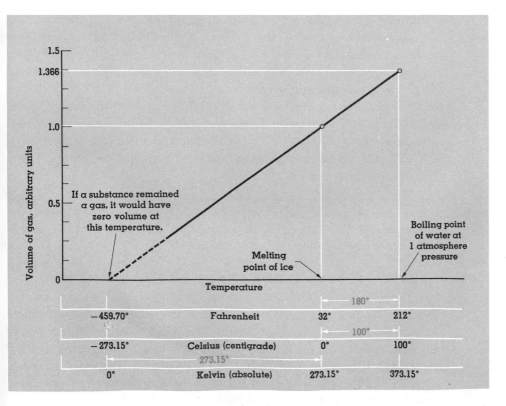

water $(P = 1$ atmosphere), and that at which the extrapolation of the line in Fig. 8-8 crosses the temperature axis. The units in which temperature is expressed are a matter of choice.

Currently three units are used to express temperature. On the *Celsius temperature scale,* the temperature range between the melting point of ice and the boiling point of water has been divided into 100° (hence the name centigrade is also used). On the *Fahrenheit temperature scale,* the same temperature range has been divided into 180°. The temperature of melting ice has been assigned a value of 0° on the Celsius scale and 32° on the Fahrenheit scale. The boiling point of water is therefore 100°C or 212°F.

In dealing with gases, it is customary to assign the number zero to the temperature corresponding to the point on the graph in Fig. 8-8 at which all gases would appear to have zero volume. Since this temperature is referred to as *absolute zero,* a temperature scale in which this temperature is assigned the number zero is called an *absolute temperature scale.* In scientific work the absolute scale most commonly used is called the *Kelvin temperature scale.* The Kelvin scale unit is defined by dividing the temperature interval from absolute zero to the freezing point of water into 273.15°. By this choice a Kelvin degree and a Celsius degree are identical.

Figure 8-8 shows not only a graph of gas volume against temperature but also relations among the Celsius, Fahrenheit, and Kelvin temperature scales. The values on the Kelvin scale are indicated by the symbol °K, whereas on the Celsius scale the symbol °C is used. Thus the freezing point of water can be stated as 0°C or as 273.15°K. Temperatures can be converted from the Celsius scale to the Kelvin scale by adding 273.15° (or for most purposes 273°) to the Celsius temperature. In working with gases, it is customary to refer to a temperature of 0°C and a pressure of 1 atmosphere as standard temperature and pressure conditions or STP.

Ex. 8-5   A 2.00–liter sample of gas changes to 3.00 liters when the temperature changes by 120°C. What change in temperature will be required for the gas sample to change from 2.00 liters to 3.60 liters?

8-6   A SET OF ASSUMPTIONS ABOUT GAS MOLECULES

To begin the interpretation of diffusion of gases and the gas laws of Charles and Boyle, a means of relating the measurements of mass, pressure, volume, and temperature to the behavior of individual molecules in a gas must be available. This essential link is provided by Avogadro's hypothesis (Section 3-5). Avogadro postulated that equal volumes of all gases, measured at the same temperature and pressure, contain equal numbers of molecules. He proposed this postulate to account for the observations of Gay-Lussac that when gases react, they do so in such a way that the ratios of their volumes, measured at the same temperature and pressure, can be expressed as the ratios of small whole numbers.

Dalton had proposed that each atom is the same as every other atom of a given element and that all molecules of a compound contain exactly the same number and kind of atoms. It is logical to conclude then that each molecule of one substance has the same mass as every other molecule of that substance. The mass of a given sample of any molecular substance is, therefore, equal to the sum of the masses of the molecules in the sample or equal to the number of molecules in the sample N multiplied by the mass of one molecule m.

$$\text{Mass of sample} = Nm$$

The significance of the Avogadro hypothesis in the development of a model for gases is that a relationship between the values of m for two different gas samples can be established. Many persons contributed to a useful set of postulates about the nature of gas molecules, but the various contributions were gathered together and given a unified interpretation by Rudolph Julius Clausius in 1857. His interpretation is presented as a list of assumptions.

1. Gases are made up of molecules and space.
   a. The molecules contain all the mass of a gas.
   b. The molecules have zero volume. (This is not an obvious postulate, and it violates both common sense and the charge cloud model of the structure of matter. On the other hand, it is consistent with the graph in Fig. 8-8 which implies that a gas could have zero volume.)
   c. All molecules of a single gaseous substance have identical mass.
2. Gas molecules are always in motion so that they collide with each other and with the walls of the container.
   a. Each molecule travels in a straight-line path with constant velocity between any two collisions with other molecules or with the wall of the container. (This postulate implies that there are no attractive forces operating between molecules. If attractive forces exist, the path of any one molecule will be influenced by other nearby molecules and the molecules will not move in a straight line between collisions.)
   b. The motion of gas molecules is random with respect to both rate and direction of motion. (That is, the rate for any one molecule may vary from essentially zero to very high values, and at any instant the individual molecules in any sample may be moving in widely different directions.)

c. Although the kinetic energy of any one molecule varies with time, at any one temperature the average kinetic energy per molecule is the same for all the molecules in all gas samples. The absolute temperature is proportional to the average kinetic energy of each molecule in a sample of gas.

d. When molecules collide, kinetic energy is conserved. (The sum of the kinetic energies of two molecules is the same after collision as it was before collision, even though this energy may then be distributed differently between the two molecules.) Collisions in which kinetic energy is conserved are sometimes referred to as perfectly elastic collisions. This postulate effectively prevents the construction of a good mechanical representation of the gas model developed by Clausius, because all collisions between real objects such as pingpong balls, golf balls, ball bearings, and even billiard balls (the closest analogy, perhaps) are inelastic to some degree. Real objects tend to lose kinetic energy and eventually (unlike molecules) will come to rest unless energy is constantly transferred to them.

e. When two gas molecules collide, the total momentum of the two molecules does not change. (The momentum of a moving object was defined in Section 5-7 as the product of its mass m and its velocity v; that is, momentum $= mv$.)

3. Avogadro's hypothesis: At the same temperature and pressure, equal volumes of gases contain equal numbers of molecules.

There is an apparent inconsistency between the assumption that the volume of the molecules is zero and the assumption that two volumeless molecules can collide. However, the first of these two assumptions simplifies the description of the model and assigns the total volume of the gas sample to the motion of the molecules. In other words, gas molecules occupy space only because of their motion. As an analogy, remember that a fan blade which occupies little space itself fills considerable space when the fan is running. The volume determined by (or filled by) the motion of gas molecules, not the volume of the molecules, is important in the gas model.

The mental model for a gas molecule, described by the set of assumptions, then, is that of a hard sphere without volume. The model itself and the postulates regarding elastic collisions of hard spheres, momentum, kinetic energy, random motion, volume, temperature, and pressure of gases are known as the **kinetic-molecular theory of gases.**

Ex. 8-6 A sample of a gas in a container at 25.0°C and 1.00 atmosphere pressure contains 1 mole of molecules. What is the gas pressure in the same container at 25.0°C if the number of moles of molecules is reduced to 0.25 mole?

8-7 ABSOLUTE ZERO

For the data plotted in Fig. 8-8, there was one temperature (absolute zero) at which gas volume was predicted to be zero. If the volume of a sample of gas that fits the postulates of Section 8-6 is due entirely to the motion of the molecules, it is necessary to conclude that the gas volume will be zero if the molecules ever stop moving. Because the volume of a gas cannot be less than zero and because the motion of the molecules cannot be less than zero, we can conceive of no temperature lower than that at which the gas volume is zero and the molecules are at rest. Since the temperature corresponding to zero motion is absolutely the lowest possible, the zero temperature on the Kelvin scale is referred to as absolute zero.

This argument ties the zero volume of the molecules (assumption 1b) to temperature as a direct measure of kinetic energy (assumption 2c). At absolute zero, the molecules would not be moving. Therefore, their average kinetic energies would be zero. At temperatures above absolute zero, a molecule has an average kinetic energy always higher than zero. The establishment of this relationship between temperature and average kinetic energy is a major achievement in developing an understanding of the behavior of gases. The relationship can be tested by attempting to find out whether the average kinetic energies of the molecules of different gases are actually equal at the same temperature.

8-8 KINETIC ENERGY OF GAS MOLECULES

To investigate the relation between average kinetic energy and temperature, samples of two gases can be used: a sample of one gas, with molecules each of mass m_1; and a sample of a second gas, with molecules of lower mass m_2, containing the same number N_1 of molecules as the first gas. These samples are at the same temperature, and each sample is placed in one of two identical spherical flasks. Since Avogadro's hypothesis (assumption 3) is that equal numbers of gas molecules are contained in equal volumes of gas at the same temperature and pressure, then, conversely, the two samples of equal numbers of molecules in flasks of identical volume and at the same temperature must exert the same pressure.

The average kinetic energies of the molecules of the two samples can be equated as specified by assumption 2c, which states that in all gas samples at the same temperature the average kinetic energies of the molecules are the same.

Average kinetic energy of molecules of gas 1
$$= \text{average kinetic energy of molecules of gas 2}$$

The kinetic energy of a moving object is defined as $\frac{1}{2}mv^2$, where m

is the mass of the object and v is its velocity. For two objects with the same kinetic energies,

$$\tfrac{1}{2}m_1v_1{}^2 = \tfrac{1}{2}m_2v_2{}^2 \qquad\qquad (Eq.\ 8\text{-}1)$$

where m_1 is the mass and v_1 is the velocity of one object, and m_2 is the mass and v_2 is the velocity of the second object.

If each side of Equation 8-1 is divided by $\tfrac{1}{2}$, by m_1, and by $v_2{}^2$, the equation becomes

$$\frac{v_1{}^2}{v_2{}^2} = \frac{m_2}{m_1} \qquad\qquad (Eq.\ 8\text{-}2)$$

Taking the square roots of both sides gives

$$\frac{v_1}{v_2} = \sqrt{\frac{m_2}{m_1}} \qquad\qquad (Eq.\ 8\text{-}3)$$

Equation 8-3 suggests that for two objects in motion with the same kinetic energy, their velocities will be inversely proportional to the square roots of their masses (Fig. 8-9).

The major problem in applying Equation 8-3 to the molecules of a gas sample is in knowing what velocity to use when every molecule may have a velocity different from that of every other molecule. Furthermore, it would be impractical to determine an individual velocity for every molecule when there are so many in a measurable sample of gas. An average velocity will be as useful, however, and for the moment suppose that it is possible to find and use an average velocity

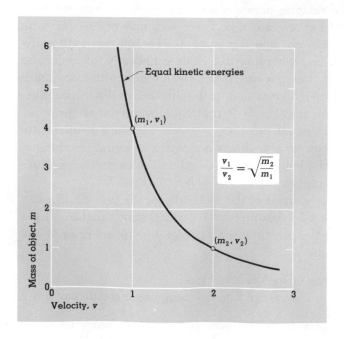

Fig. 8-9 *Graph of Equation 8-3 showing the relationships among kinetic energy, mass, and velocity of an object.*

of a sample of gas molecules. The average velocity $\bar{v}$ per molecule (read as vee bar) can be used to write Equation 8-3 in another form.

$$\frac{\bar{v}_1}{\bar{v}_2} = \sqrt{\frac{m_2}{m_1}} \qquad (Eq.\ 8\text{-}4)$$

Since there is the same number of molecules N_1 in each sample confined within equal volumes, the total number of collisions per unit of time (or collision frequency) with the wall of the container in each case will depend upon the average velocity of the molecules.

$$\frac{\text{Collision frequency 1}}{\text{Collision frequency 2}} = \frac{\bar{v}_1}{\bar{v}_2} = \frac{\sqrt{m_2}}{\sqrt{m_1}} \qquad (Eq.\ 8\text{-}5)$$

Since the surface areas of the two equal spherical containers are equal, the collisions per unit area of surface are related in the same way.

$$\frac{\text{Collision frequency 1 per unit area}}{\text{Collision frequency 2 per unit area}} = \frac{\bar{v}_1}{\bar{v}_2} = \frac{\sqrt{m_2}}{\sqrt{m_1}} \qquad (Eq.\ 8\text{-}6)$$

Equation 8-6 rests directly upon the assumption (2c) that the average kinetic energy per molecule is the same for all the molecules. Any experiment which demonstrates the validity of the relation between mass and collision frequency (Equation 8-6) will support the assumption about the kinetic energy of gas molecules. If we could count the number of collisions occurring on a unit of surface for each of two gases, the data would provide a check on assumption 2c.

Ex. 8-7 Three unidentified gases (A, B, and C) were allowed to diffuse separately through a fixed distance in a glass tube. Each gas was allowed to diffuse through the apparatus three times; the average of the three runs for each gas is given below.

Gas	Time of Diffusion Through the Tube
A	42 seconds
B	15 seconds
C	67 seconds

a. Which gas has the largest molecular mass?

b. Which gas has the lowest gas density?

Ex. 8-8 If the average velocity of oxygen molecules is 1,000 mph at 0°C, what would be the average velocity of nitrogen molecules at 0°C?

8-9 COLLISION FREQUENCY AND VELOCITY

There is no way to detect single collisions so that they can be counted directly. However, if a small unit of the surface of the sphere confining the gas were removed, each molecule that would have struck this unit

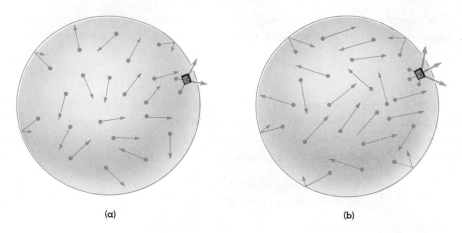

(a)   (b)

Fig. 8-10 *For molecules of different gases at the same temperature, the escape rate through a small hole is proportional to the average velocities of the molecules. At the same temperature, molecules of large mass (**a**) have lower average velocities than molecules of small mass (**b**).*

of surface inside the sphere will instead escape from the sphere. This means that the collision frequency per unit of area is equivalent to a rate of escape per unit of hole area. So a count of the molecules escaping through a hole becomes equivalent to a count of the number of molecules colliding with the same area of the wall.

It is not necessary to count the actual number of molecules escaping in each case. It will be sufficient to know the ratio of the escape rate of molecules of one gas to the escape rate of molecules of the other gas. So in the end some measurable property which is proportional to the number of molecules escaping through the hole can provide the data needed to check the theory that all gas molecules have the same average kinetic energy at the same temperature.

The volume of a sample of a gas is proportional to the number of molecules in the sample so long as pressure and temperature are kept constant. Therefore, measurements of the volume (at the same temperature and pressure) of each gas that escapes from identical small holes in each sphere during a measured time interval give data that can be used to calculate the ratio of the volumes of the escaping gases. The ratio of volumes must be the same as the ratio of the number of molecules escaping. During the same time interval, the ratios of the volumes V escaping would be the same as the ratios of the escape rates.

$$\frac{\text{Collision frequency 1}}{\text{Collision frequency 2}} = \frac{\bar{v}_1}{\bar{v}_2} = \frac{\text{escape rate 1}}{\text{escape rate 2}} = \frac{V_1}{V_2} \quad (Eq. \ 8\text{-}7)$$

where V_1 and V_2 are the volumes of each escaping gas.

What sort of experiment will produce data that can be used to evaluate the relationships between velocity and masses of molecules in a gas shown in Equations 8-5 to 8-7? The experiment must be done in such a way that those molecules which would normally strike the surface, had the unit area not been removed, will be those molecules which escape when the unit area is removed to form the hole. Moreover, the escape of molecules through the hole must not affect the rate of collision with the wall by the molecules still in the container. Molecules must not return through the hole once they have escaped, since they would then not be counted.

It turns out that these difficulties are not important if the gas pressure is low and the hole is small. Low gas pressure means a small number of molecules in a given volume and consequently a long distance between molecules. With relatively long distances between molecules, each molecule will travel a considerable distance between collisions. If the diameter of the hole in the container wall is small compared to the distance a molecule travels between collisions, then the movement of a gas through the hole reflects the motion of individual molecules. Collisions between molecules within the hole must also be kept small in number to prevent any molecules moving through the hole from getting turned around and hence not counted. Collisions within the hole are minimized by using a thin-walled container so that the hole is short and contains few molecules at any instant, and by removing all molecules of gas from the outside of the flask around the hole.

One form of apparatus for an experiment is represented schematically in Fig. 8-11. The container for the gas sample is suspended within a second container. A pump is used to evacuate the outer container, and the pump or other devices may be used to trap the escaping gas for measurement of volume. When gas in a container escapes through a small hole into a vacuum, the process is called **effusion.** In an effusion experiment it is customary to refer to the rate of escape as the **effusion rate.**

Fig. 8-11   *An apparatus for investigating the effusion of gases.*

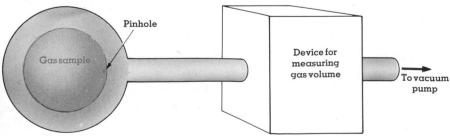

THOMAS GRAHAM 1805–1869

*A Scottish chemist, born in Glasgow. Graham entered
Glasgow University at the age of fourteen to study for
the ministry. After receiving his M.A. in 1826, he went
to Edinburgh to study chemistry in spite of the
opposition of his father. From 1829 to 1837, he taught
chemistry in Glasgow technical schools, then was
appointed professor of chemistry at the newly founded
University of London (now University College). During
the years 1837 to 1841, he published his textbook
Elements of Chemistry which was noted for its
emphasis in the early chapters on the physical principles
of chemistry. He was elected a Fellow of the Royal
Society in 1836 and the first president of the Chemical
Society of London in 1841. In 1854 he was appointed
Master of the Mint, an honorary but time-consuming
position.*

*His earliest paper (1826) dealt with the absorption of gases by liquids.
An observation by J. W. Döbereiner that a cracked bottle inverted over
water and containing hydrogen lets the hydrogen out faster than air enters
gave Graham the initial hint that led to Graham's law of gaseous diffusion.
He then studied the diffusion of solutes in liquids, first without membrane
separation, then with parchment and skin barriers. He distinguished
between crystalloids (that pass through membranes) and colloids (jelly-
like substances that do not pass through membranes). His studies became
the foundation of modern colloid chemistry. Returning to gas studies,
he found that a rubber sheet could partially separate the constituents of
air, that hydrogen but not other gases could pass through heated palladium
or platinum, and that hydrogen, associated with palladium, greatly
increased the magnetism of palladium. This last observation was considered
excellent evidence at the time for the metallic character of hydrogen.*

Thomas Graham reported the first systematic work on the effusion
process in 1846. Table 8-3 presents ratios of the effusion rates (Equation 8-7) of various gases to the effusion rate of air as reported by
Graham and also the experimentally determined densities of the gases
relative to the density of air at 0°C and 1 atmosphere pressure. At the
time of his work Graham did not have reliable molecular mass values

since the scale of atomic masses had not yet been established. The fourth column of Table 8-3 lists present-day values for the molecular masses of the gases that Graham studied.

In Chapter 3 the density of a gas was shown to be directly proportional to its molecular mass.

$$\frac{m_2}{m_1} = \frac{d_2}{d_1} \qquad \text{(Eq. 8-8)}$$

Substituting d_2/d_1 from Equation 8-8 for m_2/m_1 in Equation 8-5 gives

$$\frac{\bar{v}_1}{\bar{v}_2} = \frac{\sqrt{d_2}}{\sqrt{d_1}} = \frac{\text{collision frequency 1}}{\text{collision frequency 2}} \qquad \text{(Eq. 8-9)}$$

Substitution from Equation 8-9 into Equation 8-7 then gives

$$\frac{\text{Effusion rate 1}}{\text{Effusion rate 2}} = \sqrt{\frac{d_2}{d_1}} \qquad \text{(Eq. 8-10)}$$

In words, then, the effusion rate of a gas should be inversely proportional to the square root of the gas density. To test this conclusion, Graham's data (Table 8-3) are plotted in Fig. 8-12 with the reciprocal of effusion rate plotted against the square root of the gas density. A straight line through the origin lies close to the plotted points. This graph indicates that the rate of effusion is inversely proportional to the square root of gas density (Equation 8-10). But the relation means in turn that the average velocity of a gas molecule is inversely proportional to the square root of molecular mass (Equation 8-4). Equation 8-9 represents the conclusion that average kinetic energy and the collision frequency for molecules hitting the wall of the container are proportional. Since the discussion began with an assumption (2c) that

TABLE 8-3   DENSITIES, RATES OF EFFUSION, AND MOLECULAR MASSES FOR SEVERAL GASES

Gases	Density[a]	Rate of Effusion[a]	Molecular Mass, amu
H_2	0.0692	3.62	2.0
CH_4	0.555	1.328	16.0
C_2H_4	0.970	1.013	28.0
N_2	0.970	1.014	28.0
Air	1.000	1.000	29.0[b]
O_2	1.105	0.950	32.0
CO_2	1.530	0.831	44.0

[a] Numbers recorded are relative to air taken as 1.000.
[b] Molecular mass is a mean for the components present in air.

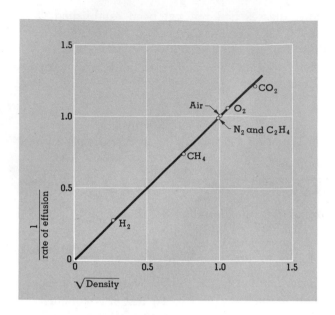

Fig. 8-12 *Graphical representation of Graham's experimental data.*

the average kinetic energy per molecule in any gas sample is proportional to the temperature, it is reasonable to conclude that Graham's experimental data do support the assumption.

Ex. 8-9   *a.* Using the data given in Table 8-3, plot the reciprocal of the effusion rate against the square root of the molecular mass for hydrogen, methane, air, oxygen, and carbon dioxide.

b. If the reciprocal of the effusion rate, relative to air, for an unknown gas is 0.93, what would be the molecular mass of this gas?

8-11   TEMPERATURE AND GAS PRESSURE

The postulate of equal average kinetic energies of gas molecules in samples at the same temperature is in agreement with experimental data (Table 8-3). Assumption 2c also included the postulate that temperature is a direct measure of the average kinetic energy of the molecules in a gas. To support this, it is necessary to show that average kinetic energy and absolute temperature are proportional. What experimental evidence is available to support the assumption that the average kinetic energy of gas molecules is proportional to the absolute temperature?

In Section 8-3 it was suggested that gas molecules exert pressure on container walls because of the collisions between the moving molecules and the stationary walls. The relation of collision frequency to velocity suggests that a study of gas pressure and temperature might provide a clue to the way kinetic energy is related to temperature.

Although the force produced by the impact of any one molecule as it hits the wall will be quite small, nonetheless the high frequency of impacts can produce a large and steady total force per unit of area. Pressure is defined as force per unit area. Therefore, the pressure exerted by a gas on the walls is the total force exerted by the gas molecules per unit area.

$$\text{Pressure of a gas} = \frac{\text{total force exerted by gas molecules}}{\text{area}} \quad (Eq.\ 8\text{-}11)$$

If the wall of the container is not allowed to move, it will have to exert an equal pressure on the gas. The total force on the wall will depend on the force exerted by each molecule multiplied by the number of molecules colliding with the wall.

$$\text{Total force} = \frac{\text{force}}{\text{molecule}} \times \text{number of molecules colliding} \quad (Eq.\ 8\text{-}12)$$

$$\text{Pressure of a gas} = \frac{1}{\text{area}} \times \frac{\text{force}}{\text{molecule}}$$
$$\times \text{ number of molecules colliding} \quad (Eq.\ 8\text{-}13)$$

A force is defined as being proportional to the momentum divided by the time (Section 5-7), and as a consequence, the force which each molecule exerts on the wall will be proportional to the momentum of the molecule divided by time.

$$\frac{\text{Force}}{\text{Molecule}} = K_1 \times \frac{\text{momentum}}{\text{molecule} \times \text{time}} \quad (Eq.\ 8\text{-}14)$$

$$\text{Pressure} = \frac{1}{\text{area}} \times K_1 \times \frac{\text{momentum}}{\text{molecule} \times \text{time}}$$
$$\times \text{ number of molecules colliding} \quad (Eq.\ 8\text{-}15)$$

In Section 8-8, the postulates for the gas model and experimental data led to the conclusion that the number of molecules colliding with the wall per unit of area and per unit of time is proportional to the average velocity of the molecules. That is,

$$\frac{\text{Number of molecules colliding}}{\text{Time} \times \text{area}}$$
$$= K_2 \times \text{average velocity of molecules} \quad (Eq.\ 8\text{-}16)$$

From Equation 8-16, then, the

$$\text{Number of molecules colliding} = \text{time} \times \text{area}$$
$$\times K_2 \times \text{average velocity of molecules} \quad (Eq.\ 8\text{-}17)$$

If Equation 8-17 is substituted in Equation 8-15 for the number of molecules colliding,

$$\text{Pressure of a gas} = \frac{1}{\text{area}} \times \frac{K_1 \text{ momentum} \times \text{time} \times \text{area}}{\text{molecule} \times \text{time}}$$
$$\times K_2 \times \text{average velocity of molecules}$$

This in turn with cancellation of terms becomes Equation 8-18.

$$\text{Pressure of a gas} = \frac{K_1 \times \text{momentum}}{\text{molecule}}$$
$$\times K_2 \times \text{average velocity of molecules} \qquad (Eq. \ 8\text{-}18)$$

But since momentum is defined as the product of mass and velocity, the pressure can equally well be written as

$$\text{Pressure of a gas} = \frac{K_1 \times \text{mass} \times \text{average velocity}}{\text{molecule}}$$
$$\times K_2 \times \text{average velocity of molecules} \qquad (Eq. \ 8\text{-}19)$$

The product of two constants (K_1 and K_2) is itself a constant K. The expression for pressure using the symbols m for mass and $\bar{v}$ for average velocity then becomes

$$\text{Pressure of a gas} = \frac{Km\bar{v}^2}{\text{molecule}} \qquad (Eq. \ 8\text{-}20)$$

The kinetic energy for any moving object is proportional to the velocity squared as long as the mass of the object remains fixed. From Equation 8-20, the pressure of a gas is proportional to the square of the average velocity of the molecules. This means that the pressure of a gas is proportional to the average kinetic energy of the molecules.

Pressure of a gas = K × average kinetic energy of the molecules

This expression implies that so long as a fixed mass of gas is kept in a container, the pressure cannot change except through a change in average kinetic energy. Experimental data relating gas pressure and gas temperature have been obtained for a number of gases. The results, in summary, indicate that, if a sample of gas is confined at low pressure in a container of fixed volume at 0°C and the temperature is then raised, the pressure increases and the increase in pressure is directly proportional to the increase in temperature. Table 8-4 presents numerical values of the pressures at 100°C for 1-liter samples of six

TABLE 8-4 RELATIONSHIP BETWEEN PRESSURE AND TEMPERATURE FOR 1-LITER SAMPLES OF GASES

Gases	Pressure at 0°C, atmosphere	Pressure at 100°C, atmospheres
Ar	1.0000	1.3675
H_2	1.0000	1.3663
He	1.0000	1.3661
O_2	1.0000	1.3676
Air	1.0000	1.3675
N_2	1.0000	1.3672

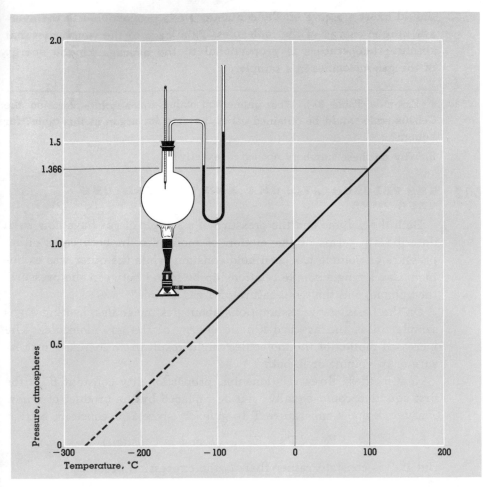

Fig. 8-13 *Relationship between pressure and temperature of a gas.*

gases with the mass chosen so each sample had a pressure of 1.0000 atmosphere at 0°C.

The pressure change between 0 and 100°C is 0.3661 atmosphere for He and 0.3676 atmosphere for O_2. The other gases have values in between these two. The changes in pressure are the same for these six gases within a range of 0.5 percent. Moreover, the value of the ratio of the pressures for a fixed volume of any one gas at the two temperatures is essentially the same as the ratio of the volume at 100°C to the volume at 0°C reported in Section 8-5 for any gas at a fixed pressure. The graph obtained when the pressure of a gas sample is plotted against temperature is shown in Fig. 8-13. The plotted line, when extended, crosses the temperature axis at the temperature previously designated as absolute zero.

Consideration of experimental data indicates that gas pressure is proportional to absolute temperature. A system of moving molecules should exert pressure on the container walls proportional to the average kinetic energy of the molecules. This leads to the conclusion that absolute temperature is proportional to the average kinetic energy of the gas molecules in a sample.

Ex. 8-10   *a.* Examine Table 8-4. What numerical value for absolute zero on the Celsius scale would be obtained using the data for argon in this table? for helium?

b. Why do these numbers not agree exactly?

8-12   GAS PRESSURE, VOLUME, AND TEMPERATURE RELATIONS

Both the volume and the pressure of a sample of gas have now been described in terms of the motion of molecules. In both cases either pressure or volume has been held constant while the other was examined. Can a single simple relationship be found between the pressure, the volume, and the temperature of a gas sample?

On the basis of the assumptions about gas molecules, heating a gas sample raises the average kinetic energy of the gas molecules. The increased motion of the molecules might result in an increase in pressure or in volume or in both.

Now in these three relationships, proportionality constant K in the first equation could equally well be replaced by the product of a new constant k and temperature T to give kT, since T is constant, so that

$$PV = kT = K \qquad (T \text{ and } m \text{ constant})$$

But if P is constant rather than T, the expression becomes

$$V = \frac{k}{P} T \qquad (P \text{ and } m \text{ constant})$$

and agrees with the second relation, $V \propto T$. If V is constant rather than T,

$$P = \frac{k}{V} T \qquad (V \text{ and } m \text{ constant})$$

in agreement with the third expression, $P \propto T$. The two previous expressions therefore follow directly from

$$PV = kT \qquad (m \text{ constant}) \qquad\qquad (Eq. \ 8\text{-}21)$$

and indicate that Equation 8-21 is a general relation between pressure, volume, and temperature of a gas, so long as the total mass of gas in the sample is constant.

It is possible to show mathematically that Equation 8-21 is correct, but perhaps the more convincing argument can be made with experimental data. Table 8-5 contains numerical values for the product of

TABLE 8-5 RELATION OF TEMPERATURE AND *PV* FOR HELIUM[a]

Temperature, °C	PV, liters × atmospheres
100	1.3659
50	1.1830
0	1.0000
−50	0.8171
−100	0.6341
−150	0.4512
−183	0.3305
−208	0.2390

[a] Mass of helium was chosen so as to give a volume of 1 liter at 0°C and 1 atmosphere pressure.

pressure and volume at different temperatures for a sample of helium having a volume of 1 liter at 0°C and 1 atmosphere pressure.

As in Table 8-4, the numerical value of *PV* at 100°C is essentially 1.366, and the graph of the *PV* product against temperature in Fig. 8-14 gives a curve identical in form to the graphs of either pressure against temperature at constant volume or volume against temperature at constant pressure. The experimental data point to the conclusion that the product of pressure and volume for a fixed mass of gas is proportional to the absolute temperature.

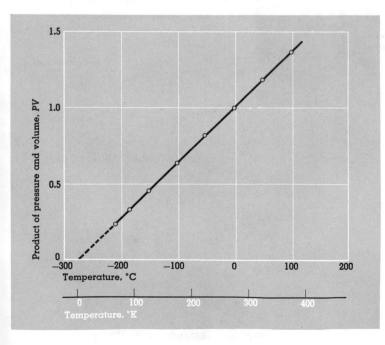

Fig. 8-14
Product of pressure and volume PV plotted against temperature for helium sample of constant mass.

311

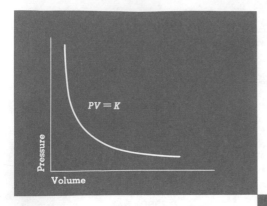

1.

The product of the pressure and volume of a gas sample is a constant provided that the total mass (g) and the temperature (T) of the sample are constant (Section 8-4).

$$PV = K \qquad (T \text{ and } g \text{ constant})$$

2.

The volume of a gas sample is proportional to the absolute temperature of the sample provided that the total mass (g) and pressure (P) of the sample are constant (Section 8-5).

$$V \propto T \qquad (P \text{ and } g \text{ constant})$$

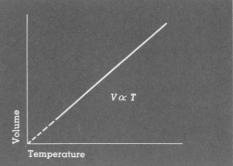

3.

The pressure of a gas sample is proportional to the absolute temperature of the sample provided that the total mass (g) and the volume (V) of the sample are constant (Section 8-11).

$$P \propto T \qquad (V \text{ and } g \text{ constant})$$

As an example of the calculations that can be made for a gas using Equation 8-21, consider the data for helium in Table 8-5. Equation 8-21 reads

$$PV = kT$$

or

$$\frac{PV}{T} = k$$

From the data in Table 8-5 at a temperature of 0°C, the absolute temperature $T = 273.15°\text{K}$ and $PV = 1.0000$, so

$$\frac{PV}{T} = k = \frac{1.0000}{273.15} = 0.003661 \text{ liter-atmosphere/deg}$$

For any other specified volume and temperature, the corresponding pressure can be computed for this sample of helium. Let us choose a volume of $V = 1.00$ liter and a temperature of $T = 200°K$.

$$\frac{P \times 1.00}{200} = 0.00366 \text{ liter-atmosphere/deg}$$

$$P = \frac{200}{1.00} \times 0.00366 = 0.732 \text{ atmosphere}$$

This is a satisfactory way of linking the changes in pressure and volume with the changes in temperature for any gas sample of fixed mass.

Ex. 8-11 A 2.00-g sample of helium is placed in a flask marked A, and a 2.00-g sample of nitrogen is placed in a flask marked B. The two flasks, A and B, are identical. The gases and the flasks are kept at constant temperature.

a. Which flask contains the greater number of molecules?

b. In which flask is the pressure greater?

c. In which flask will the molecules have the higher average kinetic energy?

8-13 THE IDEAL GAS

A gas sample whose properties correspond within experimental error to the relation

$$PV = kT$$

is called an **ideal gas.** On the basis of this operational definition, the data given in Table 8-5 and plotted in Fig. 8-14 indicate that helium behaves as an ideal gas.

The value of k in $PV = kT$ is dependent upon the volume, pressure, and temperature of the gas in a given sample. The determination of the numerical value of k for a 1-mole sample of helium at 1 atmosphere and 273°K requires a knowledge of the volume of 1 mole of helium. The density of helium is 0.1785 g/liter, and 1 mole of helium has a mass of 4.003 g. The volume occupied by 1 mole of helium at 1 atmosphere and 273°K (**standard conditions**) is calculated from the equation relating density, mass, and volume.

$$\text{Density} = \frac{\text{mass}}{\text{volume}}$$

$$\text{Volume} = \frac{\text{mass}}{\text{density}} = \frac{4.003 \text{ g}}{0.1785 \text{ g/liter}} = 22.43 \text{ liters}$$

According to Avogadro's hypothesis, equal volumes of gases contain the same number of molecules at the same temperature and pressure. Since a mole of any gas contains an Avogadro number of molecules, the volume occupied by 1 mole of helium at 1 atmosphere and 273°K would be the same as the volume occupied by 1 mole of any gas under the same conditions of temperature and pressure. The volume 22.4 liters is a constant known as the molar volume, although experimentally determined molar volumes of gases vary slightly from this numerical value (Table 8-6).

The numerical value of k for a 1-mole (22.4 liters) sample of any gas at 273°K and a pressure of 1 atmosphere is calculated from the expression

$$PV = kT$$

Solution of this equation for k gives

$$k = \frac{PV}{T} = \frac{1 \text{ atmosphere} \times 22.4 \text{ liters/mole}}{273°\text{K}}$$

$$= 0.082 \text{ liter-atmosphere/deg-mole}$$

For a 2-mole sample of any gas at 273°K and a pressure of 1 atmosphere, k is calculated in a similar manner.

$$k = \frac{PV}{T} = \frac{1 \text{ atmosphere} \times 22.4 \text{ liters/mole}}{273°\text{K}} \times 2 \text{ moles}$$

$$= 0.164 \text{ liter-atmosphere/deg}$$

The numerical value of k is proportional to the number of moles of gas in the sample. If n equals the number of moles in a sample of gas, then k for any molar quantity of gas can be determined with the expression

$$k = n \times 0.082 \text{ liter-atmosphere/deg-mole}$$

in which 0.082 liter-atmosphere/deg-mole is a proportionality constant. The expression $PV = kT$ becomes by substitution

$$PV = n \times 0.082 \times T$$

The relation $PV = kT$ can be rewritten in the form

$$PV = nRT \qquad \text{(Eq. 8-22)}$$

where n is the number of moles of gas present in the sample and R is the proportionality constant, 0.082 liter-atmosphere/deg-mole, called the gas constant. This equation is often called the **ideal gas law**. The most reliable value for R has been found experimentally to be 0.08205 liter-atmosphere/deg-mole.

In Section 8-6 a set of assumptions was proposed for the properties of gas molecules. With these assumptions as the starting point, deductions were made to show that gas molecules should exert pressure and occupy space. The logical consequences of the assumptions are that for a collection of gas molecules the product of pressure and volume is proportional to absolute temperature.

A set of assumptions and the conclusions drawn from them was called a mental model in Section 6-14. The mental model for a gas is called an ideal gas. In a sense then the mental model made up of the assumptions and conclusions in Section 8-6 can be considered to be a conceptual definition of an ideal gas.

The molecular nature of an ideal gas can be summarized.

1. The mass of a gas sample is the total mass of molecules in the sample.

2. The volume of a gas is the space between molecules. This means that the volume of the molecules themselves is zero.

3. Molecules are in motion at all temperatures above absolute zero and move in straight lines between collisions.

4. Each molecule moves at random.

5. The average kinetic energy of the molecules is proportional to the absolute temperature.

6. When two gas molecules collide, the total kinetic energy and the total momentum remain unchanged.

7. At any given temperature and pressure, equal volumes of different gases contain equal numbers of molecules. Conversely, equal numbers of different molecules occupy equal volumes at a given temperature and pressure.

The validity of the ideal gas model depends on the postulate that, when two gas molecules collide, the sum of their separate kinetic energies remains constant. Imagine for a moment that gas molecules do lose kinetic energy by colliding with one another so that the sum of their initial kinetic energies is higher than the sum of their final kinetic energies. This would imply that the molecules of the air in an inflated tire, for example, would move more and more slowly as time went by. They would, therefore, exert less and less pressure on the inside of the tire, and a flat tire would result, but without loss of air. We know from experience that this does not happen.

There is, of course, a different way of looking at the kinetic energy of colliding molecules. If the molecules were to lose energy, to what would they transfer it? If there is nothing available to which the molecules can transfer their energy, then they may pass it around among themselves as much as they like, but they cannot get rid of it by collision with other gas molecules. It is therefore reasonable to assume that kinetic energy is conserved when gas molecules collide. Heating or cooling the walls of a container of a sample of gas causes the temperature of a gas sample to change. In this operation, the gas molecules do find a source of more kinetic energy or a place to which they can transfer some of their kinetic energy, namely, the wall of the container. In what way is the wall of the container capable of furnishing or accepting energy?

8-14 KINETIC ENERGY IN SOLIDS

Certainly the atoms and molecules of the container walls do not display the same freedom of motion that is characteristic of the molecules of a gas. It is difficult to see, however, how a gas molecule can acquire kinetic energy during its contact with the container wall unless the molecule is struck by some rapidly moving particle in the container wall. The implication is strong that there is a relationship between temperature and motion of particles in solids as well as in gases. If this is so, it will be interesting to see what sort of conclusions can be based on the relationship.

The densities of solids are consistent with the idea that the structural units (atoms, molecules, or ions) in solids are virtually in contact with one another (Section 8-1). If the structural units in solids have kinetic energy, reasonably large forces must operate between the units to hold them in a rigid structure instead of allowing motion of the units in all directions. Yet some motion must be permitted or the units in the solid could not have kinetic energy. It would be reasonable to assume, then, that each unit is in motion but is held inside a cage made up of the units surrounding it so that it can move only a very short distance before rebounding. In other words, each unit vibrates or oscillates about a central position (Fig. 8-15). As the energy of this vibration increases, each unit is able to push back its neighbors and enlarge the cage slightly so that the solid expands slightly. Since nearly all solids do expand with increasing temperature, this assumption of vibrating molecules corresponds satisfactorily with observations.

8-15 KINETIC ENERGY IN LIQUIDS

When the temperature of many solids is increased sufficiently, the solids melt and become liquids. Since a liquid phase of a substance still has a density approximately the same as the solid phase, it must be that the structural units are separated no further in the liquid than in the solid. This indicates that the units in a liquid are still held together

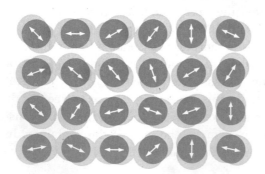

Fig. 8-15 *In a solid each molecule vibrates or oscillates about a central position.*

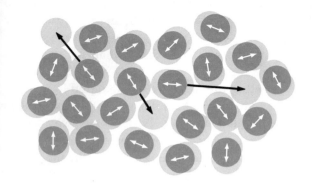

Fig. 8-16 *In a liquid, oscillating molecules may escape from the cage of their surrounding neighbors and enter a new cage.*

by relatively strong forces. Solids, however, are rigid, while liquids can flow. Some part of the force which held the solid rigid has been overcome to allow the liquid to move as a fluid.

This picture implies that the liquid structure has in it some sites in which a small group of molecules is in more vigorous motion or is separated from other groups by a greater distance than the average distance between molecules. Such sites may be referred to as high-energy sites since vigorous motion implies high kinetic energy and increased separation implies high potential energy for the group of molecules in the high-energy site. In any case, at some points in the liquid, some molecules are surrounded by neighbors less tightly held to one another than are most of the molecules which are neighbors to one another. Each molecule therefore finds itself in a cage of surrounding molecules. Such a molecule may find itself moving in a direction toward a weak place in the cage and so be able to escape from the cage of surrounding molecules and take up a new position in an adjoining cage (Fig. 8-16). In other words, diffusion can occur. Since no molecule has energy enough to make such a move with every vibration and since the length of each move is short, diffusion is much slower in the liquid than in the gas phase. The diffusion process does not depend merely upon the number of collisions (vibrations) but also upon the number of such vibrations occurring with a sufficient amount of energy concentrated at one site in the liquid to open a hole in the cage of nearest neighbors or to permit the central molecule to force its way through that cage.

Qualitative observation confirms the notion that diffusion does occur in liquids. If liquid *A* and liquid *B* are placed together in a container in which there is no stirring, each liquid diffuses into the other until no further change in composition occurs. If these liquids are completely miscible, that is, if each may dissolve the other in any ratio of amounts, the system in its final state will be homogeneous. If the two liquids are only partially miscible, the system in its final state consists of two layers. One layer is principally A saturated with B, and the other layer is B saturated with A. A much longer time is required for a system of two liquids to reach the final state by diffusion than for two gases at the same temperature and pressure.

If adequate means for detecting the presence of one liquid in another are available, the mixing of two different liquids when they have been placed in the same container can be shown. Is there any way to tell whether or not thermal motion exists in a system containing just a single substance? It is not possible to detect mixing if all the molecules are the same. Experimentally, slight differences between otherwise identical molecules of a substance can be produced by the use of isotopes. For instance, it is known that water molecules containing atoms of hydrogen with atomic mass 2 or 3 or oxygen atoms of atomic mass 18 diffuse into ordinary water which is composed almost entirely of hydrogen atoms of atomic mass 1 and oxygen atoms of atomic mass 16. Carbon tetrachloride containing radioactive chlorine atoms diffuses into carbon tetrachloride containing nonradioactive chlorine atoms. These observations suggest that random motion also takes place continuously in the liquid phase of a single substance.

In 1828, Robert Brown observed the motion of pollen grains suspended in water. Through a microscope these grains can be seen to move in erratic paths, but the individual grains are rarely seen to collide with each other. The path of any one grain might be described as a zigzag line with a straight path between each zig and zag. This zigzag motion is called Brownian movement. The irregular paths strongly suggest that the visible grains are pushed by something invisible which is moving at random. If water molecules are moving about at random, this would make the observations understandable.

Can the picture of liquid diffusion be applied equally well to at least some solids? Is it true that the structure of solids is more rigid than that of liquids? Some vibration and loosening of the structure as the temperature increases have been postulated. Casual observation suggests that the forces holding together the structure of a solid are too great to permit diffusion, but it may be only that the diffusion takes place much more slowly than in liquids. Studies of solids provide evidence that diffusion does occur at a detectable rate.

The assumption of moving particles has now been applied to gases, liquids, and solids. From the way in which a number of different kinds of observations can be linked together by assuming matter to be made up of moving particles, it is clear that this picture is of considerable significance in the study of the nature of matter. These ideas about the nature of gases, liquids, and solids are known as the **kinetic-molecular theory** or the **kinetic model of matter**.

A kinetic model for gases has been constructed by assuming that gases are systems of moving molecules. These molecules are in random motion so that the average kinetic energy per molecule is proportional to the absolute temperature. To attempt to apply this kinetic model to solids and liquids presumably means that the relation between the average kinetic energy per structural unit and absolute temperature should be the same for solids, liquids, and gases.

Kinetic energy of random motion can be present in solids and liquids only if forces operate between molecules. These forces are necessary to hold the molecules together and maintain the compact arrangement characteristic of liquids and solids. In energy terms there must be not only a kinetic energy but also a potential energy for liquids and solids. The potential energy rises as molecules separate from each other. Otherwise the solid or liquid would become a gas.

The explanation of forces between particles of matter in electrical terms has been based on charges present within the particles. The kinetic model for solids and liquids requires that there be attractive forces between neutral atoms and molecules of substances. In the charge cloud model for the atoms of the elements helium and neon, for example, the central positive charge is completely and symmetrically surrounded by an equal number of negative charges. Yet even helium and neon are liquids and solids at sufficiently low temperatures.

If atoms are neutral and rigid, these attractive forces cannot be explained in electrical terms. Perhaps the model can be modified to permit the use of electric forces. Suppose that the helium atom, for instance, is not completely rigid and that the electron cloud may, through collision, shift its position slightly with respect to the nucleus. Indeed, for the symmetrical arrangement of charge clouds around a nucleus, the net force between the nucleus and clouds is zero so there is really nothing to oppose a shift of the clouds with respect to the nucleus. Of course even the slightest shift results in a force which acts to pull the cloud and nucleus back to the symmetrical arrangement.

It would be reasonable to imagine that the electron cloud oscillates back and forth and that an atom assumes structures represented in exaggerated form in Fig. 8-17. In the cases represented by (a), (c),

Fig. 8-17 *The electron cloud in helium may oscillate back and forth in all directions with respect to the nucleus.*

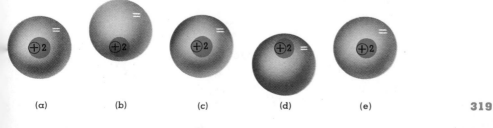

(a)   (b)   (c)   (d)   (e)

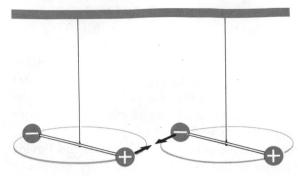

Fig. 8-18 *Atoms or molecules with separated centers of charge (dipoles) attract each other as do oppositely charged pith balls on the ends of sticks.*

and (e), the neutral atom has the nuclear charge symmetrically buried in the electron cloud, and there would be no attraction for other atoms. In (b) and (d), however, a different situation exists, for here the nucleus is no longer at exactly the center of the electron cloud. In these two cases, the centers of positive and negative charge are separated within the atom to produce an electrically unsymmetrical arrangement of charge called a **dipole.** Dipoles can be represented schematically as in Fig. 8-18. In terms of a physical model of a dipole made of oppositely charged pith balls on the ends of a stick, it is easy to see that there would be an attractive force between two of these stick-and-ball structures.

It is not possible to say whether dipoles exist naturally in individual atoms or whether they are created by some cooperation between atoms as they come close together while they move at random. We can only say that postulating the existence of dipoles provides a way of relating the charge cloud model and the kinetic-molecular theory to the experimental facts.

The total energy for a state of a system in which the structural units are separated, as in a gas, is higher than for a state of the same system in which the structural units are close together, as in a liquid or solid. The rise in total energy as a liquid or solid changes to a gas can be interpreted in terms of rise in kinetic energy related to random motion of structural units or in terms of rise in potential energy related to moving the units apart against attractive forces between units. Increase in temperature (addition of energy) results in rise in kinetic energy of structural units. Change in phase of a substance without increase in temperature in almost every case leads to expansion and hence a rise in potential energy.

8-17 BOILING POINTS OF LIQUIDS

Both liquid and gas exist together at the same temperature (the boiling point). The boiling point of a substance can be used therefore to indicate something about the magnitude of the attractive forces which produce the low potential energy for the molecules in a liquid. The higher the boiling point of a substance, the greater the attractive forces between its molecules. In Fig. 8-19 the boiling points of several substances are plotted against the total nuclear charge in each molecule. The gases helium, neon, argon, krypton, xenon, and radon make up a group called the **noble gases.** The boiling points of the noble gases increase, though somewhat irregularly, as the nuclear charge increases. The boiling points of the noble gases are lower than those of any other known system of molecules containing the same total nuclear charge with but one exception. The one exception is that argon, Ar (nuclear charge = 18), boils about 2° above fluorine, F_2 (total nuclear charge = 2×9). Are the relationships shown in Fig. 8-19 at all consistent with the idea that the center of the charge clouds in a molecule might be pushed away from the center of positive charge?

The most obvious feature of the data plotted in Fig. 8-19 is the rise in boiling point with the increase in nuclear charge. For neutral mole-

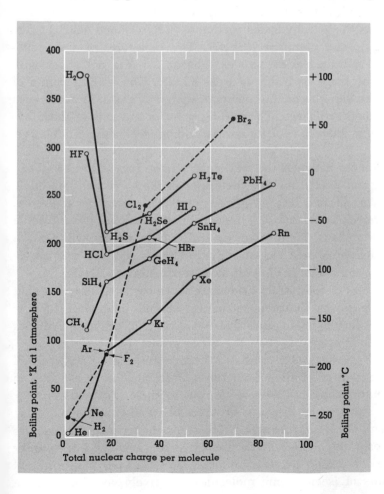

Fig. 8-19 *Boiling points of some substances plotted against total nuclear charge of a molecule of the substance. See Table 8-7.*

321

cules, an increase in nuclear charge means an increase in the number of electrons per molecule. As a general rule, an increase in the number of electrons per molecule leads to an increase in size of a molecule. Therefore, the outer electrons will usually be farther from the nucleus in a molecule of large nuclear charge than in a molecule of low nuclear charge. It seems reasonable from Coulomb's law that the outer charge clouds can be more easily shifted the greater the distance between the cloud and the nucleus which holds the cloud in the molecule. Attractive forces between molecules, based on shifting electron clouds (as described in Section 8-16) should therefore be greater in molecules of large nuclear charge than in molecules of small nuclear charge. So the general increase in boiling point with an increase in nuclear charge can be related to features of the charge cloud model and kinetic-molecular theory.

Molecules whose centers of positive and negative charge coincide are electrically symmetrical. The noble gas molecules are examples of symmetrical molecules. Other substances with electrically symmetrical molecules are the tetrahydrides methane (CH_4), silane (SiH_4), germane (GeH_4), and stannane (SnH_4). The molecules of these substances have tetrahedral structures. There is also a noble gas with which each of these hydrides is isoelectronic. The boiling points of these hydrides, like the boiling points of the noble gases, increase with increase in nuclear charge. The boiling point of any one of these hydrides is higher than that of its corresponding isoelectronic noble gas. Why?

The differences between the molecules of the four hydrides (CH_4, SiH_4, GeH_4, and SnH_4) and the molecules of the corresponding noble gases (Ne, Ar, Kr, and Rn) lie in the number of nuclei per molecule. Each hydride molecule has five nuclei, but each noble gas molecule has only one nucleus. The greater central nuclear charge will mean a greater attraction on each electron in a noble gas molecule and consequently a molecule that is difficult to distort to form a dipole.

The molecules of the tetrahydrides are more easily distorted so that the attractive forces between molecules should be higher for the hydrides than for the noble gases. This would explain why the hydrides have higher boiling points than the noble gases.

The idea of dipoles requires that attractive forces exist between all molecules regardless of their structures since the forces are due to small momentary shifts of electrons relative to nuclei. Attractive forces that can be explained on the basis of forces between temporary dipoles are called **van der Waals attraction.** The transient separation of centers of charge postulated to account for this attraction is called a **temporary dipole.** The correlation between numbers of nuclei per molecule and boiling points of isoelectronic molecules effectively accounts for the

JOHANNES DIDERIK VAN DER WAALS

1837–1923

A Dutch physicist and physical chemist. Van der Waals was born in Leiden, Holland, and studied at Leiden University from 1862 to 1865. During the next few years, van der Waals taught physics in high schools in Deventer and The Hague. He received his doctor's degree at the age of thirty-five for his thesis "On the Continuity of the Gaseous and Liquid States." He was professor of physics at the University of Amsterdam from 1877 to his retirement in 1907 and received the 1910 Nobel Prize in physics "for his work concerning the equation of state of gases and liquids."

Van der Waals attempted to explain, by means of the kinetic-molecular theory, the deviations from Boyle's and Charles's laws exhibited by gases at low temperatures and high pressures. He modified the ideal gas law, $PV = kT$, to take account of the attraction between molecules and of the volume occupied by molecules. Because of his emphasis on the attraction between like molecules in gases and liquids, the attraction between molecules has become known as van der Waals attraction. His work has influenced processes for the liquefaction of gases and industrial freezing techniques as well as theoretical studies on the phases of matter.

comparison of the noble gases and the tetrahydrides. Can a similar correlation be established for substances containing other numbers of nuclei?

The compounds hydrogen fluoride (HF), hydrogen chloride (HCl), hydrogen bromide (HBr), and hydrogen iodide (HI) make up a series called the hydrogen halides. Each of these compounds consists of diatomic molecules, containing hydrogen and a halogen atom. On the basis of attraction between molecules, the hydrogen halides should have boiling points above those of the corresponding isoelectronic noble gases, but below those of the isoelectronic tetrahydrides. The data in Fig. 8-19 show that this prediction is not borne out by the facts. Not only do the hydrogen halides, with two nuclei per molecule, have higher boiling points than the tetrahydrides, with five nuclei, but also hydrogen fluoride, with the lowest total nuclear charge, has the highest boiling point rather than the lowest of the four hydrogen halides. Some attractive force either different from or in addition to the forces due to temporary dipoles must operate between the molecules in the hydrogen halides.

For the hydrogen halide molecules, the halogen atom nucleus contains nearly all the positive charge in the molecule. If four two-electron charge clouds are arranged symmetrically around the nucleus of a halogen atom to form a halide ion, the center of positive charge and the center of negative charge are coincident. The formation of a hydrogen halide molecule can be imagined to take place by the addition of a proton to one of the two-electron charge clouds in a halide ion (Fig. 8-20). Now the proton can penetrate into one of the outer charge clouds, but as it does so, the repulsion exerted by the central nucleus will keep the proton toward the outside of the molecule and not at the center of the charge cloud. With the proton in the molecule, the center of positive charge will not be coincident with the center of negative charge for the entire molecule. A hydrogen halide molecule will therefore contain separated charges. Since this separation is not produced by the vibrations attending molecular collisions, but is present even if the molecule is considered to be rigid or stationary, the separation of charge is called a **permanent dipole.** Permanent dipoles result in attraction between molecules in addition to the attraction resulting from temporary dipoles.

The combined effect of permanent dipoles and temporary dipoles in the hydrogen halide molecules accounts for the fact that the hydrogen halides have higher boiling points than the corresponding isoelectronic noble gases and tetrahydrides. The boiling point of hydrogen fluoride is higher than that of any of the other hydrogen halides, however. Why?

Electrically symmetrical molecules with small nuclear charge should have smaller temporary dipoles than molecules with large nuclear charge. Symmetrical molecules and small nuclear charge are found in substances with low boiling points. The explanation seems to be that with smaller nuclear charge and therefore fewer electron clouds, the electron clouds are closer to the nucleus and give a more rigid struc-

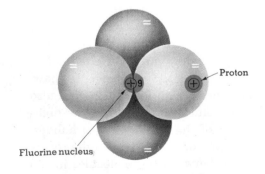

Fig. 8-20 *Model of hydrogen fluoride. The large positive nuclear charge of the fluorine atom results in the stabilization of the proton beyond the center of its electron cloud.*

ture. But comparison of the model for the hydrogen fluoride molecule with that for the hydrogen chloride molecule indicates that the fluorine nucleus ($\oplus 9$) can exert greater attractive force on 10 electrons than the chlorine nucleus ($\oplus 17$) can on 18 electrons. The proton in the hydrogen fluoride molecule will therefore be kept farther from the center of negative charge than will the proton in hydrogen chloride. These observations indicate that a hydrogen fluoride molecule must have greater charge separation than hydrogen chloride.

Although the correlation of boiling points and molecular structure has seemed to work out nicely, there are problems. One problem is indicated in Fig. 8-19 by the boiling points of the halogens. Fluorine (F_2), which is isoelectronic with argon, has a lower boiling point than argon. Yet chlorine (Cl_2) boils at a temperature not only higher than krypton but higher even than hydrogen bromide, although total nuclear charge is nearly the same for all three substances. More refined models will be needed if scientists are to account for these observations.

Ex. 8-12   Ethyl alcohol (C_2H_5OH) and methyl ether (CH_3OCH_3) both have the same molecular mass. Methyl ether has a boiling point of $-24.8°C$ and ethyl alcohol has a boiling point of $78.5°C$. In which of these substances are the attractive forces between the molecules greater? Explain.

8-18   REAL GASES

The kinetic model for the ideal gas, for which the relation $PV = nRT$ is applicable, includes the deduction that, if it were not for the container walls, all the molecules of the gas would travel away from each other since no attractive forces are assumed to be present. However, to explain the existence of liquids, an assumption was added that all molecules in liquids have attractive forces for one another, at least when the molecules are close together. Should not these attractive forces be apparent in the behavior of gases?

Any attractive forces between molecules in a gas should cause the behavior of the gas to deviate from the behavior predicted by the mental model of an ideal gas (Section 8-13). Gases whose experimental properties differ from those of an ideal gas are called *real gases.* All known gases are real gases. Attraction between molecules of real gases tends to keep the molecules from striking the walls quite as hard as they would if there were no forces. The molecules of real gases have volume. The measured volumes of gases at low temperatures or high pressures are determined in part by the volumes of the molecules themselves.

According to Avogadro's hypothesis, which is now an integral part of the ideal gas model, the volume of 1 mole (*molar volume*) of any

TABLE 8-6 MOLAR VOLUME OF SEVERAL GASES

Molecular Formula	Electrons per Molecule	Molar Volume, liters[a]
He	2	22.415
H_2	2	22.428
NH_3	10	22.077
CH_4	10	22.360
Ne	10	22.428
C_2H_2	14	22.274
CO	14	22.405
N_2	14	22.404
C_2H_4	16	22.252
O_2	16	22.394
HCl	18	22.247
H_2S	18	22.152
Ar	18	22.395

[a] Values were taken at 0°C and 1 atmosphere pressure.
SOURCE: Based on data in *Quarterly Reviews*, 4:153, 1950.

gas is the same as the molar volume of any other gas under the same conditions of temperature and pressure (Section 8-13). Table 8-6 contains experimental numerical values for the molar volumes of various gases at 0°C and 1 atmosphere. The molar volumes of gases vary in the third significant figure, yet the precision of the experimental data is great enough to mean that these variations must reflect differences in the volumes of the gases and not errors in the experimental data.

A comparison of molar volumes for different gases is a comparison of identical numbers of molecules. If Avogadro's hypothesis is in accord with experimental results, all molar volumes of different gases should be exactly the same at any given temperature and pressure. The data in Table 8-6 show that different gases have different molar volumes, so that Avogadro's hypothesis does not precisely correspond to the facts.

Molar volumes can be determined experimentally at pressures other than the 1 atmosphere used for the data in Table 8-6. The numerical values of molar volume for different gases approach each other more closely at low pressures than at high pressures. Avogadro's hypothesis describes the behavior of real gases better at low pressure than at high pressure. Both theoretically and experimentally, then, the product of pressure and volume for a given number of moles of gas should be more nearly the same for all gases (Section 8-4) at low pressure than at high pressures at any given temperature. For 1 mole of gas at 0°C and low pressure, the best experimental data give a value of 22.4145 liter-atmospheres for PV. However, for most practical applications, the value 22.4 liter-atmospheres/mole is more appropriate because it is seldom possible to calculate the properties of any given gas with more accuracy than three significant figures.

For many gases at 0°C and 1 atmosphere pressure, the molar volume of 22.4 liters describes the gas volume to within about 2 percent. Within this error it is quite proper to say that at 0°C and 1 atmosphere pressure equal volumes of different gases contain equal numbers of molecules.

At 0°C and 1 atmosphere pressure, gases such as nitrogen, oxygen, and hydrogen have molar volumes that are, for the first three significant figures, identical with 22.4 liters. The number 22.4 liters/mole can be used to relate the volume of a gas to the number of moles of gas in a system. The small densities of gases make weighing difficult, but they make volume measurements easy. Once the number of moles of gas produced or consumed in a reaction is known, it is straightforward to state the volume of the gas at 0°C and 1 atmosphere pressure since each mole will occupy 22.4 liters.

Ex. 8-13 When zinc reacts with sulfuric acid, hydrogen gas is produced according to the equation

$$Zn + H_2SO_4 \rightarrow ZnSO_4 + H_2$$

How many liters of hydrogen gas, collected at 273°K and 1.0 atmosphere pressure, will be produced when 2.5 moles of zinc reacts with sulfuric acid?

8-19 GAS-LIQUID PHASE CHANGE

The observed differences between molar volumes for gases at high and low pressures verifies the assumption that attractive forces are present between gas molecules. Attractive forces were also assumed to be present in liquids and solids to account for the compact arrangement of atoms or molecules in each of these two phases. When a liquid or a solid changes to a gas, the attraction between molecules must be overcome.

Suppose a liquid such as water is placed in a vessel from which all the air has first been removed as completely as possible. The apparatus is sealed except for a connection to a pressure-measuring device through which no gas may enter the container (Fig. 8-21). Finally the apparatus is allowed to stand in a liquid bath so that the temperature can be controlled. Under these conditions, a definite pressure can be

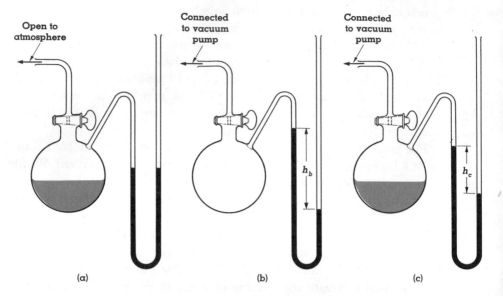

h_b

h_c

(a)   (b)   (c)

Fig. 8-21 *Determination of vapor pressure of a liquid.* **(a)** *Before evacuation of flask.* **(b)** *After evacuation of flask—no liquid present in flask.* **(c)** *After evacuation of flask—with liquid present in flask. Vapor pressure of liquid* $= h_b - h_c$.

measured in the flask. Since nearly all the air has been removed, the observed pressure must be due to the pressure of gas produced from the water. If the gas responsible is pumped out, the apparatus sealed again, and the apparatus permitted to come to the same temperature again, the pressure is found to have the same numerical value as that recorded the first time. When a sample of this gas is removed from the container, cooled, and compressed, a liquid, water, is the only substance obtained. The evidence suggests that the gas found above the water was water in vapor form. From these observations, you may conclude that water exists in the gas phase at temperatures well below the normal boiling point of water (100°C).

The existence of water in the gas phase at temperatures below 100°C is intimately associated with the presence of water vapor in the atmosphere. For example, the outside of a glass containing ice water becomes covered with drops of liquid water condensed from water vapor initially present in the air. Weather reports frequently include the humidity as an indication of the amount of water vapor in the air.

The experiment just described for measuring the pressure of water vapor over liquid water at one temperature can be repeated at a variety of temperatures. At each temperature, a different pressure is produced, whether the temperature is reached by cooling a hotter flask or by warming a colder flask to the desired temperature. In each case, this pressure is not established immediately when the temperature is changed. The flask must stand in the liquid bath for some time before all the contents have achieved the new temperature. Gas pressures and temperatures for water are plotted in Fig. 8-22.

Repeating this experiment with water vapor, using different-sized flasks or different-sized samples of water, always leads to the same pressure at any given temperature. The pressure measured over a liquid at a given temperature is a property of the liquid which is usually referred to as the **equilibrium vapor pressure.** Like density, the magnitude of the equilibrium vapor pressure varies with the temperature. An equilibrium vapor pressure is also established above ice, owing to the presence of gaseous water molecules. The magnitude of this pressure is dependent upon the temperature. Figure 8-22 shows

Fig. 8-22   *Vapor pressures of water from 0 to 100°C and ice from −40 to 0°C.*

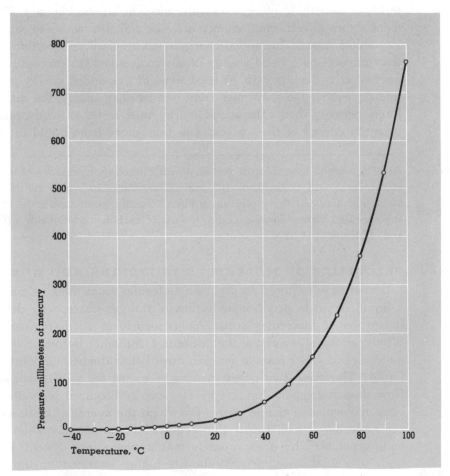

the relationship between the equilibrium vapor pressure and temperature for ice. Solids, as well as liquids, have characteristic equilibrium vapor pressures.

When the pressure on a system is below the equilibrium vapor pressure characteristic of the material in the system, vapor forms continuously. When a liquid substance changes into a gas, the process is called **evaporation.** When a solid changes to a gas, the process is called **sublimation.** Both processes are used extensively in the laboratory as techniques for separating volatile material from nonvolatile material.

How can the data in Fig. 8-22 be interpreted in terms of ideas about molecules in motion? The previously established assumption (2c) of the kinetic-molecular theory that absolute temperature and average kinetic energy are proportional requires that, at a given temperature, the average kinetic energy of a molecule in the gas phase be equal to the average kinetic energy of a molecule in the liquid or solid phase. So the existence of the molecules in the gas phase must be explained in terms of something other than differences in kinetic energies. Experiment shows that thermal energy must be added to water to convert it into water vapor. This added energy must accomplish something other than raising the kinetic energy of the molecules. On the basis of the discussion in Section 8-15, at least some of this added energy must go into separating the molecules from one another against the attractive forces between them. The added energy must, in other words, raise the potential energy of the molecules as they move from liquid to gas.

Ex. 8-14   At 20°C, carbon tetrachloride has an equilibrium vapor pressure of 91.0 mm of mercury, and chloroform 160 mm of mercury. In which liquid is the attraction between the molecules greater? Justify your answer in view of the accepted values for the boiling points of carbon tetrachloride (76.7°C) and chloroform (61.2°C).

8-20   VELOCITIES OF MOLECULES IN LIQUIDS AND GASES

If energy is required to separate molecules from their neighbors in a liquid phase to produce molecules in the gas phase, why does this separation of molecules occur spontaneously at room temperature? Why does the space above the liquid in a container become filled with molecules of vapor even at temperatures below the boiling point of the liquid? The same two questions can be raised for solids such as ice. How does it happen that the kinetic energy required is available to some molecules at temperatures for which the average kinetic energy per molecule is well below that required for vapor formation at the boiling point? Why does vapor formation occur in a system when it leads to a final state corresponding to higher energy than the initial state?

One of the basic assumptions (2b) in developing the model of the ideal gas (Section 8-13) was that the motion of molecules was random. This randomness is with respect to both direction and velocity. The initial assumption that different molecules must, at every instant have different individual velocities was not used. The ideal gas was described by conveniently dealing only with average values of the velocity or kinetic energy. However, in the case of liquids, there is some indication that the distribution of energies among molecules must be considered. Diffusion can be explained in terms of energy being sufficiently concentrated in one location to permit the escape of molecules from the cage of their surrounding neighbors. Diffusion of solids was explained similarly. So, now, can differences in energies of molecules be used to help understand how molecules may escape from their neighbors in the liquid into the vapor? For molecules to escape when the average kinetic energy of the molecules in the liquid or solid is low, there must be some molecules with a sufficiently high kinetic energy so that they can escape in spite of the attractive forces of their neighbors.

A basic postulate of the kinetic model is that the motion of gas molecules is random. This implies that collisions between molecules also occur randomly. There are some collisions in which one molecule gains kinetic energy at the expense of another molecule. If one molecule undergoes a series of collisions, each adding to its kinetic energy, it will end up with a kinetic energy higher than the average. Conversely, a molecule undergoing several collisions in which it loses kinetic energy will have a kinetic energy lower than the average.

In a collection of gas molecules, all having the same average kinetic energy, the kinetic energy will be transferred between molecules in such a way as to give the different molecules different energies. In any measurable sample of real gas, the number of molecules is so large that the fraction of the molecules having a given energy will remain constant even though the collisions and transfer of energy among the molecules continue to take place.

A graph in Fig. 8-23 shows the fraction of all the molecules having a given velocity in a sample of nitrogen gas. Each curve is based on calculations for a different temperature. The theory by which the curves are calculated was developed toward the end of the nineteenth century by James Clerk Maxwell and Ludwig Boltzmann through a careful theoretical analysis of the distribution of velocities and energies among gas molecules. Curves of the type shown in Fig. 8-23 are often referred to as Maxwell-Boltzmann distribution curves.

Although the general shape of Maxwell-Boltzmann distribution curves is fixed, raising the temperature of a gas sample increases the numerical value of the velocity represented by the largest fraction of

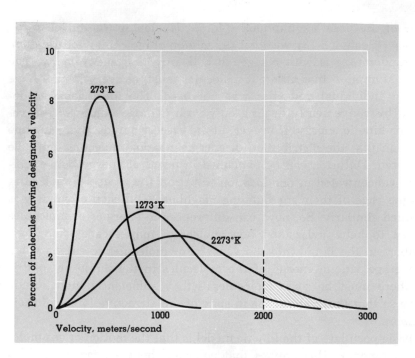

Fig. 8-23 *Maxwell-Boltzmann distribution of speeds of nitrogen molecules at three temperatures. The percentage of molecules moving at high speeds (for example, above 2,000 meters/ second) increases rapidly with temperature.*

the molecules. This is shown in the graph by the relative positions of the highest point in each curve. At the same time, the range of velocities over which the molecules are distributed is increased. Therefore, the peak of the curve shifts to the right and becomes lower as the temperature increases. The fraction of the molecules having a velocity greater than any given value, say 2,000 meters per second (meters/ second), increases rapidly as the temperature increases. The number of molecules having velocities over 2,000 meters/second is represented by the shaded area under the curve to the right of the vertical dotted line.

It would be reasonable to assume that a Maxwell-Boltzmann distribution curve can be used to represent the distribution of energies for the molecules in a liquid. There is a value for the velocities above which molecules will have a high enough kinetic energy to escape from the liquid. Molecules having lower velocity, and therefore less energy, cannot escape from the liquid. The dotted line at 2,000 meters/second in Fig. 8-23 can be thought of as dividing the total collection of molecules into two populations. One, the fast-molecule population, has more than enough kinetic energy to escape from the liquid;

whereas the other population, the slow-molecule population, does not have enough kinetic energy to escape. After a period of time the fast-molecule population will have escaped from the liquid. What will happen to the liquid as a result of the loss of its fast-molecule population?

The total collection of molecules present before any were lost had an average kinetic energy proportional to the temperature. If the fast molecules escape, the population left behind will have a lower average kinetic energy and hence a lower temperature. To keep the temperature from changing as liquid changes to vapor, the system will have to absorb energy from its environment. If it does not absorb energy, the liquid will become cooler as the fast-molecule population escapes. Quantities of energy transferred and quantities of substance in the liquid or vapor phases can be measured.

Fast molecules in the liquid that escape into the vapor will rise in potential energy as the molecules separate from each other. The rise in potential energy will result in a lowering of the kinetic energy. So finally the liquid and vapor will both be at one temperature with the same average kinetic energy for the molecules in each phase. The only energy difference between liquid and vapor will be a difference in potential energy per mole of substance.

Ex. 8-15

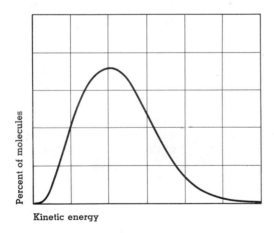

Percent of molecules

Kinetic energy

a. Explain the significance of the plot.

b. What would happen to the shape of this curve if the temperature was decreased by 10°K?

8-21 HEAT OF VAPORIZATION

It should be possible to transfer a known quantity of heat to a liquid already at its boiling point and determine the quantity of the liquid which is converted into gas as the heat is transferred. Alternatively, a known quantity of vapor might be condensed in a calorimeter and the quantity of energy that is transferred to the calorimeter thus determined. From such data it is possible to calculate the amount of heat required to vaporize 1 mole of the liquid—that is, to change 1 mole of liquid to vapor, or conversely, to condense 1 mole of vapor to liquid. The quantity of heat required to convert 1 mole of a substance from liquid to vapor is called the *molar heat of vaporization.*

Table 8-7 contains values for the molar heats of vaporization of several substances at their boiling points. Figure 8-24 shows the heat of

TABLE 8-7   MOLAR HEATS OF VAPORIZATION AND BOILING POINTS FOR SOME SUBSTANCES[a]

Substance	Nuclear Charge	Boiling Point, °K	Heat of Vaporization, kcal/mole
He	2	4.216	0.020
H_2	2	20.39	0.216
Ne	10	27.3	0.41
CH_4	10	111.67	1.955
HF	10	293.1	1.8
H_2O	10	373.15	9.717
F_2	18	85.24	1.51
Ar	18	87.29	1.558
SiH_4	18	161.8	2.9
HCl	18	188.11	3.86
H_2S	18	212.82	4.463
Cl_2	34	239.10	4.878
Kr	36	119.93	2.158
GeH_4	36	184.80	3.361
HBr	36	206.43	4.210
H_2Se	36	231.9	4.62
Xe	54	165.1	3.021
SnH_4	54	221.4	4.4
HI	54	237.80	4.724
H_2Te	54	270.9	5.55
Br_2	70	332.0	6.95
Rn	86	211.	3.92

[a] Data are arranged by isoelectronic groups.
SOURCE: *National Bureau of Standards Bulletin 500.*

vaporization data plotted against the total nuclear charge in a molecule for each substance listed in Table 8-7. This graph is similar to the plot of boiling point against nuclear charge in Fig. 8-19. The data in Fig. 8-19 were interpreted by considering attractive forces between molecules and the way these attractive forces should modify the kinetic model of the liquid. The fact that heats of vaporization in Fig. 8-24 show a relation to nuclear charge that is similar to the one found for boiling point supports the argument that both the boiling point and the molar heat of vaporization are measures of the forces which must be overcome to convert a liquid to a gas.

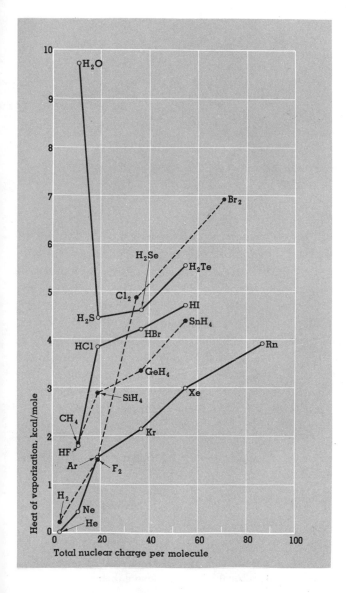

Fig. 8-24 *Molar heats of vaporization of some substances plotted against the total nuclear charge of a molecule of the substance. See Table 8-7.*

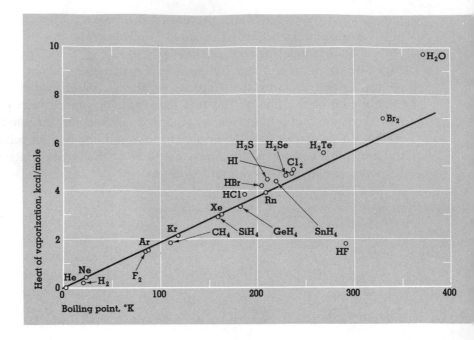

Fig. 8-25 *Boiling points and heats of vaporization of some substances.*
See Table 8-7.

If these two quantities were each a perfect measure of the attractions to be overcome, then a graph of heat of vaporization against boiling point should be a straight line. The data from Figs. 8-19 and 8-24 are combined to give a single graph in Fig. 8-25. The experimentally determined points for many substances fall reasonably close to a straight line drawn through the points obtained by plotting data for the noble gases. Hydrogen fluoride, bromine, and water, however, have numerical values much farther from the line than the values plotted for any of the other substances. It seems reasonable to conclude that many, but not all, substances do fit reasonably well into the picture of molecules in motion but with attractive forces operating between them.

Ex. 8-16 The boiling points and heats of vaporization of hydrogen sulfide (H_2S) and radon (Rn) are given below.

Gas	Boiling Point, °K	Heat of Vaporization, kcal/mole
H_2S	212.82	4.463
Rn	211.	3.92

Discuss the usefulness of boiling point and heat of vaporization as measures of the attraction between the structural units of these substances.

In Chapter 7 the charge cloud models of molecules and crystals were built without considering any possible motion of the structural units. In a sense these models can be considered to represent the situation that would exist only at absolute zero. In experimenting with chemical systems, it is necessary to work at temperatures above absolute zero. The kinetic-molecular theory developed in this chapter is based on random motion of structural units. Throughout the chapter both the mental model for structure and the mental model for random motion have been used to develop a combined model. This combined model should give an interpretation of changes in a substance as the temperature is raised to the temperature of the laboratory from some low temperature near $0°K$.

Near absolute zero, all substances are solids, and so the heating process begins with the transfer of heat into a solid at a low temperature. For example, graphite is a solid at all temperatures below about $4000°C$. Any addition of energy to solid graphite results in a temperature increase for the solid. At temperatures near $0°K$, a $1°$ change in the temperature of 1 mole of graphite requires the transfer of 0.06 cal/deg-mole. To effect the same temperature change in 1 mole of graphite at room temperature, about 2 cal/deg-mole is required.

For any substance, whether solid, liquid, or gas, the ratio of the quantity of energy absorbed to the change in temperature is called heat capacity. For a mole of the material, the heat capacity is called the *molar heat capacity.* The molar heat capacity of carbon is small at low temperature and increases gradually as the temperature rises. This is true of all solid substances. Most crystalline elements at room temperature and above have molar heat capacities of about 6 cal/deg-mole.

When a solid melts, energy is absorbed even though temperature does not change while solid and liquid are both present in the system, that is, at the melting point. At the melting point of any substance, the liquid phase always has a higher energy than the same mass of solid. The energy absorbed to melt 1 mole of solid is called the *molar heat of fusion.* The molar heat capacity for many substances in the liquid phase is larger in magnitude than the molar heat capacity of the substance in the solid phase. The heat capacities of several liquids and solids are tabulated in Table 8-8. As is the case with solids, the heat capacities of liquids increase as temperatures rise.

The transformation of liquid to vapor is discussed in Sections 8-19 and 8-21. In this transformation, the amount of energy absorbed per mole of a substance converted to gas is called the molar heat of vaporization. The molar heat capacities of most gases do not change with temperature. Heat capacities for some gases are listed in Table 8-9.

TABLE 8-8 MOLAR HEAT CAPACITIES FOR SOME LIQUIDS AND SOLIDS

Substance	Temperature, °K	Molar Heat Capacity, cal/deg-mole[a]	
		Solid	Liquid
CO	68	12.4	14.4
H_2O	73	3.2	
C_3H_8	85	12.6	20.2
Cl_2	172	13.3	16.0
H_2O	273	9.0	18.0
Cu	298	5.9	
Zn	693	7.1	7.5

[a] Values were taken at 1 atmosphere pressure.
SOURCE: G. N. Lewis and M. Randall, *Thermodynamics*, 2d ed., McGraw-Hill Book Company, Inc., New York, 1961.

TABLE 8-9 MOLAR HEAT CAPACITIES FOR SOME GASES AT CONSTANT PRESSURE

Gas	Formula	Molar Heat Capacity, cal/deg-mole[a]
Monatomic molecules:		
Helium	He	4.97
Neon	Ne	4.97
Argon	Ar	4.97
Diatomic molecules:		
Hydrogen	H_2	6.84
Nitrogen	N_2	6.96
Oxygen	O_2	7.02
Hydrogen chloride	HCl	7.04
Chlorine	Cl_2	8.10
Triatomic molecules:		
Carbon dioxide	CO_2	8.83
Water	H_2O	8.67
Sulfur dioxide	SO_2	9.65
Polyatomic molecules:		
Ammonia	NH_3	8.80
Ethane	C_2H_6	12.35

[a] Values were taken at 293.1°K and 1 atmosphere pressure.

The data in Table 8-9 are grouped by the number of atoms in each molecule. For gases with monatomic molecules, the heat capacity is about 5 cal/mole-deg. But gases with two atoms per molecule have heat capacities of about 7 cal/mole-deg. More complex molecules have still larger heat capacities. Of course, if the heat capacities for gases with diatomic molecules are calculated in terms of a mole of atoms rather than a mole of molecules, all the values would be about 3.5 cal/deg-mole of atoms. Gases with molecules more complex than diatomic ones have heat capacities of less than 3.5 cal/deg-mole of atoms.

A basic assumption has been that the average kinetic energy of the molecules in an ideal gas is directly proportional to the absolute temperature. The heat capacity of an ideal gas should therefore be a measure of the energy required to change the kinetic energy of the molecules and a measure of nothing else. Real gases with monatomic molecules (for example, helium and neon) are more similar to ideal gases than any other known gases. On this basis it would be reasonable to assume that the heat capacity of an ideal gas is about 5 cal/mole-deg.

Why do systems with structures more complex than those of monatomic molecules have heat capacities different from those of an ideal gas?

Ex. 8-17   The heat capacity of aluminum is 0.216 cal/g-deg. What is the molar heat capacity of aluminum?

Ex. 8-18   A mass of 10.0 g of magnesium at a temperature of 35.0°C is added to 100. g of water in a calorimeter. The initial temperature of the water is 20°C. What will be the final temperature of the magnesium and water? The heat capacity of magnesium is 0.246 cal/g-deg at 25°C.

8-23   STRUCTURE AND ENERGY

A fundamental assumption in the kinetic-molecular theory has been that temperature is associated with the motion through space of the molecule as a unit. On this basis, the average kinetic energy of molecules in an ideal gas is directly proportional to the absolute temperature, and the energy required to change the kinetic energies of the molecules is the same for each gas. The energy of a molecule moving through space is called *translational energy.* The energy required to change the translational energy of a gas cannot be higher than that required for a monatomic gas. Therefore, some other processes which require energy must be taking place in gases which have more than one atom per molecule and which have heat capacities larger than 5 cal/mole-deg.

For diatomic molecules there are two possible motions which could take place and which are different from the translational motion of the entire molecule. A diatomic molecule might well rotate like the baton of an expert twirler. Alternatively, the two joined atoms might vibrate back and forth along the line of centers as if they were connected by a spring. This vibrational motion is somewhat similar to the type of motion that was described for solids and liquids in the kinetic model. If the molecules tumble faster at higher temperatures and if the centers of the atoms move farther apart with each vibration at higher temperatures, these motions could account for the larger heat capacities of diatomic gases. Generally speaking, the number of ways in which energy could be absorbed would increase as the number of atoms in the molecules increased, and this is consistent with experimental observations. The energy going into tumbling or rotating the molecules is called **rotational energy,** and that causing the molecules to vibrate is called **vibrational energy.** The energy required to change the temperature of a sample of gas is made up of three parts.

Total energy = translational energy
+ rotational energy + vibrational energy

This relationship means that only a part of the heat absorbed by a gas whose molecules contain more than one atom goes to raise the kinetic energy of the molecules and hence the temperature. This explains the nature of the differences in the values for the molar heat capacities of gases listed in Table 8-9.

When atoms are joined in complex and extensive structures, vibration of atoms is important while the motion of atoms through the system is less significant. Solids are systems then in which heat capacity is the result primarily of vibration rather than translational motion of structural units.

The development of a theory which combines both structure and motion suggests a limitation on the electron charge cloud model developed in Chapter 7. In essence, the models of molecules considered in Chapter 7 are applicable only at absolute zero since none of the postulates and assumptions in the charge cloud model were concerned with the energy of motion within the molecules. For systems at temperatures above absolute zero, the effects of motion of the structural units must be included to give a complete picture of the properties of matter. Because of relative motion within molecules, small additional attractive forces are developed between molecules. But the major effect of motion is that molecules tend to separate from one another and that atoms in molecules tend to move away from each other. At room temperature a few substances like helium and neon are monatomic gases, but the attraction between structural units within most substances is still relatively strong.

Many substances with which the chemist works can exist in the solid, the liquid, or the gas phase. Yet the charge cloud model for the structure of atoms and molecules proposed in Chapter 7 does not by itself account for the existence or properties of the three phases of matter. Indeed, all matter behaves as if there is a built-in tendency to expand throughout the space provided. This tendency to expand is kept in check only by attractions between atoms or by container walls or by gravitational attraction.

Gases are substances made up of units which can move in all directions to fill any container. When gases escape through small holes, the rate of escape is related to the gas density. Experiments have also shown that the pressure, volume, and temperature of a gas are all related to one another. These experimental observations can be related to each other by means of a mental model which assumes each gaseous substance to be composed of molecules in rapid motion. By assuming that the motion is random in all directions, an explanation is given for the way in which a gas expands and escapes through holes. The average kinetic energy of the moving molecules is assumed to be proportional to absolute temperature, and in this way the relationship between pressure, volume, and temperature of gases is explained.

For gases the relation between pressure, volume, and temperature, $PV = nRT$, is called the ideal gas law. The lower the pressure used, the more closely real gases conform to this relationship. An ideal gas is thought not only to have molecules that move at random but also to have molecules without volume and a total kinetic energy that is exactly proportional to the absolute temperature.

Liquids and solids differ from gases not in the absence of random motion but in the presence of strong attraction (van der Waals attraction), which hold the structural units of solids and liquids together. The attraction which holds together the structural units of liquids and solids are also present in gases. In a gas, however, attractions between structural units are relatively weak and serve only to reduce the gas volume slightly below that expected if no forces of any kind operated.

The kinetic model based on moving molecules is extended to include solids and liquids by adding attractive forces between molecules. In this general form, the set of assumptions and conclusions about the nature of matter is called the kinetic-molecular theory or the kinetic model of matter.

A kinetic model was developed because gases expand in all directions at every opportunity. In a sense, then, the kinetic model pictures a kind of disruptive process going on in a gas. If this process is unimpeded, it leads to a system that increases in volume without limit. On the other hand the charge cloud model is based on electrostatic forces that hold atoms together so as to form structures in which attractive forces (bonds) and disruptive processes (random motion) are joined in battle in a proportion sufficient to account for the observed properties of a system. In this way, solids, liquids, and gases do fit into a general scheme that can be understood in terms of the charge cloud and kinetic models.

Ex. 8-19 The density of liquid ammonia is 0.68 g/ml. Calculate the volume available for each molecule of ammonia.

Ex. 8-20 a. On the basis of the kinetic-molecular theory, explain why deviations from ideal numerical values for molar gas volumes are smallest at low gas pressure.

b. Which of the following isoelectronic gases with 18 electrons per molecule would you predict to exhibit the greater deviation from ideal molar gas volume: ethane (C_2H_6) or fluorine (F_2)?

Ex. 8-21 The space-filling capacity of gases, compared to that of solids and liquids, has been discussed in the past in terms of the following ideas: (a) gas molecules fill space by rapid motion, or (b) gas molecules fill space by expanding to any size needed. Discuss the relative merits of these two ideas.

Ex. 8-22 Match the expressions in the left-hand column with an expression in the right-hand column which best completes a correct statement regarding the kinetic-molecular theory.

1. The average kinetic energy of gas molecules is
2. Gas molecules move
3. The volume of a single molecule of an ideal gas is
4. All collisions between molecules of an ideal gas are
5. The space occupied by a gas is filled by the gas because of
6. Equal volumes of gases at the same temperature and pressure
7. Both the total kinetic energy and the total momentum are

a. equal to the mass of 1 mole of gas molecules.
b. conserved when gas molecules collide.
c. contain equal numbers of gas molecules.
d. at constant average velocities and in straight lines between collisions.
e. proportional to the temperature of the gas.
f. the rapid motion of the gas molecules.
g. perfectly elastic.
h. zero.

Ex. 8-23 a. Discuss the interrelationship of potential energy, translational kinetic energy, attraction between molecules, and change in phase for a liquid evaporating at constant temperature.

b. How can the amount of heat required to change a mole of substance from a liquid to a gas be interpreted in terms of the attraction between the molecules of a substance?

Ex. 8-24 *a.* Robert Boyle used a mercury manometer (similar to the apparatus shown in Fig. 8-5) to measure the pressure of the atmosphere. How does such an apparatus measure the pressure of the atmosphere?

b. Pressure is expressed as force divided by area. An operational definition such as the height of a mercury column is often used to represent the pressure of a gas. How is the force per unit area related to the height of the mercury column?

Ex. 8-25 A sample of gas which occupies 1.0 liter at 300°K and 1.0 atmosphere pressure would occupy what volume at 400°K and 1.0 atmosphere pressure? at 200°K and 1.0 atmosphere pressure?

Ex. 8-26 Use the listed effusion rates and molecular masses for methane (CH_4) and oxygen (O_2) to show that the effusion rates of these gases are inversely proportional to the square roots of the molecular masses.

	Molecular Mass	*Effusion Rate*
Methane	16	1.36
Oxygen	32	0.95

Ex. 8-27 A sample of 100 ml of an aqueous barium chloride solution at 30.0°C is mixed with 100 ml of the same solution at 20.0°C. The heat capacity of the barium chloride solution is 0.78 cal/g-deg, and the density of the solution is 1.180 g/ml. What will be the final temperature of the mixture?

Ex. 8-28 Why is the ratio PV/g, where P is the pressure of a gas, V is the volume of a gas, and g is the mass of the gas, a characteristic property?

Ex. 8-29 In Fig. 8-6b, the volume of a gas was plotted as a function of the reciprocal of the pressure (1/pressure). Pressure and density data for oxygen at 273°K are given in the table. Make a graph of these data, plotting density as a function of pressure. Compare the curve in this graph with the curve in Fig. 8-6b.

Pressure, atmospheres	*Density, g/liter*
0.50	0.715
1.0	1.43
1.5	2.14
2.0	2.86
2.5	3.58

Ex. 8-30 The molecular masses, gas densities, and average velocities of molecules of four gases, measured at 1.0 atmosphere pressure and 273°K, are given in the table.

Gas	*Molecular Mass, g/mole*	*Gas Density, g/liter*	*Average Velocity, meters/second*
H_2	2.0	0.0899	
He	4.0	0.178	1.24×10^3
O_2	32.0	1.43	0.44×10^3
CO_2	44.0	1.96	0.38×10^3

a. Using the data in the table, show that the ratio of the square root of gas densities can be used in place of the ratio of the square root of molecular masses to calculate the ratio of effusion rates of two gases.

b. What average velocity would be estimated for molecules of hydrogen, H_2, by using an equation developed from gas density ratios?

Ex. 8-31 The table contains data resulting from the calculated volume-temperature-pressure relationships for 1 mole of helium gas.

Case	Volume, liters	Pressure, atmospheres	Temperature, °K
I	11.2	2.0	273.0
II	14.2	1.0	173.0
III	15.3	2.0	373.0
IV	22.4	0.50	136.5
V	22.4	1.0	273.0
VI	22.4	2.0	546.0
VII	30.6	1.0	373.0
VIII	44.8	0.50	273.0
IX	61.2	0.50	373.0

According to these data,

a. For which cases is the value of the product of pressure and volume PV a constant?

b. For which cases is the numerical value of the ratio V/T a constant?

c. For which cases is the numerical value of the ratio P/T a constant?

d. Calculate the PV/T ratio for each of the cases listed in the table. What do these calculated values indicate?

e. When the value of the expression PV/T is calculated for n moles of gas, it appears as $PV/nT = R$. In what units is R expressed?

f. Using the expression given in question *e*, what volume will 1 mole of helium occupy at 100°K and 0.1 atmosphere pressure?

g. What volume will 10^{-6} mole of helium occupy at standard temperature and pressure?

Ex. 8-32 Figure 8-23 represents Maxwell-Boltzmann distribution curves for nitrogen gas at three different temperatures.

a. What is the approximate maximum velocity of the nitrogen molecules at 300, 900, and 1500°K?

b. How do the total areas under each of the three curves compare?

Ex. 8-33 A student placed an electric heating coil and a thermometer in a small calorimeter containing 30 g of ice. He recorded the temperature and heating time. These data are graphically illustrated at the top of page 345.

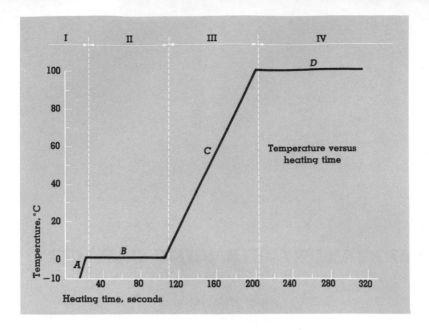

Temperature versus
heating time

a. What is the significance of the point where lines C and D meet?

b. Why does the temperature remain constant for approximately 87 seconds along line B?

c. In which time interval are the contents of the calorimeter a mixture of ice and liquid water? all liquid water? boiling water?

d. In which time interval is the heat that the system is absorbing called the heat of fusion? called the heat of vaporization?

e. Why is the slope of the line during time interval I different from the slope during time interval III?

Ex. 8-34   When potassium chlorate is heated, it decomposes to form potassium chloride and oxygen. The equation for the reaction is

$$2KClO_3 \rightarrow 2KCl + 3O_2$$

a. How many liters of oxygen, measured at 273°K and 760 mm pressure, will be produced when 24.5 g of $KClO_3$ is decomposed?

b. What volume will the oxygen produced according to part a occupy if the temperature of the gas increases to 300°K and the pressure decreases to 740 mm?

345

TEMPERATURE-CHANGING CAPACITY

THE MAJOR USE that people make of chemical systems is for the production of energy. About 3,000,000,000 tons of chemicals are used each year in systems that undergo change where the principal practical purpose is to obtain energy. The reaction products are simply discarded. For each of these systems, oxygen is one of the initial reactants and the other is a fuel such as coal, oil, natural gas, or wood. In Chapter 3, the significance of the change in temperature that occurs when zinc is added to a water solution of copper sulfate was discussed as an indication of change in the system. The observed change in temperature of the calorimeter is interpretable in terms of the transfer of energy from the system to the calorimeter.

Temperature changes or energy transfers are involved with every chemical change in some intimate fashion. Can these observations be interpreted in terms of the models that have been developed for the structures of substances?

One chemical that is of considerable industrial importance as an energy source is methane. Methane reacts with oxygen to give carbon dioxide and water. In Chapter 7 charge cloud models were developed for the molecules of methane, oxygen, carbon dioxide, and water. On the basis of the charge cloud model, *chemical change* means breaking bonds in the reactants and making new bonds to form the products. It should be possible to relate the transfer of heat that can be measured in the laboratory either to the symbols in equations and features of charge cloud models that can be shown on paper or to the three-dimensional models that you can hold in your hands. Here is a chemical black box!

9-1   **USE OF A CALORIMETER TO MEASURE TEMPERATURE-CHANGING CAPACITY**

In Experiment 8 in *Investigating Chemical Systems*, known quantities of water and hydrochloric acid were mixed. The temperature of the system was observed and recorded before and after mixing, and the change in temperature was calculated. Two changes occurred simultaneously in the experiment. First, water was mixed with the solution of hydrochloric acid. Second, the temperature of the mixture changed. Two changes, mixing of reactants and change in temperature, were the only observations made. A system that can undergo a change in state is described as having a temperature-changing capacity.

After mixing the hydrochloric acid and water, the system in its final state does not itself have a temperature-changing capacity. Its temperature can be changed, however, provided it is placed in contact with an environment at a different temperature. If this environment is at a lower temperature, it is possible in fact to return the temperature of the hydrochloric acid–water system to its initial temperature. As the temperature of the system falls, the temperature of the environment rises.

When two systems at different temperatures are connected, heat is transferred from one system to the other. If water is used for the environment, 1 kcal of heat transferred from the reacting system will effect an increase of 1° in the temperature of each kilogram of water. A device for carrying out measurements of the quantities of heat transferred, a calorimeter, is shown in Fig. 3-10.

The changes occurring in the hydrochloric acid–water system during mixing can be reconsidered. The mixing can be carried out in a calorimeter in such a manner that the system remains at constant temperature, whereas in the earlier procedure the temperature increased. If the system remains at constant temperature, heat must be transferred from the system to the calorimeter.

In the procedure followed in Experiment 8, that is, where the temperature of the reacting system changes, it is possible to calculate the amount of heat that would have to be removed to return the system to the initial temperature. To do this, the heat capacity of the final solution must be known. No matter which of the two procedures is used for determining the quantity of energy, the crucial condition is

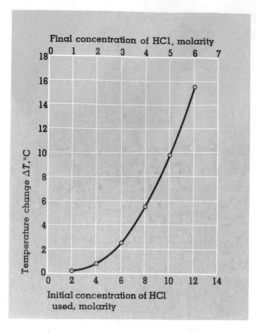

Fig. 9-1 *Temperature changes observed when 100 ml of water is mixed with 100-ml samples of hydrochloric acid of different concentrations.*

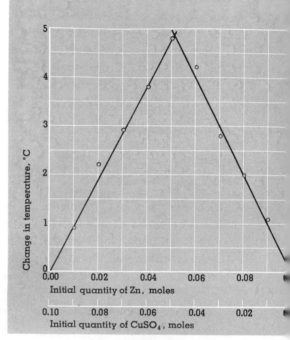

Fig. 9-2 *Temperature changes observed when zinc is added to copper sulfate solutions.*

that the initial and final states of the system be compared at constant temperature and constant pressure. Data obtained from mixing 100 ml of water with 100-ml portions of hydrochloric acid solutions of several initial concentrations are plotted in Fig. 9-1.

The temperature change was also determined for the mixing of zinc and copper sulfate. The data discussed in Section 3-19 for this system are plotted in Fig. 9-2. Here the conclusion is that the amount of temperature change is directly related to the extent or amount of change in chemical composition which occurs in the system.

Ex. 9-1   *a.* When 1 g of ammonia gas (NH_3) is formed from gaseous hydrogen (H_2) and nitrogen (N_2), 0.647 kcal of thermal energy is evolved. What is the heat transferred per mole of NH_3 formed?

b. Write the chemical reaction that represents the formation of 1 mole of NH_3.

Generalizations relating the transfer of energy to changes in atomic, molecular, or electrical structures will be more easily found by consideration of systems composed of relatively simple molecules. Ideally, these systems will undergo changes accompanied by the evolution or absorption of large amounts of heat. The following equations describe some reactions used for supplying large quantities of heat.

$$C \ (s) + O_2 \ (g) \rightarrow CO_2 \ (g) \qquad (Eq. \ 9\text{-}1)$$

$$2H_2 \ (g) + O_2 \ (g) \rightarrow 2H_2O \ (l) \qquad (Eq. \ 9\text{-}2)$$

$$CH_4 \ (g) + 2O_2 \ (g) \rightarrow CO_2 \ (g) + 2H_2O \ (l) \qquad (Eq. \ 9\text{-}3)$$

$$2CO \ (g) + O_2 \ (g) \rightarrow 2CO_2 \ (g) \qquad (Eq. \ 9\text{-}4)$$

Carbon, in the form of coal or coke, and methane (CH_4), as a constituent of natural gas, are widely used fuels of great commercial value. Carbon monoxide is frequently produced during the burning of these fuels. If sufficient air is available, the carbon monoxide burns to produce carbon dioxide. The reaction of hydrogen with oxygen is sometimes used to produce high-temperature flames for special purposes such as cutting steel plate. A mixture of hydrogen with carbon monoxide called water gas is also used as a fuel. Water gas is produced by the reaction between carbon and steam (Equation 9-5) at a temperature of about 1000°C.

$$C \ (s) + H_2O \ (steam) \rightarrow CO \ (g) + H_2 \ (g) \qquad (Eq. \ 9\text{-}5)$$

To make reliable measurements on the transfer of heat in such reactions, all reactants and products must be held within the calorimeter throughout the reaction. This is the only way that precise information about both the initial and the final states can be obtained. For calorimetric measurements on reactions of substances with oxygen, a sealed container, called a bomb calorimeter, is ordinarily used so that no reactant or product is lost from the system (Fig. 9-3). After the reactants have been sealed in the container, the reaction can be started easily by the heat from a small electric ignition coil inside the calorimeter.

Many calorimetric measurements have been made for the burning of graphite (an allotrope of carbon) in oxygen to give carbon dioxide. The analysis of the data shows that 7.8311 ± 0.0009 kcal of heat per gram of graphite burned at 25°C and 1 atmosphere pressure is transferred from the system. To obtain this value, the graphite sample used must be free of other material, and the temperature and pressure must be the same for both the initial and final states of the system. Experimental measurements show that the total amount of heat transferred

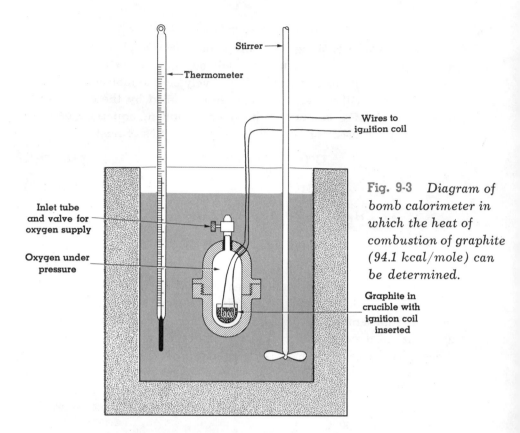

Inlet tube and valve for oxygen supply

Oxygen under pressure

Thermometer

Stirrer

Wires to ignition coil

Fig. 9-3 *Diagram of bomb calorimeter in which the heat of combustion of graphite (94.1 kcal/mole) can be determined.*

Graphite in crucible with ignition coil inserted

from the reacting system is not influenced by variations in the temperature during the reaction. For the initial state the temperature most frequently used is 25°C. During the reaction the temperature may increase (or decrease), but the system can be cooled (or warmed) to give a temperature reading of 25°C for the final state of the system. The total quantity of heat transferred to restore the system to the temperature of the initial state will be the same, regardless of how high the temperature rose (or fell) during the reaction. Such a statement is based on the idea that heat transfer in the system is perfect, that is, that a complete transfer of heat can be accurately determined by temperature measurements during the reaction. If undesired heat losses to the calorimeter or from the calorimeter occur in the system, these heat losses must be accounted for. In other words, the statement depends on the conservation of energy and on the ability to determine the amount of heat transferred.

In the combustion of graphite, the quantity of heat evolved is directly proportional to the mass of carbon burned. The heat of reaction could therefore be recorded as the quantity of heat transferred per gram of graphite burned. For interpretation of chemical systems, however, the quantity of heat transferred per mole of reactant is the more useful

TABLE 9-1 HEATS OF REACTION FOR FOUR SYSTEMS

System	Heat of Reaction[a]
$C\ (s) + O_2\ (g) \rightarrow CO_2\ (g)$	94.1 kcal
$2H_2\ (g) + O_2\ (g) \rightarrow 2H_2O\ (l)$	136.6 kcal
$CH_4\ (g) + 2O_2\ (g) \rightarrow CO_2\ (g) + 2H_2O\ (l)$	212.8 kcal
$2CO\ (g) + O_2\ (g) \rightarrow 2CO_2\ (g)$	135.4 kcal

[a] Values were taken at 25°C and 1 atmosphere pressure.

form for the data. For graphite (C), the quantity of heat transferred per mole can be calculated.

$$7.8311 \text{ kcal/g} \times 12.011 \text{ g/mole of C} = 94.059 \text{ kcal/mole of C}$$

The amount of heat transferred (evolved or absorbed) during a reaction in a chemical system of known composition is called the **heat of reaction.** To be meaningful, a numerical value for a heat of reaction must be associated directly with a chemical equation representing the change under discussion. Heats of reaction for the four systems represented by Equations 9-1 to 9-4 are listed in Table 9-1.

If thermal energy is transferred into or out of a system, there must be a corresponding rise or fall in the total quantity of energy stored in the system. But there is no way to measure the total quantity of energy which may be stored in a system. Calorimetric measurement, however, can provide reliable numerical values for quantities of heat transferred to or from a system and hence for the energy changes which a system undergoes.

9-3 ENTHALPY

For a chemical system that undergoes a change at constant pressure, the total energy stored in the system is called the **enthalpy** and designated by H. When the system undergoes a change in state, the enthalpy change ΔH is given by

$$H_2 - H_1 = \Delta H$$

where H_2 is the enthalpy of the system in its final state and H_1 is the enthalpy of the system in its initial state. When the initial and final temperature and pressure are each the same, the heat of reaction is a measure of ΔH.

A reaction which gives off heat to the surroundings is said to be **exothermic,** and H_2 is less than H_1, so that ΔH has a negative value. This is the case for the reaction between hydrogen and oxygen,

$$2H_2\ (g) + O_2\ (g) \rightarrow 2H_2O\ (l) \qquad \Delta H = -136.6 \text{ kcal}$$

A reaction which absorbs heat from the surroundings is said to be **endothermic,** and H_2 is greater than H_1, so that ΔH has a positive value.

Enthalpy changes can be shown in diagrammatic form. An enthalpy diagram (Fig. 9-4) is often helpful as an aid to interpretation of enthalpy changes. If the number zero were assigned to the enthalpy of the system containing hydrogen gas and oxygen gas in the initial state, then the enthalpy for the system containing water in the final state would be downhill from the enthalpy for the initial state or starting point (Fig. 9-4). Consequently, the change in enthalpy is expressed as $\Delta H = -136.6$ kcal/mole of O_2. When ΔH is negative, heat is evolved. Only changes in enthalpy and not the enthalpy for a particular state of a system can be calculated from measurements of changes in the laboratory. A reference point for the enthalpy within a system can be chosen in any manner that is consistent and convenient. This choice of reference point is similar to the designation of sea level as zero in measuring the heights of mountains and the depths of the oceans. The reference point for measurements of enthalpy changes (that is, the point at which enthalpy is zero) is established by assigning zero enthalpy to the elements in the pure form at 25°C and 1 atmosphere pressure.

For the reaction of hydrogen and oxygen to form water as described by Equation 9-2, the system in its final state was chosen to be liquid water at 25°C and 1 atmosphere pressure. The final state could equally well have been chosen to be gaseous water (steam) at some other temperature and pressure. All that would be required is sufficient volume in the calorimeter bomb to ensure that all water would remain in the gas phase. An experiment carried out in this way evolves 115.6 kcal of heat per 2 moles of steam formed or per mole of oxygen used.

$$2H_2 \ (g) + O_2 \ (g) \rightarrow 2H_2O \ (g) \qquad \Delta H_2 = -115.6 \text{ kcal/mole of } O_2$$
$$(Exp. \ 9\text{-}6)$$

This can be compared to the evolution of 136.6 kcal of heat per 2 moles of liquid water formed or per mole of oxygen used. In both expressions, ΔH is calculated at 25°C and 1 atmosphere pressure.

$$2H_2 \ (g) + O_2 \ (g) \rightarrow 2H_2O \ (l) \qquad \Delta H_1 = -136.6 \text{ kcal/mole of } O_2$$
$$(Exp. \ 9\text{-}7)$$

The data indicate that between gaseous water and liquid water, there is an enthalpy difference of 21.0 kcal/2 moles of H_2O at 25°C and 1 atmosphere pressure.

In Chapter 8 the energy difference between the liquid and gas phases of a substance was defined as heat of vaporization. In Experiment 21 of *Investigating Chemical Systems* an experimental method is developed for calculating heats of vaporization for water and other liquids

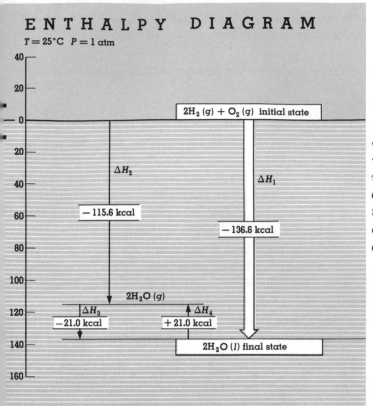

ENTHALPY DIAGRAM

$T = 25°C \quad P = 1$ atm

$2H_2$ (g) + O_2 (g) initial state

ΔH_2

ΔH_1

-115.6 kcal

-136.6 kcal

$2H_2O$ (g)

ΔH_3
-21.0 kcal

ΔH_4
$+21.0$ kcal

$2H_2O$ (l) final state

Fig. 9-4 *Enthalpy change for the formation of 2 moles of water from hydrogen and oxygen at a temperature of 25°C and a pressure of 1 atmosphere.*

from data obtained in the laboratory. The **heat of vaporization** and the **heat of fusion** of a substance are enthalpy changes and can be called **enthalpy of vaporization** and **enthalpy of fusion,** respectively. Enthalpy changes accompanying phase changes can be treated in exactly the same way as enthalpy changes accompanying any chemical change. The calculated numerical value for the molar heat of vaporization of water at 25°C is 10.5 kcal/mole of H_2O.

$$H_2O \ (l) \rightarrow H_2O \ (g) \quad \Delta H_4 = 10.5 \text{ kcal/mole of } H_2O \quad (Exp. \ 9\text{-}8)$$

For 2 moles of water, $\Delta H_4 = 21.0$ kcal. The reverse process, in which gas is condensed to liquid, gives the same numerical value, but the heat is evolved instead of absorbed so that $\Delta H_3 = -10.5$ kcal/mole of H_2O.

$$H_2O \ (g) \rightarrow H_2O \ (l) \quad \Delta H_3 = -10.5 \text{ kcal/mole of } H_2O \quad (Exp. \ 9\text{-}9)$$

The changes in enthalpy are shown graphically in Fig. 9-4 which relates ΔH_1, ΔH_2, ΔH_3, and ΔH_4 to the chemical reactions. Other heats of vaporization are given in Table 8-7.

353

a. Make an enthalpy diagram similar to that shown in Fig. 9-4 for the enthalpy change for the reaction between N_2 (*g*) and H_2 (*g*) to form NH_3 (*g*).

b. What is the enthalpy change for the reaction as indicated by the diagram?

9-4 HESS'S LAW

Hydrogen and oxygen can be allowed to react to form liquid water by two different pathways. By Pathway I (Fig. 9-4), the reactants form liquid water directly in one step for which $\Delta H_1 = -136.6$ kcal/2 moles of H_2O. By Pathway II the reactants form steam in the first step with $\Delta H_2 = -115.6$ kcal/2 moles of H_2O, and then the steam is condensed to liquid water for the second step with $\Delta H_3 = -21.0$ kcal/2 moles of H_2O. For Pathway II, the enthalpy change is $\Delta H_2 + \Delta H_3 = -115.6 + (-21.0) = -136.6$ kcal/2 moles of H_2O which is the same as for Pathway I. So the number of steps in the path from initial to final state does not affect the experimentally obtained and calculated values for enthalpy change during a reaction.

What consequences would follow if one pathway differed from another in going from the initial state to the same final state and if the total enthalpy changes were not the same by the two pathways? This would mean that, in one way or another, energy would have been lost or gained and not conserved. In spite of repeated tests of the principle of the conservation of energy, no case has yet been found in which energy is not conserved.

Indeed the impossibility of creating or destroying energy is the basis for the definition of enthalpy. When heat is the only form of energy being transferred into or out of a system, enthalpy is imagined to be energy in the system which must change by exactly the amount necessary to account for the heat transferred. The additivity of enthalpy data was implicit in the discussion of the reaction of hydrogen and oxygen to form water. The additivity of enthalpy data as a particular case of the law of conservation of energy was recognized by G. H. Hess as early as 1840.

Underlying the additivity of enthalpy data obtained at constant pressure are two assumptions.

1. For each state of a system there is just one numerical value of the enthalpy.

2. If two states of a system differ in enthalpy, energy exactly equal to the difference is absorbed or evolved during the change from initial to final state provided that for the two states the system has the same pressure.

As a consequence of these two assumptions about enthalpy, the magnitude of the change in enthalpy is fixed once the initial and final

states of the system are fixed. No matter what pathway between the
two states is chosen, the enthalpy change will always be the same.

The additivity of enthalpy data is usually referred to as **Hess's law,**
which may be stated thus: The change in enthalpy accompanying a
change in a system from the initial to final state is independent of the
pathway between the initial and final state. To illustrate, consider a
system in which the initial state is represented by the symbol A and
the final state by the symbol D, and suppose that there are two ways
by which the system can change from state A to state D.

$$A \rightarrow D$$
$$A \rightarrow B \rightarrow C \rightarrow D$$

Hess's law requires that the enthalpy change accompanying the change
from A directly to D be identical to the sum of the three enthalpy
changes accompanying the three changes from A to B to C to D (Fig.
9-5). The direct change from A to D represents a downhill pathway,
or exothermic reaction, during which the system changes from the
initial state A to the final state D. The circuitous pathway, including

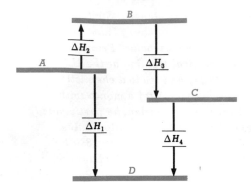

Fig. 9-5 *Hess's law in diagrammatic form.*

the endothermic change from A to B, followed by two exothermic changes B to C and C to D, arrives at the same final state D of the system. According to the assumptions for additivity of enthalpy data,

$$\Delta H_1 = \Delta H_2 + \Delta H_3 + \Delta H_4$$

or $$H_D - H_A = \Delta H_1 = \Delta H_2 + \Delta H_3 + \Delta H_4$$

An analogy for Hess's law is found in mountain climbing. Suppose that you decide to climb to a mountain peak 1 mile above your lodge. This decision defines your initial and final states. There may be many paths up the mountain. Every path, however, has to conform to one requirement. No matter how different the paths may be, every path must end in your being exactly 1 mile above the lodge. Vertical distance is conserved in the mountain-climbing analogy. You cannot alter the height of the mountain by the path you take. Vertical distance in the analogy corresponds to enthalpy in Hess's law. You cannot alter the enthalpy difference between the states of the system by choosing different pathways, that is, different sequences of reactions.

Ex. 9-3   *a.* If the reaction of N_2 (g) and H_2 (g) to produce NH_3 (g) is carried out in such a way that the NH_3 (g) formed is dissolved in water as a dilute solution, the heat evolved is 19.32 kcal/mole of NH_3. Determine the enthalpy difference between gaseous ammonia and aqueous ammonia, and write the equations which describe each step of the overall change from the free elements to dissolved ammonia.

b. Make an enthalpy diagram representing the series of reactions you have written in part *a*.

9-5   COMBUSTION OF GRAPHITE

On the basis of Hess's law, the combustion of graphite can be considered in a new way. In its initial state the system represented in

Equation 9-1 consists of 1 mole of solid graphite and 1 mole of oxygen gas at 25°C and 1 atmosphere. During the reaction

$$C\ (s) + O_2\ (g) \rightarrow CO_2\ (g) \qquad\qquad (Eq.\ 9\text{-}1)$$

the system gives up 94.1 kcal of heat per mole of graphite, per mole of oxygen, or per mole of carbon dioxide. In its initial state the system consists of pure elements under the conditions for which they have zero enthalpy. Consequently, $CO_2\ (g)$ can be placed at −94.1 kcal on an enthalpy diagram for this exothermic reaction (Fig. 9-6). Therefore, for the change in state of the system represented by Equation 9-1, there is a change in enthalpy of −94.1 kcal; $\Delta H = -94.1$ kcal/mole of C, O_2, or CO_2.

The reference state of an element is sometimes called the standard state. Conventionally, the **standard state** of an element is a particular allotrope free of other materials and at a temperature of 25°C and a pressure of 1 atmosphere. The enthalpy of an element in its standard state is zero. The standard state of carbon is the allotrope graphite at 25°C and 1 atmosphere pressure. For the reaction represented by Expression 9-10, the heat of reaction $\Delta H = -135.4$ kcal per mole of O_2 or per 2 moles of CO.

$$2CO\ (g) + O_2\ (g) \rightarrow 2CO_2\ (g) \quad \Delta H = -135.4\ \text{kcal} \quad (Exp.\ 9\text{-}10)$$

The chemical equation in Expression 9-10 can be divided by 2 to give

Fig. 9-6 *Using Hess's law, the enthalpy of formation for CO from C and O_2 can be calculated.*

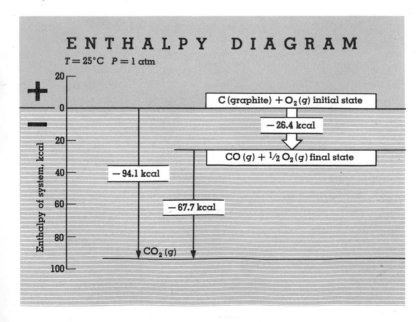

ENTHALPY DIAGRAM

$T = 25°C \quad P = 1\ atm$

Enthalpy of system, kcal

C (graphite) + O_2(g) initial state

− 26.4 kcal

CO (g) + ½ O_2(g) final state

− 94.1 kcal

− 67.7 kcal

CO_2 (g)

the equation in Expression 9-11. The enthalpy change must be divided by 2 also.

$$CO\ (g) + \tfrac{1}{2}O_2\ (g) \rightarrow CO_2\ (g) \quad \Delta H = -67.7\ \text{kcal} \quad (Exp.\ 9\text{-}11)$$

In the strict sense, the chemical equation in Expression 9-10 has one interpretation that cannot be applied to the chemical equation in Expression 9-11. Two molecules of carbon monoxide react with one molecule of oxygen to give two molecules of CO_2 (Expression 9-10), but it would be a different matter to say that one molecule of carbon monoxide reacts with one-half molecule of oxygen since molecules are structural units. Furthermore, it would not be correct to write

$$CO\ (g) + O\ (g) \rightarrow CO_2\ (g)$$

to mean the same as Expression 9-11 since the oxygen is here represented to be in the monatomic form which has quite different properties from the diatomic form of oxygen. However, Expression 9-11 certainly can mean that 1 mole of CO reacts with $\tfrac{1}{2}$ mole of O_2 to give 1 mole of CO_2.

A line can be placed on the energy diagram in Fig. 9-6 to represent the enthalpy of the system with composition $CO\ (g) + \tfrac{1}{2}O_2\ (g)$ at a level such that the enthalpy for composition $CO_2\ (g)$ is downhill 67.7 kcal ($\Delta H = -67.7$ kcal). The enthalpy for composition $CO\ (g) + \tfrac{1}{2}O_2\ (g)$ must therefore be higher than the enthalpy for composition $CO_2\ (g)$. From the enthalpy diagram in Fig. 9-6 and from Hess's law, it follows that the change in enthalpy for the reaction of graphite and oxygen to yield CO is -26.4 kcal/mole of graphite.

$$C\ (s) + O_2\ (g) \rightarrow CO\ (g) + \tfrac{1}{2}O_2\ (g) \quad \Delta H = -26.4\ \text{kcal/mole of C}$$

This can also be written as shown in Expression 9-12 since O_2 appears on both sides of the equation.

$$C\ (s) + \tfrac{1}{2}O_2\ (g) \rightarrow CO\ (g) \quad \Delta H = -26.4\ \text{kcal/mole of C}$$
$$(Exp.\ 9\text{-}12)$$

It is impossible to carry out in the laboratory a reaction in which carbon reacts with oxygen to produce only carbon monoxide. Nonetheless, from data for reactions which can be performed in the laboratory, an enthalpy change has been calculated for the formation of carbon monoxide from carbon and oxygen. The basic assumption that energy is conserved in every step indicates that the enthalpy change calculated for any step cannot be more precise than the experimental data for the reactions which are performed in the laboratory.

9-6 COMBUSTION OF DIAMOND

Hess's law is a most valuable generalization. Through its use, the enthalpy of a great many reactions can be computed. Consider, for example, the enthalpy changes for the burning of graphite and diamond. The reactions of these two substances with oxygen were discussed briefly in Section 2-13 where it was shown that graphite and diamond are allotropic forms of the same element, carbon.

The reactions, as carried out experimentally with high precision, are

C (graphite) $+ O_2$ (g) $\rightarrow CO_2$ (g) $\Delta H = -94.059$ kcal/mole of C
C (diamond) $+ O_2$ (g) $\rightarrow CO_2$ (g) $\Delta H = -94.512$ kcal/mole of C

Since oxygen and carbon dioxide are identical in all respects in both systems, any difference between the enthalpy changes for the burning of diamond and graphite must be assigned to differences between their energies.

C (diamond) $\rightarrow$ C (graphite) $\Delta H = -0.453$ kcal/mole of C

So 1 mole of graphite is 0.453 kcal lower in energy than 1 mole of diamond. When the standard state of carbon is referred to at 25°C and 1 atmosphere, graphite is the allotropic form used.

Ex. 9-4   *a.* Draw an enthalpy diagram for the two systems graphite–oxygen–carbon dioxide and diamond–oxygen–carbon dioxide. Show on the diagram the enthalpy change for

C (diamond) $\rightarrow$ C (graphite)

b. What would be the minimum amount of energy required to change 1 kg of graphite to 1 kg of diamond?

Ex. 9-5   Show how the enthalpy of formation for gaseous ammonia, NH_3 (g), can be calculated from the following reactions.

a. Combustion of ammonia

NH_3 (g) $+ \frac{3}{4}O_2$ (g) $\rightarrow \frac{3}{2}H_2O$ (g) $+ \frac{1}{2}N_2$ (g) $\Delta H = -75.7$ kcal

b. Formation of water

$\frac{3}{2}H_2$ (g) $+ \frac{3}{4}O_2$ (g) $\rightarrow \frac{3}{2}H_2O$ (g) $\Delta H = -86.7$ kcal

9-7   NOMENCLATURE

Every chemical reaction at constant pressure and constant temperature is accompanied by a change in enthalpy. Regardless of the nature of the reaction or of the conditions under which the reaction is carried out, the quantity of heat transferred into or out of a particular system at constant pressure is referred to as the **enthalpy of reaction** or **heat of reaction**. To provide more restricted meanings, the temperature and pressure are specified and the quantities of one or more reactants or products are designated. Heats of reaction listed in tables are commonly specified for reactions carried out at a constant temperature (for example, 25°C), at a constant pressure of (1 atmosphere), and for a definite quantity of one reactant or product (1 mole).

TABLE 9-2 ENTHALPIES (heats) OF COMBUSTION FOR SEVERAL SUBSTANCES

Reaction	ΔH, kcal/mole of Substance Burned[a]
$C\ (s) + O_2\ (g) \rightarrow CO_2\ (g)$	-94.1
$CH_4\ (g) + 2O_2\ (g) \rightarrow CO_2\ (g) + 2H_2O\ (l)$	-212.8
$C_2H_6\ (g) + \frac{7}{2}O_2\ (g) \rightarrow 2CO_2\ (g) + 3H_2O\ (l)$	-372.8
$C_2H_4\ (g) + 3O_2\ (g) \rightarrow 2CO_2\ (g) + 2H_2O\ (l)$	-337.2
$C_2H_2\ (g) + \frac{5}{2}O_2\ (g) \rightarrow 2CO_2\ (g) + H_2O\ (l)$	-310.6
$CO\ (g) + \frac{1}{2}O_2\ (g) \rightarrow CO_2\ (g)$	-67.7
$H_2\ (g) + \frac{1}{2}O_2\ (g) \rightarrow H_2O\ (l)$	-68.3
$H_2\ (g) + \frac{1}{2}O_2\ (g) \rightarrow H_2O\ (g)$	-57.8
$NH_3\ (g) + \frac{3}{4}O_2\ (g) \rightarrow \frac{3}{2}H_2O\ (l) + \frac{1}{2}N_2\ (g)$	-91.4

[a] Values were taken at 25°C and 1 atmosphere pressure.

TABLE 9-3 ENTHALPIES (heats) OF FORMATION FOR SEVERAL PRODUCTS

Reaction	ΔH, kcal/mole of Product Formed[a]
$C\ (s) + O_2\ (g) \rightarrow CO_2\ (g)$	-94.1
$C\ (s) + \frac{1}{2}O_2\ (g) \rightarrow CO\ (g)$	-26.4
$H_2\ (g) + \frac{1}{2}O_2\ (g) \rightarrow H_2O\ (l)$	-68.3
$\frac{1}{2}H_2\ (g) + \frac{1}{2}F_2\ (g) \rightarrow HF\ (g)$	-64.2
$C\ (s) + 2H_2\ (g) \rightarrow CH_4\ (g)$	-17.9
$\frac{1}{2}N_2\ (g) + \frac{3}{2}H_2\ (g) \rightarrow NH_3\ (g)$	-11.0
$\frac{1}{2}H_2\ (g) + \frac{1}{2}Cl_2\ (g) \rightarrow HCl\ (g)$	-22.0
$C\ (s) + \frac{3}{2}H_2\ (g) + \frac{1}{2}Cl_2\ (g) \rightarrow CH_3Cl\ (g)$	-19.6
$Mg\ (s) + \frac{1}{2}O_2\ (g) \rightarrow MgO\ (s)$	-143.8

[a] Values were taken at 25°C and 1 atmosphere pressure.
SOURCE: *National Bureau of Standards Bulletin 500.*

For further convenience in reference and also by tradition, heats of reaction (ΔH values) are frequently assigned names to indicate something about the nature of the reaction itself. For instance, the reactions of substances with oxygen are frequently referred to as **combustion reactions**. The change in enthalpy during the reaction of 1 mole of the substance being burned at 25°C and at 1 atmosphere pressure is then referred to as the **enthalpy of combustion** or **heat of combustion**. Enthalpy changes for the combustion of C, H_2, CH_4, CO, and some other substances are listed in Table 9-2.

Reactions in which a substance is prepared from its constituent elements are called **formation reactions**. The enthalpy change accompanying the formation of 1 mole of a substance from the elements in their standard states at a given temperature and 1 atmosphere pressure is known as the **enthalpy of formation** or **heat of formation**. From tables of enthalpies of formation, enthalpy changes for other reactions can be calculated using Hess's law. Because not all formation reactions can be carried out in a manner that will permit direct calorimetric measurement, many heats of formation are calculated by using Hess's law, for example, as was done in calculating the heat of formation of carbon monoxide (Section 9-5). Table 9-3 lists enthalpies of formation for several substances.

When a mole of a substance decomposes so as to form atoms of the constituent elements in the gas phase at 1 atmosphere and 25°C, the enthalpy change accompanying the reaction is called an **enthalpy of dissociation** or **heat of dissociation**. Some enthalpies of dissociation for elements are given in Table 9-4.

TABLE 9-4 ENTHALPIES (heats) OF DISSOCIATION OF SOME ELEMENTS

Reaction	ΔH, kcal/mole of Atom Formed[a]
$\frac{1}{2}F_2\ (g) \rightarrow F\ (g)$	+18.3
$\frac{1}{2}H_2\ (g) \rightarrow H\ (g)$	+52.1
$\frac{1}{2}Cl_2\ (g) \rightarrow Cl\ (g)$	+28.9
$\frac{1}{2}Br_2\ (l) \rightarrow Br\ (g)$	+26.7
$\frac{1}{2}I_2\ (s) \rightarrow I\ (g)$	+25.5
$\frac{1}{2}O_2\ (g) \rightarrow O\ (g)$	+59.2
$\frac{1}{2}N_2\ (g) \rightarrow N\ (g)$	+112.5
$C\ (s) \rightarrow C\ (g)$	+171.7

[a] Values were taken at 25°C and 1 atmosphere pressure.
SOURCE: *National Bureau of Standards Bulletin* 500.

Determine the overall change in enthalpy for the following reactions by algebraically summing the reactions and enthalpy changes. In each case note whether the overall reaction is endothermic or exothermic.

a.
$$K\ (s) \rightarrow K\ (g) \qquad \Delta H = 21.5\ \text{kcal}$$
$$\tfrac{1}{2}Cl_2\ (g) \rightarrow Cl\ (g) \qquad \Delta H = \text{(from table)}$$
$$K\ (g)\ +\ Cl\ (g) \rightarrow KCl\ (s) \qquad \Delta H = -154.7\ \text{kcal}$$

$$K\ (s)\ +\ \tfrac{1}{2}Cl_2\ (g) \rightarrow KCl\ (s) \qquad \Delta H = \text{(to be calculated)}$$

b.
$$Mg\ (s) \rightarrow Mg\ (g) \qquad \Delta H = 35.9\ \text{kcal}$$
$$\tfrac{1}{2}O_2\ (g) \rightarrow O\ (g) \qquad \Delta H = \text{(from table)}$$
$$Mg\ (g)\ +\ O\ (g) \rightarrow MgO\ (s) \qquad \Delta H = -238.9\ \text{kcal}$$

$$Mg\ (s)\ +\ \tfrac{1}{2}O_2\ (g) \rightarrow MgO\ (s) \qquad \Delta H = \text{(to be calculated)}$$

c.
$$\tfrac{1}{4}P_4\ (s) \rightarrow P\ (g) \qquad \Delta H = 75.2\ \text{kcal}$$
$$\tfrac{3}{2}H_2\ (g) \rightarrow 3H\ (g) \qquad \Delta H = \text{(from table)}$$
$$P\ (g)\ +\ 3H\ (g) \rightarrow PH_3\ (g) \qquad \Delta H = -229.3\ \text{kcal}$$

$$\tfrac{1}{4}P_4\ (s)\ +\ \tfrac{3}{2}H_2\ (g) \rightarrow PH_3\ (g) \qquad \Delta H = \text{(to be calculated)}$$

9-8 AN ANALOGY FOR ENERGY

One fundamental characteristic of energy is that energy is conserved when it is transferred from one system to another. In this regard, energy and money share a common feature. You may find it helpful to think of money as an analogy for energy.

Money is transferred from one person to another, from one industry to another, and from one bank to another. Bookkeepers in banks assume that money does not increase or decrease during the transfer. Money is conserved. It is therefore possible to develop a bookkeeping system which keeps track of money transactions. The bookkeeper insists that a complete record will show that the differences between the money which came in and which went out must equal what is in storage. When he can show arithmetically that this is true, he says his books balance.

A bookkeeper can balance his books by actually inspecting and precisely counting the money in storage. For energy in storage, a precise measure is not available. Only changes in stored energy are computed from energy transfers and from the assumption that energy is conserved.

For all ordinary transactions, money is transferred without increase or decrease. If we suspect some individual of possessing more money than he has taken in, we are tempted to believe he is a counterfeiter.

In any discussion of energy, it is of considerable scientific interest to wonder about the connection between mass and energy. Each has been developed as an item that is conserved. So far we have assumed that mass within a system is conserved when a system changes from the initial to the final state. We have assumed that energy is conserved in the coupling between two systems that interact with each other.

Mass is identified as a property associated with atoms. In this way conservation of mass is dealt with by chemists as conservation of atoms.

In systems where nuclear changes take place, the amounts of energy transferred may be as large as several billion kilocalories per mole of material. The fission of uranium-235 is an example of a system in which nuclear changes occur. Experiments show that the transfer of energy to the surroundings in large amounts is accompanied by transfers of mass to the surroundings even though no atoms are transferred out of the system.

Albert Einstein concluded in 1905 that the mass and energy of a system are proportional,

$$E = Km$$

and that the proportionality constant is about 2×10^{13} kcal/kg. So you can say that mass has energy or energy has mass. Every exothermic reaction in a system must involve a transfer of mass from the system to its environment.

In the chemistry laboratory, measurements of energy transfers of less than 100 kcal/g are generally involved. A transfer of 100 kcal of energy means, according to the Einstein equation, a mass transfer of only 0.000000005 g. Chemical reactions are therefore accompanied by mass transfers too small to detect with any available devices for measuring the mass of the system. So although Einstein's mass-energy equivalence is assumed to hold in all chemcial reactions, nonetheless, for practical operations, a chemical system is always treated as having constant mass.

9-9 FORMATION OF METHANE

Computation of the enthalpy of formation of methane requires information about a chemical reaction that cannot be carried out directly in the laboratory,

$$C\ (s) + 2H_2\ (g) \rightarrow CH_4\ (g)$$

Reactions involving each of the three components of the chemical system can be carried out.

$$C\ (s) + O_2\ (g) \rightarrow CO_2\ (g) \quad \Delta H = -94.1 \text{ kcal/mole of } O_2$$
$$(Exp.\ 9\text{-}13)$$

If 94.1 kcal/mole of oxygen is evolved in the combustion of graphite as written in Expression 9-13, 94.1 kcal of energy would be absorbed if the reaction could be reversed to form graphite and oxygen.

$$CO_2 \ (g) \rightarrow C \ (s) + O_2 \ (g) \quad \Delta H = +94.1 \text{ kcal/mole of } O_2$$
$$(Exp. \ 9\text{-}14)$$

Reversing the equation in an expression made up of an equation and the accompanying enthalpy change makes it necessary to change the algebraic sign of the enthalpy change. This is so because reversing a reaction in which heat is evolved ($\Delta H < 0$) requires that heat be added ($\Delta H > 0$) for the reverse reaction.

Besides Expression 9-13, two additional expressions are needed to compute the enthalpy of formation of methane (Tables 9-2 and 9-3).

$$2H_2 \ (g) + O_2 \ (g) \rightarrow 2H_2O \ (l) \quad \Delta H = -136.6 \text{ kcal/mole of } O_2$$
$$(Exp. \ 9\text{-}15)$$

$$CH_4 \ (g) + 2O_2 \ (g) \rightarrow CO_2 \ (g) + 2H_2O \ (l)$$
$$\Delta H = -212.8 \text{ kcal/2 moles of } O_2 \quad (Exp. \ 9\text{-}16)$$

In this set of reactions, Expressions 9-13 and 9-15 together describe a system which forms carbon dioxide and water from carbon, hydrogen, and oxygen. Similarly, Expression 9-16 describes a system which forms carbon dioxide and water, but in this case from methane and oxygen.

If Expression 9-16 is reversed, the three expressions can be added to obtain the expression for the enthalpy of formation of methane. Figure 9-7 shows the enthalpy of formation of methane in diagrammatic form.

$$C \ (s) + O_2 \ (g) \rightarrow CO_2 \ (g) \quad \Delta H = -94.1 \text{ kcal} \quad (Exp. \ 9\text{-}13)$$

$$2H_2 \ (g) + O_2 \ (g) \rightarrow 2H_2O \ (l) \quad \Delta H = -136.6 \text{ kcal} \quad (Exp. \ 9\text{-}15)$$

$$CO_2 \ (g) + 2H_2O \ (l) \rightarrow CH_4 \ (g) + 2O_2 \ (g) \quad \Delta H = 212.8 \text{ kcal}$$
$$(Exp. \ 9\text{-}17)$$

$$C \ (s) + 2H_2 \ (g) \rightarrow CH_4 \ (g) \quad \Delta H = -17.9 \text{ kcal/mole of } CH_4$$
$$(Exp. \ 9\text{-}18)$$

The addition of the three expressions indicates that 1 mole of methane is 17.9 kcal lower in enthalpy than 1 mole of solid carbon and 2 moles of gaseous hydrogen; $\Delta H = -17.9$ kcal/mole of CH_4.

The procedure outlined for computing the enthalpy of formation for methane can be expressed in general terms.

1. Treat the chemical equations as if they are algebraic equations.
2. Add the enthalpies algebraically.
3. Manipulate the equations so that equal numbers of moles of undesired substances can be canceled to obtain the expression for the enthalpy of formation of the desired substance.

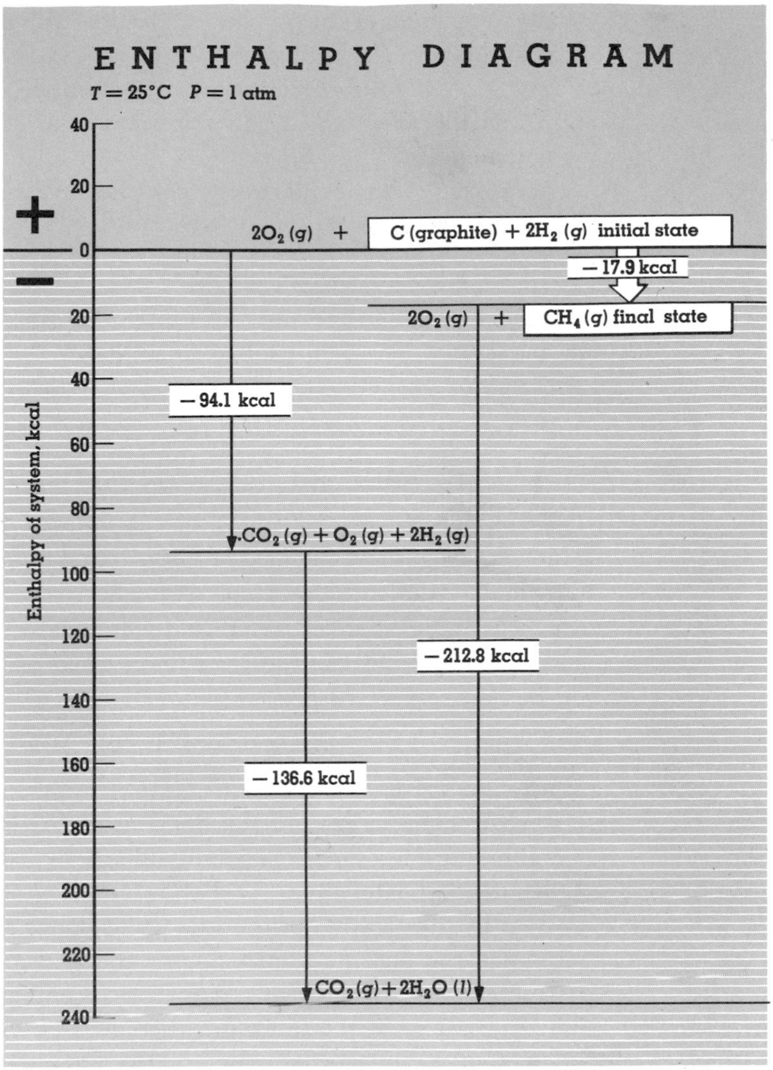

ENTHALPY DIAGRAM

$T = 25°C$ $P = 1$ atm

(y-axis: Enthalpy of system, kcal — marked 40, 20, 0, 20, 40, 60, 80, 100, 120, 140, 160, 180, 200, 220, 240)

$2O_2$ (g) + C (graphite) + $2H_2$ (g) initial state

−17.9 kcal

$2O_2$ (g) + CH_4 (g) final state

−94.1 kcal

CO_2 (g) + O_2 (g) + $2H_2$ (g)

−212.8 kcal

−136.6 kcal

CO_2 (g) + $2H_2O$ (l)

Fig. 9-7 Calculation of the enthalpy change for the formation of CH_4 from C (graphite) and H_2 (g).

9-10 BOND ENERGY IN HYDROGEN CHLORIDE

A chemical reaction can be viewed as a change in which bonds in reactants are broken and new bonds are made in products. Can enthalpy data be used to give values for the enthalpy changes associated with the breaking or making of a bond of a particular type?

When a chemical bond is formed in a system, the energy of the system becomes lower, that is, energy is transferred from the system. To break the same bond, an equivalent amount of energy must be transferred into the system. On this basis, **bond energy** can be defined as the enthalpy change when a mole of gaseous molecules separates into the constituent gaseous atoms. Gaseous molecules are specified so that the term bond energy can be limited to just that energy necessary to disrupt bonds within the mole of molecules. The energy necessary to separate molecules from each other in the liquid (heat of vaporization) or the solid (heat of sublimation) to effect a change in phase is not included.

For example, the bond energy per mole of HCl is the enthalpy change for the reaction in Equation 9-19.

$$HCl\ (g) \rightarrow H\ (g) + Cl\ (g) \qquad\qquad (Eq.\ 9\text{-}19)$$

A related reaction represented by Expression 9-20 can be carried out in the laboratory. The change in enthalpy for Expression 9-20 is the enthalpy of formation for 2 moles of HCl gas.

$$H_2\ (g) + Cl_2\ (g) \rightarrow 2HCl\ (g) \quad \Delta H = -44.0\ kcal \qquad (Exp.\ 9\text{-}20)$$

or $\quad \frac{1}{2}H_2\ (g) + \frac{1}{2}Cl_2\ (g) \rightarrow HCl\ (g) \quad \Delta H = -22.0\ kcal$

Enthalpy changes for two more reactions—the heat of dissociation of hydrogen gas and the heat of dissociation of chlorine gas—are needed to calculate the enthalpy change for the reaction represented in Equation 9-19. The changes in enthalpy for these two reactions are also equal to the bond energies of 1 mole each of hydrogen and chlorine molecules, respectively.

$$H_2\ (g) \rightarrow 2H\ (g) \quad \Delta H = ?$$
$$Cl_2\ (g) \rightarrow 2Cl\ (g) \quad \Delta H = ?$$

For the bond energy of the bond in the hydrogen molecule, experimental calorimetry data are available. If hydrogen gas made up of H_2 molecules is heated to several thousand degrees, hydrogen atoms are formed by dissociation of the molecules. Once formed, these atoms can be blown rapidly into a calorimeter and allowed to recombine to form H_2 molecules. Energy evolved in the recombination is transferred to the calorimeter and can be measured (Fig. 9-8). The change in enthalpy for the recombination is -104.2 kcal/mole of H_2 (Table 9-4).

$$H_2\ (g) \rightarrow 2H\ (g) \quad \Delta H = 104.2\ kcal/mole\ of\ H_2$$

For chlorine gas, satisfactory direct calorimetric measurements of the bond energy (enthalpy of dissociation) have never been made. Indirect techniques, however, give a bond energy of 57.8 kcal/mole of Cl_2.

$$Cl_2\ (g) \rightarrow 2Cl\ (g) \quad \Delta H = 57.8\ kcal/mole\ of\ Cl_2$$

These three enthalpies of reaction can be used to calculate the hydrogen–chlorine bond energy.

$$\frac{1}{2}H_2\ (g) + \frac{1}{2}Cl_2\ (g) \rightarrow HCl\ (g) \quad \Delta H = -22.0\ kcal$$
$$H\ (g) \rightarrow \frac{1}{2}H_2\ (g) \quad \Delta H = -52.1\ kcal$$
$$Cl\ (g) \rightarrow \frac{1}{2}Cl_2\ (g) \quad \Delta H = -28.9\ kcal$$

$$\overline{H\ (g) + Cl\ (g) \rightarrow HCl\ (g) \quad \Delta H = -103.0\ kcal/mole\ of\ HCl\ (g)}$$

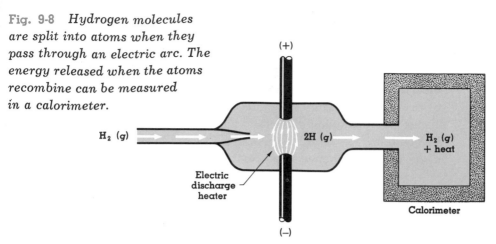

Fig. 9-8 *Hydrogen molecules are split into atoms when they pass through an electric arc. The energy released when the atoms recombine can be measured in a calorimeter.*

The last expression gives the enthalpy of formation of 1 mole of HCl gas from the gaseous atoms ($\Delta H = -103.0$ kcal). The reverse of the equation representing the dissociation of HCl to give gaseous atoms and the accompanying enthalpy change defines the bond energy of 1 mole of HCl molecules as 103.0 kcal/mole. An enthalpy diagram for arriving at the same conclusion is shown in Fig. 9-9.

Three bond energies have been discussed.

$$
\begin{array}{lll}
\text{H—H} & \Delta H = & 104.2 \ \text{kcal/mole} \\
\text{Cl—Cl} & \Delta H = & 57.8 \ \text{kcal/mole} \\
\text{H—Cl} & \Delta H = & 103.0 \ \text{kcal/mole}
\end{array}
$$

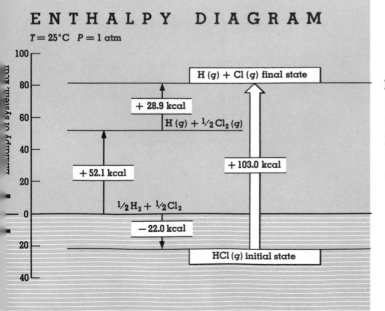

Fig. 9-9 *Calculation of the enthalpy change for the dissociation of HCl gas.*

In each of these three bonds, the dissociation of diatomic molecules into the two isolated atoms involved breaking only one type of bond. Hence, the energy absorbed as the molecules dissociated could be set equal to the bond energy. How can the enthalpy change be interpreted when a substance such as water (HOH), with two bonds per molecule, dissociates into atoms? For molecules with several bonds, the enthalpy change accompanying dissociation into atoms must equal the sum of the bond energies of all the bonds. Is it possible to determine what part of the enthalpy change is associated with each bond?

9-11 AVERAGE BOND ENERGIES

The imaginary steps in the synthesis of a water molecule from hydrogen and oxygen atoms are indicated in Expressions 9-21 to 9-24. Figure 9-10 presents the same data in the form of an enthalpy diagram.

Fig. 9-10 *Enthalpy change for the formation of water from hydrogen and oxygen atoms.*

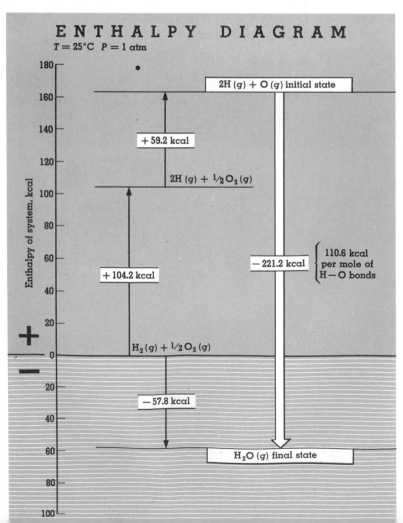

ENTHALPY DIAGRAM

$T = 25°C$ $P = 1$ atm

Enthalpy of system, kcal

2H (g) + O (g) initial state

+ 59.2 kcal

2H (g) + ½O₂ (g)

$$2H (g) + \tfrac{1}{2}O_2 (g)$$

+ 104.2 kcal

− 221.2 kcal

110.6 kcal per mole of H—O bonds

$$H_2 (g) + \tfrac{1}{2}O_2 (g)$$

− 57.8 kcal

H_2O (g) final state

If Expression 9-6 is reversed and divided by 2 to form Expression 9-23, and added to Expressions 9-21 and 9-22, Expression 9-24 is obtained.

$$H_2 \ (g) \to 2H \ (g) \quad \Delta H = 104.2 \ \text{kcal} \qquad (Exp. \ 9\text{-}21)$$

$$\tfrac{1}{2}O_2 \ (g) \to O \ (g) \quad \Delta H = 59.2 \ \text{kcal} \qquad (Exp. \ 9\text{-}22)$$

$$\underline{H_2O \ (g) \to H_2 \ (g) + \tfrac{1}{2}O_2 \ (g) \quad \Delta H = 57.8 \ \text{kcal} \qquad (Exp. \ 9\text{-}23)}$$

$$H_2O \ (g) \to 2H \ (g) + O \ (g) \quad \Delta H = 221.2 \ \text{kcal/mole of } H_2O$$
$$(Exp. \ 9\text{-}24)$$

Expression 9-24 represents the complete dissociation of water molecules into hydrogen and oxygen atoms. The reaction in Expression 9-24 requires the breaking of two hydrogen–oxygen bonds in each water molecule. The charge cloud model (Section 7-17) indicates that the two hydrogen–oxygen bonds in the intact water molecule are identical. The bond energy for each hydrogen–oxygen bond in water then must be 110.6 kcal/mole of H—O bonds.

The calculation of the bond energy of the hydrogen–carbon bonds in methane may also be carried out by the same method used to determine the hydrogen–oxygen bond energy in gaseous H_2O. Figure 9-11 is an enthalpy diagram which permits the determination of the enthalpy change for the reaction

$$C \ (g) + 4H \ (g) \to CH_4 \ (g)$$

The result is −398.0 kcal/mole of CH_4. Consequently, the bond energy for one H—C bond in methane at 25°C is one-fourth of 398.0 or 99.5 kcal/mole of H—C bonds.

In ethane (H_3C—CH_3) there are two different types of bonds, six carbon–hydrogen bonds and one carbon–carbon bond (Fig. 7-22a). How can experimental data be used to calculate a bond energy for the carbon–carbon bond linking the two carbon atoms? The change in enthalpy associated with the formation of ethane gas from the isolated C and H atoms represents the sum of all seven bond energies. The assignment of proper proportions of the enthalpy change among the carbon–hydrogen and carbon–carbon bonds requires some independent way of arriving at the magnitude of the bond energy of either the C—C bond or the C—H bond. If each of the C—H bonds in ethane is assumed to have the same bond energy as one of the bonds in methane, the bond energy for the carbon–carbon bond in ethane can be calculated.

Figures 9-12 and 9-13 are enthalpy diagrams which give enthalpy data for ethane (C_2H_6). The enthalpies of combustion of ethane, graphite, and hydrogen can be used to obtain a numerical value of −20.3 kcal for the ethalpy of formation of 1 mole of ethane from 2 moles of graphite and 3 moles of hydrogen gas (Fig. 9-12).

$$2C \ (s) + 3H_2 \ (g) \to C_2H_6 \ (g) \quad \Delta H = -20.3 \ \text{kcal} \qquad (Exp. \ 9\text{-}25)$$

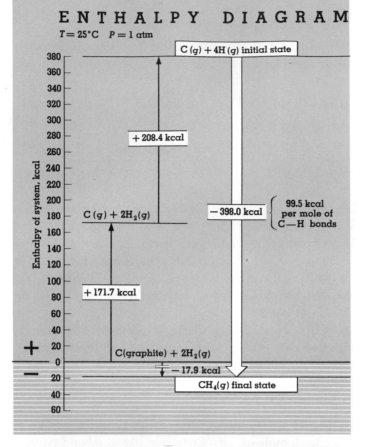

Fig. 9-11 *Enthalpy change for the reaction* C (g) + 4H (g) → CH₄ (g).

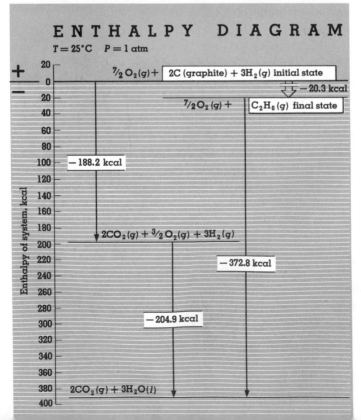

Fig. 9-12 *Enthalpy change for the formation of ethane from graphite and hydrogen.*

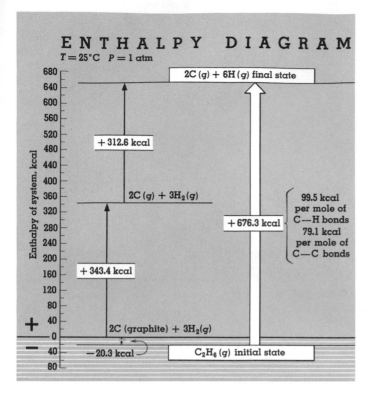

ENTHALPY DIAGRAM
$T = 25°C$ $P = 1$ atm

680
640
600
560
520
480
440
400
360
320
280
240
200
160
120
80
40
0
40
80

Enthalpy of system, kcal

$+$

$-$

2C (g) + 6H (g) final state

+ 312.6 kcal

2C (g) + 3H₂(g)

+ 676.3 kcal

99.5 kcal
per mole of
C—H bonds
79.1 kcal
per mole of
C—C bonds

+ 343.4 kcal

2C (graphite) + 3H₂(g)

− 20.3 kcal

C₂H₆ (g) initial state

Fig. 9-13 *Enthalpy change for the dissociation of ethane.*

The dissociation of ethane to atoms,

$$C_2H_6 \ (g) \rightarrow 2C \ (g) + 6H \ (g)$$

is indicated on the diagram as $\Delta H = 676.3$ kcal/mole of C_2H_6 (Fig. 9-13). The breaking of 6 moles of carbon–hydrogen bonds identical to those in methane requires $6 \times 99.5 = 597.0$ kcal. Therefore, the energy required to break 1 mole of carbon–carbon bonds in ethane is the difference between 676.3 kcal and 597.0 kcal, or 79.3 kcal.

$$C—C \rightarrow 2C \ (g) \quad \Delta H = 676.3 - 597.0 = 79.3 \text{ kcal}$$

The calculation of bond energies for bonds in other substances containing carbon–carbon and carbon–hydrogen bonds gives numerical values in many cases that agree with the bond energies in ethane to within about 5 percent. It is reasonable to assume then that carbon–hydrogen and carbon–carbon bond energies are practically constant from one molecule to another. In methane, which, of course, contains no carbon–carbon bond, the bond energy for the carbon–hydrogen bond differs from the same bond in other carbon–hydrogen compounds by 0.7 kcal/mole of C—H bonds. Bond energies are given in Table 9-5.

TABLE 9-5 BOND ENERGIES AT 25°C

Bond	Bond Energy, kcal/mole
H—H	104.2
Cl—Cl	57.8
H—Cl	103.0
O—O	33.2[a]
O—O	118.3[b]
Br—Br	46.1
H—Br	87.5
C—C (from ethane)	79.3
C—C (average for many different substances)	83.1
C—H (from methane)	99.5
C—H (average for many different substances)	98.8
C—Cl	78.5

[a] Value given is for O—O bond in hydrogen peroxide.
[b] Value given is for O—O bond in O_2 molecule.

A bond energy represents an enthalpy change for an imagined reaction. If the equations for reactions and the enthalpy changes for the reactions can be combined so as to give a sum which includes all the bonds in a mole of a particular substance, then the sum of the corresponding bond energies will represent the energy absorbed when a mole of the substance dissociates into free atoms.

Bond energies can be used in the same ways and for the same purposes that enthalpies of formation can be used. Enthalpies of formation are based on the elements in their standard states, but bond energies are based on the elements as free, gaseous atoms.

If the bond energy of a particular type of bond is assumed to be constant from one molecule to the next, the enthalpy change accompanying a chemical reaction can be calculated. For example, the enthalpy of reaction for the formation of HCl and CH_3Cl (methyl chloride) by the reaction of chlorine and methane can be calculated.

$$CH_4 + Cl_2 \rightarrow CH_3Cl + HCl$$

The calculations can be performed in tabular form, proceeding on the assumption that all old single bonds in reactants are broken and that all new single bonds are formed in the products.

Bonds Broken		Bonds Formed	
4 C—H (4 × 99.5) = +398.0 kcal		H—Cl = −103.0 kcal	
Cl—Cl = +57.8 kcal		3 C—H (3 × 99.5) = −298.5 kcal	
+455.8 kcal		C—Cl = −78.5 kcal	
		−480.0 kcal	

The net enthalpy change then is $-480.0 + 455.8 = -24.2$ kcal/mole of either reactant or either product. The experimentally determined enthalpy change for this reaction is -28 kcal/mole of CH_4, which agrees with the calculated value within 4 kcal/mole.

Ex. 9-7   A reaction of nitrogen atoms and hydrogen atoms and the corresponding enthalpy change are given as

$$N \ (g) + 3H \ (g) \rightarrow NH_3 \ (g) \qquad \Delta H = -279.8 \text{ kcal/mole of } NH_3$$

Calculate the bond energy for the nitrogen–hydrogen bond in ammonia, NH_3.

Ex. 9-8   Calculate from bond energies the enthalpy change for the reaction

$$3CH_4 \rightarrow C_3H_8 + 2H_2$$

9-12   BOND ENERGIES AND STRUCTURAL MODELS

The use of the term bond energy implies that the energies in Table 9-5 have some relationship to the bonds that have been postulated to explain the structural models of compounds. The energies in Table 9-5 were derived from measurements of energy transferred during a reaction. Models were used only to decide that there was one single bond in a hydrogen chloride molecule, two single bonds in a water molecule, or four single bonds in a methane molecule. In Chapter 8 the point was made that the charge cloud models developed in Chapter 7 were for structures at absolute zero. At other temperatures each molecule has an energy higher than that at $0°K$. This higher energy results from the absorption of energy to increase translational, rotational, and vibrational energies (Section 8-23).

The bond energies recorded in Table 9-5 are based on data obtained at 25°C. Does the contribution of the kinetic energy of the molecule at 25°C seriously complicate the interpretation of bond energies in terms of features of the structural models for the components of the system?

One solution to the problem would be to conduct the measurement of bond energies at $0°K$ where the kinetic energy of the structural units is zero. However, no one has ever been able to have a reaction take place at absolute zero. There is another way to an answer, however.

In measurements of the enthalpy of combustion of methane, all that is necessary is an initial state of 25°C and a final state of 25°C. The reaction itself raises the temperature momentarily to several hundred degrees above 25°C. But for the overall enthalpy change, only the initial and final temperatures need be considered.

It is possible to carry out reactions in such a way that the initial and final states of the system are at a temperature close to 0°K even though the reaction will not occur at absolute zero. The reactants are warmed to some higher temperature at which the reaction (change in structure) takes place, and the products of the reaction are cooled. The quantity of heat that must be transferred from the system to cool it to the temperature of the initial state following the reaction must be measured. A specially designed low-temperature calorimeter is needed. The data obtained for the bond energies which correspond to numerical values that would have been measured at 0°K are listed in Table 9-6. The first entries in the table are for molecules with single bonds, and the last three entries show molecules with multiple bonds.

Bond energy data in Table 9-6 show that between values at 0°K and 298°K the differences are not more than about 1 kcal/mole. This is a relative change of about 1 percent in the bond energy for a change in temperature of about 300°. The contribution of the kinetic energy of molecules to bond energies at 25°C therefore proves to be minor. It is reasonable to assume that bond energies do indeed reflect the quantities of energy transferred from the system when two atoms join together. For all calculations where an accuracy of about 1 kcal/mole is adequate, bond energy data at 25°C should be satisfactory and are more convenient to obtain than bond energy data at 0°K. The small difference between bond energies at 25°C and 0°K makes it reasonable to interpret the values for bond energies at 25°C in terms of the electron charge cloud model. The effects of kinetic energy of molecules can be ignored in thinking about the relation of bond energy to the structure of matter for a system whose temperature is within a few hundred degrees of absolute zero.

TABLE 9-6   BOND ENERGIES AT 0°K AND 298°K

Bond	Substance Used	Bond Energies, kcal/mole	
		at 0°K	at 298°K
F—F	F_2	35.6	36.6
Cl—Cl	Cl_2	57.2	57.8
H—Cl	HCl	102.2	103.0
H—H	H_2	103.2	104.2
H—O	H_2O	109.5	110.6
H—C	CH_4	98.2	99.5
C—C	C_2H_6	77.7	79.3
C=C	C_2H_4	139.9	143.3
C≡C	C_2H_2	193.3	194.4
N≡N	N_2	225.0	226.0

The bond energies in Table 9-6 range from a low numerical value for the fluorine–fluorine bond in fluorine gas to a high numerical value for the carbon–carbon bond in acetylene. In the sequence of carbon–carbon bonds present in ethane, ethylene, and acetylene, the numerical values increase in stepwise fashion. In ethylene the C—C bond energy is nearly twice the bond energy for the C—C bond in ethane, whereas the numerical value for the bond in acetylene is nearly three times the numerical value for the C—C single bond in ethane.

In Section 7-20 ethane, ethylene, and acetylene were considered to have a single, a double, and a triple bond between the two carbon atoms, respectively. The magnitudes of the carbon–carbon bond energies for C_2H_6, C_2H_4, and C_2H_2 can be arranged in an order that corresponds to the order single, double, and triple.

Ex. 9-9   Applying data from tables in this chapter and a method similar to that used to calculate the bond energy for the carbon–carbon single bond in ethane, determine the bond energy for the carbon–carbon double bond in ethylene, C_2H_4.

9-13   BOND ENERGIES IN CARBON DIOXIDE

It is possible to calculate the enthalpy change for the reaction shown in Expression 9-26 and Fig. 9-14.

$$CO_2 \text{ (g)} \rightarrow CO \text{ (g)} + O \text{ (g)} \quad \Delta H = 126.9 \text{ kcal} \qquad (Exp.\ 9\text{-}26a)$$

For the decomposition of carbon dioxide into carbon atoms and oxygen atoms, the enthalpy change is

$$CO_2 \text{ (g)} \rightarrow C \text{ (g)} + 2O \text{ (g)} \quad \Delta H = 384.2 \text{ kcal} \qquad (Exp.\ 9\text{-}26b)$$

If the equation in Expression 9-26a is reversed and added to the equation in Expression 9-26b,

$CO \text{ (g)} + O \text{ (g)} \rightarrow CO_2 \text{ (g)}$	$\Delta H = -126.9 \text{ kcal}$	
$CO_2 \text{ (g)} \rightarrow C \text{ (g)} + 2O \text{ (g)}$	$\Delta H = 384.2 \text{ kcal}$	
$CO \text{ (g)} \rightarrow C \text{ (g)} + O \text{ (g)}$	$\Delta H = 257.3 \text{ kcal}$	$(Exp.\ 9\text{-}27)$

the result implies that the second oxygen atom in carbon dioxide is held by a bond energy of 126.9 kcal and the first by a bond energy of 257.3 kcal. On the other hand, the data for complete decomposition of carbon dioxide (384.2 kcal) could be interpreted as representing two bonds of equal energy of 192.1 kcal. Which is the better choice?

A charge cloud model for carbon dioxide was described in Section 7-20. With three nuclei in a CO_2 molecule, the repulsion of the oxygen nuclei for each other would explain the structure in which an oxygen atom is located on each side of the carbon nucleus. Of the 22 electrons in carbon dioxide, six form three compact two-electron clouds that

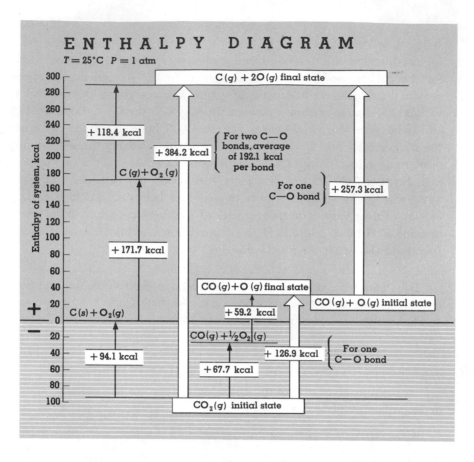

Fig. 9-14 *Enthalpy changes for the decomposition of carbon dioxide and carbon monoxide.*

make up the kernels of the three atoms. The remaining 16 electrons are arranged in eight two-electron charge clouds, which are represented by the compact set of spheres in Fig. 9-15. This is the low-energy arrangement in which eight two-electron clouds can be assembled around one carbon and two oxygen kernels. The model for the structure of the CO_2 molecule indicates that the two oxygen atoms occupy equivalent positions relative to the carbon nucleus within the molecule. Therefore, each of the two carbon–oxygen bond energies in CO_2 should be equal to each other and have a magnitude of 192.1 kcal.

Ex. 9-10   If the charge cloud model of CO_2 in Fig. 7-28 and the bond energy of the carbon–oxygen bonds, 192.1 kcal, are accepted, explain why the numerical value $\Delta H = 126.9$ kcal for the reaction

$$CO_2 \ (g) \to CO \ (g) + O \ (g)$$

is different from the numerical value $\Delta H = 192.1$ kcal for breaking one double bond in CO_2.

In Experiment 8 in *Investigating Chemical Systems,* when dilute hydrochloric acid was added to water, the temperature of the resulting solution was observed to be higher than the temperature of the initial unmixed liquids. In other words, a system in which water and dilute hydrochloric acid are present initially in separate containers has a temperature-changing capacity in comparison with the same system in which the water and hydrochloric acid have been finally mixed. That is, the enthalpy change for the reaction at constant temperature is negative. What changes within the system are associated with the enthalpy change?

In terms of the relationship between enthalpy changes and structural changes, as the hydrochloric acid is diluted with water, some rearrangement must occur among the charge clouds and nuclei of the system. The rearrangement produces a final state with lower enthalpy than the initial state since heat is transferred out of the system.

When gaseous hydrogen chloride is mixed with water, an exothermic reaction occurs. When this reaction occurs to produce a product in which 12 moles of HCl are dissolved per liter of the final solution, the change in enthalpy is about 14.2 kcal/mole of HCl dissolved. When a solution is prepared from the separated components, hydrogen chloride and water, the change in enthalpy per mole of solute is called the **enthalpy of solution** or **heat of solution.**

When an initial solution that is 12 M in HCl is diluted to produce a final solution that is 6 M in HCl, about 2 kcal of heat is evolved per mole of HCl. The dilution of a solution by a solvent gives a change in enthalpy that is called **enthalpy of dilution** or **heat of dilution.**

Hydrogen chloride gas and water can be combined in various ratios to produce final solutions covering a range of concentration from near

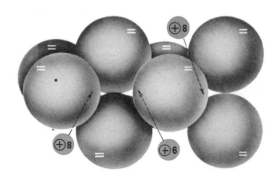

Fig. 9-15   *Charge cloud model of carbon dioxide.*

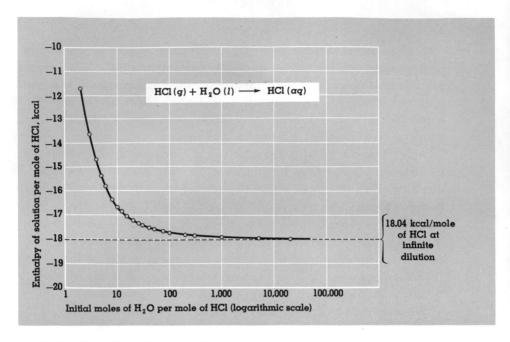

The graph shows enthalpy of solution per mole of HCl, kcal on the y-axis (from -10 to -20) and Initial moles of H₂O per mole of HCl (logarithmic scale) on the x-axis (from 1 to 100,000).

The equation on the graph reads: $HCl(g) + H_2O(l) \longrightarrow HCl(aq)$

The y-axis is labeled "Enthalpy of solution per mole of HCl, kcal" and the x-axis is labeled "Initial moles of H₂O per mole of HCl (logarithmic scale)". The dashed horizontal line is labeled "18.04 kcal/mole of HCl at infinite dilution".

Fig. 9-16   *Enthalpy changes when hydrogen chloride dissolves in water.*

0 *M* to about 12 *M*. In Fig. 9-16 the enthalpies of solution are plotted against final concentration. The curve describing the enthalpy of solution approaches a limiting magnitude of 18.0 kcal/mole of HCl as the concentration of the solution approaches zero. For high concentrations, the enthalpy of solution changes considerably for a small change in concentration. In other words, at high concentration the curve has a greater slope than at low concentration. As the solution becomes progressively more dilute, the curve becomes more nearly horizontal. When the concentration is so small that adding more solvent does not detectably change the properties of the solution, the solution is said to be at **infinite dilution.**

Solutions are homogeneous, which means that the dissolved material in a solution is spread uniformly throughout the solvent. In a solution containing a given number of dissolved particles at high concentration, the number of particles per unit volume is large. If the same number of particles are dissolved to produce a solution of low concentration, there will be fewer particles per unit volume.

As a solution is diluted, the dissolved particles in a solution are separated farther and farther from each other. Separating the particles in a hydrochloric acid solution by dilution lowers the enthalpy of the system, that is, energy is transferred from the system. Since no such change in enthalpy is found when hydrogen chloride gas is allowed to expand in the absence of water, it would be reasonable to conclude that the hydrogen chloride and the water interact when they are mixed. The enthalpy of dilution indicates that the addition of more water produces more interaction which results in the transfer of energy from the system.

Hydrochloric acid solutions will conduct electricity, so that ions must be present. If the properties of hydrogen chloride are analogous to those of hydrogen fluoride, a proton-transfer reaction could take place similar to that described for hydrogen fluoride in Section 7-22. This suggests that the dissolving of hydrogen chloride is a chemical reaction represented by

$$HCl \ (g) + H_2O \ (l) \rightarrow H_3O^+ \ (aq) + Cl^- \ (aq) \quad \Delta H = -18.0 \ \text{kcal}$$
$$(Exp. \ 9\text{-}28)$$

where aq means that the ions are in water (aqueous) solution.

Enthalpies of solution and enthalpies of dilution not only provide data to aid in the interpretation of the nature of solutions, but they have other uses as well. As one example, consider the problem of determining the enthalpy of formation of solid ammonium chloride (prepared in Experiment 18 in *Investigating Chemical Systems* by the reaction of gases). This compound is prepared in Experiment 22 by adding aqueous ammonia to aqueous hydrogen chloride.

The enthalpy of formation of NH_4Cl, however, is the enthalpy change accompanying the following reaction.

$$\tfrac{1}{2}N_2 \ (g) + 2H_2 \ (g) + \tfrac{1}{2}Cl_2 \ (g) \rightarrow NH_4Cl \ (s)$$

To calculate the enthalpy of formation of NH_4Cl from data for the reaction in aqueous solutions, knowledge of the enthalpies of solution of the various components of the system is required. Experiment 22 is a search for the data needed and an analysis of the data to calculate the enthalpy of formation for solid ammonium chloride.

Enthalpy changes give evidence of and point the way to an interpretation of interactions in a system. Enthalpy changes by themselves, however, are insufficient to permit a complete interpretation. A more complete understanding seems to be provided by considering both the enthalpy changes and the structural changes which must occur together.

9-15 VOLUME CHANGE AND ENTHALPY CHANGE

In Chapter 8 phase changes for a substance were related to the transfer of energy. A change in phase of a system at constant temperature is always accompanied by a transfer of energy to or from the surroundings. The change from liquid to gas is always endothermic and is always accompanied by a volume increase for the system. All changes from

TABLE 9-7 DENSITIES AND VOLUMES PER MOLE OF HYDROGEN
CHLORIDE IN TWO SOLUTIONS AT 25°C

Concentration, moles of HCl/liter	Density, g/ml	Quantity of Solution per Mole of HCl	
		Volume, ml	Mass, g
12.0	1.183	83.3	98.5
6.0	1.098	166.7	183.0

solid to liquid are endothermic, and most, but not all, known melting phenomena are accompanied by volume increase for the system.

The dilution of 12.0 M hydrochloric acid to 6.0 M is accompanied by an enthalpy change of about -2 kcal/mole of HCl. From the densities of the solutions, the mass of each solution per mole of HCl can be calculated. The volume of solution per mole of HCl can be calculated as 1,000 ml divided by the molarity. The data are collected in Table 9-7. To dilute 83.3 ml of 12.0 M HCl solution to 166.7 ml of 6.0 M HCl solution requires the addition of 84.5 ml of water instead of only 83.4 ml as one might expect. The change in volume ΔV as the system goes from the initial state to the final state is therefore

$$\Delta V = 166.7 - (83.3 + 84.5) = -1.1 \text{ ml}$$

In the dilution of hydrochloric acid, then, enthalpy decrease in the system is accompanied by decrease in volume.

In Experiment 6, lead iodide was precipitated by the reaction

$$Pb(NO_3)_2 \ (aq) + 2KI \ (aq) \rightarrow PbI_2 \ (s) + 2KNO_3 \ (aq)$$

From the mass per mole and the densities, the volume occupied by a mole of each component as a solid can be calculated. The volumes obtained are listed in Table 9-8.

TABLE 9-8 DENSITIES AND VOLUMES PER MOLE OF COMPONENTS
FOR LEAD IODIDE FORMATION

Component	Molar mass, g	Density, g/ml	Volume of 1 Mole, ml
$Pb(NO_3)_2$	331.2	4.53	73.1
KI	166.0	3.13	53.1
KNO_3	101.1	2.11	47.9
PbI_2	461.0	6.16	74.7

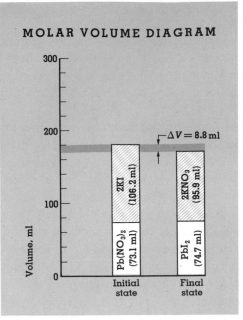

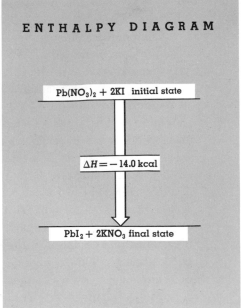

Fig. 9-17 *In the system represented by the equation*
$Pb(NO_3)_2 + 2KI \rightarrow PbI_2 + 2KNO_3$, *there is a
decrease in volume of 8.8 ml/mole of PbI_2 and an
enthalpy change of 14.0 kcal/mole of PbI_2.*

Comparison of the solid components present in reactants and products
gives a volume decrease of 8.8 ml/mole of PbI_2.

$$\Delta V = 74.7 + 2(47.9) - 73.1 - 2(53.1) = -8.8 \text{ ml/mole } PbI_2$$

The enthalpy change is -14.0 kcal/mole of PbI_2.

$$Pb(NO_3)_2 \ (aq) + 2KI \ (aq) \rightarrow PbI_2 \ (s) + 2KNO_3 \ (aq)$$
$$\Delta H = -14.0 \text{ kcal}$$

In this case also a decrease in enthalpy in the system accompanies a
decrease in volume.

There appears to be a general correlation between volume decrease
and enthalpy decrease. It may be possible to interpret this correlation
in terms of changes in structure. In Chapter 7 chemical change was
interpreted in terms of rearrangement of charge clouds and nuclei resulting in an arrangement of the charges to give lower energy. If the
charges fit together more compactly, this should reduce the volume of
the system. The fall in electrostatic energy should manifest itself as a
decrease in enthalpy in the system.

There are exceptions to the correlation of volume decrease and enthalpy decrease. One example is the freezing of water. This is an
exothermic process which is accompanied by a volume increase. A
tendency to form more compact systems is an important but not the
only reason for change in a system.

Temperature change and chemical change have a close association in a number of systems. This association has been studied in laboratory experiments with the dilution of hydrochloric acid, the vaporization of a liquid, the reaction of an acid and a base, and the formation of ammonium chloride.

Whenever separated substances make up the reactants of a system, the system has a capacity to change temperature as the system goes from its initial to its final state. It is possible to connect the system to its surroundings so that an energy (heat) transfer takes place. Transferring heat makes it possible to keep the system at a constant temperature and to convert the temperature-changing capacity into an energy-transferring capacity. Enthalpy is the aspect of the state of a system that is related to the energy-transferring capacity of the system. During chemical change at constant temperature, the enthalpy of a chemical system changes as a result of the transfer of heat.

Enthalpy changes are conveniently measured for the reaction of oxygen with many substances. The enthalpy changes are called enthalpies of combustion. Some compounds can be prepared directly from elements so that direct measurements give the enthalpy of formation.

Energy transferred must indicate a corresponding energy change within a system. Whatever the sequence of steps between initial and final state, the total enthalpy change must always be the same. This conclusion is called Hess's law. The conclusion that enthalpy change is determined only by initial and final states makes it possible to construct a bookkeeping system.

The enthalpy changes in a sequence of reactions can be added algebraically so as to give a magnitude for the overall change. By this trick, using Hess's law, enthalpies of formation can be computed for compounds which cannot be prepared directly from the elements in the laboratory. To develop enthalpies of formation that have greatest usefulness, it is necessary to define a standard state for each element. The standard state of an element is taken as the free form of each element at 1 atmosphere pressure and a specified temperature, commonly 25°C.

Numerical values can be obtained for the energy absorbed as each element in its standard state is converted into a state made up of gaseous atoms. With these data it is possible to compute the enthalpy changes for the breaking up of gaseous molecules to give gaseous atoms. The enthalpy always increases in this change and the numerical values obtained are called bond energies.

Bonds between atoms were proposed as the result of a study of structural models. The interpretation of an enthalpy change as a bond energy is therefore based on the assumption that there is a link between reaction energies and structure changes.

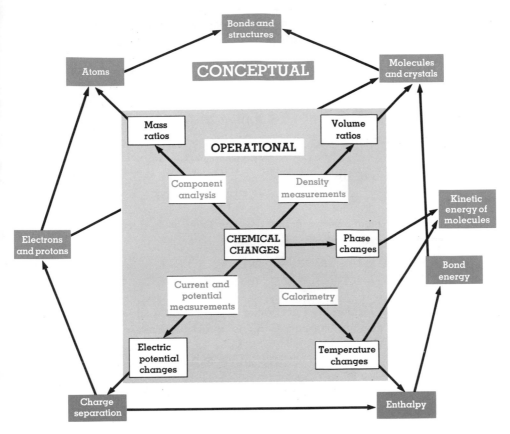

Fig. 9-18 *Changes in properties related to chemical changes and to concepts (mental models) that have been devised to explain chemical changes.*

When solutions are formed, energy changes occur. These changes must be tied to some interaction between the substances which form the solution. The enthalpy change produced by adding 1 mole of a substance to a solvent to form a solution is called a heat of solution. The change of concentration of a solution by the addition of solvent produces an enthalpy change called the heat of dilution.

An enthalpy decrease in a system is often accompanied by a volume decrease. This fits in with an earlier discussion of a chemical system in terms of its electrical properties. In an electrical system, change is likely to produce a final state which places positive and negative charges closer together. As the electric charges draw closer together, the system achieves a more compact structure and lower total energy.

Much of the discussion of enthalpy and the relationship between bond energy and features of structural models can be summarized by a diagram. Figure 9-18 is an adaptation and enlargement of Fig. 5-1.

How many kilocalories of heat are necessary to decompose 13.5 g of H_2O (g) into H_2 (g) and O_2 (g) at 25°C and 1 atmosphere pressure?

Ex. 9-12 From the information given in Table 9-4 and below, determine the bond energy of the H—Br bond.

a. Dissociation of H_2

$$H_2 \ (g) \rightarrow 2H \ (g)$$

b. Vaporization of Br_2

$$Br_2 \ (l) \rightarrow Br_2 \ (g) \qquad \Delta H = 7.0 \ kcal$$

c. Formation of HBr

$$H_2 \ (g) + Br_2 \ (l) \rightarrow 2HBr \ (g) \qquad \Delta H = -17.3 \ kcal$$

Ex. 9-13 Using the bond energy data given in Table 9-5, calculate the change in enthalpy for the following reactions.

a. $\frac{1}{2}H_2 \ (g) + \frac{1}{2}Br_2 \ (g) \rightarrow HBr \ (g)$

b. $CH_4 \ (g) + 4Cl_2 \ (g) \rightarrow CCl_4 \ (g) + 4HCl \ (g)$

Ex. 9-14 The heat of formation of acetylene, C_2H_2, is 54.2 kcal, and the heat of formation of gaseous benzene, C_6H_6, is 20 kcal. Calculate the change in enthalpy for the reaction

$$3C_2H_2 \ (g) \rightarrow C_6H_6 \ (g)$$

Ex. 9-15 A chemist conducted an experiment in which he exploded a flash bulb in a calorimeter. Some of the observations he made for this experiment are given in the table.

Flash Bulb	Mass of Bulb before Exploding, g	Mass of Bulb after Exploding, g	Heat Released, kcal	Mass of Al_2O_3 Produced, g
1	9.58	9.57	0.41	0.10
2	9.42	9.43	0.39	0.09
3	9.75	9.75	0.42	0.11

a. How much mass transfer out of the bulb would the quantities of energy in the table represent?

b. How can the data presented in the table and the answer to part a be used to explain the fact that chemists are not usually concerned with changes in mass which accompany the absorption or evolution of heat by a system?

Ex. 9-16 The reaction

$$\frac{1}{2}H_2 \ (g) + \frac{1}{2}Cl_2 \ (g) \rightarrow HCl \ (aq)$$

can be thought of as proceeding via the following steps.

a. $\frac{1}{2}H_2 \ (g) \rightarrow H \ (g) \qquad \Delta H =$ (Use tables in this chapter.)

b. $\frac{1}{2}Cl_2 \ (g) \rightarrow Cl \ (g) \qquad \Delta H =$ (Use tables in this chapter.)

c. H (g) + Cl (g) → HCl (g) $\Delta H = -103.0$ kcal

d. HCl (g) → HCl (aq) $\Delta H = -17.0$ kcal

Make an enthalpy diagram for the net reaction. From the diagram you have made, what is the enthalpy change of the net reaction?

Ex. 9-17 Using equations from the chapter, calculate the amount of heat liberated by the formation of the following.

a. 2.0 g of HBr (g) from H_2 (g) and Br_2 (g)

b. One molecule of HBr (g) from H_2 (g) and Br_2 (g)

Ex. 9-18 a. The assigned enthalpy for each free element in its reference state is zero. For example, H_2 (g) and O_2 (g) are each assigned zero enthalpy. Does this indicate that the energy stored in each of these gases at 25°C and 1 atmosphere pressure is zero? Explain your answer.

b. What is the convention for assigning positive and negative signs to changes of enthalpy?

c. How does Hess's law of heat summation (additivity of enthalpy data) represent the law of conservation of energy?

Ex. 9-19 a. Using the data given in Table 9-4, and the expressions

$$H_2 \ (g) + F_2 \ (g) → 2HF \ (g) \qquad \Delta H = -128.5 \text{ kcal}$$
$$H_2 \ (g) + I_2 \ (s) → 2HI \ (g) \qquad \Delta H = 12.4 \text{ kcal}$$

calculate the bond energy for the H—F bond in hydrogen fluoride and the H—I bond in hydrogen iodide.

b. Using the bond energy data in Table 9-5, compare the bond energies for the bonds in HF, HI, HCl, and HBr.

Ex. 9-20 The heat of formation of gaseous CF_4 is -162.5 kcal/mole. Estimate the bond energy for the C—F bond. Why is the C—F bond energy different from the C—Cl bond energy?

$$C \ (s) → C \ (g) \qquad \Delta H = 171.7 \text{ kcal}$$

Ex. 9-21 Use the following information to determine the C—C bond energy in acetylene, C_2H_2.

a. Formation of acetylene

$$H_2 \ (g) + 2C \ (s) → C_2H_2 \ (g) \qquad \Delta H = 54.2 \text{ kcal}$$

b. Sublimation of graphite (carbon)

$$C \ (s) → C \ (g) \qquad \Delta H = 171.7 \text{ kcal}$$

c. Dissociation of hydrogen

$$H_2 \ (g) → 2H \ (g) \qquad \Delta H = 104.2 \text{ kcal}$$

d. Formation of methane (formation of four C—H bonds)

$$C \ (g) + 4H \ (g) → CH_4 \ (g) \qquad \Delta H = -398.0 \text{ kcal}$$

Ex. 9-22 Refer to Fig. 9–16 and answer the following questions by interpreting the graph in which ΔH per mole of HCl is plotted against moles of water.

a. What is the heat of solution per mole of HCl for a system consisting of 5 moles of water per mole of HCl? for a system consisting of 10 moles of water per mole of HCl?

b. Apply Hess's law to the production of an infinitely dilute HCl solution containing 1 mole of HCl. Prepare the dilute solution (1) by preparing a concentrated 12 M solution of HCl and diluting this solution with a large volume of water, and (2) by dissolving HCl gas in water to form a solution whose concentration is the same as that formed in (1).

Ex. 9-23 Compute the heat of formation of gaseous CCl_4 from energy of sublimation of graphite and bond energy data. Although the four C—F bonds have a bond energy only about 80 kcal more than for four C—Cl bonds, the difference between heats of formation is considerably greater than 80 kcal. Why?

Ex. 9-24 It is observed in many chemical systems that an exothermic change is accompanied by a decrease in volume, even though the mass remains fixed. In terms of the charge cloud model, how are energy and volume connected so as to indicate the reasonableness of the association?

Ex. 9-25 The enthalpy of solution of solid sodium chloride, NaCl (s), is $+0.4$ kcal/ mole of NaCl dissolved. Estimate the enthalpy change if enough NaCl is dissolved in 100 ml of water to form a saturated solution. The solubility of NaCl (s) is 6.2 moles/liter of solution at 25°C. What is the approximate change in the temperature of the resulting solution?

Ex. 9-26 In each part of this question, write the chemical equation from the word description given, indicate the number of moles of oxygen required to react with 1 mole of reactant and the number of moles of each product formed, and determine the mass of each product formed per gram of reactant.

a. One mole of carbon disulfide, CS_2, reacts with oxygen to produce carbon dioxide, CO_2, and sulfur dioxide, SO_2.

b. One mole of propanol, C_3H_7OH, reacts with oxygen to produce water and carbon dioxide.

c. One mole of phosphine, PH_3, reacts with oxygen to produce phosphorus oxide, P_4O_{10}.

ELECTRONS, NUCLEI, AND ORBITALS

WHEN A CHEMICAL CHANGE in a system occurs in such a way that no energy can be transferred into or out of the system, some temperature change always accompanies the chemical change. The temperature of some systems in their final states may be many hundreds of degrees above that for the initial states.

In Chapter 9, the quantities of energy transferred into or out of chemical systems were measured for changes that occurred in such a way that the system had the same initial and final temperatures. The measured quantities of energy were interpreted as enthalpies of formation and as bond energies.

Bond energies computed from energy changes provide a link between experimental observations and models relating the structure and properties of atoms and molecules. Molecules are structures which are essentially described in terms of the electric interaction of electrons and nuclei. What observations can be made if chemical changes are studied in systems arranged so that the final temperature is quite high? Do systems at high temperature exhibit any properties that provide further insight into the nature of chemical change?

When charcoal, or coal, or solid carbon burns in air, the temperature of the reacting system will usually be at least 400°C and may range upward to 3000°C or even higher. The temperature depends on the

TABLE 10-1 TEMPERATURE AND INCANDESCENT COLORS

Temperature, °C	Color
600–900	Dull red
900–1000	Cherry red
1000–1100	Orange
1100–1200	Yellow
1200–1300	White
1300–1500	Brilliant white
Above 1500	Dazzling white

SOURCE: N. A. Lange, *Handbook of Chemistry*, 10th ed., McGraw-Hill Book Company, Inc., New York, 1961.

concentration of oxygen in the gas mixture in contact with the carbon and the rate at which the heat produced by the reaction is dissipated to the surroundings.

If, for example, the mole ratio of oxygen to carbon is increased by substituting pure oxygen for air in the system, the temperature of the system will rise. Along with the increase in temperature, the color of the solid carbon changes. At about 600°C the solid carbon glows with a faint dull-red color. As the temperature is increased, the red color becomes brighter and yellower. At temperatures above 1500°C the color of the carbon is an intense dazzling white. The changes in the color of carbon as it is heated seem to proceed smoothly and continuously with change in temperature, so that one color blends into another. The same sequence of colors can be produced by gradually increasing the temperature of a tungsten filament in a light bulb, a platinum wire, or many other solids. A solid giving off light in the manner just described is said to be **incandescent.** A rough guide to the relation between color and temperature of a solid is given in Table 10-1.

When methane burns in air, alterations in the concentration of the air or oxygen in the initial gas mixture results in changes in temperature of the flame. This is the way the temperatures of the flames of laboratory burners are adjusted. As the methane and oxygen react the flame gives off a blue glow, which becomes more intense as the temperature increases. However, the color does not change visibly. How can the difference between the colors of incandescent burning solid carbon and of glowing burning gaseous methane be explained?

10-1 FLAMES

Not only the methane and oxygen mixtures but also a number of other gaseous mixtures give off light when they burn. Examples of other systems in which reactions are accompanied by the evolution of visible light are carbon monoxide and oxygen, hydrogen and oxygen, and hydrogen and chlorine. After ignition, if streams of these gases are mixed continuously, a reaction proceeds in a small volume with the evolution of light. The visible glowing region of the reacting system is called a **flame.**

Different systems of gases produce flames of different colors. A change in the mole ratios of the gases in a system that reacts to form a flame will alter the temperature of the flame. However, as the temperature of a flame increases, the color of the light emitted remains constant over a considerable range of temperature (Plate 3). In contrast, as the temperature of an incandescent solid such as platinum or carbon is increased, the color of the light emitted by the solid varies from red to yellow to white but the color of the flame itself remains unaffected.

When some solids are placed in flames, they become incandescent. Other solids not only become incandescent but also cause the flame to glow with a characteristic color. If a solid piece of sodium chloride is heated in a flame, the flame glows with an intense yellow light. If the temperature of the flame is increased, the color of the light from the flame does not change but the intensity of the yellow light does increase. Several examples of flame colors are listed in Table 10-2.

The behavior of solid sodium chloride is different in other respects from that of solid carbon when each substance is heated in a flame. The yellow color produced when sodium chloride is heated in a flame spreads throughout the flame, and the hot solid lump of sodium chloride is incandescent. A hot solid lump of carbon is also incandescent, but the flame is not colored. The sodium chloride appears to give off a gas which causes the flame to glow with an intense yellow color. In

TABLE 10-2 EXAMPLES OF FLAME COLORS PRODUCED WHEN SOLIDS ARE HEATED IN A BUNSEN BURNER FLAME

Substance	Boiling Point, °C	Characteristic Flame Color
Sodium	889	Yellow
Copper chloride	1366	Emerald green
Lithium chloride	1382	Carmine
Sodium chloride	1465	Yellow
Calcium chloride	1600	Yellow-red
Sodium fluoride	1704	Yellow
Calcium oxide	2850	The color of the flame does
Platinum	4010	not change. The solid sub-
Carbon	4347	stance becomes incandescent.

Table 10-2 the substances are listed in order of increasing boiling point to show that those substances which produce only incandescence are also the group with the highest boiling points.

From a flame that becomes yellow by heating a lump of solid sodium chloride, a dust consisting of solid sodium chloride can be recovered from the gases above the flame. Thus, the sodium chloride does not appear to be changed chemically by being heated. Its behavior in a flame is solely dependent upon its forming a gas. Within the flame, this gas glows with a yellow light. Every substance in Table 10-2 which produces a characteristic flame color vaporizes to some extent when it is heated in a flame.

The color of incandescent solids depends upon the temperature alone, whereas the color of glowing gases in flames depends primarily upon the nature of the substance being heated. Glowing gases and incandescent solids emit light; the phenomenon is called **emission.** Why should solids and gases differ so markedly in the character of the light emitted?

The kinetic-molecular model developed in Chapter 8 for gases and solids included postulates that were based on one major difference between gases and solids. A gas is composed of molecules separated by relatively large distances. In the monatomic gases such as helium and neon, the atoms have little effect on each other. Solids, on the other hand, are composed of atoms or molecules packed closely together with relatively little space between them. This tight packing in solids results because the atoms or molecules do attract each other. The colored flames may be a consequence of some property of individual atoms or molecules, whereas incandescence may be associated with an interaction between closely packed atoms or molecules. On this basis, observations of glowing gases may provide experimental data that will permit interpretation of changes in chemical systems in terms of models that have been developed or may provide data that will lead to a new model.

10-2 EMISSION SPECTRA

The light emitted by a glowing gas or flame has a color characteristic of each of the elements present in the gas. Any substance which, when heated in a flame to form a gas, causes the flame to glow with the same yellow color as that produced by sodium chloride vapor or sodium metal vapor in a flame is found to contain the element sodium. In 1859 Robert Bunsen, a German chemist, developed a laboratory method of analysis based on the fact that each element in a glowing gas emits light of a characteristic color.

The procedure which Bunsen developed includes an operation based on an observation made by Isaac Newton in 1666. Newton saw that a

ROBERT WILHELM BUNSEN *1811–1899*

A German chemist. Bunsen once said, "A chemist who is not a physicist is nothing," a quotation that is pertinent today. Bunsen's fame began with his early studies of organic arsenic compounds, which are poisonous, vile-smelling, highly flammable, and often explosive (he lost an eye and almost his life). These studies contributed to the understanding of the composition of organic compounds. His studies on light and photochemical effects with H. E. Roscoe and on spectrum analysis of chemicals on the earth and in the sun with G. Kirchhoff were also important. With the spectroscope that he and Kirchhoff invented, he discovered traces of two new elements in some mineral waters; from 40 tons of these waters he then isolated 17 g of a mixture of the chlorides of rubidium and cesium. His first spectroscope consisted of a prism, a cigar box, and the ends of two discarded telescopes. The burner that he used as a light source for his spectroscope has come to be known as the bunsen burner. Probably the principle of the bunsen burner, however, is the result of earlier work by Faraday.

He was educated at Göttingen University, taught at Kassel and Marburg Universities, and was a professor at Heidelberg University from 1852 to 1889. Both Lothar Meyer and D. I. Mendeleev studied in his laboratories.

---

beam of sunlight from a pinhole formed a circle of white light when it fell directly on a screen. If the beam of sunlight passed through a glass prism, the beam was bent from its original path. On the screen, the light emerging from the prism formed an oval which was not white. The oval was, in fact, red at one end and violet at the other—with shades of orange, yellow, green, and blue between the red and violet. Newton concluded that white light was composed of light of many colors and that, when white light passes through a prism, the light of the different component colors is bent in different amounts. The pattern of colors that Newton observed in the oval is commonly referred to as a **spectrum.** The type of spectrum obtained when light emitted by an object is passed through a prism is called an **emission spectrum.** Instruments were devised by Bunsen and others that could be used to produce spectra and to analyze any light beam in order to determine the colors of the light in the beam. An instrument used to produce and to analyze light is known as a **spectroscope.**

Instead of a circular pinhole, Bunsen used a narrow slit designed to form a ribbon of light which passes through the prism. If the source emits white light, a rectangle of light appears on the screen, but none of the rectangle appears to be white. Instead, a pattern of colors extends across the rectangle. On the other hand, if the light source emits but a single color, a single line of colored light appears on the screen.

When light from incandescent objects is analyzed in a spectroscope, a lighted rectangle appears on the screen. Red light is at one end of the rectangle, violet light is at the other end, and a continuous sequence of colors is between. A light pattern of this type in an emission spectrum is called a **continuous spectrum.** When flames emitting colored light (for example, the flames described in Table 10-2) are used as light sources for the spectroscope, the spectrum obtained is made up of one or more colored lines separated by dark spaces. This type of emission spectrum is called a **line spectrum.** The color and position of a line in a line spectrum is always consistent with the position of the same color in the continuous spectrum. Plate 4 shows a continuous spectrum and examples of line spectra.

The hot wire in an electric light bulb emits light that gives a continuous spectrum. Electric light bulbs are often referred to as incandescent lights. On the other hand, a neon sign, a mercury vapor lamp, and a sodium vapor lamp each emit light of a different color, and the light from each produces a different and characteristic line spectrum.

10-3 ABSORPTION SPECTRA

If white light from an incandescent object is passed through a tube containing sodium metal vapor at a temperature somewhat below the temperature at which the vapor glows, an example of a third type of spectrum is obtained. This spectrum is identical to a continuous spectrum except for one remarkable feature. Without sodium vapor in the light path, the white light gives a continuous spectrum. When sodium vapor is placed in the light path, dark lines are seen in the otherwise continuous spectrum. These dark lines which indicate a low intensity or absence of light are at exactly the same position within the spectrum as the lines observed in a line spectrum for sodium. A dark line spectrum is also called an **absorption spectrum.**

These observations suggest that sodium vapor can either emit light of a characteristic color or absorb light of exactly the same color. What does the emission and absorption of light imply about the nature of substances?

10-4 THE NATURE OF LIGHT

Experimental studies indicate that light has several characteristic properties. When light shines on an object with a dull black surface, the temperature of the object rises. What is observed is that an object which is said to give off light (the light source) produces a temperature rise in another object (the light absorber) at a distance from the source. The one object alters the temperature of the other object even though the source and absorber may be separated by great distances. Thus the sun raises the temperature of objects on the earth even though the sun is 93,000,000 miles away.

In Chapter 9, temperature changes in systems were interpreted in terms of energy changes. Light is therefore a form of energy transfer between two objects. It is often said that light is radiant energy, and like work and heat, light is energy being transferred.

When an object absorbs light, the temperature rise can be used to calculate the amount of energy absorbed. The quantity of energy delivered per second per square meter of absorber surface is called the intensity of the light. A light source that delivers a large amount of energy in a short time is said to be a high-intensity source.

Numerous experiments have shown that, when a light source is turned on, a measurable time passes before the light reaches a distant point. Although the times are extremely short for distances of a few miles on the earth, the short times can be measured with sensitive instruments. These observations are interpreted to mean that light has a velocity. Approximately eight minutes are required for light to travel 93,000,000 miles from the sun to the earth.

The characteristics of light discussed so far can be summarized as follows.

1. Light is radiant energy.
2. Light has intensity (energy transferred per second per unit area).
3. Light has color.
4. Light beams are bent when they pass through prisms, and the amount of bending is related to the color of the light.
5. Light has velocity.

10-5 THE WAVE THEORY OF LIGHT

In the nineteenth century a theory of light, based on the assumption that light is a wave, was generally used by scientists. In other words, light was assumed to have the properties of waves.

If a light wave is assumed to be like a wave produced on the surface of a quiet pool of water, the properties of a light wave can be described as follows.

1. A wave has energy.
2. A wave has wavelength.
3. A wave has amplitude.
4. A wave has velocity.
5. A wave has frequency.

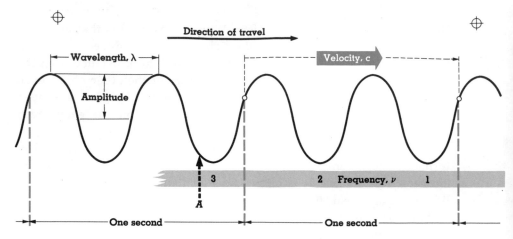

Fig. 10-1 *Schematic diagram showing wavelength, amplitude, frequency, and velocity of a wave.*

Figure 10-1 is a diagram showing the various properties of a wave. The **frequency** of a wave is the number of waves that travel past a given point in one second.

The **velocity** of a wave describes the distance traveled in one second by some point on the wave. For light the velocity in empty space is found to be the same no matter what the color or intensity of the light may be. For light waves there is a relation between wavelength λ (lambda), frequency ν (nu), and velocity c

$$\nu\lambda \;=\; c$$

where ν is the number of waves per second and λ is given in meters per wave, so that the velocity c is in meters per second. The experimentally determined velocity of light c is 2.998×10^8 meters/second.

The observable properties of light are assumed to be related to the wave theory as follows.

1. Light is energy being transferred, and a wave transfers energy.
2. Light intensity is related to wave amplitude.
3. Light color corresponds to wavelength.
4. Light beams can bend, and a wave can be bent.
5. Light has velocity and a wave has velocity.

Up until just before the end of the nineteenth century, scientists believed the wave theory of light was entirely satisfactory. It is possible to show that visible light has wavelengths between about 7,000 A for red light and about 4,000 A for violet light. Photographic film, sensitive thermometers, or other light-sensitive instruments were used to demonstrate that radiant energy is not always visible but can have longer wavelengths than that of red light and shorter wavelengths than that of violet light. This made it possible to build spectroscopes which extended the investigation of spectra beyond violet light into ultra-violet spectra as well as beyond red light into infrared spectra.

A light beam that consists of light of all wavelengths gives a continuous spectrum. A light beam that consists of a single wavelength gives a spectrum which contains but a single line.

10-6 THE PHOTON THEORY OF LIGHT

About the end of the nineteenth century there seemed to be just two difficulties in the interpretation of the properties of light in terms of the wave theory. One difficulty was concerned with the interpretation of the nature of incandescence. Briefly stated, the difficulty was that no one could account quantitatively for the continuous spectra which characterized the light emitted by incandescent objects.

The other difficulty had to do with interpreting the nature of the photoelectric effect described in Section 6-3. In the photoelectric production of electrons, it was found that a metal which emitted electrons when it was illuminated with blue light might fail to give any electrons at all when it was illuminated with red light no matter how intense a beam of red light was used. Experimentally it was found that each substance emitted electrons only when it was illuminated by light of wavelengths shorter than some wavelength characteristic of the metal. Changing the intensity of the light changed only the number of electrons emitted. Shorter wavelengths of light did not change the number of electrons emitted but did increase the velocity and hence produced electrons that had higher kinetic energies as they left the metal surface.

A scheme that could account for the production of continuous spectra from the light emitted by incandescent objects was worked out by Max Planck. He found it necessary to assume that energy in matter is in bundles. He called a bundle of energy a **quantum.** A bundle of energy emitted as light is called a **photon.** The energy in a photon of light is best thought of as a bundle of energy, that is, as a quantum. Planck suggested that the energy E in a photon is proportional to wave frequency ν so that

$$E = h\nu = \frac{hc}{\lambda} \qquad (Eq.\ 10\text{-}1)$$

where h, known as Planck's constant, has the numerical value 6.625 $\times$ 10^{-34} joule-second/quantum and E is expressed in units of joules per quantum (joules/quantum).

The photoelectric emission of electrons was interpreted by Albert Einstein in terms of light photons. Einstein proposed that the production of an electron in photoelectric emission is the result of the absorption of a quantum of energy. Electron emission could occur, however, only if the energy of the photon of light is greater than some minimum energy. Light quanta with too little energy are completely ineffective in causing the emission of electrons and only serve to raise the temperature of the absorber. When light photons with sufficient energy are absorbed, one electron is emitted for each photon absorbed. The number of electrons emitted is therefore equal to the number of photons with sufficient energy that are absorbed.

The observed properties of light discussed in Section 10-4 are represented by the assumptions of quantum theory.

1. Light is energy being transferred, and a photon of light is a bundle of energy in motion.

2. Light intensity corresponds to the number of photons striking a unit area of absorber per second.

3. Light color corresponds to the energy per photon.

4. Light can bend, but photon theory finds this difficult to explain.

5. Light has velocity and a photon has velocity.

Neither wave theory nor photon theory alone completely accounts for all the experimental properties of light. Light, then, must be regarded as being partially like waves and partially like photons or particles. The equation proposed by Planck,

$$E = h\nu$$

does provide a quantitative relation which links the two theories together. How can the production of line spectra by isolated atoms be related to either or both theories of light?

Ex. 10-1   a. Which has the higher energy, a photon of violet light with wavelength 4,000 A or a photon of red light with wavelength 7,000 A?

b. A photon of light with wavelength 6,000 A has an energy E. A photon of light of what wavelength would correspond to an energy $2E$?

c. What is the energy in joules of a light photon of 6,000 A?

10-7 THE BOHR ATOM MODEL

Of all the line spectra produced by gases, the spectrum with the fewest lines is that of monatomic hydrogen gas. All attempts to account for line spectra have therefore started with the study of the hydrogen spectrum.

In 1913, in order to account for the line spectrum of hydrogen, Niels Bohr proposed a model for the structure of the hydrogen atom. Some aspects of Bohr's model were discussed in Section 7-2.

In the model developed by Bohr, the electron was assumed to be a particle traveling in a circular orbit around the proton. Bohr proposed that the atom would maintain its structure because of the counteraction of two tendencies. He assigned the electron a kinetic energy that tended to cause the electron to move at ever-increasing distances from the proton. The opposing tendency was the electric potential energy

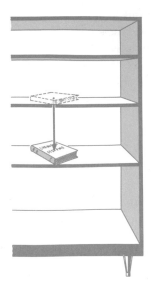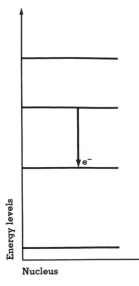

Nucleus

Fig. 10-2 *The energy of an electron in an atom, like the potential energy of a book on a bookshelf, can change only in steps called quanta.*

resulting from the electrostatic forces operating between the proton and electron. The sum of the kinetic energy of the electron and the electric potential energy is the total energy of the atom exclusive of any translational energy the atom as a whole may possess. Bohr assumed that there was a numerical value for the total energy of the atom that ensured a stable atomic structure in which the electron moved in a single circular orbit.

The hydrogen atom could absorb energy (for example, light of suitable wavelength) only by having the electron move to a circular orbit farther from the nucleus. When the electron returned to its original orbit, an equal quantity of energy in the form of light would be emitted. If orbits of any possible radius are permitted, however, then an electron shifting from one orbit to another should be accompanied by energy changes of all possible magnitudes. In other words, if orbits of any radius are permitted, light of all possible wavelengths would be emitted or absorbed and analysis of emitted light would produce a continuous spectrum. In order to account for the observed line spectrum of hydrogen, Bohr proposed that orbits of only certain sizes were possible (Fig. 10-2). This would mean that a change from one orbit to another would cause a transfer of a quantum of energy representing the difference between the total energies corresponding to the two orbits (Fig. 10-2). A quantum of energy emitted then corresponds to light of a particular wavelength and to a line in the spectrum. An electron in the orbit closest to the nucleus is said to occupy the lowest, or 1st, **energy level** of the atom, whereas an electron in an orbit at a greater distance from the nucleus is said to occupy the 2nd, 3rd, 4th, . . . , nth energy level. When the electron in a hydrogen atom occupies the lowest energy level, the atom is said to be in its **ground state.** When the electron is in any other energy level, the atom is said to be in an **excited state.** The energies of the first and second energy levels can be designated by E_1 and E_2, respectively. The wavelength of the light emitted (corresponding to a line in the spectrum) when an electron shifts from the second to the first energy level is related to the difference between energy levels by Equation 10-2.

$$E_2 - E_1 = \frac{hc}{\lambda}$$

or

$$\lambda = \frac{hc}{E_2 - E_1}$$

(Eq. 10-2)

Since h and c are known constants, the wavelength of emitted light gives direct information about the difference between the energies corresponding to the different energy levels in an atom.

For Bohr, the requirement of discrete energy levels for electrons in atoms was a postulate chosen solely because it fitted experimental observations. Bohr could propose no reason at the time to explain why electrons in atoms should have only a limited number of possible energies. Ten years after Bohr's proposal, Louis de Broglie, a French scientist, supplied a hint that was helpful. De Broglie argued that since light had not only wave properties but also particle properties, as suggested by Planck and Einstein, electrons probably had particle properties as well as wave properties. C. J. Davisson and L. H. Germer in the United States and G. P. Thomson in England tested this proposal and found

Fig. 10-3 *Water waves produce an interference pattern when they pass through two slits in a barrier.*

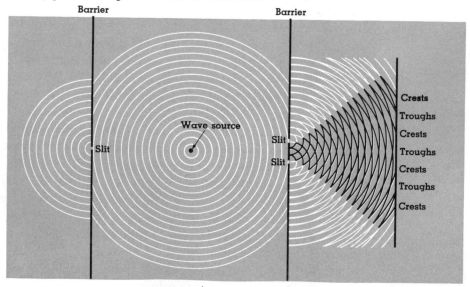

that electrons did have both sets of properties. Beams of electrons striking the edge of a crystal produced interference patterns similar to those characteristic of water waves and light (Fig. 10-3).

If electrons are wavelike, it would be reasonable to ask what sort of wave will be present when an electron is confined within an atom by the electrostatic attraction of a nucleus. Even before the Davisson-Germer-Thomson experiments, Erwin Schroedinger in Germany had enlarged on de Broglie's suggestion and worked out a theory based on the idea that matter is wavelike. The calculations in Schroedinger's theory correspond approximately to the analysis of the possible vibrations in a spherical piece of jelly or in a balloon floating in the upper atmosphere. Before considering the perhaps unfamiliar vibrating balloons or spheres of jelly, let us first examine wave motion in more familiar systems.

A violin string or a rope stretched and tied at both ends will vibrate if it is plucked or if a vibrator is attached to one end. If a string tied at both ends is plucked near one end, a wave travels along the string to the other end, is reflected, travels back along the string, is reflected again, and so on. When one end of the string is tied securely and a vibrator attached to the other end, waves travel back and forth.

Now if the tension and the length of the string and the frequency of the vibration are properly adjusted, the reflected waves will combine with the advancing waves to produce a stationary pattern of loops. Several possible stationary patterns are illustrated in Fig. 10-4. The

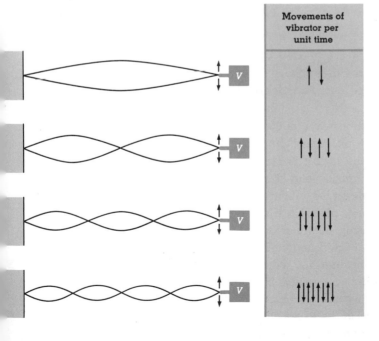

Movements of vibrator per unit time

Fig. 10-4 *Standing waves produced in a string by a vibrator V at one end. Standing waves are produced only at certain definite frequencies of the vibrator. The diagram shows the relationship between these frequencies and the number of nodes in the standing waves.*

patterns shown in Fig. 10-4 are referred to as *standing waves.* Each standing wave consists of a series of loops, all of which in any one pattern are the same in size. The complete set of loops just exactly occupies the distance between the two ends of the string. No matter how complex the pattern of standing waves may be, a fractional number of loops (for example, $3\frac{1}{3}$ loops or any set of loops not corresponding to a whole number) is never observed.

A string is described by its length, and standing waves in a string are referred to as one-dimensional standing waves. To describe a one-dimensional standing wave, only an integer n is required to identify the number of loops. For $n = 1$, there is one loop between the ends; while for $n = 2$, there are two loops, and so forth for any other whole-number value of n.

Two-dimensional standing waves can be produced in drumheads. A thin layer of sand sprinkled on a square drumhead will show where the loops are. In this case, however, the drumhead is tied all around and the loops in the standing waves will extend in two directions at right angles. Two integers will be necessary to describe the arrangement of loops across the surface of the drumhead.

Ex. 10-2   The energy of the photon of light emitted when an electron shifts from the second energy level to the ground state in an atom of hydrogen is 1.63 $\times$ 10^{-18} joule. What is the wavelength of the light corresponding to photons of this energy? Is the wavelength of the corresponding light within the spectrum of visible light?

10-8   THE WAVE MECHANICS MODEL OF THE ATOM

Three integers are needed to describe the three-dimensional standing wave patterns in a sphere. The mathematics for vibrating spheres has been worked out, and Schroedinger used it to develop his ideas about atoms.

When a standing wave is considered in terms of energy, two different energies are necessary. For a string, a standing wave can be produced only if the string is stretched tightly. But stretching a string places it under tension and stores energy. A stretched string therefore has potential energy. A vibrating string is obviously in motion and so has kinetic energy also. Each standing wave pattern corresponds to a unique relationship between potential and kinetic energy.

In the electron orbit model of the hydrogen atom, Bohr had to assume that only certain energies were possible. Schroedinger developed the ideas of standing waves also to show that only certain total energies are associated with electrons. The development of atomic structure theory in terms of standing waves is often called *wave mechanics.*

In wave mechanics an electron in an atom is assumed to be a standing wave. The electrostatic attraction between positive and negative charge produces the potential energy, and the standing wave provides the kinetic energy. For a hydrogen atom the electron wave completely surrounds the nucleus to give a three-dimensional pattern of loops. To describe the pattern of loops, a set of three different numbers is needed.

Any one pattern of loops in the three-dimensional electron wave corresponds to a certain total energy for the atom. When the total energy of the atom changes, the pattern changes; or conversely, when the pattern changes, the energy changes. Since the wave pattern (as in the violin string) can involve just whole numbers, only certain magnitudes of energy are possible.

Wave mechanics provides a model for a hydrogen atom that corresponds to the experimentally observed fact that hydrogen can only emit or absorb energies of certain magnitudes. Standing wave patterns and line spectra are therefore assumed to be related. To explore further the relationship between wave mechanics and energy levels requires additional experimental information regarding energy-level patterns in other atoms as well as in hydrogen.

Ex. 10-3   Answer the following questions in terms of the wave mechanics model.

a. How is the kinetic energy of the standing electron wave described?

b. How is the potential energy of the standing electron wave described?

c. Why can the electron wave have only certain magnitudes of total energy?

d. How can changes in total energy be related to line spectra?

10-9 IONIZATION ENERGIES

Experimental determination of the energies of electron waves in atoms can be done not only from the analysis of spectra but also from measurements of the energy absorbed when ions are formed from neutral atoms. Electricity can be used to form ions from gaseous atoms.

In Section 6-1 experimental evidence was presented to show that gases can conduct electricity. The gas discharge process exhibits the following characteristics.

1. Gases conduct best at low pressures.

2. A minimum voltage is required before conduction begins.

3. During conduction, the gas glows and emits light.

These characteristics can be interpreted by saying that when charge flows, the gas is ionized to form electrons and charged atoms or charged molecules and that the gas absorbs energy from the electricity during the ionization process. As the electrons and ions recombine, energy in the form of light is emitted. In other words, the gas discharge tube converts electric energy to light energy.

The fact that a minimum voltage is required to produce electric con-

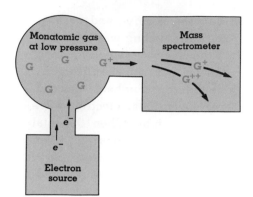

Fig. 10-5 *An apparatus for measuring ionization energies.*

duction in a gas suggests that some minimum quantity of energy is required to produce ions from otherwise neutral molecules or atoms. In the simplest case of ionization, one electron would be removed from a single atom. The energy required to remove one electron from an atom is called the **first ionization energy.** To measure ionization energies, some means are needed to produce ions under circumstances in which a known quantity of energy can be supplied to a known number of atoms.

One experimental procedure uses an apparatus, indicated schematically in Fig. 10-5, which combines an electron source and a mass spectrometer, both of which were described in Chapter 6. The electron source produces a beam of electrons whose energy can be controlled and measured. The electron beam is directed at a sample of a monatomic gas. Positive ions formed in the process (Section 6-7) can be detected in a mass spectrometer. The ions are drawn into the mass spectrometer by a negatively charged electrode. The mass spectrometer can only discriminate between ions with different charge/mass ratios. But if a single monatomic gas of known atomic mass is used, the charge on each type of positive ion can be determined since all the ions will have the same mass. In this way, it is possible to decide how many electrons the atom must have lost to produce each different type of ion.

There is a level, which is characteristic of each element, for the energy of the electrons in a bombarding electron beam below which no positive ions are formed in the sample of the element. As the energy of the electron beam is increased, an energy is reached for which positive ions with a single positive charge appear in the mass spectrometer. With hydrogen atoms there is only the one ionization energy. With helium atoms there is a first ionization energy associated with loss of one electron and also a second higher ionization energy associated with the production of doubly charged positive ions. Lithium atoms show three different ionization energies.

Ionization energies for the elements with atomic numbers 1 to 11 are listed in Table 10-3. The ionization energies can be reported simply

TABLE 10-3 IONIZATION ENERGIES OF SOME ELEMENTS[a]

Ionization Energy	H	He	Li	Be	B	C	N	O	F	Ne	Na
First											118
Second										497	1,090
Third									402	943	1,650
Fourth								314	804	1,470	2,280
Fifth							335	811	1,450	2,220	3,200
Sixth						260	682	1,270	2,010	2,900	3,980
Seventh					191	572	1,090	1,780	2,630	3,620	4,820
Eighth				215	579	1,100	1,780	2,630	3,620	4,770	6,090
Ninth			124	420	874	1,490	2,260	3,180	4,270	5,490	6,910
Tenth		566	1,746	3,550	5,980	9,040	12,700	17,000	21,900	27,400	33,700
Eleventh	313	1,247	2,810	4,990	7,800	11,200	15,300	20,000	25,400	31,100	

[a] Numerical values are in kilocalories per mole.
SOURCE: Data are calculated from Arnold Eucken (ed.), *Landolt and Börnstein Tables*, 6th ed., Springer-Verlag OHG, Berlin, 1950.

as the potential difference used to give each electron in the bombarding electron beam its kinetic energy. This potential difference is expressed in volts per bombarding electron or joules per electron. Chemists find ionization energies expressed in units of kilocalories per mole of atom or ion involved more useful. For any element listed in Table 10-3, the successive ionization energies are in a vertical column under the symbol for the element, with the ionization energy for the most easily removed electron at the top of the column. The first ionization energies for eleven elements are shown along the diagonal labeled "First" on the right side of the table.

According to Table 10-3, the quantity of energy necessary to remove the first electron from helium is 566 kcal/mole of He. This quantity of energy is absorbed by 1 mole of helium in the reaction $He \rightarrow He^+ + e^-$. A much larger quantity of energy, 1,247 kcal/mole of He^+, is required to remove the second electron in the reaction $He^+ \rightarrow He^{++} + e^-$. That the energy to remove the second electron from the helium atom should be larger than the first is reasonable because the second electron has to be removed from an already positively charged ion (He^+) which has a strong attraction for the second electron in the atom.

The first ionization energies can be considered to be measures of the

TABLE 10-4 ENERGY TRANSFERS

Change	Energy, kcal/mole
Ionization Energies:	
$Li\ (g) \rightarrow Li^+\ (g) + e^-$	124.
$O\ (g) \rightarrow O^+\ (g) + e^-$	314.
$F\ (g) \rightarrow F^{9+}\ (g) + 9e^-$	62,500[a]
Enthalpies of Reaction:	
$2H\ (g) \rightarrow H_2\ (g)$	−104.2
$\frac{1}{2}H_2\ (g) + \frac{1}{2}F_2\ (g) \rightarrow HF\ (g)$	−64.2
$CH_4\ (g) + 2O_2\ (g) \rightarrow CO_2\ (g) + 2H_2O\ (l)$	−212.8
$CH_4\ (g) \rightarrow C\ (g) + 4H\ (g)$	398.0
$H_2O\ (l) \rightarrow H_2O\ (g)$	10.5
$C\ (s) \rightarrow C\ (g)$	171.7
Work Done Against Gravitational Attraction:	
Auto (sea level) → auto (mountaintop elevation 1 mile)	3,440[b]

[a] Obtained from Table 10-3 by adding figures in the column for F.
[b] Kilocalories per compact car of 1-ton mass.

(a) *Flame color for methane burning in oxygen.*

(b) *Flame color for hydrogen burning in oxygen.*

PLATE 3

(c) *Flame color for hydrogen burning in chlorine.*

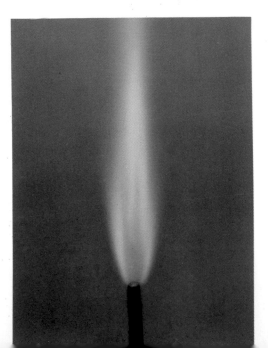

quantity of energy absorbed when 1 mole of atoms is ionized to produce 1 mole of ions and 1 mole of electrons. Some idea of the relative magnitudes of ionization energies can be gained by comparing them with the quantities of heat evolved or absorbed in chemical reactions and with quantities of energy expended as work is done against gravitational attraction as shown in Table 10-4.

Lithium has a low ionization energy by comparison with helium and beryllium in Table 10-3, but even 124 kcal/mole is nearly twice the quantity of energy produced when hydrogen and fluorine gas react to form 1 mole of hydrogen fluoride. Yet the reaction between hydrogen and fluorine is one of the most strongly exothermic chemical reactions per mole of product.

The experimental procedure described for determining the ionization energies of an element depends upon producing the element in the form of a monatomic gas. Only a few elements can be converted to monatomic gases. Fortunately, analysis of spectroscopic data for elements can also provide ionization energies for most elements.

Ex. 10-4   Refer to Table 10-3.

a. What is the least amount of energy required to remove 1 mole of electrons from 1 mole of neon atoms?

b. What is the least amount of energy required to remove 2 moles of electrons from 1 mole of beryllium atoms? Write the equation representing this change.

Ex. 10-5   Assuming that the enthalpy change could be converted completely to work, what is the smallest number of moles of methane (CH_4) that must react with oxygen to lift a 150-lb student to a height of 10 miles above the earth?

10-10   ENERGY LEVELS IN ATOMS

In the Bohr model of a hydrogen atom, the electron was assumed to travel in a circular path, or orbit, around the proton. When energy is absorbed by the atom, the electron is considered to move to an orbit farther from the proton. Each different orbit that an electron can occupy corresponds to an energy level.

In the wave mechanics model, on the other hand, each energy level corresponds to a different three-dimensional standing electron wave enveloping the nucleus. Both models arrive at the same equation for the total energy E_n of a one-electron atom or one-electron ion whose nucleus carries a charge $\oplus Z$ (Equation 10-3).

$$E_n = -2m \left(\frac{\pi Z e^2}{nh} \right)^2 \qquad (Eq.\ 10\text{-}3)$$

In Equation 10-3, h is Planck's constant, m is the mass of an electron, e is the charge on an electron, and n is the number of the orbit occupied

TABLE 10-5 CONSTANTS USED IN CALCULATIONS FOR THE BOHR ATOM AND WAVE MECHANICS MODELS

Symbol	Constant
m	9.108×10^{-31} kg/electron
e	1.60×10^{-19} joule/volt
h	6.625×10^{-34} joule-second/quantum

by an electron, with $n = 1$ corresponding to the orbit closest to the nucleus, and $n = 2$ corresponding to the second orbit from the nucleus, and so on. Numerical values for e, h, and m are given in Table 10-5. The number n not only designates the orbit occupied by an electron in a Bohr atom model but also designates the energy level of the atom. When $n = 1$, the value for E_n is called the energy of the ground state.

The assumption that electrons are standing waves in the wave mechanics model leads to an interpretation of n that is more complex than in the Bohr atom model. Essentially, n describes the size of the standing electron wave that envelops the nucleus of the atom.

The number designated by n is called the **principal quantum number.** The energies corresponding to shifts of an electron between orbits corresponding to different values of n in the hydrogen atom are shown in the form of an energy-level diagram in Fig. 10-6.

In calculating the energy of the ground state of a hydrogen atom for $n = 1$ in Equation 10-3, exactly the same numerical value is obtained for the charge cloud model, the Bohr model, and the wave mechanics model. The Bohr and wave mechanics models can be used also to calculate the energies of excited states. There is no way of calculating the energies of excited states in the charge cloud model.

When the atoms in a gas are excited so that the gas can emit light, the spectrum of the light is altered slightly if the excited gas is placed between the poles of a powerful magnet. With the magnet in place, the spectrum of the emitted light shows more lines than does the spectrum from the excited gas that is not between the magnet poles.

Atoms of certain elements are affected by a magnet under other circumstances. If an input beam of hydrogen atoms passes between the poles of a magnet (Fig. 10-7), two diverging output beams are formed with half the initial atoms in one beam and half in the other. Lithium atoms show the same behavior. A beam of helium atoms is not split, but a beam of helium ions, He^+, is. The experiments suggest that some atoms have properties that permit them to be influenced by a magnet.

The description of a model that will account for the effect of a magnet on some atoms requires an involved mathematical analysis. The conclusions of the analysis, however, are usually summarized by using quantum numbers in addition to the integer n to describe the energy levels of an atom. Just as the principal quantum number describes the energy level of an electron within a hydrogen atom, so can other quantum numbers be used to describe additional properties. A set of four quantum numbers is necessary to describe the relation between each electron and the rest of the atom in which it is present.

Neither the charge cloud model nor the Bohr atom model provides any easy way to describe the energy levels of an atom beyond the description provided by the principal quantum number. Through the

Fig. 10-6 *Energy-level diagram for hydrogen, showing ionization energy, energies of transition between energy levels, and wavelengths of lines in the emission spectrum produced when electrons undergo these transitions.*

ENERGY–LEVEL DIAGRAM

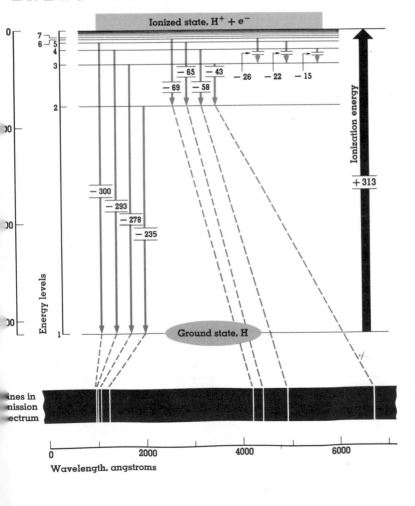

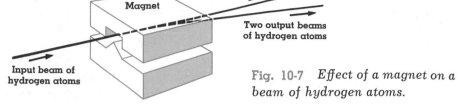

Fig. 10-7 *Effect of a magnet on a beam of hydrogen atoms.*

Input beam of hydrogen atoms

Magnet

Two output beams of hydrogen atoms

theory based on three-dimensional standing electron waves, the wave mechanics model does provide the equivalent of three quantum numbers. Although these three quantum numbers are strictly related only to energy, they can be correlated in general terms with geometrical relations within an atom to give a pictorial interpretation.

Ex. 10-6 Equation 10-3 describes the ground state energy for a one-electron atom or ion whose nuclear charge is Z. For hydrogen $Z = 1$, and the equation gives a ground state energy of -313 kcal/mole. If the value of Z is doubled from 1 to 2, how does the ground state energy change? What ion corresponds to the one-electron ion when $Z = 2$? What is the ground state energy for Li^{++}?

10-11 ELECTRON WAVE DESCRIPTIONS

A three-dimensional standing electron wave can be pictorially interpreted to have a size, a shape, and an orientation. The size is described by the principal quantum number so that the larger the value of n, the larger the radius of the standing electron wave.

The shape of the electron wave pattern is described by a second quantum number which chemists designate by one of the letters s, p, d, f, or g. Each letter represents a different shape for an electron wave. The number of possible shapes for an electron wave is related to the size of the wave, that is, to the principal quantum number. The relationships between the principal quantum number and the second quantum number are listed in Table 10-6. Thus, for $n = 1$, there is only one possible wave shape designated by s; while for $n = 2$, there are two possibilities, s and p; and so forth.

TABLE 10-6 PERMISSIBLE SECOND QUANTUM NUMBERS GOVERNING THE SHAPE OF THE ELECTRON WAVE FOR PRINCIPAL QUANTUM NUMBERS 1 TO 4

Principal Quantum Number n	Second Quantum Number
1	1s
2	2s, 2p
3	3s, 3p, 3d
4	4s, 4p, 4d, 4f

Principal Quantum Number n	Third Quantum Number
1	$1s$
2	$2s$
	$2p_x 2p_y 2p_z$
3	$3s$
	$3p_x 3p_y 3p_z$
	$3d_{xy} 3d_{xz} 3d_{z^2} 3d_{yz} 3d_{x^2-y^2}$

The principal quantum number and the second quantum number together determine the possible numerical values for the third quantum number. The third quantum numbers are indicated as differentiating subscripts, as indicated in Table 10-7. For a wave of shape indicated by s, there is just one possible orientation for each principal quantum number. On the other hand, for a wave with shape indicated by p, there are three different orientations and the subscripts x, y, and z are used to indicate these possibilities as p_x, p_y, and p_z. With waves of shape specified by d, the five possible orientations are indicated by d_{xy}, d_{xz}, d_{yz}, d_{z^2}, $d_{x^2-y^2}$. For waves of shape specified by f, there are seven orientations to be described; but chemists do not ordinarily encounter problems that require consideration of f shapes, and so the s, p, d, f notation does not include provision for details of shape f.

Some atoms also have a magnetic property as indicated by the splitting of a beam of hydrogen atoms into two beams by a magnet. The behavior of the hydrogen beam suggests that there are two kinds of hydrogen atoms which can be differentiated on the basis of their magnetic properties. To account for two different types of hydrogen atoms, it has been postulated that each electron in an atom spins like a top. A spinning negative charge would be expected to behave like a small magnet and so would be attracted to one of the poles of a magnet. The magnetic properties of electrons were mentioned in Section 7-13 when the properties of molecular oxygen were discussed.

For an electron spinning within an atom, there are just two possibilities. The electron can spin clockwise or counterclockwise. If a large number of hydrogen atoms is examined, one-half of the atoms will have electrons of one spin and the other half will have electrons of opposite spin. This would explain the observed behavior of a hydrogen beam when it passed between the poles of a magnet. Chemists indicate the two directions of electron spin by an arrow pointing either up or down.

The quantum-number designations for an electron wave can be

TABLE 10-8 COMPARISON OF TWO TYPES OF NOTATION FOR QUANTUM NUMBERS IN RELATION TO ELECTRONIC CONFIGURATIONS

s,p,d,f notation	$1s$	$2s$	$2p_x$	$2p_y$	$2p_z$	$3s$	$3p_x$	$3p_y$	$3p_z$	$3d_{xy}$	$3d_{xz}$	$3d_{z^2}$	$3d_{yz}$	$3d_{x^2-y^2}$
Principal quantum number n	1	2				3								
Second quantum number l	0	0	1			0	1			2				
Third quantum number m	0	0	-1	0	$+1$	0	-1	0	$+1$	-2	-1	0	$+1$	$+2$
Spin quantum number s	$+\frac{1}{2}\ -\frac{1}{2}$	$+\frac{1}{2}\ -\frac{1}{2}$	$+\frac{1}{2}\ -\frac{1}{2}$	$+\frac{1}{2}\ -\frac{1}{2}$	$+\frac{1}{2}\ -\frac{1}{2}$	$+\frac{1}{2}\ -\frac{1}{2}$	$+\frac{1}{2}\ -\frac{1}{2}$	$+\frac{1}{2}\ -\frac{1}{2}$	$+\frac{1}{2}\ -\frac{1}{2}$	$+\frac{1}{2}\ -\frac{1}{2}$	$+\frac{1}{2}\ -\frac{1}{2}$	$+\frac{1}{2}\ -\frac{1}{2}$	$+\frac{1}{2}\ -\frac{1}{2}$	$+\frac{1}{2}\ -\frac{1}{2}$
Number of electrons with each l quantum number	2	2	6			2	6			10				
Number of electrons with each n quantum number ($= 2n^2$)	2	8				18								

brought together into a symbol that describes the energy and form of the wave. Thus, in the first energy level with a principal quantum number of 1, the electrons are referred to as $1s$ electrons. For the principal quantum number of 2, the electrons are designated by $2s$, $2p_x$, $2p_y$, or $2p_z$. In similar fashion, symbols can be written for the electrons in other energy levels.

Physicists have developed a different set of symbols for quantum numbers based entirely on digits. For each energy level the principal quantum number $n = 1, 2, 3, \ldots$, which means n is an integer. A second quantum number is designated by the symbol l where $l = 0, 1, 2, 3, \ldots, (n - 1)$ which means l can be any integer up to a number that is one less than the principal quantum number. The l values of 0, 1, 2, and 3 correspond to the chemist's designations of s, p, d, and f, respectively. A third quantum number is designated by m where $m = 0, \pm 1, \pm 2, \pm 3, \ldots, \pm l$. Here the p_x, p_y, and p_z electrons correspond to m values of 0, +1, and −1, respectively. A fourth quantum number designates the spin of an electron and has just two values, either $+\frac{1}{2}$ or $-\frac{1}{2}$. The assignment of quantum numbers to electrons and their correlation with the s, p, d, f notation is summarized in Table 10-8. The s, p, d, f notation is more useful for chemists than the digit notation which is primarily needed for the mathematical analysis in wave mechanics. Only the s, p, d, f notation is used in this book.

10-12 ATOMS OTHER THAN HYDROGEN

In the wave mechanics model of hydrogen, the energy level of an atom can be described by the principal quantum number. The total energy of the hydrogen atom will be determined by the size, shape, and orientation of the standing electron wave present in the atom. The electron is represented by a standing wave which has an energy. When the principal quantum number n is greater than 1, the standing electron wave may have more than one shape and orientation. In every energy level the electron will also have a spin.

A model for atoms other than hydrogen will include the designation of the size, shape, and orientation for all the electron waves present simultaneously around the nucleus. This has yet to be accomplished in complete detail for any element other than hydrogen. Because complete description is not yet possible, it is assumed that in atoms other than hydrogen a set of energy levels exists, similar to those already described for the hydrogen atom. The s, p, d, f notation is used for other atoms also.

There is one problem, however. With several electrons to be assigned energy levels, why do they not all end up in the lowest energy level described by the symbol $1s$? Much the same problem was encountered in locating electrons in the charge cloud model (Section 7-5).

WOLFGANG PAULI *1900–1958*

An Austrian-American physicist, born in Vienna, where he received his early education. Pauli received his doctorate from Munich University, Germany, in 1921, then studied a year with Max Born in Göttingen and a year with Niels Bohr in Copenhagen. He was lecturer at Hamburg University from 1923 to 1928, became professor of theoretical physics at the Zürich Institute of Technology in 1928, and after 1940, held also the position of professor of theoretical physics at the Institute for Advanced Study at Princeton. He received the Nobel Prize in physics in 1945 for the enunciation of the exclusion principle that now bears his name. In 1946 he became a citizen of the United States.

Pauli was led to the exclusion principle through a series of lectures given by Bohr in Göttingen. Bohr pointed out that his atomic model, though giving an adequate description of the hydrogen spectrum, was quite incapable of accounting for the periodicity of properties exhibited by the chemical elements. Some principle was required, limiting the number of electrons in each energy level. Pauli's year in Copenhagen brought him no closer to the answer, but on his return to Hamburg his studies on the periodic system of the elements finally led him to the simple conclusion that no two electrons in an atom can have completely identical properties, or, as it was phrased soon afterward, no two electrons in an atom can have the same four quantum numbers.

Wolfgang Pauli first pointed out the necessity to assume some limitation on the number of electrons that possess the same set of quantum numbers. His postulate can be stated thus: No two electrons in an atom can have identical sets of the four quantum numbers. This assumption is called the Pauli exclusion principle and is related to the exclusion principle adopted for the charge cloud model. With the aid of the exclusion principle, electrons can be assigned to energy levels in atoms containing more than one electron. Therefore only two $1s$ electrons can be in an atom, one spinning clockwise and the other counterclockwise.

Each of the symbols $1s$, $2p$, and so on, of Table 10-6 represents an energy level for an atom. It is convenient to consider that the symbols each represent a region in the space around a nucleus which may be occupied by zero, one, or two electron waves but never more than two. Such a region of space is called an **orbital.** When an orbital contains two electrons, the electrons must have opposite spins (Pauli exclusion principle).

In the wave mechanics model of the hydrogen atom, each principal quantum number other than $n = 1$ refers to several different orbitals, all at the same energy level (Fig. 10-8). Thus the $2s$ and the $2p$ orbitals provide for identical energies when they are occupied by elec-

Fig. 10-8 *The first four principal quantum numbers for the orbitals of calcium and hydrogen. The bottom of each box corresponds to the energy level. The arrows in the boxes show the number of electrons in each of the orbitals in the ground state. All energies are lower than zero and should be read as negative numbers.*

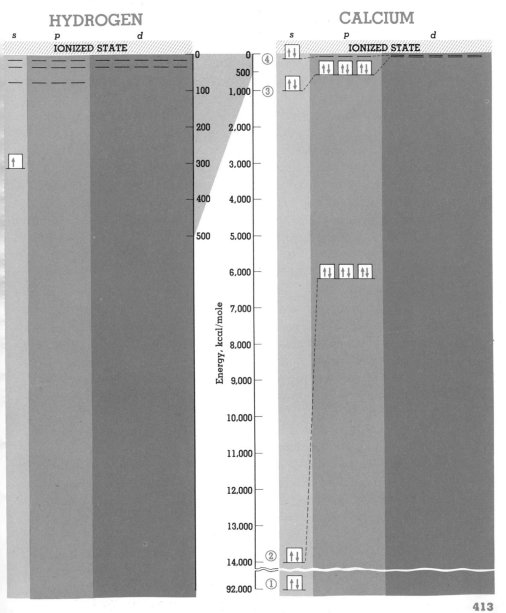

tron waves. For more complex atoms with several electrons, the situation is different. When not one but several electron waves are present, they interact with each other so that in addition to energy differences between the energy levels designated by the principal quantum numbers, there are also small energy differences between the orbitals within a principal level. For example, the $2s$ and $2p$ orbitals are of different energy in calcium (Fig. 10-8). Within a set of p orbitals of the same principal quantum number, all the p orbitals have the same energy. For an atom in the vicinity of a powerful magnet, however, the energies of the p orbitals change to give three energy levels which differ slightly from one another.

The distribution of orbitals by energy levels can be represented better in a diagram than in words. Figure 10-8 shows a diagram for calcium and also for hydrogen.

Complete separation of electron waves from a nucleus corresponds to zero total energy for the atom (Section 5-15). All other arrangements therefore correspond to energies lower than zero. Electron waves in the $1s$ orbital always have lower total energies than in any other orbital of the atom. When electron waves in orbitals with the same quantum-number designation are compared in different atoms, the electron wave in the atom with the larger nuclear charge will have the lower total energy. The orbitals in calcium (atomic number 20) will have lower total energies than the corresponding orbitals in hydrogen with atomic numbers 1 (Fig. 10-8).

10-13 AN ATOMIC ORBITAL MODEL

The quantum-number notation (often referred to as the s, p, d, f notation) provides a means for describing the arrangement of energy levels within an atom. Figure 10-8 shows diagrammatically the energy differences between corresponding orbitals for hydrogen and for calcium. Each energy level is designated by a box representing an orbital. Each electron wave within an orbital is indicated by an arrow. Electron waves with spins in opposite directions are shown by arrows with heads pointing in opposite directions.

For many purposes it is unnecessary to know the energy differences between energy levels. Only the order in which the orbitals are occupied by electron waves is needed. For lithium (atomic number 3) and nitrogen (atomic number 7) the ground state electronic configuration is given in the electron-in-a-box diagrams in Fig. 10-9a and b. For calcium (atomic number 20) the order of filling boxes is shown schematically in Fig. 10-9d or symbolically as $1s^2 2s^2 2p^6 3s^2 3p^6 4s^2$, where the superscripts refer to the number of electron waves in the designated energy level. The energy of the electron waves rises from left to right in the orbitals designated in the symbolic representation. For

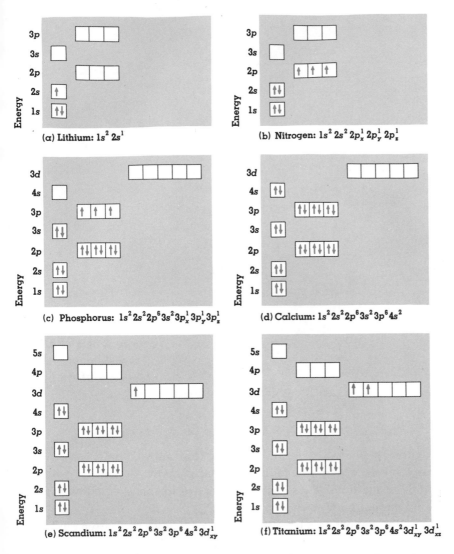

Fig. 10-9 *Electron-in-a-box diagrams and electronic configurations for (a) lithium, (b) nitrogen, (c) phosphorus, (d) calcium, (e) scandium, and (f) titanium.*

phosphorus with 15 electron waves the order in which orbitals are occupied is given as a set of boxes in Fig. 10-9c or as a set of symbols $1s^2 2s^2 2p^6 3s^2 3p^3$. For nuclear charge greater than 20 the order of filling orbitals by electron waves follows a pattern somewhat different from that for the elements hydrogen through calcium. Thus elements with atomic numbers 21 and 22, scandium and titanium, are described in Fig. 10-9e and f. After the 4s orbital is occupied by electron waves, a set of five 3d orbitals becomes available and is filled by ten electron waves before any electron waves enter the 4p orbitals.

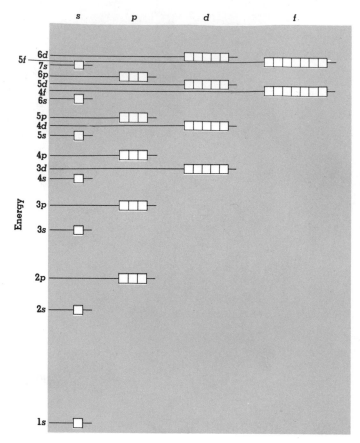

Fig. 10-10 *Relative energy levels of atoms of the elements with atomic numbers 1 to 20.*

Figure 10-10 is a diagram showing the approximate sequence of energy levels which determines the assignment of electron waves to orbitals in an atom. These assignments are for an isolated atom in its ground state, or lowest energy state.

The filling of orbitals by electron waves follows the pattern indicated in Fig. 10-10 and three additional rules.

1. The number of electron waves in an atom must equal the number of protons (equal to the nuclear charge) in its nucleus, so that the atom will be electrically neutral.

2. No more than two electron waves can be present in any one orbital (Pauli exclusion principle).

3. Each new electron wave added to the atom will go to the orbital which has the lowest energy and which is not already filled. If two orbitals of the same energy are unfilled, the entering electron wave will enter an empty orbital, rather than one which already contains one electron wave, since the negative electron waves repel each other. For example, the diagram for nitrogen in Fig. 10-9b shows that each of the 2p electron waves occupies a separate orbital.

This description of electron wave arrangements in terms of orbitals is often referred to as the *atomic orbital model.* Is it possible to show that this model is useful in interpreting experimental evidence about the elements? Since the atomic orbital model has been developed from spectral information about isolated atoms, experimental evidence about isolated atoms may be more easily interpreted by means of this model. Ionization energies have already been described but have not been interpreted.

Ex. 10-7   How many orbitals has the principal quantum number $n = 3$? What is the s, p, d, f notation for each of these orbitals?

Ex. 10-8   What are the n and l values for a $3d$ electron? for a $1s$ electron?

Ex. 10-9   Write the correct orbital notation for each of the following sets of quantum numbers: $n = 1, l = 0, m = 0$; $n = 2, l = 1, m = -1$; $n = 3, l = 2, m = 1$.

Ex. 10-10   Draw electron-in-a-box diagrams for the elements carbon, sodium, neon, and potassium.

10-14   FIRST IONIZATION ENERGIES AND ORBITALS

The ionization energy of hydrogen is 313 kcal/mole and the first ionization energy of helium is 566 kcal/mole. In the atoms of both elements, the electron waves are in the $1s$ orbital. The $1s$ orbital in helium has a lower energy level than the $1s$ orbital in hydrogen. The larger nuclear charge in the helium atom lowers the energy more than the repulsion between the electron waves in the same s orbital raises the energy for an atom.

Lithium has a first ionization energy of 124 kcal/mole, which is smaller than that of either hydrogen or helium. Lithium atoms have three electron waves, and the orbital arrangement in the ground state called the *electronic configuration* is $1s^2 2s^1$ (Fig. 10-9a). Since the $2s$ electron wave is in a higher energy level than the $1s$ electron waves, the energy required to separate the $2s$ electron wave from the attraction of the nucleus is smaller than that required to ionize the $1s$ electron wave in hydrogen or helium. The lithium nucleus and the two $1s$ electron waves together constitute a kernel with a net charge of $\oplus 1$. The lithium kernel has the same net charge as a hydrogen nucleus. The $2s$ electron wave is, then, held in the lithium atom, much as a $1s$ electron wave is held in a hydrogen atom. The main difference between the two atoms is that, because of the Pauli exclusion principle, the $2s$ electron wave must remain outside the $1s$ electron waves. This results in a smaller first ionization energy for lithium than for hydrogen.

For beryllium the first ionization energy is 215 kcal/mole. The electron waves are arranged in the configuration $1s^2 2s^2$, so that the first electron removed is from the $2s$ orbital. The greater nuclear charge in

TABLE 10-9 ENERGY LEVELS AND ELECTRONIC CONFIGURATIONS OF ATOMS WITH NUCLEAR CHARGE 1 TO 40

Atom	Charge	Energy Levels and Electronic Configurations									
Hydrogen	1	$1s^1$									
Helium	2	$1s^2$									
Lithium	3	$1s^2$	$2s^1$								
Beryllium	4	$1s^2$	$2s^2$								
Boron	5	$1s^2$	$2s^2$	$2p_x^1$							
Carbon	6	$1s^2$	$2s^2$	$2p_x^1 2p_y^1$							
Nitrogen	7	$1s^2$	$2s^2$	$2p_x^1 2p_y^1 2p_z^1$							
Oxygen	8	$1s^2$	$2s^2$	$2p_x^2 2p_y^1 2p_z^1$							
Fluorine	9	$1s^2$	$2s^2$	$2p_x^2 2p_y^2 2p_z^1$							
Neon	10	$1s^2$	$2s^2$	$2p_x^2 2p_y^2 2p_z^2$							
Sodium	11	$1s^2$	$2s^2$	$2p^6$	$3s^1$						
Magnesium	12	$1s^2$	$2s^2$	$2p^6$	$3s^2$						
Aluminum	13	$1s^2$	$2s^2$	$2p^6$	$3s^2$	$3p_x^1$					
Silicon	14	$1s^2$	$2s^2$	$2p^6$	$3s^2$	$3p_x^1 3p_y^1$					
Phosphorus	15	$1s^2$	$2s^2$	$2p^6$	$3s^2$	$3p_x^1 3p_y^1 3p_z^1$					
Sulfur	16	$1s^2$	$2s^2$	$2p^6$	$3s^2$	$3p_x^2 3p_y^1 3p_z^1$					
Chlorine	17	$1s^2$	$2s^2$	$2p^6$	$3s^2$	$3p_x^2 3p_y^2 3p_z^1$					
Argon	18	$1s^2$	$2s^2$	$2p^6$	$3s^2$	$3p_x^2 3p_y^2 3p_z^2$					
Potassium	19	$1s^2$	$2s^2$	$2p^6$	$3s^2$	$3p^6$		$4s^1$			
Calcium	20	$1s^2$	$2s^2$	$2p^6$	$3s^2$	$3p^6$		$4s^2$			
Scandium	21	$1s^2$	$2s^2$	$2p^6$	$3s^2$	$3p^6$	$3d_{xy}^1$	$4s^2$			
Titanium	22	$1s^2$	$2s^2$	$2p^6$	$3s^2$	$3p^6$	$3d_{xy}^1 3d_{xz}^1$	$4s^2$			
Vanadium	23	$1s^2$	$2s^2$	$2p^6$	$3s^2$	$3p^6$	$3d_{xy}^1 3d_{xz}^1 3d_{z^2}^1$	$4s^2$			
Chromium	24	$1s^2$	$2s^2$	$2p^6$	$3s^2$	$3p^6$	$3d_{xy}^1 3d_{xz}^1 3d_{z^2}^1 3d_{yz}^1 3d_{x^2-y^2}^1$	$4s^1$			
Manganese	25	$1s^2$	$2s^2$	$2p^6$	$3s^2$	$3p^6$	$3d_{xy}^1 3d_{xz}^1 3d_{z^2}^1 3d_{yz}^1 3d_{x^2\to y^2}^1$	$4s^2$			
Iron	26	$1s^2$	$2s^2$	$2p^6$	$3s^2$	$3p^6$	$3d_{xy}^2 3d_{xz}^1 3d_{z^2}^1 3d_{yz}^1 3d_{x^2-y^2}^1$	$4s^2$			
Cobalt	27	$1s^2$	$2s^2$	$2p^6$	$3s^2$	$3p^6$	$3d_{xy}^2 3d_{xz}^2 3d_{z^2}^1 3d_{yz}^1 3d_{x^2-y^2}^1$	$4s^2$			
Nickel	28	$1s^2$	$2s^2$	$2p^6$	$3s^2$	$3p^6$	$3d_{xy}^2 3d_{xz}^2 3d_{z^2}^2 3d_{yz}^1 3d_{x^2-y^2}^1$	$4s^2$			
Copper	29	$1s^2$	$2s^2$	$2p^6$	$3s^2$	$3p^6$	$3d_{xy}^2 3d_{xz}^2 3d_{z^2}^2 3d_{yz}^2 3d_{x^2-y^2}^2$	$4s^1$			
Zinc	30	$1s^2$	$2s^2$	$2p^6$	$3s^2$	$3p^6$	$3d^{10}$	$4s^2$			
Gallium	31	$1s^2$	$2s^2$	$2p^6$	$3s^2$	$3p^6$	$3d^{10}$	$4s^2$	$4p_x^1$		
Germanium	32	$1s^2$	$2s^2$	$2p^6$	$3s^2$	$3p^6$	$3d^{10}$	$4s^2$	$4p_x^1 4p_y^1$		
Arsenic	33	$1s^2$	$2s^2$	$2p^6$	$3s^2$	$3p^6$	$3d^{10}$	$4s^2$	$4p_x^1 4p_y^1 4p_z^1$		
Selenium	34	$1s^2$	$2s^2$	$2p^6$	$3s^2$	$3p^6$	$3d^{10}$	$4s^2$	$4p_x^2 4p_y^1 4p_z^1$		
Bromine	35	$1s^2$	$2s^2$	$2p^6$	$3s^2$	$3p^6$	$3d^{10}$	$4s^2$	$4p_x^2 4p_y^2 4p_z^1$		
Krypton	36	$1s^2$	$2s^2$	$2p^6$	$3s^2$	$3p^6$	$3d^{10}$	$4s^2$	$4p_x^2 4p_y^2 4p_z^2$		
Rubidium	37	$1s^2$	$2s^2$	$2p^6$	$3s^2$	$3p^6$	$3d^{10}$	$4s^2$	$4p^6$		$5s^1$
Strontium	38	$1s^2$	$2s^2$	$2p^6$	$3s^2$	$3p^6$	$3d^{10}$	$4s^2$	$4p^6$		$5s^2$
Yttrium	39	$1s^2$	$2s^2$	$2p^6$	$3s^2$	$3p^6$	$3d^{10}$	$4s^2$	$4p^6$	$4d_{xy}^1$	$5s^2$
Zirconium	40	$1s^2$	$2s^2$	$2p^6$	$3s^2$	$3p^6$	$3d^{10}$	$4s^2$	$4p^6$	$4d_{xy}^1 4d_{xz}^1$	$5s^2$

beryllium (compared to that in lithium) leads to a larger ionization energy for an electron from the 2s orbital.

Boron has a first ionization energy of 191 kcal/mole, which is smaller than that of beryllium. The electronic configuration is $1s^2 2s^2 2p_x{}^1$ (Table 10-9). The outermost electron is in a 2p orbital, somewhat more distant from the nucleus than the 2s orbital.

Carbon and nitrogen have electronic configurations $1s^2 2s^2 2p_x{}^1 2p_y{}^1$ and $1s^2 2s^2 2p_x{}^1 2p_y{}^1 2p_z{}^1$ (Fig. 10-9b) and ionization energies of 260 and 335 kcal/mole, respectively. The electron waves are arranged in separate p orbitals (of the same energy level) rather than in the same orbital because of the mutual repulsion of electron waves. The higher ionization energies of carbon and nitrogen can be explained by the fact that carbon and nitrogen have larger nuclear charges than boron. The ionization energy of oxygen is 314 kcal/mole, which is less than that of nitrogen. The electronic configuration in the ground state of oxygen is $1s^2 2s^2 2p_x{}^2 2p_y{}^1 2p_z{}^1$ (Table 10-9). Two of the electron waves are now in the same $2p_x$ orbital and subject to mutual repulsion. This raises the energy of the system slightly and makes the ionization energy of oxygen less than that of nitrogen.

In the orbital models for fluorine and neon, additional electron waves are added to p orbitals, with an accompanying increase in first ionization energy. Neon has an electronic configuration in which all orbitals with principal quantum numbers 1 and 2 are filled.

In the atoms of the elements from sodium through argon, the order of filling of orbitals outside the orbitals with principal quantum numbers 1 and 2 repeats the pattern proposed for lithium through neon (Table 10-9). The pattern of the graph obtained when first ionization energies (Table 10-3) are plotted against atomic number for the set of elements sodium through argon closely parallels the pattern for lithium through neon (Fig. 10-11). This repeating or periodic pattern suggests that there is some possibility for correlating the atomic orbital model with observations of properties of chemical systems.

10-15 THE NOBLE GASES

Of the elements in any one period, helium, neon, argon, krypton, xenon, and radon have the highest ionization energies of those in Table 10-3 and Fig. 10-11. Some properties of the noble gases are listed in Table 10-10. These six elements are found in the atmosphere as uncombined gases. All six were discovered about 1900 as a result of the studies by an Englishman, William Ramsay, on the composition of air.

With the exception of helium, the noble gases have electronic configurations in the highest energy level represented by $s^2 p^6$. The electronic configuration $s^2 p^6$ in an atom is called a completed or **filled level**. The highest energy levels of the noble gases then are filled levels.

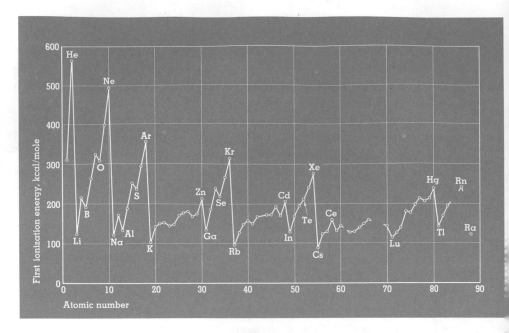

Fig. 10-11 *First ionization energies of the elements. The energies plotted are for the removal of the first electron from the atoms in 1 mole of the element.*

The six noble gases have monatomic molecules. A great many attempts have been made to prepare compounds of these elements but without success. For this reason the group has been called the inert gases as an indication of their unreactivity.

In 1962 it was discovered that xenon forms compounds with fluorine, provided the initial mixture of the elements is heated to about 400°C. Most previous attempts to prepare compounds of the noble gases were carried out at a low temperature since it was presumed that any com-

TABLE 10-10 PROPERTIES OF THE NOBLE GASES

Element	Atomic Number	Atomic Mass	First Ionization Energy, kcal/mole	Melting Point, °C	Boiling Point, °C	Electronic Configuration in Outer Orbitals
Helium	2	4.0	566	—270	—269	$1s^2$
Neon	10	20.2	497	—249	—246	$2s^2 2p^6$
Argon	18	39.9	363	—189	—186	$3s^2 3p^6$
Krypton	36	83.8	323	—157	—153	$4s^2 4p^6$
Xenon	54	131.3	280	—112	—108	$5s^2 5p^6$
Radon	86	222.	248	—71	—62	$6s^2 6p^6$

pounds would be unstable at a higher temperature. Two substances, XeF_4 and XeF_2, have been isolated and identified. Both XeF_4 and XeF_2 are stable, colorless solids at room temperature. Reports of experiments in early 1963 indicated the existence of XeF_6 and also that two of the other noble gases can form compounds with fluorine. Radon forms RnF_4 and krypton forms KrF_4.

Knowledge of the chemical properties of the noble gases will certainly be developed further on the basis of these discoveries. Ionization energy data show that argon, krypton, xenon, and radon have first ionization energies lower than that of fluorine, whereas the ionization energies of helium and neon are higher than that of fluorine. The magnitudes of the ionization energies of helium and neon in comparison to the ionization energies of the other noble gases suggest that helium and neon are unlikely to form compounds even though other elements in the group do so.

The filled highest energy levels of their atoms correspond with the observation that the noble gases are unreactive although not entirely inert. The failure of these gases to form many compounds and their low boiling points (Table 10-10 and Section 8-17) do set them apart from other elements so that the term noble is appropriate.

10-16 PERIODIC BEHAVIOR OF THE CHEMICAL ELEMENTS

A striking pattern is observed when the first ionization energies of the elements are plotted against atomic numbers (Fig. 10-11). The first ionization energy increases, decreases, and increases in a repeating pattern as the atomic number steadily increases. This repeating pattern is said to be periodic, and the property of the elements plotted (for example, first ionization energy) is said to show **periodicity.** In other words, first ionization energy is a periodic property. Is the periodicity in first ionization energy related to a periodicity in other properties of the elements?

More than one hundred years ago, accumulation of experimental evidence led chemists to suspect that there was some kind of pattern in the properties of the elements which could be used as a basis for classifying the elements. In 1869 two chemists, Dmitri Mendeleev in Russia and Lothar Meyer in Germany, published classification schemes for the known elements called **periodic tables.** The original basic form of Mendeleev's periodic table has been retained through all the modifications necessitated by new chemical information. Since Mendeleev's original work, the number of known elements has increased from about 60 to 103. One of the great triumphs of the periodic table was the ease with which the subsequently discovered noble gases and other elements could be incorporated in it.

A major feature of the periodic table is that its organization conforms to the discovery that some properties of the elements are periodic. Another property for which periodicity has been demonstrated is atomic volume. *Atomic volume* is defined as the volume (in milliliters) occupied by one mole of atoms of an element in solid form. Lothar Meyer used atomic volume to prepare his classification scheme of the elements. The atomic volume of a solid is calculated by dividing the atomic mass (grams per mole) by the density (grams per milliliter) of the solid. Plotting the atomic volume of the solid elements with atomic numbers 1 to 92 against the atomic number gives the curve in Fig. 10-12. The repeating pattern in Fig. 10-12 shows that atomic volume is a periodic property. Sodium, potassium, rubidium, and cesium are at peaks. When other properties of the elements are plotted against atomic number, the curves obtained rise and fall in magnitude in repeating patterns. As another example, the melting points of the elements are plotted against atomic number in Fig. 10-13.

LOTHAR MEYER *1830–1895*

A German chemist and physician. Meyer received his medical degree from Würzburg in 1854, then studied chemistry at Heidelberg and mathematical physics at Königsberg. Meyer taught at the Universities of Breslau, Karlsruhe (from 1868), and Tübingen (from 1876 to 1895) where he was professor of chemistry. During the Franco-Prussian War (1870–1871), he acted as army surgeon in Karlsruhe when his institute was turned into a hospital.

He attended the Karlsruhe International Chemical Congress in 1860 and was strongly influenced by Cannizzaro. His book Modern Theories of Chemistry *was influential in clarifying chemical concepts. In 1869 he published evidence for the periodic classification of the elements by demonstrating the periodicity of atomic volume, melting point, volatility, malleability, brittleness, and electrochemical behavior. Meyer and Mendeleev jointly received the Davy Medal of the Royal Society for their independent establishment of the periodic law.*

Meyer's early work was on the chemistry of the blood. In later years he directed over sixty doctoral candidates in numerous organic and inorganic studies. He was actively interested in problems of high school and university education.

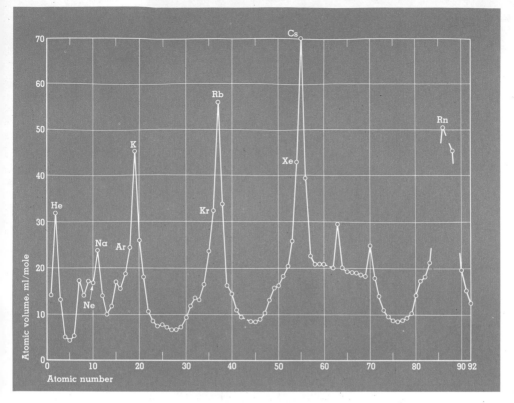

Fig. 10-12   *Periodicity of the atomic volumes of the elements.*

Fig. 10-13   *Periodicity of the melting points of the elements.*

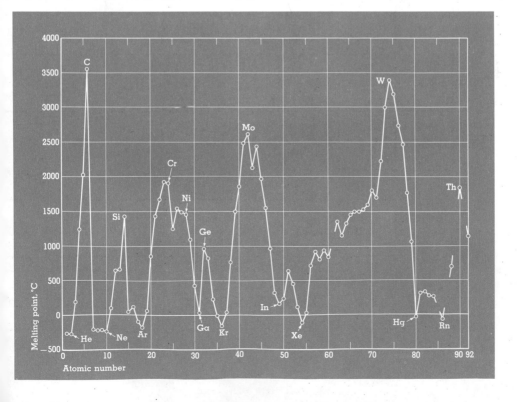

	I	II

| H 1 | |

| Li 3 | Be 4 |
| Na 11 | Mg 12 |

K 19	Ca 20	Sc 21	Ti 22	V 23	Cr 24	Mn 25	Fe 26	Co 27
Rb 37	Sr 38	Y 39	Zr 40	Nb 41	Mo 42	Tc 43	Ru 44	Rh 45
Cs 55	Ba 56	See below 57-71	Hf 72	Ta 73	W 74	Re 75	Os 76	Ir 77
Fr 87	Ra 88	See below 89-

| La 57 | Ce 58 | Pr 59 | Nd 60 | Pm 61 | Sm 62 | Eu 63 |
| Ac 89 | Th 90 | Pa 91 | U 92 | Np 93 | Pu 94 | Am 95 |

		III	IV	V	VI	VII	O
							He 2
		B 5	C 6	N 7	O 8	F 9	Ne 10
		Al 13	Si 14	P 15	S 16	Cl 17	Ar 18
Ni 8	Cu 29	Zn 30	Ga 31	Ge 32	As 33	Se 34	Br 35	Kr 36
Pd 6	Ag 47	Cd 48	In 49	Sn 50	Sb 51	Te 52	I 53	Xe 54
Pt 8	Au 79	Hg 80	Tl 81	Pb 82	Bi 83	Po 84	At 85	Rn 86

Gd 4	Tb 65	Dy 66	Ho 67	Er 68	Tm 69	Yb 70	Lu 71
Cm 6	Bk 97	Cf 98	Es 99	Fm 100	Md 101	No 102	Lw 103

CHEMICAL ELEMENTS: THEIR SYMBOLS, ATOMIC NUMBERS, AND ATOMIC MASSES—1961

Name	Symbol	Number	Mass[a]	Name	Symbol	Number	Mass[a]
Actinium	Ac	89	(227)	Mercury	Hg	80	200.59
Aluminum	Al	13	26.9815	Molybdenum	Mo	42	95.94
Americium	Am	95	(243)	Neodymium	Nd	60	144.24
Antimony	Sb	51	121.75	Neon	Ne	10	20.183
Argon	Ar	18	39.948	Neptunium	Np	93	(237)
Arsenic	As	33	74.9216	Nickel	Ni	28	58.71
Astatine	At	85	(210)	Niobium	Nb	41	92.906
Barium	Ba	56	137.34	Nitrogen	N	7	14.0067
Berkelium	Bk	97	(249)	Nobelium	No	102	(253)
Beryllium	Be	4	9.0122	Osmium	Os	76	190.2
Bismuth	Bi	83	208.980	Oxygen	O	8	15.9994
Boron	B	5	10.811	Palladium	Pd	46	106.4
Bromine	Br	35	79.909	Phosphorus	P	15	30.9738
Cadmium	Cd	48	112.40	Platinum	Pt	78	195.09
Calcium	Ca	20	40.08	Plutonium	Pu	94	(242)
Californium	Cf	98	(249)	Polonium	Po	84	210.
Carbon	C	6	12.01115	Potassium	K	19	39.102
Cerium	Ce	58	140.12	Praseodymium	Pr	59	140.907
Cesium	Cs	55	132.905	Promethium	Pm	61	(145)
Chlorine	Cl	17	35.453	Protactinium	Pa	91	231.
Chromium	Cr	24	51.996	Radium	Ra	88	226.05
Cobalt	Co	27	58.9332	Radon	Rn	86	222.
Copper	Cu	29	63.54	Rhenium	Re	75	186.2
Curium	Cm	96	(245)	Rhodium	Rh	45	102.905
Dysprosium	Dy	66	162.50	Rubidium	Rb	37	85.47
Einsteinium	Es	99	(251)	Ruthenium	Ru	44	101.07
Erbium	Er	68	167.26	Samarium	Sm	62	150.35
Europium	Eu	63	151.96	Scandium	Sc	21	44.956
Fermium	Fm	100	(253)	Selenium	Se	34	78.96
Fluorine	F	9	18.9984	Silicon	Si	14	28.086
Francium	Fr	87	(223)	Silver	Ag	47	107.870
Gadolinium	Gd	64	157.25	Sodium	Na	11	22.9898
Gallium	Ga	31	69.72	Strontium	Sr	38	87.62
Germanium	Ge	32	72.59	Sulfur	S	16	32.064
Gold	Au	79	196.967	Tantalum	Ta	73	180.948
Hafnium	Hf	72	178.49	Technetium	Tc	43	(99)
Helium	He	2	4.0026	Tellurium	Te	52	127.60
Holmium	Ho	67	164.930	Terbium	Tb	65	158.924
Hydrogen	H	1	1.00797	Thallium	Tl	81	204.37
Indium	In	49	114.82	Thorium	Th	90	232.038
Iodine	I	53	126.9044	Thulium	Tm	69	168.934
Iridium	Ir	77	192.2	Tin	Sn	50	118.69
Iron	Fe	26	55.847	Titanium	Ti	22	47.90
Krypton	Kr	36	83.80	Tungsten	W	74	183.85
Lanthanum	La	57	138.91	Uranium	U	92	238.03
Lawrencium[b]	Lw	103		Vanadium	V	23	50.942
Lead	Pb	82	207.19	Xenon	Xe	54	131.30
Lithium	Li	3	6.939	Ytterbium	Yb	70	173.04
Lutetium	Lu	71	174.97	Yttrium	Y	39	88.905
Magnesium	Mg	12	24.312	Zinc	Zn	30	65.37
Manganese	Mn	25	54.9380	Zirconium	Zr	40	91.22
Mendelevium	Md	101	(256)				

[a] The numbers in parentheses are the mass numbers of the most stable isotopes.
[b] The existence of this element has not yet been confirmed.

SOURCE: *Journal of the American Chemical Society*, **84**:4175, 1962.
Journal of Chemical Education, **38**:625, 1961.

DMITRI IVANOVICH MENDELEEV

1834–1907

A Russian chemist, born in Tobolsk, Siberia. Mendeleev was the youngest of a family of seventeen. His father died young. To support the family, his mother ran a glass factory. When this burned down, the family moved to St. Petersburg (Leningrad) where he studied chemistry. He worked with Bunsen in Heidelberg, Germany, during 1859 and attended the Karlsruhe International Chemical Congress in 1860, where he was influenced by Cannizzaro. In the 1860s he taught at the St. Petersburg Technological Institute and became professor of chemistry at the University of St. Petersburg. In the attempt to put some order into chemical topics for his textbook, The Principles of Chemistry, *he proposed the "Periodic Law" (1869) and used it to predict the properties of as yet unknown elements and to indicate that a number of currently accepted values of atomic masses were probably incorrect. The discovery of gallium by P. Lecoq de Boisbaudran (1875), scandium by L. F. Nilson (1879), and germanium by C. Winkler (1886), all of which had the properties predicted by Mendeleev, established his fame.*

Mendeleev's major experimental contributions were in solution chemistry, liquid-vapor studies, and research on the nature and origin of petroleum. He was adviser to a major oil refinery (he visited Pennsylvania oil fields in 1876) and was interested in the study of the atmosphere and the possibility of air travel. Because of his liberal views on political issues, he was never elected to the Imperial Academy of Sciences. In 1890 he resigned his chair in protest against the government's oppressive treatment of students and the lack of academic freedom at the university. From 1893, he was director of the Bureau of Weights and Measures in Russia where he continued his scientific studies. Element 101 was named mendelevium in his honor.

Figure 10-11 indicates that ionization energies are highest for the series of elements with atomic numbers 2, 10, 18, 36, 54, and 86 (the noble gases), while ionization energies are lowest for the series of elements with atomic numbers 3, 11, 19, 37, and 55. It is possible to arrange the elements in such a manner that the elements in the first series (the noble gases) are listed in one vertical column and those in

$LiCl$	$BeCl_2$											BCl_3	CCl_4	NCl_3	OCl_2	FCl	
$NaCl$	$MgCl_2$											$AlCl_3$	$SiCl_4$	PCl_5	SCl_4	$ClCl$	
KCl	$CaCl_2$											$GaCl_3$	$GeCl_4$	$AsCl_3$	$SeCl_4$	$BrCl$	
$RbCl$	$SrCl_2$											$InCl_3$	$SnCl_4$	$SbCl_5$	$TeCl_4$	ICl_3	
$CsCl$	$BaCl_2$												$PbCl_4$	$BiCl_3$			

Fig. 10-14   *Periodicity of the formulas for the chlorides of some elements.*

the second series are listed in another vertical column. A table which includes all the elements arranged on a similar basis is called a **periodic table of the elements.** In the accompanying periodic table the atomic number for each element is given as a subscript to the left of the symbol for the element. The chemical properties of elements in each vertical column are similar, and the chemical properties of the elements along any horizontal row change in a regular fashion. Elements listed in one vertical column of the periodic table are referred to as being in one **family** or **group,** whereas the elements listed in a horizontal row are members of one **period.** Lithium, sodium, and potassium, referred to previously in the discussion of periodicity in atomic volume (Fig. 10-12), for example, are members of a family called the **alkali metals.**

The periodicity of chemical properties of elements is illustrated by the formulas of the compounds that some elements form with chlorine. These compounds are called chlorides. The formulas for the chlorides of several elements, containing the largest percentage of chlorine for which a compound of the element with chlorine has been isolated, are listed in the form of a periodic table in Fig. 10-14. The formulas for the compounds in the left-hand vertical column (group I) show that each element in that column combines with chlorine in a 1:1 atom ratio, whereas the elements in the second column (group II) combine with chlorine in a 1:2 atom ratio. There are exceptions to periodicity in the formulas of chlorides (for example, in groups V, VI, and VII). Predictions of properties based on periodicity must therefore always be verified by experiment.

Enthalpies of formation for the chlorides of the elements hydrogen

ALBERT EINSTEIN   *1879–1955*

*A German-Swiss-American physicist. Einstein
was the creator of the special and general theory
of relativity. He received the 1921 Nobel Prize in
physics "for his contributions to mathematical
physics and especially for his discovery of the law
of the photoelectric effect." He was born in Ulm,
Germany, went to school mainly in Munich, and
then proceeded to university studies at the Polytechnic School in Zürich, Switzerland. Unable to
obtain a university teaching position, he took a
minor post at the Berne Patent Office which gave
him ample time for his scientific pursuits. During the single year of 1905,
he published the special theory of relativity incorporating the constancy of
the speed of light c and the mass-energy relationship, $E = mc^2$; the theory
of Brownian movement; and the explanation of the photoelectric effect in
terms of quanta or photons of light. The same year he received his doctorate.
He was a professor at Prague (Austria, now Czechoslovakia) in 1911 and
in Zürich in 1912. He became director of the newly founded Kaiser Wilhelm
Institute of Physics in Berlin in 1913. He traveled widely, partly in the cause
of Zionism. On Hitler's accession to power in Germany, Einstein lost his
positions there and from 1933 was professor of mathematics at the Institute
for Advanced Study at Princeton, New Jersey. Although a pacifist all his
life, he wrote the famous letter to Roosevelt in 1939 alerting him to German
preparations for nuclear warfare, a letter which led to the production of the
first fission bomb by the United States. A man with a strong social
conscience, he wrote and spoke on world government, total disarmament,
and the proper utilization of science.*

*His theories of relativity have helped to transform the view of the universe
held by men in this century and have been an enormous stimulus to
astronomical studies. Application of the energy relationship promises to
make available to mankind almost unlimited sources of energy unless its
misapplications destroy us all. Element 99, first detected in the fallout from
a hydrogen bomb explosion on Eniwetok Island (1952), was named
einsteinium in his honor.*

(atomic number 1) to calcium (atomic number 20) are plotted against
atomic number in Fig. 10-15. The shape of the graph is similar to that
obtained for other periodic properties.

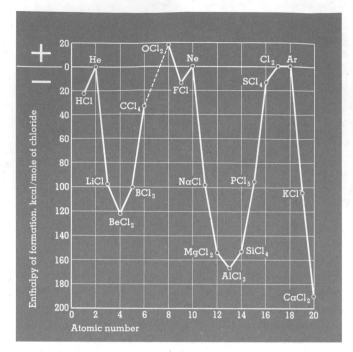

Fig. 10-15 *Enthalpies of formation for the chlorides of some elements.*

The periodic table is based on experimental data for the properties of elements and therefore is completely independent of any model for atomic structure. Can the atomic orbital model be developed to describe compound formation in such a way that the periodicity of chemical properties (formulas of chlorides, for example) can be understood?

10-17 THE ATOMIC ORBITAL MODEL AND COMPOUND FORMATION

In terms of the charge cloud model, atoms combine to form molecules if, as a result of the combination, the negative charge density around the positive nuclei is increased. One way in which negative charge density can be increased is to have electron charge clouds attracted to two nuclei. In the atomic orbital model, compound formation results in an increase in negative charge density around the positive nucleus when one or more standing electron waves occupy the orbitals of two atoms simultaneously.

In this way one or more of the electron waves in each of two atoms can be simultaneously attracted by the nuclei of the two atoms. Such an attraction can result in an arrangement of two atoms in a molecule that has lower total energy than the two atoms separated. This will mean that there is a bond between the two atoms in the molecule. Although it has not been possible to calculate total energies for most of the molecules which interest chemists, it is possible to use a set of operational rules that satisfactorily account for compound formation.

Several factors must be considered in discussing the spatial characteristics of orbitals that are designated by the quantum numbers l and m (Table 10-8) governing shape and orientation, respectively. Central among these factors is the electrostatic principle that a rise in the energy possessed by an electron and nucleus is accompanied by an increase in the distance between the two. On this basis, those electrons in the highest energy orbitals of an atom are assumed to be on the outside of the atom. In the diagram for calcium in Fig. 10-8, the two $4s$ electrons are closest to the ionization level. Therefore, considerably less energy must be supplied to the atom in order to separate the two $4s$ electrons from the calcium atom than to separate other electrons.

In studying orbital geometry, it is necessary to confine discussion to the hydrogen atom. This is so because orbital geometry has been deduced from a mathematical analysis of the wave mechanics model developed only for the hydrogen atom. The orbital geometry in other atoms is assumed to be similar.

The $1s$ orbital in a hydrogen atom is arranged symmetrically about the nucleus. The most symmetrical three-dimensional geometric structure is a sphere since one measurement, the radius, describes a sphere completely. The $1s$ orbital can therefore be taken to be spherical in shape. The s orbitals of higher principal quantum numbers, $2s$ and $3s$, for example, are also spherically symmetrical and, since they are of higher energy, occupy spherical shells concentric with, but outside, the $1s$ sphere.

Since the three p orbitals have equivalent energies, all three must have identical relations to the nucleus. The differences among the three orbitals are only differences in orientation. When each of the three p orbitals is occupied by electron waves, which cause the orbitals to repel each other, the orbitals can be farthest apart if they extend outward from the nucleus along lines at right angles to each other. Since three mutually right-angle axes are possible in three-dimensional space, the three p orbitals fit into such an arrangement. Each p orbital will extend along an axis running through the nucleus and will have a shape somewhat like that of two pears fastened together at their small ends. A model of the arrangement of three p orbitals (p_x, p_y, and p_z) is shown in Fig. 10-16. Chemists often say that the p orbital has the shape of a dumbbell.

The five d orbitals of equal energy have more complex geometric shapes than p orbitals, and again differ from each other by their orientations in space. The d orbitals are important in discussions of the structure of atoms in the fourth row of the periodic table.

A single hydrogen atom in its ground state possesses a spherical s orbital occupied by one electron wave. The orbital model allows two

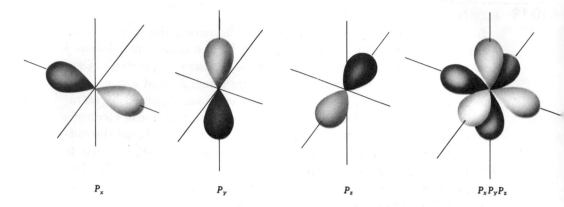

P_x P_y P_z $P_xP_yP_z$

Fig. 10-16   *Models showing the spatial arrangement for* p_x, p_y, *and* p_z *orbitals with respect to the nucleus of an atom.*

electron waves to occupy one orbital if the electron waves have opposite spins. The atoms in a stable H_2 molecule share a pair of electron waves between the nuclei so that the two electron waves occupy the 1s orbitals of both atoms. Since the electron waves in the separated atoms would be in separate spherical s orbitals, the bond between the hydrogen atoms is called an *s-s* bond and the orbitals are said to overlap (Fig. 10-17). An orbital in one atom that can overlap an orbital in another atom to form a bond is called a **bonding orbital.**

10-19   HYDROGEN FLUORIDE

When a hydrogen atom and a fluorine atom (Table 10-9) combine, the electron wave in the s orbital of the hydrogen is available for bond formation. But the s orbitals of the fluorine atom, $1s^2$ and $2s^2$, with two electron waves in each are already filled and therefore cannot form bonds. One of the p orbitals in fluorine, however, contains only one electron wave and provides an orbital where charge density can be increased by bond formation. In this way, the spherical s orbital in hydrogen and one p orbital in fluorine can overlap, so that the two electron waves form a bond between the two nuclei. This is called an

Fig. 10-17   *The 1s orbitals of two hydrogen atoms overlap to form an s-s bond.*

Hydrogen $1s^1$ Hydrogen $1s^1$ Hydrogen molecule

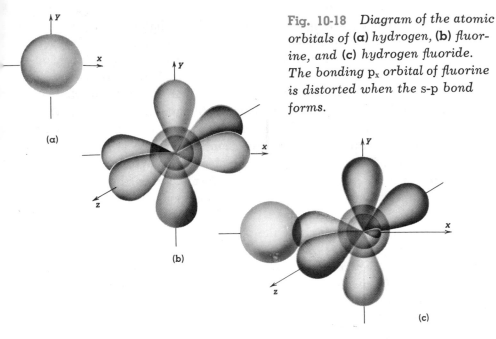

Fig. 10-18 *Diagram of the atomic orbitals of* (**a**) *hydrogen,* (**b**) *fluorine, and* (**c**) *hydrogen fluoride. The bonding* p_x *orbital of fluorine is distorted when the s-p bond forms.*

(a)

(b)

(c)

s-p bond. A sketch of the orbital model for hydrogen fluoride is given in Fig. 10-18c.

The formation of an *s-p* bond between hydrogen and fluorine leaves all bonding orbitals of both atoms filled with two electron waves. No further bond formation can take place by the overlapping of orbitals. Experimentally it is found that atoms of hydrogen and fluorine combine in a 1:1 ratio. The atomic orbital model for hydrogen fluoride is consistent with the experimental evidence for the composition of hydrogen fluoride, HF.

10-20 FLUORINE

From the atomic orbital model, it is reasonable to predict that two fluorine atoms can unite to form a diatomic molecule by the overlap of two *p* orbitals. The resulting bond is referred to as a *p-p* bond. The diatomic molecule predicted by the atomic orbital model is in agreement with experimental data showing that the molecular mass of fluorine gas corresponds to the formula F_2.

10-21 WATER AND AMMONIA

According to the atomic orbital model, hydrogen and oxygen atoms should be able to form *s-p* bonds to give a molecule with the formula H_2O. On the same basis, hydrogen and nitrogen can form *s-p* bonds to give a molecule with the formula NH_3. The experimentally determined atomic ratios and molecular masses for these two compounds correspond to the formulas H_2O and NH_3, respectively.

The geometric arrangement of the nuclei in diatomic molecules must be linear since two nuclei (assumed to be points) determine a line. Therefore, no question of bond angle was raised in the discussion of H_2, HF, and F_2. The charge cloud model predicted tetrahedral bond angles for H_2O and NH_3. What bond angles would be predicted for H_2O and NH_3 molecules on the basis of the atomic orbital model?

In Section 10-18 it was stated that the three p orbitals with a given principal quantum number were oriented in space at right angles to each other. The total energy of a molecular structure will be lowest, and hence the strongest bond will be formed when the orbitals of the combining atoms overlap the maximum amount. Maximum overlap of a dumbbell-shaped p orbital with a spherical s orbital in an s-p bond will occur when the axis of the p orbital passes through the center of the s orbital. On the basis of the atomic orbital model, therefore, a bond angle of $90°$ would be predicted for H—O—H in water. The same bond angle of $90°$ would be predicted for H—N—H in ammonia as illustrated in Fig. 10-19.

Table 10-11 lists the experimentally determined bond angle for H_2O as $104°28'$ and for NH_3 as $107°20'$. These are considerably larger than the $90°$ angles predicted by the model. Before you conclude that the atomic orbital model is not useful in predicting bond angles, you should note that the experimentally determined angles in H_2S, H_2Se, H_2Te, PH_3, AsH_3, and SbH_3 are very nearly $90°$. This is the angle predicted by the orbital model since the outer electronic configurations (Table 10-9) of S, Se, and Te are identical with that of O and the outer electronic configurations of P, As, and Sb are identical with that of N. This would suggest that there is something unusual in H_2O and NH_3 which causes the bond angles to be larger than predicted.

Fig. 10-19 *Orbital models of water and ammonia.*

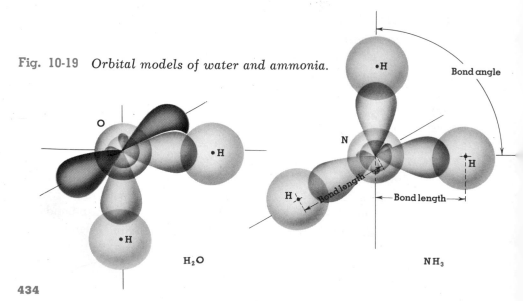

H₂O   NH₃

TABLE 10-11   BOND ANGLES IN SEVERAL HYDRIDES

CH_4	109°28′	NH_3	107°20′	H_2O	104°28′
SiH_4	109°28′	PH_3	93°20′	H_2S	92°10′
GeH_4	109°28′	AsH_3	91°50′	H_2Se	91°
		SbH_3	91°20′	H_2Te	89°30′

SOURCE: Linus Pauling, *Nature of the Chemical Bond and the Structure of Molecules and Crystals*, 3d ed., Cornell University Press, Ithaca, N.Y., 1960.

The distortion of the bond angles in water and ammonia molecules from the 90° angles predicted on the basis of the atomic orbital model could be explained in terms of the mutual repulsion of hydrogen nuclei. These nuclei are nearer to each other in H_2O and NH_3 than they are in H_2S and PH_3. Since more energy levels in atoms of sulfur and phosphorus are occupied by electron waves than in oxygen and nitrogen atoms, it is reasonable to conclude that sulfur and phosphorus atoms are larger than oxygen and nitrogen atoms, respectively. A larger size would imply a greater distance between hydrogen nuclei within molecules of hydrides of elements in the same group. The hydrogen nuclei in H_2S and PH_3 ought, therefore, to be farther apart, and so they repel each other less than in H_2O and NH_3.

10-22 HYBRIDIZATION

The electronic configurations of the elements with atomic numbers 4, 5, and 6 (beryllium, boron, and carbon) are listed in Table 10-9. On the basis of the discussion of bond formation given in Sections 10-17 to 10-20, it would be reasonable to conclude that beryllium would be an inert element, since it has no half-filled orbitals. On the same basis, a boron atom should form only one bond with other atoms and carbon should form only two bonds with other atoms. Experimental observations do not agree with these conclusions. Beryllium is not inert. Beryllium reacts with other elements to form compounds with 1:2 atomic ratios, for example, BeH_2 and $BeCl_2$. Boron forms compounds in which the atomic ratio is 1:3, for example, BF_3 and BCl_3. Carbon forms over a million compounds in which each carbon atom is bonded to four other atoms.

These contradictions between experimental observations and predictions based on the atomic orbital model indicate that the atomic orbital model as presented thus far is incomplete. The atomic orbital model was developed by assuming that the experimental observations and computations for the behavior of electrons in hydrogen atoms could be extended to atoms containing more than one electron. In the hydrogen atom all the orbitals (s, p, d, and f) of a given principal quantum number represent the same total energy. Experimental evidence for

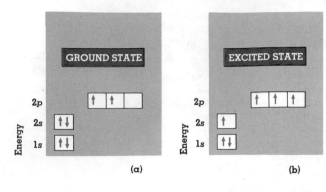

Fig. 10-20 *Electron-in-a-box diagrams for carbon* **(a)** *in the ground state and* **(b)** *in an excited state.*

atoms with more than one electron wave indicates that all the orbitals with the same principal quantum number cannot represent the same total energy.

When one atom combines with another to form a molecule, each atom introduces electrons into the orbitals of the other atom by the overlapping of orbitals in the molecules. It is quite possible that the overlapping of orbitals changes the orbitals from their nature in isolated atoms. Consideration of compounds of beryllium, boron, and carbon leads to some further rules for using the atomic orbital model to explain the formation of bonds in molecules.

The formation of molecules from atoms depends upon the electric attraction between electrons and nuclei. The greater the density of negative charge around the nuclei in a molecule, the lower the energy of the system, and hence, the greater the attraction. This principle was referred to repeatedly in the development of the charge cloud model in Chapter 7. It applies to the atomic orbital model as well.

Consider an atomic orbital model for an isolated carbon atom. The electronic configuration for carbon in the ground state is shown in Fig. 10-20a. Such an arrangement provides orbitals for only two bonds with hydrogen, and consequently the carbon nucleus can surround itself with but six electron waves having the principal quantum number 2. On the other hand, the electron waves with quantum number 2 can be arranged so that there is one electron wave in the 2s orbital and one electron wave in each of the 2p orbitals as shown in Fig. 10-20b. An isolated carbon atom with the electronic configuration of the excited state shown in Fig. 10-20b has a higher energy than is characteristic of a carbon atom in the ground state. In the excited state the carbon nucleus can become surrounded with eight electron waves rather than six having the principal quantum number 2 during bond formation. This should result in a further lowering of the energy of the system. If the four additional electrons are provided by four hydrogen atoms, the compound formed will have the formula CH_4. This would indicate that a system of carbon and hydrogen atoms can have a lower energy in a compound corresponding to the formula CH_4 than in a compound with the formula CH_2.

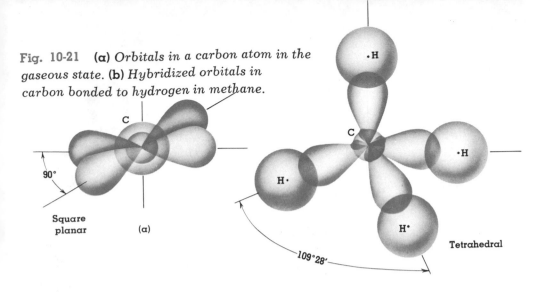

Fig. 10-21 **(a)** *Orbitals in a carbon atom in the gaseous state.* **(b)** *Hybridized orbitals in carbon bonded to hydrogen in methane.*

90°

Square planar   (a)

109°28′

Tetrahedral

(b)

The rearrangement of electrons among the orbitals for a given principal quantum number leads to the production of a new set of orbitals. All these new orbitals are equivalent when they are involved in bond formation. Thus in the methane molecule, the new orbitals are not made up of one *s* orbital and three *p* orbitals. Instead a new set of four equivalent orbitals is formed. Each orbital is designated as an *sp*³ orbital (Fig. 10-21).

The redistribution of orbitals representing different energies in an isolated atom to form a new set of equivalent orbitals in a molecule is called **hybridization.** The electrons will repel each other as usual. For this reason, the four orbitals will keep as far from each other as possible. Geometrically, this is equivalent to having the orbitals directed toward the corners of a regular tetrahedron.

An atomic orbital model of methane using hybridized orbitals corresponds to the formula CH_4 and to a molecule with bond angles of 109°28′. The hybridized atomic orbital model then comes to the same set of conclusions for the geometric structure of methane that were found with the charge cloud model. Figure 10-22 shows the electronic

Fig. 10-22 *Electronic configurations for Be, B, and C in the ground state and in an excited state. Hybridized orbitals are underlined.*

	Be			B			C		
	1s	2s	2p	1s	2s	2p	1s	2s	2p
Ground state	↑↓	↑↓		↑↓	↑↓	↑	↑↓	↑↓	↑ ↑
Excited state	↑↓	↑	↑	↑↓	↑	↑ ↑	↑↓	↑	↑ ↑ ↑
Hybridized state	$1s^2 2s^1 2p_x^1$			$1s^2 2s^1 2p_x^1 2p_y^1$			$1s^2 2s^1 2p_x^1 2p_y^1 2p_z^1$		
Orientation of hybridized orbitals	Linear (180°)			Trigonal (120°)			Tetrahedral (109°28′)		

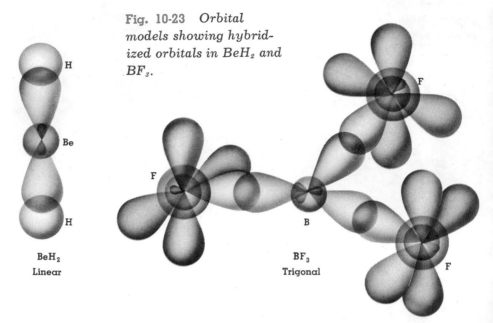

Fig. 10-23 *Orbital models showing hybridized orbitals in BeH₂ and BF₃.*

H

Be

H

BeH₂
Linear

F

B

F

F

BF₃
Trigonal

configurations for some hybridized orbitals for beryllium, boron, and carbon. The orientation of these hybridized orbitals is illustrated in Figs. 10-21b and 10-23. The names used to describe these orientations are given in Fig. 10-22.

Hybridization is not, however, to be regarded as a process that atoms go through. Instead hybridization is a way of trying to modify the orbital model as developed for isolated atoms to explain the formation of molecules. More explicitly it can be said that electron waves know nothing about hybridization or about orbitals. Electron waves and nuclei simply arrange themselves according to the forces that operate upon them. The atomic orbital model and the hybridized orbitals are terms used to designate two mental attempts to describe the arrangement of electron waves in a systematic way.

10-23 HYBRIDIZATION IN MULTIPLE BONDS

According to the charge cloud model, the properties of some molecules are best correlated with models which have more than one two-electron charge cloud shared between two nuclei. When two or three two-electron charge clouds are involved in a bond, the bonds are called double or triple bonds, respectively. How would atomic orbital models for molecules containing double and triple bonds be constructed?

In hybridization, the maximum possible number of hybridized orbitals does not always have to be used. In carbon, for example, hybridization need not always result in the formation of four sp^3 hybrid orbitals that would give four tetrahedral bond angles. Compounds with different atomic ratios and molecules with different geometrical structures are formed if fewer than four atoms are available to form bonds with each carbon atom. This more limited type of hybridization occurs fairly commonly in carbon compounds. Compounds containing nitrogen and oxygen atoms also exhibit limited hybridization. Besides sp^3 hybridization, then, carbon compounds are known in which hybridization of carbon orbitals produces bonds that are described as sp^2 and sp.

The planar, or flat, molecules of ethylene with formula C_2H_4 are described by the charge cloud model as an arrangement of six two-electron charge clouds around two carbon kernels. Each of the two two-electron clouds at each carbon atom holds a proton, and the remaining two clouds are shared between the two carbon atoms.

In the atomic orbital model, the ground state of carbon is represented by the symbol $1s^2 2s^2 2p_x^1 2p_y^1$ (Table 10-9). A hybridized state of carbon may be described by the symbol

$$1s^2 \underline{2s^1 2p_x^1 2p_y^1} 2p_z^1$$

in which one $2s$ electron wave has been placed in the $2p_z$ orbital. If three sp^2 (underlined) orbitals of a carbon atom are used in forming bonds to two hydrogen atoms and to the other carbon atom, one p orbital remains occupied by one electron wave. In Fig. 10-24a the half-filled p orbital on each carbon atom is shown in an orientation perpendicular to the plane of the six atoms (four H atoms and two C atoms). Sidewise overlap of the two perpendicular orbitals will occur if the carbon atoms are close enough together in the molecule. Sidewise overlapping of two half-filled orbitals produces a **pi bond.**

The description of the steps in the formation of a pi bond in ethylene is a convenient way to describe the nature of the pi bond and the structure of ethylene. However, there is no way to know whether atoms go through any corresponding steps, although bonding must be described in consecutive sentences.

In acetylene, C_2H_2, still fewer hydrogen atoms are available to furnish $2s$ electrons for bonds. In this molecule, in which the electronic configuration of each carbon in a hybridized state may be designated by the symbol $1s^2 \underline{2s^1 2p_x^1} 2p_y^1 2p_z^1$, there are four half-filled orbitals. Only two sp (underlined) hybridized orbitals are used by each carbon atom in forming bonds to hydrogen and the second carbon atom. The acetylene molecule is linear in shape (Fig. 10-24b). Consequently, two half-filled p orbitals that are mutually perpendicular to the line of H—C—C—H nuclei are available at each carbon atom for sidewise overlap in pi bonding. The two pi bonds may be thought of as forming four regions of high electron density around the axis of the linear molecule.

In ethylene each carbon atom may be said to form three sp^2 hybrid

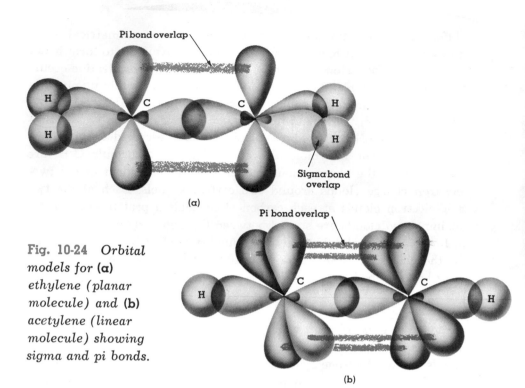

Fig. 10-24 *Orbital models for (a) ethylene (planar molecule) and (b) acetylene (linear molecule) showing sigma and pi bonds.*

bonds plus one pi bond. In acetylene, each carbon atom may be said to form two *sp* hybrid bonds plus two pi bonds.

The charge cloud model indicates a linear structure for the carbon dioxide, CO_2, molecule. The carbon atom is at the center of the molecule (Section 7-21). One possible hybridized state for carbon and the ground state for oxygen are

$$C \qquad 1s^2\underline{2s^12p_x^1}2p_y^12p_z^1 \qquad\qquad O \qquad 1s^22s^22p_x^22p_y^12p_z^1$$

Since there are two oxygen atoms bonded to a carbon atom in CO_2, it would be reasonable to start with two *sp* (underlined) hybrid orbitals in carbon to form an *sp-p* bond with each of the two oxygen

Fig. 10-25 *Orbital model of CO_2 showing pi bonding.*

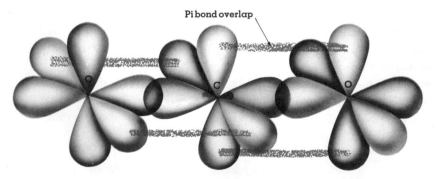

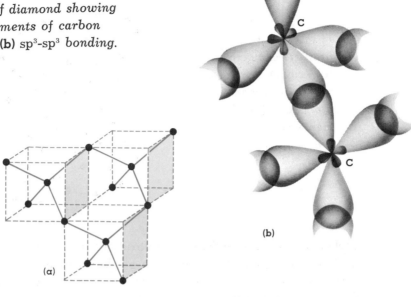

Fig. 10-26 *Diagram of the structure of diamond showing* (**a**) *arrangements of carbon atoms and* (**b**) sp^3-sp^3 *bonding.*

(b)

(a)

atoms. Two half-filled p orbitals remain on the carbon atom, arranged at right angles to the sp-p bond. One p orbital from each oxygen atom was used in the sp-p bond to carbon, and one half-filled p orbital remains in each oxygen atom. The electron density between the carbon and oxygen nuclei can be increased if the nuclei are close enough together to permit pi-bond formation with the remaining two p orbitals on the carbon atom and one p orbital on each oxygen atom. The pi bonds and two sp-p bonds are then said to hold the carbon atom and two oxygen atoms together in CO_2 (Fig. 10-25). Carbon supplies two sp hybrid orbitals plus two p orbitals for the sp-p bond and the pi bond to each oxygen atom.

X-ray diffraction patterns for diamond and graphite, which are allotropes of carbon, can be analyzed to indicate that in diamond each carbon atom is surrounded at the corners of a regular tetrahedron by four other carbon atoms. The bond angles of 109°28′ indicate that the bonds between adjacent carbon atoms are formed by the overlap of two sp^3 orbitals, endwise, to give the maximum overlap and maximum electron density, consistent with lowest total energy. The bond between two adjacent carbon atoms in diamond can be described as sp^3-sp^3 (Fig. 10-26).

Graphite, in contrast to diamond, has a layer structure in which carbon atoms are joined in a pattern of interlocking hexagons with bond angles of 120° so that each carbon atom is surrounded by three other carbon atoms in the layer (Fig. 10-27). The bonding between

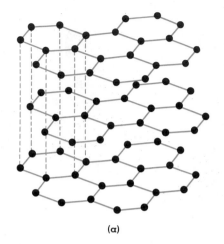

Fig. 10-27 *Diagram of the structure of graphite showing* (**a**) (right) *arrangements of carbon atoms and* (**b**) (far right) *sp²-sp² bonding.*

(a)

carbon atoms involves three sp^2 hybrid orbitals from each carbon atom (sp^2-sp^2 bond), but this leaves one p orbital containing only one electron wave at each carbon atom. This p orbital is considered to be a dumbbell-shaped orbital at right angles to the plane of the sp^2 hybrid orbitals. Above and below each hexagon, then, there are six half-filled p orbitals. Above and below the plane of the hexagon, sidewise overlap of p orbitals can be imagined to occur to give a doughnut-shaped ring of relatively high electron density. This sidewise overlap of p orbitals provides for six electron waves belonging to the doughnut above and below the hexagon. Not one of the six electron waves belongs to a specific carbon atom. Such electron waves belonging to more than two atoms are said to be **delocalized.** The delocalized electron waves in graphite that form bonds by overlap of p orbitals is another example of pi bonding. In graphite the overlapping sp^2 hybrid orbitals in the two-dimensional sheets form strong bonds, but the layers are held apart by the repulsion of the pi electron waves for the next layer and the repulsive forces of carbon nuclei in adjacent layers. Graphite is rather easily split into sheets; whereas diamond, with an endless array of sp^3-sp^3 bonds, is the hardest substance known.

Where bonds are formed by the overlap of orbitals along their axes, these bonds are called **sigma bonds.** Examples of sigma bonds which have already been considered are indicated in orbital notation as s-s, s-p, p-p, sp^3-s, and sp^3-sp^3 bonds. A single bond joining two atoms along the axes of the orbitals is always called a sigma bond. Pi bonds, on the other hand, are formed by sidewise overlap of p orbitals. For atoms joined by pi bonds, the internuclear distance is always less than for the same atoms joined by sigma bonds alone.

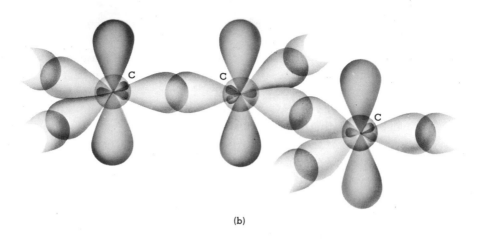

(b)

Ex. 10-11 From the discussion on the bonding in diamond and graphite, predict which allotropic form of carbon (*a*) is harder and (*b*) has the greater density. Give reasons for your choices, and check your answer with a handbook.

10-24 COMPARISON OF CHARGE CLOUD AND ORBITAL MODELS

Interpretations of structure and properties of matter based on the atomic orbital model in which maximum hybridization occurs in sp^3 bonds are quite similar to those based on the charge cloud model. How are the two models to be regarded? Is one clearly inferior to the other so that it should be discarded? If both models always lead to the same conclusions, then there is no reason to retain both of them. Presumably the easiest one to use would then be kept, and the other discarded. On the other hand, if conclusions based on the two models only partially agree, it may be unwise to keep just one. The test of a desirable model is that it be effective both in agreeing with what is already known and in suggesting conclusions not suspected previously.

One comparison of the charge cloud and atomic orbital models can be made with ammonia, phosphine (PH_3), water, and hydrogen sulfide (H_2S). Bond angles for the molecules of these compounds are discussed briefly in Section 10-21 and compared with the experimental data given in Table 10-11. In agreement with experimental observation, the charge cloud model and the atomic orbital model both suggest approximately tetrahedral bond angles in the molecules for ammonia and water. The two models make different predictions for the bond angles in molecules of phosphine and hydrogen sulfide. Here the measured bond angles are 93°20′ and 92°10′, respectively, or nearly right angles. Atomic orbitals without hybridization predict a 90° bond angle. No bond angles of 90° have been predicted on the basis of the charge cloud model, so the atomic orbital model appears to correspond more closely to observations of the properties of some molecules than does the charge cloud model.

To invoke hybridization of atomic orbitals for some cases and not for others is arbitrary, however. As a general rule, it appears that hybridization of s and p orbitals is useful in interpreting the properties of only the first 10 elements. Just why this should be so is not entirely clear to chemists at the present time.

It seems reasonable then to conclude that, for some problems, the charge cloud model is useful, whereas for others (for example, when limited hybridization in sp and sp^2 bonds is involved), the atomic orbital model is the better choice. Although the charge cloud model is useful in interpreting compound formation and molecular geometry in a number of covalent substances, the charge cloud model does not lend itself easily to interpretation of excited states of atoms and of the spectra of elements, nor to multiple bond formation. The atomic orbital model was developed through a consideration of energy levels for electron waves in atoms. It is, therefore, not surprising that the orbital model is more useful than the charge cloud model in interpreting the excited states of atoms. It must be emphasized that three-dimensional models for atomic and molecular structure are essential because no one at the present time knows how to solve the mathematical equations which occur in the detailed wave mechanics treatment of the structure of matter. Thus, it is not only in introductory courses in chemistry that these simple geometrical models have to be used, but throughout all of chemistry.

One assumption which is probably too drastic in both the charge cloud model and the atomic orbital model is the requirement that electrons be paired. For clarity in describing systems and ease in making calculations, it is usually assumed that electrons occur in pairs in atoms and molecules. However, the Pauli exclusion principle only forbids more than two electrons from occupying the same orbital and does not require that electrons pair at all. Indeed, some recent calculations indicate that because of the electron–electron repulsion the electrons will form two-electron clouds or two-electron waves only if this results in a considerable increase in charge density close to the positive nuclei. Thus, electrons will consist of four pairs in the CH_4 molecule because of the influence of the four hydrogen nuclei. However, in neon there is no real advantage if the outer clouds are two-electron clouds. The distribution of electrons in space may be better described as two sets of four one-electron clouds that partially overlap, than as one set of four two-electron clouds. Conclusions such as these result from an approach which has recently been suggested and which has been called the "double quartet model." It will undoubtedly be developed more fully by chemists in the future.

Gases at high temperature emit light with characteristic colors that form line spectra. The line spectra are quite unlike the continuous spectrum formed by the light emitted by incandescent solids. Analysis of the spectra for gaseous elements has led to the idea that atoms possess energy levels.

To account for energy levels, first an atomic model with electrons in circular orbits (the Bohr atom) and, later, a model with standing electron waves (the wave mechanics model) were devised. As the electrons go from lower to higher energy levels, energy is absorbed, but energy is emitted as the electrons go from higher to lower energy levels. The emitted energy behaves like a wave whose wavelength (hence, color) is determined by the energy difference between the two levels.

An electron in an atom behaves in some ways like a three-dimensional standing wave. There are four characteristics of the wave which describe each electron: (1) size, (2) shape, (3) orientation, and (4) spin. These characteristics are identified by a set of four quantum numbers. In any atom no two electron waves can have identical sets of quantum numbers. To identify a person living in the United States takes information analogous to five quantum numbers: name, house number, street, city, and state. No two persons (not even twins!) in the United States have the same set of five quantum numbers.

The spin quantum number has only two possible values corresponding to a clockwise or counterclockwise spin of the electron. For this reason, pairs of electrons will be found in multielectron atoms for which all quantum numbers are the same except for the spin quantum number. The reservation of space available around a nucleus for occupancy by such an electron pair or by a single electron is called an orbital.

Orbital assignments for atoms are worked out primarily from spectroscopic data. These data provide a basis for determining the orbitals that contain two, one, or zero electron waves. Combination of atoms to form molecules can occur when orbitals of two atoms overlap to permit electron waves from both atoms to occupy the overlapping orbitals. Such an overlap can form sigma bonds of the *s-s*, *s-p*, and *p-p* types.

The orbitals also have geometrical relations to one another. For hydrogen atoms, these relations have been worked out in detail from the theory. Other atoms with many electron waves are assumed to have similar relations among their orbitals. This simplified picture of hydrogen-like orbitals has to be modified to account for the behavior of many molecules in which the interaction of electron waves is complex in nature. Hybridization of orbitals results in compounds for which the bonding may be described as *s-sp, s-sp², s-sp³, p-sp³, sp³-sp³*, and *sp²-sp³*, for example all of which are called sigma bonds.

When there are not enough atoms available to utilize all possible hybridized orbitals, the resulting structures may be described in part by pi bonding and in part by sigma bonding. The description on paper of pi bonding involves sidewise overlap of orbitals as contrasted with head-on overlap in sigma-bond formation.

Ex. 10-12 Match the middle column listed below with each outer column.

Geometric Shape	Molecule	Type of Hybridization
Tetrahedral	BF_3	sp
Linear	CF_4	sp^2
Trigonal	BeF_2	sp^3

Ex. 10-13 Construct a table indicating the electronic configurations of the alkali metals. How do these configurations differ?

Ex. 10-14 Draw orbital pictures for the outer electrons to show bonding in the following covalent molecules: Br_2, HI, H_2O, PCl_3.

Ex. 10-15 Explain why, in terms of the atomic orbital model, it is reasonable to expect the following elements to occur as diatomic molecules: F_2, I_2, H_2.

Ex. 10-16 Explain what is meant by orbital hybridization.

Ex. 10-17 Draw orbital model representations of the following covalent molecules, and predict what geometric structures each molecule will exhibit: $BeCl_2$, BF_3, $SiCl_4$.

Ex. 10-18 Draw orbital model sketches and charge cloud model sketches, and write Lewis structures for the molecules and ions in the following reactions.

a. $NH_3 + H_2O \rightarrow NH_4^+ + OH^-$

b. $HF + H_2O \rightarrow H_3O^+ + F^-$

Ex. 10-19 A chemistry teacher filled three unlabeled bottles with solutions *A, B,* and *C* and put them in the laboratory. The teacher knew that the three solutions were lithium chloride, sodium chloride, and calcium chloride but did not tell which solution was in which bottle. One of the students in the class tested the solutions by first cleaning a platinum wire with nitric acid and burning off the acid, then dipping the wire in the unidentified solutions and holding the wire in the flame of a burner. The student recorded the following observations.

Bottle *A*	Yellow-red-orange flame color
Bottle *B*	Yellow color
Bottle *C*	Faint red

On the basis of these data, what conclusions could be drawn about the contents of each of the three bottles?

Ex. 10-20 Sketch an atomic orbital model for N_2.

Ex. 10-21 Describe the bonds and the bond angles in BeH_2 and $AlCl_3$, using the atomic orbital model.

Ex. 10-22 Explain what happens in the following statements.

a. A photon of light with energy less than that necessary to cause photoelectric emission is absorbed by a metal.

b. A photon of light with energy greater than that necessary to cause photoelectric emission is absorbed by a metal. Speculate as to whether the excess energy of the photon is converted to electron kinetic energy or produces heat in the absorbing metal.

c. An atom in an excited state returns to its ground state.

Ex. 10-23 a. According to the atomic orbital model, what shape is assigned to s orbitals? to p orbitals?

b. Make a sketch showing the shape and spatial arrangement of the three p atomic orbitals in the neon atom.

Ex. 10-24 Show the probable geometric changes in this reaction (see Fig. 7-13).

$$P_4 \xrightarrow{O_2} P_4O_6 \xrightarrow{O_2} P_4O_{10}$$

Ex. 10-25 On the basis of spectroscopic observations, list the following items in two columns, one entitled line spectra and the other continuous spectra: electric incandescent lamp, colored flame, glowing charcoal, mercury vapor lamp, infrared heat lamp, sodium vapor lamp, white hot iron, neon light.

Ex. 10-26 According to the Bohr atom model, how is kinetic energy stored in the hydrogen atom? How is potential energy stored in the hydrogen atom?

Ex. 10-27 Match the terms with the statements.

Terms	Statements
1. Ionization energy	a. Hybridization of orbitals
2. Highest first ionization energy	b. Electron of an atom, molecule, or ion with higher energy than that corresponding to ground state
3. Lowest first ionization energy	
4. Dark line spectra	c. Limits number of electrons per orbital to two electrons
5. Pauli exclusion principle	
6. Excited state	d. Group I of the periodic table
	e. Energy absorbed when a mole of electrons is separated from a mole of a gaseous species.
	f. Group 0 of the periodic table
	g. Called absorption spectra

Ex. 10-28 Answer these questions regarding the periodic table.

a. How many elements are in the fourth period?

b. How many elements are in the group headed by the element beryllium (group II)?

c. How are the elements copper, silver, and gold similar to the elements in the alkali metal family? How are they different from the elements in the alkali metal family?

Ex. 10-29 Defend or refute the following statements.

a. As the temperature of an incandescent solid is increased, the color of the emitted light changes from red to yellow to white.

b. As the temperature of a flame produced by hot gaseous substances increases, the intensity of the flame color decreases and the flame color changes.

c. When any compound which contains sodium is heated to a high temperature in a flame, the color of the flame is always an intense yellow.

d. When the light emitted by a hot incandescent solid is analyzed with a spectroscope, a continuous spectrum will be observed. If colored light from a high-temperature flame is analyzed with a spectroscope, a line spectrum will be observed.

e. A gaseous substance absorbs light of a certain wavelength. The same gaseous substance, when excited, radiates light of exactly the same wavelength.

f. When the light emitted by excited gaseous atomic hydrogen is analyzed spectroscopically, the most complex line spectrum for any known substance is found.

Ex. 10-30 From Fig. 10-6, what amount of energy is required to remove the electron from the influence of the hydrogen nucleus (proton) when the electron is in the second energy level, $n = 2$? in the third energy level, $n = 3$? in the fourth energy level, $n = 4$?

Ex. 10-31 Refer to a table of physical constants of the elements in a handbook of chemistry; make a list of the boiling points of the liquid phases and densities of the solid phases for the elements with atomic numbers 1 to 20. Determine whether boiling point and density are periodic properties by plotting boiling points and densities against atomic numbers.

Ex. 10-32 a. What general relationship exists between first ionization energy and the arrangement of electron waves in the outer orbitals of an atom?

b. Examination of Table 10-3 reveals that oxygen (atomic number 8) and sulfur (atomic number 16) have lower first ionization energies than do the elements nitrogen (atomic number 7) and phosphorus (atomic number 15). Similarly boron (atomic number 5) and aluminum (atomic number 13) have lower ionization energies than do the elements beryllium (atomic number 4) and magnesium (atomic number 12). Explain.

Ex. 10-33 a. Discuss the bond angles formed by hydrogen and the central atom of the hydrides listed in Table 10-11 in terms of the orbital model.

b. Describe the bonding in graphite and diamond.

Ex. 10-34 a. From a consideration of the atomic orbital model, describe the sigma bonds for the molecules BF_3, H_2O, and OF_2.

b. Make a sketch of the orbital structure for the bonds in each of the molecules listed in part *a.*

Ex. 10-35 *a.* What assumption has been made to explain why all the electron waves in a multielectron atom do not occupy the lowest energy level of the atom?

b. What is the maximum number of electron waves possible in each of the three $2p$ orbitals?

c. Using Table 10-9 and Fig. 10-9, write electron-in-a-box notations for the silicon atom (atomic number 14), sulfur atom (atomic number 16), magnesium atom (atomic number 12), and titanium atom (atomic number 22).

Ex. 10-36 *a.* Write the correct formulas for the following compounds by using the atomic orbital model for compound formation: lithium fluoride, beryllium hydride, carbon tetrachloride, nitrogen fluoride, oxygen fluoride, hydrogen fluoride.

b. Sketch charge cloud pictures for beryllium hydride and oxygen fluoride.

c. From the atomic orbital model, what geometric shape would you expect each of the following compounds to have: beryllium hydride, carbon tetrachloride, nitrogen fluoride, oxygen fluoride, and hydrogen fluoride?

d. Write Lewis structures for the compounds in part *a.*

e. Write Couper structures for the compounds in part *a.*

Ex. 10-37 Carbon burns in oxygen to produce a mixture of carbon monoxide and carbon dioxide. At 400°C and in a limited amount of oxygen, the product of the combustion will be primarily carbon monoxide. At 400°C and in an excess of oxygen, the product will be primarily carbon dioxide.

a. If 48 g of carbon is burned under each of the conditions described, in which case will the mass of product be greater? How much greater?

b. In which case will a larger volume of gaseous product be formed at 0°C and 1 atmosphere pressure? How much larger volume?

PART THREE: MODELS AS AIDS TO THE INTERPRETATION OF SYSTEMS

Chapters 7 to 10

OUR INTERPRETATION of chemical change has proceeded through the development of several ideas. An idea developed into a set of assumptions and into the logical consequences of the assumptions is called a mental model. The diagram on page 451 is a schematic representation of the major ideas and their connections with experimental information related to chemical change.

Matter was defined in Chapter 1 as the stuff that has mass and occupies space. These two aspects of all matter, mass and volume, are therefore fundamental to any interpretation of the nature of substances and their chemical reactions. Measurements of mass suggest that mass is conserved in chemical change. Volume is usually not conserved.

How do the mass and volume of matter arise? This question was first dealt with, although briefly, in Chapter 6, based on a set of postulates called the nuclear atom. The choice of the best set of postulates was governed solely by the conclusions which could be drawn logically from the postulates. If a set of conclusions is logical and in agreement with experimental data, the set of postulates is accepted as satisfactory.

Several mental models have been developed in Chapters 7 to 10. In the order of their discussion these were the electron charge cloud model, the kinetic-molecular theory, energy, and the atomic orbital model. As a means for summarizing the ideas developed so far, let us consider how these four models deal with the space-filling property of matter.

The most curious suggestion about how to regard mass and volume was mentioned in Chapter 6. Rutherford proposed an atomic model for which mass and volume can be considered separately. In this model, nearly all the mass of an atom is associated with a nucleus near the center of an atom, whereas nearly all the volume of the atom is occupied only by the electrons outside the nucleus.

With the electrons filling space and providing negative charge and with the nucleus providing mass and positive charge, the connection between nucleus and electrons was made through electrostatics as described by Coulomb's law. Our first attempt to interpret the electrical structure of matter ran into trouble, however, because of the nature of electrostatic potential energy.

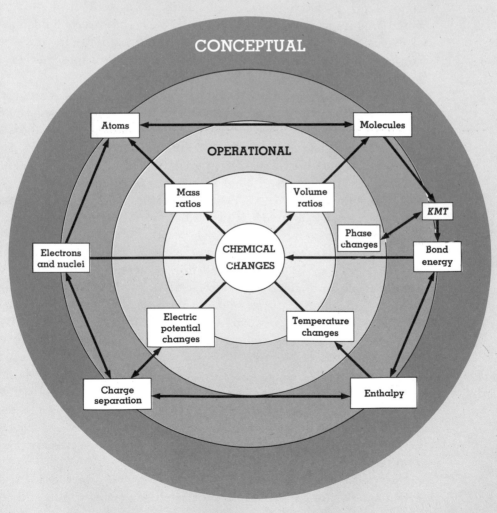

The trouble was that the electrical nature of the system indicates the arrangement of lowest energy is the one with positive and negative charges coincident. This would have the tragic effect of making volume disappear and the electrical model useless! To avoid this catastrophe, a nonelectric energy was postulated for each electron cloud. This energy was called a kinetic energy and assigned a nature such that electron charge clouds of large size would have low kinetic energy. The electrostatic attraction between electron and nucleus, would, however, give a system of low potential energy for a charge cloud of small size. A system of low total energy is selected on the basis of the sum of potential and kinetic energy.

A second trouble then arose because the potential energy and the kinetic energy together imply that a system of low total energy should result if a large number of charge clouds coalesce to produce a single cloud of many electrons with high charge density. Such a situation would produce an atom of small volume. To avoid this second dilemma, an exclusion principle was added to the list of postulates for the electron charge cloud model. Through the exclusion principle, merger of electron clouds was limited to two electrons at a time.

A set of postulates for the electron charge cloud model gives conclusions about the shapes of polyatomic molecules in nice agreement with experimental data. Two geometric shapes (spheres and tetrahedra) are found to be characteristic of many different kinds of molecules. The experimental data that bear out the usefulness of the charge cloud model are measurements of bond lengths and bond angles, although at least two simple molecules, H_2S and PH_3, have bond angles that suggest the charge cloud model may not be entirely satisfactory for predicting geometric aspects of molecules.

The charge cloud model implies that systems of nuclei and electrons are most likely to be found in low-energy arrangements. In atomic orbital language, nuclei and electrons adopt the ground state configuration. Two different types of low-energy arrangements are found. (1) For some elements, neutral molecules are formed with only a few atoms per molecule. (2) For other elements, an unlimited number of atoms can be assembled in an endlessly repeated structure.

For either type of element, the structure formed is uncharged, and so no electrical repulsive forces exist between the structural units. This implies that every substance should be an aggregate of atoms or molecules in contact with each other. The attractive forces between units of the aggregate might be strong or weak, but no electric forces are present to keep them apart.

Every solid element, however, can be converted into a gas. But a certain quantity of an element in the gas phase occupies about a thousand times as great a volume as the same quantity of the element in the solid phase. Nothing in the charge cloud model provides for this large difference in volume. Again, the volume occupied by matter presents itself as a puzzle in our picture of the nature of matter.

The comparatively large volume of a gas is provided for by an energy. Just as a kinetic energy is assigned to an electron cloud to keep it from collapsing, so a kinetic energy is assigned to a gas to account for gas volume. Unlike the kinetic energy in a fluffy charge cloud, the kinetic energy in the gas is identified with the random and incessant motion of molecules within the gas. For gases at ordinary pressures (1 atmosphere or less), the space occupied by the molecules, if they were not in motion, is not more than one-thousandth of the space between the moving molecules in the gas.

Volume is a feature provided for in each of our mental models for matter by virtue of nonelectric energy terms. In gases nearly all the volume is imagined to be the result of the random motion of gas molecules which possess kinetic energy. This random motion leads to a large amount of space between comparatively small molecules. For solids, volume is built into the nuclear atom model by a kinetic energy term not associated with motion of a particle but with a cloud- or wavelike character and an exclusion principle. These together result in electrons which are rather like fluffy clouds.

Mass is built into all the models for matter by simply identifying mass as a property of atomic nuclei. For most atoms, less than 0.1 percent of the mass is contributed by electrons. Little more can be said about mass at the present time than the assumption that mass is associated with atomic nuclei.

In the melting of a solid or in the vaporizing of a liquid, the mass of the system remains constant. Observations always indicate that, when any phase change takes place so that the final temperature is identical with the initial temperature, the change is accompanied by some alteration in the environment of the system as well. It is as if the system could not be completely isolated for study but in some way is coupled to the environment. Whenever a system changes phase at constant temperature, the environment changes too. The coupling between the change inside and the change outside the system is called energy transfer. For changes in phase at constant temperature, energy is transferred between environment and system as heat or thermal energy. The magnitude of the change in the system and in the surroundings is always related in a constant way. As is the case with mass which is conserved, so is energy conserved.

A common accompaniment of chemical change is temperature change. Experimental data for the temperature change in a system have been interpreted by means of thermal energy transfer. When temperature and pressure are held constant, the energy change within the system is called an enthalpy change and is equivalent to the thermal energy transferred. The idea of enthalpy change not only provides a bookkeeping system for energy changes but also can be used to develop a tie between the structural changes in a chemical reaction (bond breaking and bond making) and energy transferred whenever a system undergoes a change in state.

The link between energy and the structural model is provided by defining bond energy as the thermal energy absorbed when a mole of bonds are broken as molecules dissociate into gaseous atoms. The same amount of energy is evolved when the atoms unite again to form the same molecules. The contribution that a bond between a particular pair of atoms makes to the bond energy of a molecule is nearly the same no matter how simple or complex the molecule. This allows the use of Hess's law in estimating heats of reaction for even untried reactions of some substances whose molecular structures are known.

To tie together more effectively the mental models of energy and structure, other aspects of chemical systems were explored. The colors of gas flames, the production of line spectra, and the electrical properties of gases are interpreted by assuming that elements consist of atoms in which the nucleus–electron systems have discrete energy levels. Although the charge cloud model is capable of only a limited interpretation of energy levels, the atomic orbital model is a much more effective aid to interpretation of energy levels. In the orbital model, electrons are considered to be analogous to three-dimensional standing waves. Each standing electron wave is located in a region of space (an orbital) close to the nucleus so that the energy of the system is determined by the distance between the orbital and the nucleus. An orbital may be occupied by not more than two standing electron waves.

As in the charge cloud model, the postulates of kinetic energy and the Pauli exclusion principle are introduced to account for the volume of an atom or molecule in the orbital model. The attractive forces are provided entirely by electrostatic interactions between nuclei and electrons. The interactions of electrons in orbitals lead to hybridized orbitals in bond formation. The orbital model provides for compound formation by orbital overlap and gives satisfactory geometrical structures for many covalent compounds. In principle the orbital model is capable of providing complete answers to questions about structure and energy. In practice the mathematics often proves so difficult as to allow only approximate solutions for use in interpreting the nature of matter. For most purposes the charge cloud model gives a reasonable insight into the geometrical structures of molecules, whereas the orbital model gives a reasonable insight into the energies of atoms and molecules.

Atoms were introduced in Part One as structural units with the idea that matter is made up of a collection of separate atoms. Charge cloud theory (and atomic orbital theory) pictures the electrons of atoms as merging (overlapping) to form molecules or crystals. The fundamental structural units have become electrons and nuclei rather than separate atoms. For the chemist the individual atoms in a compound are defined only by the separated nuclei. There are always enough electrons in a compound so that positive and negative charges add up to zero net charge. It is not possible, however, to identify each electron with a separate atom in a compound.

Four big ideas are involved in the models developed to interpret changes in the states of chemical systems: (1) structure, (2) random motion, (3) mass, and (4) energy. Structure is interpreted by the charge cloud model to deal with the fact that every system has form and to take into account the space-filling property exhibited by each system. Random motion supplements our idea of the space-filling properties of matter and suggests a way in which changes in structure can actually occur. Mass is an idea related to a major unchanging property of matter in a system whose state undergoes change. When a system changes in state, something called energy may change within the system, but if so, the total quantity of energy remains unaltered when the system and its environment are considered together. Energy and mass are each conserved.

METALS

11

OF THE 103 elements 3 are liquids, 11 are gases, and 89 are solids at room temperature. Each of the elements can exist as solid, liquid, or gas. All that is necessary to effect the transition of an element from one phase to another is sufficient change in temperature of the system containing the element. Is there a set of ideas that can be used to interpret the observed temperature ranges in which each of the three phases occur for the different elements?

The ideas developed in Chapters 7 to 10 relate the properties of matter to the interaction of electrons and nuclei. These interactions provide energy and structure relationships that can be used to interpret observations of phase changes and of chemical reactions.

The properties of a small group of elements, those in the upper right-hand, or northeast, corner of the periodic table, have been considered in evaluating the usefulness of models developed for the structure of matter in Chapters 7 to 10. However, 11 of the 14 liquid and gaseous elements are found in the northeast corner of the periodic table. Do these facts mean that the charge cloud and atomic orbital models are limited in their applicability to just a few elements?

11-1 METALS AND PERIODICITY

In general, the elements in the northeast corner of the periodic table have melting and boiling points below 500°C, and the solid and liquid

456

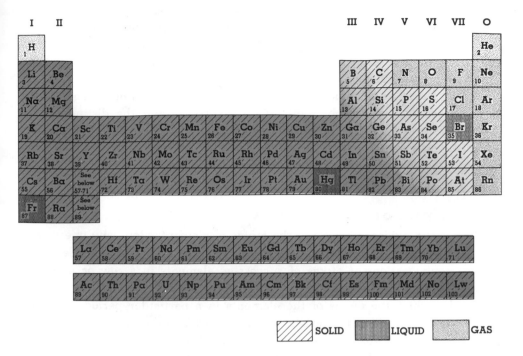

I	II												III	IV	V	VI	VII	O
H 1																		He 2
Li 3	Be 4												B 5	C 6	N 7	O 8	F 9	Ne 10
Na 11	Mg 12												Al 13	Si 14	P 15	S 16	Cl 17	Ar 18
K 19	Ca 20	Sc 21	Ti 22	V 23	Cr 24	Mn 25	Fe 26	Co 27	Ni 28	Cu 29	Zn 30	Ga 31	Ge 32	As 33	Se 34	Br 35	Kr 36
Rb 37	Sr 38	Y 39	Zr 40	Nb 41	Mo 42	Tc 43	Ru 44	Rh 45	Pd 46	Ag 47	Cd 48	In 49	Sn 50	Sb 51	Te 52	I 53	Xe 54
Cs 55	Ba 56	See below 57-71	Hf 72	Ta 73	W 74	Re 75	Os 76	Ir 77	Pt 78	Au 79	Hg 80	Tl 81	Pb 82	Bi 83	Po 84	At 85	Rn 86
Fr 87	Ra 88	See below 89															

La 57	Ce 58	Pr 59	Nd 60	Pm 61	Sm 62	Eu 63	Gd 64	Tb 65	Dy 66	Ho 67	Er 68	Tm 69	Yb 70	Lu 71
Ac 89	Th 90	Pa 91	U 92	Np 93	Pu 94	Am 95	Cm 96	Bk 97	Cf 98	Es 99	Fm 100	Md 101	No 102	Lw 103

SOLID   LIQUID   GAS

Fig. 11-1 *Of all the elements about two-thirds are metals (green shading), about one-sixth are nonmetals, and about one-sixth have properties intermediate between those of metals and nonmetals.*

phases of these elements do not conduct electricity. The atoms of these elements either form no bonds at all or tend to form covalent bonds with each other. Of the 103 known elements, fewer than 20 are included in the cluster of elements in this part of the periodic table.

Most of the elements that are found in the remainder of the periodic table are solids, have relatively high melting points and high boiling points, have a lustrous gray color, and conduct electricity in both the solid and liquid phases. When they are finely divided, these elements have brown or black colors. Of the elements in this large group, about 70 are so similar in properties that chemists have found it profitable to think of them collectively. These elements with similar properties (roughly two-thirds of all known elements) are called **metals** or **metallic elements.** Elements which do not have the properties of metals are called **nonmetals.** The elements in the northeast corner of the periodic table are the nonmetals. Figure 11-1 is a periodic table modified to show the division of the elements into two sets: metal and nonmetal—as shown by the gradation in color.

The terms metal and nonmetal as defined here are used throughout the book to refer only to separate chemical elements. Any compound,

457

mixture, or solution which may have properties similar to the properties of metals is said to have metallic character. Thus, brass (a mixture of copper and zinc) has metallic character. Similarly, methane is a non-metallic substance but not a nonmetal because methane is a compound of two elements.

Does the fact that the nonmetals are clustered in one corner of the periodic table imply something systematic about the distinction between metals and nonmetals? Is there any way that either the atomic orbital model or the charge cloud model can be related to the observable properties which are used to decide whether an element is a metal or a nonmetal?

11-2 ELECTRONS PER ORBITAL

The nuclear charges of the atoms of elements along any one row of the periodic table increase from left to right in the row. The electronic configurations of atoms of successive elements in a row or period of the periodic table differ by increments of one electron. The electrons by which the atoms of the elements in a particular period differ are arranged in a characteristic set of orbitals. For the first period, this set of orbitals consists of just the 1s orbital. For either the second or third periods, the characteristic set of orbitals consist of four orbitals—one s orbital and three p orbitals. These orbitals, which are progressively filled in the atoms of the elements in one period of the periodic table, are called the **outer** or **available orbitals** of that period. The electrons that can occupy available orbitals are called **outer electrons.** A comparison of the atoms in the second and third periods shows that at the left end there is just one electron in the available orbitals, while at the right end there are eight electrons in the available orbitals. For example, in the second row of the periodic table, both lithium and neon have four available orbitals. A lithium atom has only one electron, whereas neon has eight electrons. The ratio of electrons present to available orbitals increases from 1:4 for lithium to 8:4 for neon. In other words, the ratio of electrons to orbitals increases from left to right in a row of the periodic table. Does this mean that metallic properties of elements are associated with a low value of the ratio of electrons to available orbitals?

In the second row of the periodic table, there are two metals: lithium and beryllium; and in the third row there are three metals: sodium, magnesium, and aluminum. If a low value for the ratio of electrons to available orbitals is associated with metallic character, it will be necessary to explain why there are more metals in the third row than in the second row.

In the fourth row of the periodic table, there are eighteen elements and a maximum of nine available orbitals. These nine orbitals are made up of one 4s, three 4p, and five 3d orbitals (Table 10-9). Of the eighteen elements in the fourth row, fourteen are metals. The first element in the fourth row is a metal, potassium ($_{19}K$), which, like lithium and sodium, has one outer electron. The fourteenth element in the fourth row is a metal, germanium ($_{32}Ge$), which has fourteen outer electrons and nine available orbitals. So it appears that the ratio of the number of outer electrons to the number of available orbitals has some relation to the metallic character of elements even though there must be some other factor involved besides the magnitude of this ratio.

When a family of elements (group V, for example) is considered instead of a row, or period, of the periodic table, metallic properties appear to be associated with a large atomic number. Bismuth ($_{83}Bi$) is a metallic element, whereas nitrogen ($_7N$) is a nonmetal. Within one family all elements have the same electronic configuration for the available orbitals in each different atom, but the principal quantum numbers of the outer orbitals are different. The orbital models for the atoms of the elements in a family differ only in nuclear charge and in the number of filled orbitals in the kernel of the atom which is made up of the nucleus and the filled orbitals. The nuclear charge in the atoms of the nitrogen family changes from $\oplus 7$ in nitrogen to $\oplus 83$ in bismuth. The number of filled orbitals in the kernels of atoms changes from 1 in nitrogen (2 electrons) to 39 in bismuth (78 electrons).

Not only does boiling point increase in the nitrogen family of elements as atomic number increases, but other properties change as well. Melting points increase, although not by the same amount as boiling points. The electric conductivities of nitrogen and phosphorus are so low as to be almost unmeasurable, whereas arsenic, antimony, and bismuth do conduct electricity moderately well.

TABLE 11-1 ELECTRONIC CONFIGURATIONS OF THE ELEMENTS IN THE NITROGEN FAMILY

Element	Boiling Point, °C	Filled Orbitals in the Kernel	Outer Orbitals	
$_7N$	−196	$1s^2$	2s ↑↓	2p ↑ ↑ ↑
$_{15}P$	280	$1s^2 2s^2 2p^6$	3s ↑↓	3p ↑ ↑ ↑
$_{33}As$	610	$1s^2 2s^2 2p^6 3s^2 3p^6 3d^{10}$	4s ↑↓	4p ↑ ↑ ↑
$_{51}Sb$	1440	$1s^2 2s^2 2p^6 3s^2 3p^6 3d^{10}$ $4s^2 4p^6 4d^{10}$	5s ↑↓	5p ↑ ↑ ↑
$_{83}Bi$	1420	$1s^2 2s^2 2p^6 3s^2 3p^6 3d^{10}$ $4s^2 4p^6 4d^{10} 4f^{14} 5s^2$ $5p^6 5d^{10}$	6s ↑↓	6p ↑ ↑ ↑

The kernels of all the atoms in any one group will possess the same net positive charge. In the nitrogen family, the net charge on the kernel of an atom of each member element is ⊕5. In a family of elements, the kernels of the elements with larger atomic number have a larger radius. This means that electrons in the outer orbitals of the atoms will be farther from the nucleus in atoms of the elements with large atomic number than in atoms of the elements with small atomic number. The outer electrons of any atom are held to the kernel by the attractive force between the electrons and the positive charge on the kernel.

The kernel of an atom behaves electrically as if it is an equivalent sphere with the net charge concentrated at the center of the sphere. The size of the kernel gives it two properties: (1) the larger the kernel, the greater the distance between the electrons in the outer orbitals and the central charge, and (2) the larger the kernel, the more space around its outer surface for a given number of electrons to fit.

In terms of potential energy and kinetic energy for kernels that have the same net positive charge, an increase in the size of a kernel will raise the electric potential energy of the atom so far as the electrons outside the kernel are concerned. This will also mean that the outer electrons in atoms with large kernels will have low kinetic energy compared to outer electrons in an atom with a small kernel. The relationship between kernel size and atomic number provides a basis for understanding the differences in the metallic characters of the elements in the nitrogen family.

Of course it is possible that some unusual forces that are not electrical in nature must be considered if the structure of metals is to be understood. Before electric forces are rejected as an aid to understanding metals, it will be interesting to consider the magnitudes of the bond energies in metals. Bond energies in metals can be compared, for example, with bond energies in nonmetals and compounds.

Ex. 11-1 In which group of the periodic table do the atoms of the elements have the smallest kernel charge compared with the corresponding elements in other groups? What is the charge on the kernel of the fluorine atom? of the iodine atom? List the atoms of group VII in order of increasing kernel size.

11-3 BOND ENERGIES IN METALS

The gas phase of a metal consists of single atoms in most cases. To form a gas from a solid metal must therefore mean that bonds present in the solid are broken in the vaporizing process. The gas phase of a nonmetal, in contrast to that of a metal, commonly consists of diatomic or polyatomic molecules. Dissociation of a mole of molecules of gaseous nonmetal to give atoms requires the absorption of a considerably larger quantity of energy than is required for the vaporization of a mole of the same molecules from the liquid phase. In other words, the total bond energy for all the bonds in a mole of a nonmetallic element is much greater than the molar heat of vaporization of the element.

Energy requirements for the formation of atoms by vaporizing metals can be compared to the formation of atoms by dissociating nonmetal molecules by considering the enthalpy changes in each case. The enthalpies of the elements in their standard states at 25°C (enthalpy = 0) can be compared to the enthalpies of the separated atoms in the gas phase at 25°C. The enthalpy changes listed in Table 11-2 are computed on the basis of 1 mole of gaseous atoms formed not only from various elements in their standard states but also from several compounds. The fractional coefficient in front of each reactant is therefore determined by the total number of atoms in the molecule of the reactant. The data in Table 11-2 are diagramed in Fig. 11-2.

The range of numerical values for the enthalpies of formation of a mole of gaseous metal atoms from a solid metal is essentially the same as the range of numerical values for the enthalpies of formation of a mole of atoms for other types of substances as shown in Fig. 11-2.

In Chapters 7 and 10 the bonds between atoms were interpreted in terms of the electrostatic attraction between electrons and nuclei. If this is the only way by which energy is lowered in the formation of bonds, it is reasonable to expect that enthalpies of formation for atoms from all elements in their standard states should be of the same order of magnitude. Since the enthalpy changes accompanying the production of atoms from metals and from other substances are of the same order of magnitude, it is reasonable to assume that there is only one type of attractive force involved in the bonding of atoms. Ionically bonded, covalently bonded, and metallically bonded systems should all be understandable through the characteristics of models based on electrical properties. These models combine electric potential energy, electron kinetic energy, and the Pauli exclusion principle.

Both the charge cloud model and the atomic orbital model describe an atom in terms of an electrostatic potential energy and a kinetic energy of the electron. Together these two energies account for the total energy of an atom, and the sum of the energies for all the atoms in a system is the total energy of the system. The lower the total energy of the system, the more stable is the system with respect to separation into parts. This statement applies equally to the separation of atoms into electrons and nuclei and to the separation of molecules into isolated atoms.

The considerable differences observed between the properties of metals and of nonmetals need not be explained by introducing some

TABLE 11-2 ENTHALPY OF FORMATION OF 1 MOLE OF ATOMS IN THE GAS PHASE FROM VARIOUS SUBSTANCES IN THEIR STANDARD STATES

Formation Reaction	ΔH, kcal/mole of Atoms Formed[a]
$W\ (s) \rightarrow W\ (g)$	+201.6
$C\ (s)\ graphite \rightarrow C\ (g)$	+171.7
$\frac{1}{2}CO\ (g) \rightarrow \frac{1}{2}C\ (g) + \frac{1}{2}O\ (g)$	+128.6
$\frac{1}{2}MgO\ (s) \rightarrow \frac{1}{2}Mg\ (g) + \frac{1}{2}O\ (g)$	+119.0
$\frac{1}{2}N_2\ (g) \rightarrow N\ (g)$	+113.0
$Ti\ (s) \rightarrow Ti\ (g)$	+112.4
$\frac{1}{2}LiF\ (s) \rightarrow \frac{1}{2}Li\ (g) + \frac{1}{2}F\ (g)$	+100.8
$Fe\ (s) \rightarrow Fe\ (g)$	+96.7
$\frac{1}{5}Mg_3N_2\ (s) \rightarrow \frac{3}{5}Mg\ (g) + \frac{2}{5}N\ (g)$	+88.7
$Cu\ (s) \rightarrow Cu\ (g)$	+81.5
$\frac{1}{5}CH_4\ (g) \rightarrow \frac{1}{5}C\ (g) + \frac{4}{5}H\ (g)$	+79.6
$\frac{1}{5}CH_3Cl\ (g) \rightarrow \frac{1}{5}C\ (g) + \frac{3}{5}H\ (g) + \frac{1}{5}Cl\ (g)$	+75.4
$\frac{1}{5}CH_2Cl_2\ (g) \rightarrow \frac{1}{5}C\ (g) + \frac{2}{5}H\ (g) + \frac{2}{5}Cl\ (g)$	+70.9
$\frac{1}{4}NH_3\ (g) \rightarrow \frac{1}{4}N\ (g) + \frac{3}{4}H\ (g)$	+69.9
$\frac{1}{5}CHCl_3\ (l) \rightarrow \frac{1}{5}C\ (g) + \frac{1}{5}H\ (g) + \frac{3}{5}Cl\ (g)$	+68.4
$Mn\ (s) \rightarrow Mn\ (g)$	+68.3
$\frac{1}{5}CCl_4\ (l) \rightarrow \frac{1}{5}C\ (g) + \frac{4}{5}Cl\ (g)$	+64.2
$\frac{1}{2}O_2\ (g) \rightarrow O\ (g)$	+59.2
$\frac{1}{2}LiH\ (s) \rightarrow \frac{1}{2}Li\ (g) + \frac{1}{2}H\ (g)$	+55.4
$S\ (s) \rightarrow S\ (g)$	+53.3
$\frac{1}{2}H_2\ (g) \rightarrow H\ (g)$	+52.1
$Pb\ (s) \rightarrow Pb\ (g)$	+46.3
$Li\ (s) \rightarrow Li\ (g)$	+37.1
$Zn\ (s) \rightarrow Zn\ (g)$	+31.2
$\frac{1}{2}Cl_2\ (g) \rightarrow Cl\ (g)$	+28.9
$Na\ (s) \rightarrow Na\ (g)$	+26.0
$Cs\ (s) \rightarrow Cs\ (g)$	+18.8
$\frac{1}{2}F_2\ (g) \rightarrow F\ (g)$	+18.3

[a] Numerical values were taken at 25°C and 1 atmosphere pressure.

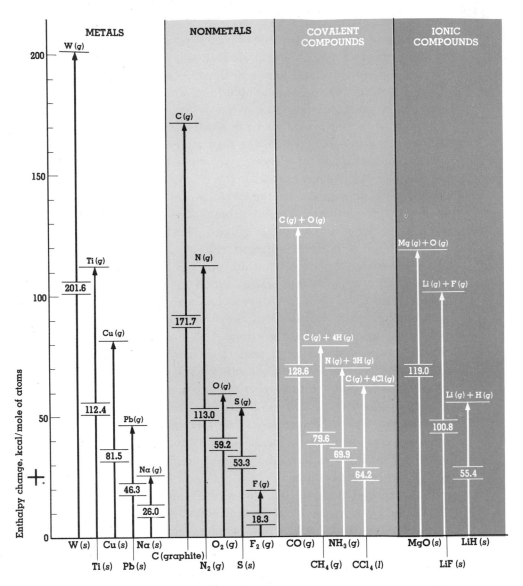

Fig. 11-2 *Enthalpy changes for conversion of various substances in their standard state to gaseous atoms at 25°C.*

special nonelectric force. If the bond energies in elements are to be understood only in electrical terms, differences in the number and arrangement of atomic orbitals must account for the differences between the properties of nonmetals and the properties of metals.

Ex. 11-2 **Explain why ionic and metallic crystals have higher heats of vaporization than do covalent molecular crystals.**

What evidence indicates that the number of electrons present for a given number of available orbitals makes a difference in the distribution of the electrons and hence in the type of bonding? Since the orbitals represent the spaces available for electrons in an atom, the question can be put in another way. What evidence is there to suggest that the amount of space available for electrons around the kernel of an atom has anything to do with the way atoms join together?

The effect of space for electrons around a kernel was discussed first in Chapter 7, in connection with the charge cloud model for lithium metal. According to the charge cloud model, solid lithium metal is a collection of positively charged lithium ions surrounded by an equal number of one-electron charge clouds. The lithium ions exert an attractive force on several adjacent charge clouds. Since each charge cloud is equally close to several lithium ions, there is no basis for considering that a particular charge cloud is associated with any one lithium ion. Thus, it is not unreasonable to assume that the charge clouds might shift readily from one lithium ion to the next. An electron wave or charge cloud not bound to a single nucleus but spread out around several nuclei is said to be *delocalized* (Section 10-23).

In a fluorine molecule, on the other hand, each electron has a specific relative position with respect to the two nuclei in any one diatomic molecule. Electrons which maintain fixed relative positions around a nucleus are said to be *localized.* The electrons in the kernels of each atom are considered to be localized. Outside the kernel, the electrons may be delocalized as in metals or in pi bonds or localized as in sigma bonds of covalent compounds.

In an isolated atom, all the electrons are firmly held to the nucleus. This is indicated by the large first ionization energies found for isolated atoms (Section 10-9). When isolated atoms join together to form molecules, ions, or metals, it is possible, however, that some electrons outside the kernels become delocalized.

Localized electrons occupy less volume than do delocalized electrons. By comparison, delocalized electrons have low kinetic energy. The assumption that delocalized electrons are present in metals means that electrons in metals have low kinetic energy. If the delocalized electrons can also remain close to positively charged kernels, then the metal structure will have a low potential energy. In this way delocalized electrons can provide a means to achieve low kinetic energy, low potential energy, and hence low total energy in a structure made up of metal atoms.

Just how the electrons occupy the volume in a metal cannot be decided experimentally. Sometimes the electrons in a metal are best described as moving from atom to atom. At other times electrons in a metal are best described as being spread out to enclose many atoms at once. Which description of the electrons is used depends more on the particular property of metals being discussed than upon any logical or experimental decision. The only feature common to both descriptions is that the delocalized electrons occupy more volume than the localized electrons around any given nucleus.

According to the model for the structure of metals based on delocalized electrons, the atoms in a piece of metal are bonded together as a whole. No bond can be considered to exist solely between just two atoms in a metal crystal. The difference between bonding in crystals made up of metal atoms and in crystals made up of molecules is indicated schematically in Fig. 11-3. The bonds between metal atoms tie the whole system of atoms together. Metals are best discussed in terms of the properties of crystals of metal and not in terms of the properties of isolated metal atoms.

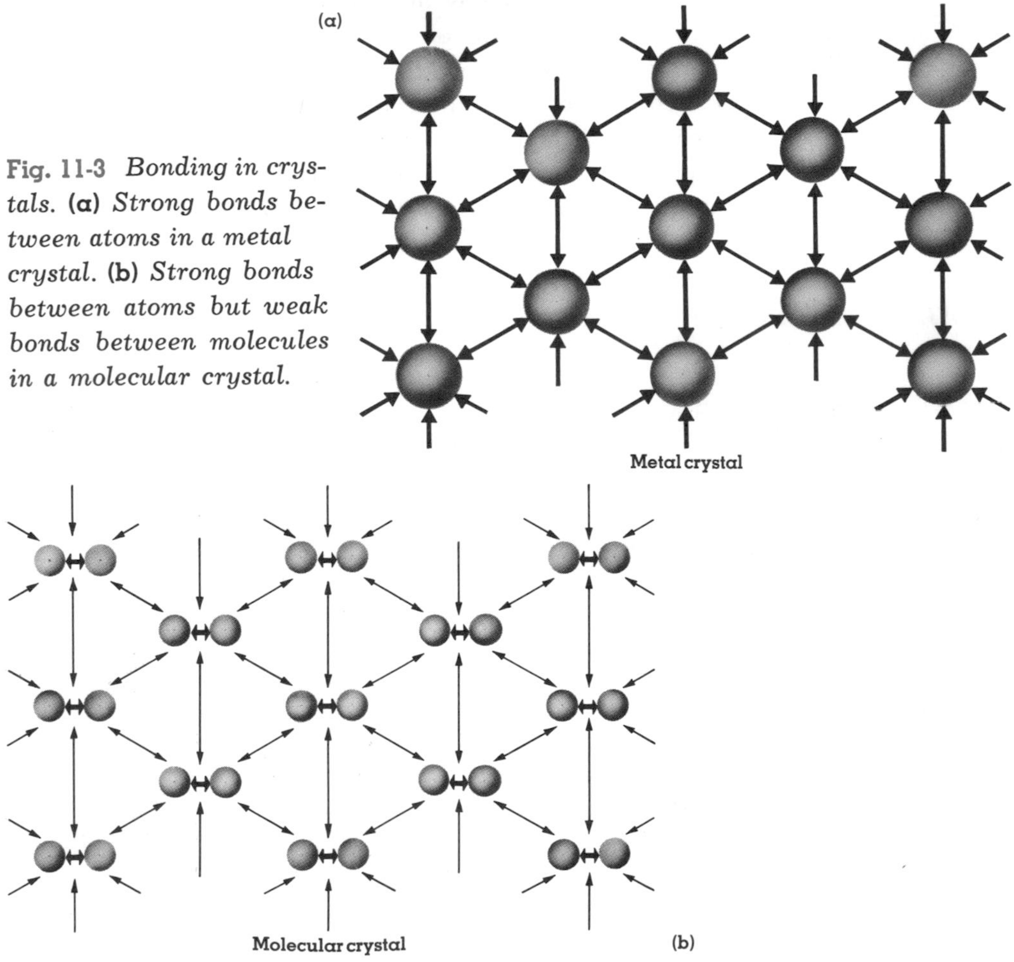

(a)

Fig. 11-3 *Bonding in crystals.* (a) *Strong bonds between atoms in a metal crystal.* (b) *Strong bonds between atoms but weak bonds between molecules in a molecular crystal.*

Metal crystal

Molecular crystal

(b)

11-5 CHARACTERISTIC PROPERTIES OF METALS

The usefulness of the delocalized-electron model for the bonds in metals can be judged only on the basis of how well the model can be used to interpret the observed properties of metals. In Table 11-3 the properties which distinguish metals from nonmetals are listed. The suitability of the model for interpreting these properties will be used as the criterion for judging the usefulness of the delocalized-electron model. Table 11-3 also lists the sections of Chapter 11 in which the distinguishing properties are discussed. °

11-6 PHASE CHANGES IN METALS

With a few exceptions, the metallic elements melt at temperatures above 500°C. Most metals are liquids through a considerable temperature range. Table 11-4 gives temperature ranges for the liquid phases of some metals with widely differing melting points and corresponding data for some nonmetals. Nonmetallic elements are liquids through temperature ranges of only a few hundred degrees at most, whereas most metals are liquids through temperature ranges of about 1000°C.

According to the delocalized-electron model for the metallic bond, a metal crystal consists of a group of atom kernels bound together by delocalized electrons. The delocalization of the electrons is possible because the atoms of metals possess many unfilled orbitals. The atoms are close enough together to permit the delocalized electron waves of

TABLE 11-3 PROPERTIES THAT DISTINGUISH METALS FROM NONMETALS

Metals	Section in Which discussed	Nonmetals
High melting points Liquids over wide temperature ranges	11-6	Melting points usually low Liquids over narrow temperature ranges
Good conductors of electricity	11-7	Poor conductors of electricity
Good conductors of heat	11-8	Poor conductors of heat
Opaque	11-9	Transparent or translucent
Metallic luster	11-9	Dull appearance
High tensile strength	11-15	Low tensile strength
Malleable and ductile Can be pounded into sheets or drawn into wires	11-15	Brittle Will shatter when pounded

TABLE 11-4 PROPERTIES OF SOME METALS AND NONMETALS

Element	Melting Point, °C	Boiling Point, °C	Liquid Range, °C[a]	First Ionization Energy, kcal/mole	Light Transmission
Na	98	889	791	118	Opaque
Bi	271	1420	1149	169	Opaque
Mg	650	1120	470	178	Opaque
Al	660	2327	1667	139	Opaque
Cu	1083	2528	1445	179	Opaque
Fe	1535	2800	1265	181	Opaque
Pt	1769	4010	2241	206	Opaque
H	−259	−253	6	313	Transparent, colorless
N	−210	−196	14	335	Transparent, colorless
Cl	−101	−34	67	329	Transparent, yellow-green
S	119	445	326	240	Transparent, yellow

[a] Liquid range = boiling point − melting point.

one atom to spread out and overlap the delocalized electron waves in the orbitals of the other atoms in the crystal. In this type of arrangement of kernels and delocalized electrons, the system has a low total energy. This means that the separation of atoms from the crystal requires the transfer of a large quantity of energy into the system.

When a solid melts to form the liquid phase, there is only a small increase in volume. This means that the nuclei are not much farther apart in the liquid than in the solid. Delocalized electrons can, therefore, be present to interact with the nuclei in a liquid metal. The system in the liquid phase should not have an appreciably higher total energy than it did in the solid phase. This conclusion is substantiated by the fact that heats of fusion for metals are generally not more than 1 or 2 kcal/mole.

Boiling a molten metal results in the separation of metal atoms to form the gas phase. Because vaporization increases the distance between metal atoms, the opportunity to form a metallic bond by delocalization of electrons disappears in the gas phase. The low kinetic energy provided by delocalized electrons in a metal crystal cannot be achieved in the gas phase. This means that the total energy of a metal system in the gas phase would be quite high. This prediction based on the model for the metallic bond is in agreement with the observation that the heats of vaporization for metals generally range from 20 to 100 kcal/mole. In Section 8-21, a high heat of vaporization was found to be associated with a high boiling point. Thus the high boiling points of metals are in accord with properties predicted on the basis of the de-localized-electron model for bonding of atoms in metals.

11-7 CONDUCTION OF ELECTRICITY IN METALS

Metals conduct electricity whenever a potential difference is established between two points in solid or liquid metal. Unlike the situation at the surfaces of electrodes during electrolysis, no reactions occur at the points where the charge enters and leaves the metal. No minimum potential difference is necessary for establishing the flow of charge in a solid or liquid metal. On the other hand, a minimum potential difference is necessary to establish the flow of charge in metals in the gas phase. The total energy of a system of nuclei and electrons is raised when there is a potential difference between two points in the system. As the total energy of the metal rises, the electrons tend to shift toward the positively charged side of the conductor. When any one electron shifts its position, all the other electrons in the conductor must shift as well (Fig. 11-4). In other words, a slight shift in the position of an electron near the negative end of a conductor will be accompanied by a corresponding shift in position of an electron at the positive end of the conductor.

Fig. 11-4 *An electron entering a metal from a negative terminal causes a slight shift in the delocalized electrons in the metal. For each electron that enters the metal from the negative terminal, an electron leaves the metal at the positive terminal.*

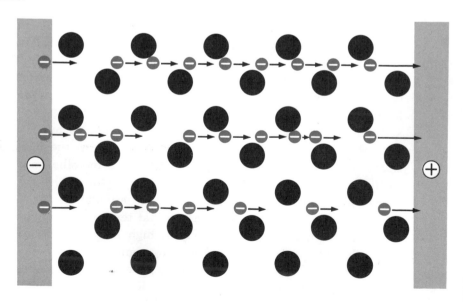

The mobility of delocalized electrons can account for the assumption that charge flows in a conductor and for the observation that, when charge enters a metallic conductor, an equivalent quantity of charge leaves at another point in the conductor.

As electrons move in a solid or liquid metal, the temperature of the metal rises. A rise in temperature implies a rise in the average kinetic energy of the metal atoms. In other words, passing electricity through a metal makes the metal atoms vibrate more rapidly and at random. This is explained by saying that the moving electrons can transfer some of their kinetic energy to the kernels of the atoms to raise their vibrational energy in the solid phase.

The electric resistance of metallic conductors increases as the temperature of the conductor is raised. Ionic solutions and gases show precisely the opposite effect; that is, ionic solutions and gases show a decrease in resistance to charge flow as the temperature rises.

As the temperature of a metal sample is raised, the positively charged kernels move more rapidly because of the rise in their kinetic energy. Presumably the movement of the kernels will interfere with the flow of electrons through the metal sample. It is therefore reasonable that the resistance of a metal should increase as the temperature of the metal rises.

Ex. 11-3 One of the best electric insulators is solid sulfur. In terms of electronic configuration, why is sulfur an insulator?

11-8 HEAT TRANSFER THROUGH METALS

Copper is used as wire for electric transmission because of its excellent electric conductivity, that is, its low electric resistance. Because of its excellent ability to conduct heat, copper is used on the bottom of cooking utensils. Quite generally, materials which conduct electric charge readily also conduct heat readily. At first glance, however, charge transfer and heat transfer through a substance seem unrelated.

Yet the delocalized electrons around positively charged kernels suggest a possible connection. Heat transfer through a piece of metal occurs whenever one side of the piece is at a higher temperature than the other side. Higher temperature on one side of the metal means that the kernels in that side have a higher average kinetic energy than the kernels in the other side. But a rise in the kinetic energy of the kernels can alter the kinetic energy of the delocalized electrons just as it is possible for the delocalized electrons to interact with the kernels to transfer kinetic energy from the electrons to the atomic kernels. In other words, the vibrating kernels can transfer kinetic energy to the electrons. The highly mobile delocalized electrons can then move

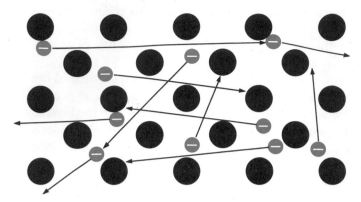

Fig. 11-5 *Electrons, free to travel distances equal to many atomic diameters before transferring their kinetic energies to other electrons or to kernels, can account for the good heat conductivity of metals.*

through the metal crystal to transfer kinetic energy to kernels in relatively distant parts of the crystal (Fig. 11-5).

In nonmetals, on the other hand, the transfer of heat is solely a result of the random motion and collisions of atoms and molecules. This process based on random collisions of relatively massive particles takes place more slowly than the transfer of heat in metal systems where the motion of the highly mobile delocalized electrons makes the heat transfer more rapid.

11-9 LIGHT ABSORPTION BY METALS

Finely divided metals are brown or black in color when they are viewed in white light. A black object is one that absorbs all colors present in white light. As the light is absorbed, the temperature of the metal rises. The absorption of the entire spectrum of visible light by a finely divided metal is quite in contrast to the behavior of nonmetals. Some nonmetals are colorless and transparent; that is, they transmit rather than absorb visible light. Other nonmetals are colored and thus absorb just a few colors of the spectrum of visible light. The temperature of a nonmetal also rises when it absorbs light.

Absorption of light and the resulting rise in temperature are not the only ways that metals may respond to light. In Sections 6-3 and 10-6 the photoelectric effect was discussed. Some metals arranged as negatively charged electrodes in an evacuated space will emit electrons when light shines on them. For the photoelectric effect to occur with a particular metal, the light used must have a wavelength shorter than a particular numerical value characteristic of the metal. This is interpreted to mean that a certain minimum quantity of energy is required for the emission of electrons from a metal.

A gas made up of metal atoms will also absorb light and produce electrons. For this to happen, the only light that is effective is light with a wavelength shorter than some maximum. Presumably electron emission from a metal means a rise in electric potential energy as the electron separates from the rest of the atom and leaves behind a positively charged ion.

Another type of interaction between light and metals is the phenomenon of reflection. The surface of a piece of metal can be polished until it becomes quite smooth. A highly polished metal surface can be used as a mirror to reflect images without distortion. The polished surface of most metals has a silvery luster which is characteristic of most substances containing delocalized electrons. The color of the polished surfaces of all but a few metals is silvery. Two of the exceptions are copper and gold.

Light absorption by a powdered metal to give the characteristic black color can be interpreted in terms of a partial separation of electrons from kernels. Even though the separation is only slight, it implies a rise in electric potential energy of the system and a rise in the kinetic energy of the delocalized electrons. The delocalized electrons can transfer kinetic energy to the kernels of the atoms in the metal so that the atoms move more rapidly but at random. Therefore, the metal absorbs light of all wavelengths to produce a rise in temperature.

Reflected light is light that has been absorbed by a metal and then emitted without change except in direction. Delocalized electrons must be involved in an interpretation of the luster of metals and the reflection of light by metals, but the nature of the involvement of delocalized electrons is not clear to scientists at the present time.

11-10 CRYSTAL STRUCTURE OF METALS

Crystals of copper, silver, and gold are found in natural deposits. In Section 2-12 the characteristic shapes of crystals were interpreted to mean that atoms or molecules have a regular pattern of arrangement in a crystal. There is no evidence to suggest that the solid phase of metals is made up of molecules. On this basis it would be reasonable to conclude that metallic crystals are structures based on regular arrangements of atoms. Is it possible to determine the arrangement of atoms in a sample of metal?

An effective experimental technique for determining the arrangement of atoms in a metal crystal is based on x-ray interference patterns. X-rays, like visible light, may be characterized by wavelength. Visible light has wavelengths in the range from about 4,000 to 7,000 A. X-rays have wavelengths of less than 1,000 A.

When light beams pass through appropriately spaced parallel slits, interference patterns of light and dark areas are produced (Section 10-7). The details of the interference pattern depend upon the wavelength of the light and the spacing between the slits. X-rays, like light, will produce interference patterns which can be detected with photographic film. The details of the interference pattern depend upon the wavelength of the x-rays. Instead of a set of slits, however, a thin crystal is used to produce the interference patterns for x-rays. Analysis of these interference patterns of x-rays yields detailed information concerning the arrangement of the atoms in the crystal.

X-ray interference patterns produced by the interaction of x-rays with crystals of metallic elements indicate that the arrangements of the atoms in about 80 percent of the metals can be classified into three different categories. Moreover, these three types of arrangement correspond to three ways for packing identical spheres close together in regular patterns.

The positively charged atomic kernels in metal crystals have been described as positively charged spheres that are immersed in a sea of delocalized electrons. According to electrostatic principles, the kernels should repel other similar kernels uniformly in all directions. However, the attractive forces between the kernels and the delocalized electrons act to bind the kernels together. The attractive forces between each kernel and all the electrons surrounding it tend to pack the spherical kernels into as small a space as possible but at the same time maintaining the same distance between each pair of adjacent spheres. An arrangement of this type is known as *closest packing of spheres.* Two closest-packed arrangements of atoms found in solid metals are discussed in Section 11-11. A third arrangement that differs somewhat from closest packing is discussed in Section 11-12.

11-11 CLOSEST PACKING OF SPHERES

Analogies for the packing of spherical atoms are provided by the packing of sets of spherical objects such as ball bearings, marbles, ping-pong balls, or any balls of uniform size. The first layer of spheres is arranged on a flat plane. The two arrangements of spheres differ in the way in which the successive layers are arranged one above the other.

In the arrangement shown in Fig. 11-6a, each sphere in layer A will be in contact with six other spheres in the layer. The spheres of a second layer B, which is identical with layer A, can then be placed on layer A so that spheres in layer B fit into the indentations in the first layer A. Each sphere in layer A is now in contact with three spheres in layer B to make a total of nine contacts per sphere. .

When a third layer of spheres is placed on top of and in the indentations of layer B, there are two alternative ways in which the spheres in the third layer may be fitted into the indentations in layer B. With respect to layer B, these two positions for the third layer are equivalent. However, the two positions are not equivalent with respect to layer A.

In one position, the third layer is placed so that each sphere is di-

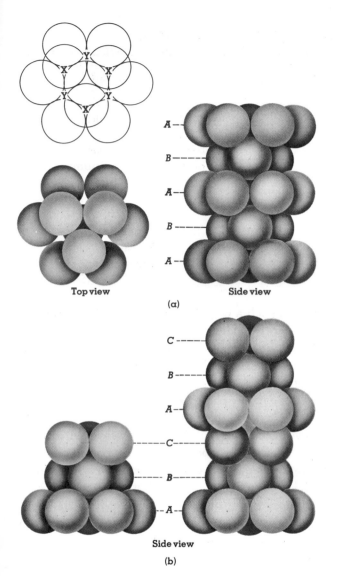

Top view   Side view

(a)

Side view

(b)

Fig. 11-6 *Closest-packing systems. Six spheres can be placed around a single sphere in a plane.* (a) *The open-circle diagram shows how three more spheres can be placed on the original array of seven spheres, with the centers of the three over the spaces marked X. In hexagonal closest-packing arrangement (side view), alternate planes of spheres are identical.* (b) *The third layer can be placed in a way different from the A and B layers, with centers of spheres in the third layer over holes in the first layer (marked Y in the open-circle diagram). This type of arrangement of spheres is called face-centered cubic closest packing.*

rectly above a sphere in layer *A* (Fig. 11-6a). This arrangement makes the third layer like layer *A* in every respect so it can be designated by the letter *A*, also. A fourth layer can be placed in position directly above layer *B* so that the fourth layer can be designated by the letter *B*, also. Alternating *A* and *B* layers can be extended upward as far as one wishes to go. It is convenient to designate the pattern by the letters *ABABAB*, where the letters correspond to the successive vertical layers of spheres. Spheres arranged so that each sphere touches 12 other spheres and with layers in the pattern *ABABAB* are said to be **hexagonal closest packed.**

In structures made up of spheres of uniform size, no more than 12

TABLE 11-5 SOME ELEMENTS THAT FORM CRYSTALS CORRESPONDING TO CLOSEST-PACKED ARRANGEMENTS

Hexagonal Closest Packed	Face-centered Cubic Packed	
Beryllium	Aluminum	Gold
Cadmium	Calcium	Iron
Calcium	Chromium	Lead
Lithium	Cobalt	Lithium
Magnesium	Copper	Manganese
Zinc		
Helium	Neon	
	Argon	
	Krypton	

spheres can be assembled in such a way that each of the 12 spheres is in contact with a thirteenth central sphere. Hence, the hexagonal closest-packed arrangement is an arrangement in which a given number of identical spherical objects can be packed into the smallest volume.

With two layers of spheres (A and B) arranged one on top of the other, the third layer (C) can be placed on the B layer so that the spheres of layer C are not directly above the spheres in layer A (Fig. 11-6b). For this case, layer C is different from either layer A or layer B. The fourth layer can be directly above the A layer and the fifth above the B layer so that the pattern of arrangement can be represented by ABCABCABC. Spheres arranged so that each one is in contact with 12 other spheres with the layers in the pattern of an ABCABCABC structure are said to be **face-centered cubic packed.** This is a close-packed arrangement just as is the hexagonal closest-packed structure. Each sphere touches 12 others.

Hexagonal closest packing and face-centered cubic packing represent the two ways in which identical spheres may be closest packed in regular patterns. They are models for the arrangements of atoms in the crystals of approximately 60 percent of the metals as determined by x-ray measurements. Table 11-5 lists some of the metals that form crystals corresponding to each pattern. Four noble gas elements are also included as examples of substances other than metals that form close-packed crystals.

11-12 BODY-CENTERED CUBIC PACKING

About 20 percent of the metallic elements form crystals in which each atom is in contact with only eight other atoms rather than twelve.

Fig. 11-7 *Body-centered cubic packing.*

Spheres can be arranged in this way as indicated in Fig. 11-7. In this arrangement, nine spheres form a cube in which a sphere is at each corner and a sphere is in the center of the cube. The name applied to this arrangement is **body-centered cubic packing.** Table 11-6 lists some metals that form crystals for which x-ray measurements show the atoms to be arranged in body-centered cubic packing.

Several metals can exist in more than one crystal form. Thus chromium, iron, lithium, and manganese can form crystals with either body-centered cubic packing or face-centered cubic packing. Calcium can form crystals with hexagonal close packing as well as with body-centered cubic packing and face-centered cubic packing. The different crystal forms, called **phases,** are stable over different temperature ranges. A crystal of a substance can change from one phase to another at a characteristic temperature called the transition temperature. Because it corresponds to a change in phase, a **transition temperature** is similar to a melting point or boiling point. Just as diamond and graphite with different structures represent two allotropic forms of carbon, so crystals with different arrangements (different structures) represent different allotropic forms of metals. No model has yet been devised that will enable us to predict the crystal form of a metal. For each metal, the crystal form must be determined experimentally.

Measurement of the distance between the centers of spheres in

---

TABLE 11-6 SOME ELEMENTS THAT FORM CRYSTALS WITH BODY-CENTERED CUBIC PACKING

Barium	Cobalt	Manganese	Sodium
Calcium	Iron	Potassium	Tungsten
Cesium	Lithium	Rubidium	Vanadium
Chromium			

closest-packing arrangements and in the body-centered cubic-packing arrangement shows that the spheres in the body-centered cubic structure are almost but not quite as closely packed as are the spheres in the closest-packing arrangements. In an arrangement of spheres those spheres in contact with a single central sphere are referred to as **nearest neighbors** of the central sphere. Each sphere in a closest-packed structure has twelve nearest neighbors, whereas each sphere in the body-centered cubic structure has only eight nearest neighbors. The smaller the number of nearest neighbors, the less compact the packing.

In the body-centered cubic structure, however, each central sphere has a second set of six neighbors only a little farther away from the central sphere than the nearest neighbors. These nearby spheres are referred to as **next nearest neighbors.** In the closest-packed structures the spheres beyond the nearest twelve are much farther away from the central sphere than are the next nearest neighbors of the body-centered cubic structure. Therefore, body-centered cubic packing is only slightly less effective as a way of filling space with spheres than the two closest-packed arrangements.

The number of nearest neighbors which an atom has is called its **coordination number.** The coordination number characteristics of the two closest-packed structures is 12 and that of the body-centered cubic structure is 8, although the body-centered cubic structure is sometimes said to have a coordination number of 8 plus 6. The crystals of some metals are structures that correspond to distortions of these three packing patterns. In these distorted patterns, each atom is surrounded by nearest neighbors arranged in a nonuniform rather than uniform way.

Ex. 11-4 Iron changes from the body-centered cubic lattice to the face-centered cubic lattice at 916°C. How would the density of iron change during this transition?

11-13 UNIT CELLS

Metal crystal structures have been discussed thus far as analogs of the arrangements of spheres of identical radii. Arrangements of spheres can be described by taking just the point at the center of each sphere to represent the positions of the spheres. The arrangement of the points is called a **lattice.** It is customary then to represent the structure of a metal crystal in terms of the positions of the atomic nuclei as if the nuclei are points. It is difficult to deal quantitatively with the geometry of an entire lattice containing an unlimited number of points, however. Considerable simplification can be achieved by extracting from each lattice a simple repeating unit of structure. When these units are arranged side by side, the lattice is produced in all directions without

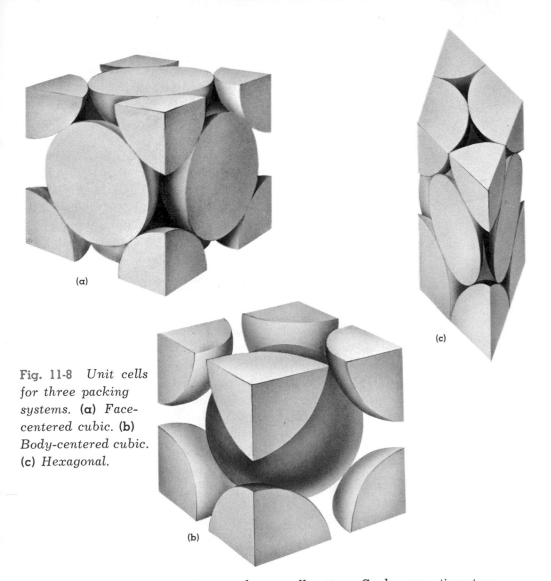

Fig. 11-8 *Unit cells
for three packing
systems.* (**a**) *Face-
centered cubic.* (**b**)
Body-centered cubic.
(**c**) *Hexagonal.*

(a)

(c)

(b)

any gaps or interruptions in the overall pattern. Such a repeating structural unit which is characteristic of a given lattice is called the **unit
cell** of that lattice. The unit cell is the smallest repeating structural
unit representing an integral number of atoms.

The closest-packed lattices can be differentiated from each other by
establishing the positions of the centers of the atoms for three layers of
each lattice. Figure 11-8 shows models of the unit cells of the three
lattices characteristic of metal crystals. The unit cell of the *ABCABC*
type of closest-packed lattice is a cube (Fig. 11-8a). The center of a
sphere lies at each of the eight corners of the cube and also at the
center of each face of the unit cell. Such a lattice is known, therefore,
as a **face-centered cubic lattice.** The unit cell of the **body-centered cubic
lattice** also has the center of a sphere at each corner of a cube and a

sphere at the center of the cube, as in Fig. 11-8b. The unit cell of the *ABABAB* type of closest-packed lattice has vertical faces at right angles to the bottom face, but in the top and bottom of this unit cell the angles are not right angles. Two angles are 60° and two are 120° (Fig. 11-8c). Such a lattice is known as the **hexagonal closest-packed lattice.**

Each unit cell must contain an integral number of spheres. The unit cells in Fig. 11-8 can be shown to contain an integral number of spheres. For example, in the unit cell of the face-centered cubic lattice in Fig. 11-8a, there is one-half of a sphere in each of six faces, which gives a total of three spheres. At each of the eight corners there is one-eighth of a sphere, which gives one more sphere. So a face-centered cubic unit cell contains exactly four spheres. The unit cells of other lattices can also be shown to contain integral numbers of spheres.

11-14 ATOMIC RADII

The density of an element is equal to the ratio of atomic mass to the atomic volume as well as being equal to the mass/volume ratio of a particular object made of the element. If the atomic volume of an element is divided by the Avogadro number, the result is the apparent volume of a single atom of the element. The apparent volume of a single atom is based on the assumption that the atoms of an object completely fill the space occupied by the object. Spherical atoms cannot completely fill the space occupied by an object, however. For this reason, the atomic volume calculated from the density of a crystal cannot be used alone to compute a numerical value for the volume of a single atom.

Since the unit cells of a crystal lattice completely fill the space occupied by a crystal, the apparent volume of an atom calculated from crystal density must be directly related to the volume of a unit cell. It is possible to calculate the ratio of the volume of a unit cell to the volume of the spheres within the unit cell. With this information about unit-cell volume in relation to sphere volume, the volume of an individual sphere can be calculated. Analogous calculations for the volumes of atoms in crystals can be carried out. An example will show how the calculations are handled.

Crystals of copper have a density of 8.95 g/ml, an atomic mass of 63.54 g/mole, and a face-centered cubic crystal lattice. So the apparent volume of an atom of copper is

$$\text{Apparent volume} = \frac{63.54 \text{ g/mole}}{8.95 \text{ g/ml} \times 6.02 \times 10^{23} \text{ atoms/mole}}$$
$$= 1.179 \times 10^{-23} \text{ ml/Cu atom}$$

In a unit cell of a face-centered cubic lattice there are four spheres.

Each face of the cube in the face-centered cubic lattice (Fig. 11-8a) has a diagonal whose length is equal to four times the radius of one sphere so that the length of the edge of the cube from the Pythagorean theorem must be $2\sqrt{2}\,R$ where R is the radius of one sphere. The volume of one unit cell is then $(2\sqrt{2}\,R)^3 = 16\sqrt{2}\,R^3$, while the volume of one sphere is $\frac{4}{3}\pi R^3$. There are four spheres per unit cell in the face-centered cubic lattice. Therefore, the fraction of the volume of a unit cell occupied by the four spheres is

$$\text{Fraction of volume} = \frac{4 \times \frac{4}{3}\pi R^3}{16\sqrt{2}\,R^3} = \frac{\pi}{3\sqrt{2}} = 0.740$$

For a copper crystal the actual volume of an atom must be 0.740 times the apparent volume of an atom. The volume per copper atom will then be

$$\text{Volume} = 1.179 \times 10^{-23}\ \text{ml} \times 0.740 = 8.72 \times 10^{-24}\ \text{ml/Cu atom}$$

It is customary to describe the size of an atom by its radius rather than its volume. For a spherical copper atom the radius can be calculated readily from the volume V since

$$V = \tfrac{4}{3}\pi R^3$$

The result for copper is a radius of 1.28×10^{-8} cm or 1.28 A.

When experimental data for crystals are used to calculate radii, the numerical values obtained are called **atomic radii**. The assumptions upon which the calculations are based are listed below. These assumptions are used in Experiment 23 of *Investigating Chemical Systems* to interrelate density and sphere radius for spheres packed together in a lattice.

1. All the atoms in a crystal have the same radius.
2. The atoms are arranged in a regular or repeating pattern.
3. Each atom is a hard sphere.
4. Each atom is in contact with its nearest neighbors.

Atomic radii have been calculated for most of the metallic elements. The radii, represented by circles, are shown in a modified periodic table in Fig. 11-9. Atomic radius is a periodic property of the elements. Along a single row of the periodic table the atomic radius decreases as the atomic number increases. The members of any family in the periodic table show an increase in atomic radius with an increase in atomic number.

The relation between atomic radius and atomic number can be interpreted in terms of the arrangement of electrons in the orbitals of atoms and in terms of nuclear charge. In the atoms of elements along any one

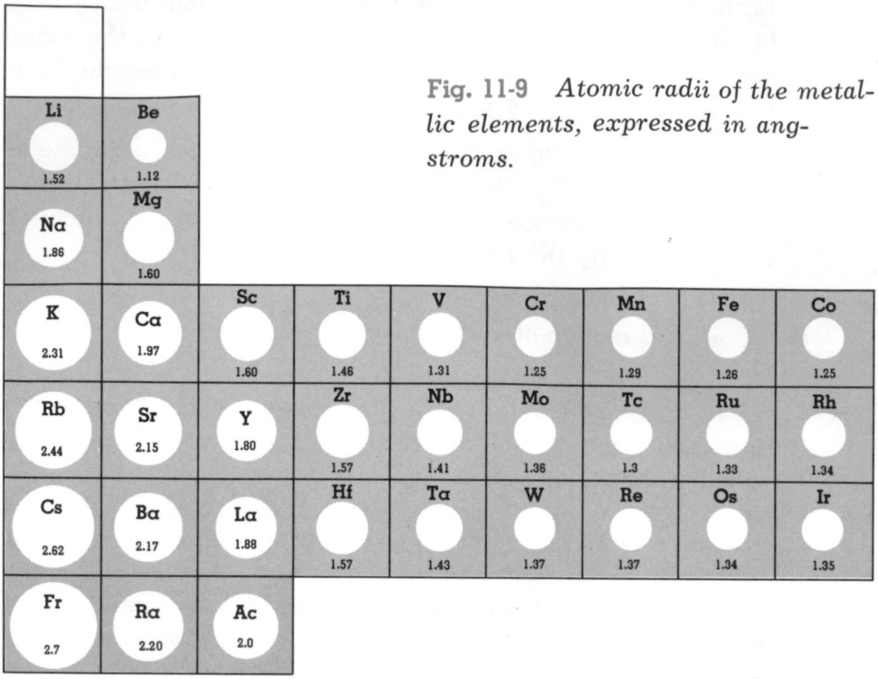

Fig. 11-9 *Atomic radii of the metallic elements, expressed in angstroms.*

Li 1.52	Be 1.12							
Na 1.86	Mg 1.60							
K 2.31	Ca 1.97	Sc 1.60	Ti 1.46	V 1.31	Cr 1.25	Mn 1.29	Fe 1.26	Co 1.25
Rb 2.44	Sr 2.15	Y 1.80	Zr 1.57	Nb 1.41	Mo 1.36	Tc 1.3	Ru 1.33	Rh 1.34
Cs 2.62	Ba 2.17	La 1.88	Hf 1.57	Ta 1.43	W 1.37	Re 1.37	Os 1.34	Ir 1.35
Fr 2.7	Ra 2.20	Ac 2.0						

row, the electrons in the outer orbitals are arranged around a kernel containing the same number of filled levels. Increase in nuclear charge pulls the electrons more tightly around the nucleus, and thus the atomic radius is reduced. This increased attraction more than balances the repulsion between the added electron and any other outer electrons. For a family of elements, the atoms of each successive member have a larger kernel containing more filled levels. Hence the electrons in the unfilled orbitals are farther from and less tightly held by the nucleus. This results in an increase in atomic radius as the atomic number increases among the elements in a single group.

Ex. 11-5 Show by calculation that the fraction of unit-cell volume occupied by spheres of the body-centered cubic lattice is not 0.74.

Ex. 11-6 Is it possible for a manufacturer of marbles to fill more than 74 percent of a large box with marbles of uniform size? If his shipping charges are determined by volume and not mass, what portion of these charges can be regarded as charges for shipping empty space?

Ex. 11-7 Metallic cerium occurs both as hexagonal and face-centered cubic close-packed crystals. Would you expect the density of the face-centered cubic close-packed cerium crystal to be much different from the density of the hexagonal close-packed cerium crystal? Why or why not?

			Al					
			1.43					
Ni	Cu	Zn	Ga	Ge	As			
1.24	1.28	1.33	1.22	1.22	1.21			
Pd	Ag	Cd	In	Sn	Sb			
1.38	1.44	1.49	1.62	1.4	1.41			
Pt	Au	Hg	Tl	Pb	Bi	Po		
1.38	1.44	1.52	1.71	1.75	1.46	1.4		

11-15 DEFORMATION OF METALS

If a piece of ice is hammered or twisted hard enough, the ice does not bend but shatters into many small pieces. When most metals are hammered or twisted, they do not shatter, however, but flatten out or bend. The behavior of metals is described by saying that metals can be deformed.

Processes in which metals are deformed are of great industrial importance. For example, the stamping, forging, drawing, and spinning of metal sheets to form items of complex shape for use in automobiles, refrigerators, watches, dishpans, and a great many other objects are processes of basic importance in twentieth-century technology. If metal sheets could not be bent or twisted or hammered without shattering, industrial manufacturing processes and products would be far different from what they are.

A material which can be hammered into sheets and twisted or bent without breaking is said to be **malleable.** Materials which can be drawn through dies to produce wire are described as **ductile.** Metals are both malleable and ductile. Metals are also able to resist stretching without breaking. This property of metals is called **tensile strength.** Substances such as ice which have covalent bonds are neither malleable nor ductile, nor do they have great tensile strength. How can these differences be understood?

To this point the discussion of metals has used the idea of metal structure based on delocalized electrons and positively charged kernels. In most metals it is not known exactly how many electrons are delocalized. Probably not all the electrons outside the kernel should be thought of as being equally free to move around. With this uncertainty it is better to think just of a positive ion and one or two delocalized electrons. A metal crystal is, in these terms, a collection of positive ions immersed in a sea of negative charge. The attractive forces between the sea of negative charge and the positive ions are large and hold the structure tightly together. The tensile strength of a metal is a measure of the attractive forces between electrons and ions.

Since the delocalized electrons surround each ion symmetrically, the ions can be moved past each other relatively easily as long as the average distance between ions is not changed and as long as the delocalized electrons are available for bonding. Suppose, for example, that the group of ions shown in Fig. 11-10a is moved to a new position shown in Fig. 11-10b. In terms of the crystal itself, nothing has been changed except at the crystal edges. In the interior of the crystal, the environment of each metallic ion is the same before and after displacement. The nearest neighbors of ions in metal crystals, then, can be changed easily, and new strong bonds will form readily with new nearest neighbors. This illustrates a striking difference between the nondirectional bonding of metals and the directed bonding in covalent molecules. The displacements shown in Fig. 11-10 give an explanation of why metals are ductile. Continued slippage of ions past each other will allow the metal to be drawn into wire without breaking. At the same time, because the forces between atoms are large in metal crystals, considerable force has to be exerted to stretch a metal.

Figure 11-10 shows the initial and final states of a deformation, but it does not describe the intermediate stages. It must not be supposed that the whole set of ions moves bodily from one place to another simultaneously. For bodily movement of a large number of ions to take place to produce holes, the atoms would have to separate against the powerful forces that hold the metal crystal together. Instead, one ion

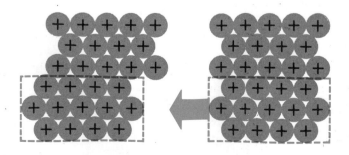

Fig. 11-10 *Displacement of metal ions in a metal crystal.*

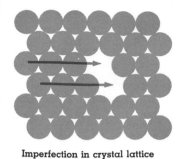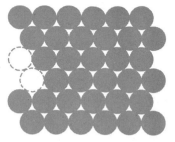

Imperfection in crystal lattice   Imperfection removed

Fig. 11-11 *Model showing that migration of atoms in a metal crystal removes imperfections.*

moves at a time, and the dislocation moves more or less gradually across the crystal. Most crystals, in fact, are imperfect because there are small vacant places in the crystal lattice where one or more ions are missing or because there are extra planes of ions which disturb the regularity of the crystal structure. Deformation of the crystal at the points of imperfection is then somewhat easier since the deformation itself may serve to straighten out the crystal pattern along these imperfections (Fig. 11-11).

Relatively little force is required to bend a straight copper wire sharply. This is interpretable in the delocalized-electron model in terms of the positive ions in a sea of negative charge. Yet straightening out a bent wire proves to be difficult, not so much because of the force required but because it is difficult to eliminate completely the kink which was introduced initially. An attempt to straighten the kink always seems to bend the wire at some other point nearby. The wire behaves as if it is slightly stiffer at the kink than at other places along side the kink. Any deformation tends to make a metal harder and stiffer. Practical use is made of this property of metals to prepare metal products which are hard and tough.

A sharp bend in a metal wire or sheet will separate some ions so far from adjacent delocalized electrons and nearest ion neighbors that the orderly crystal pattern is broken. Even though these breaks in the pattern may not be large enough to be seen as cracks or visible flaws, nonetheless they represent regions where the edges of crystal planes no longer join smoothly (Fig. 11-12). In effect, a sharp bend produces many little crystals out of what was initially one crystal or a small number of large crystals. Any attempt to push the little crystals back together will be difficult since the planes and edges formed during the bending do not necessarily fit together again to form an orderly crystal pattern.

The deformation of metals can be understood in terms of two ideas.

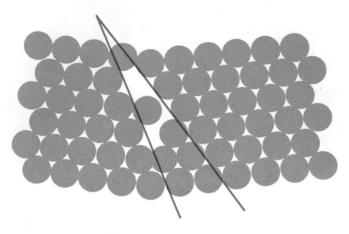

Fig. 11-12 *Two-dimensional model of a crystal imperfection. Lines show different orientations of two metal lattices. Note the irregular, loose packing between the lines.*

The fact that deformation occurs without shattering fits in with the idea of delocalized electrons. On the other hand, the stiffness produced by deformation fits in with the idea of a crystal lattice. Metals are understood best then as combining some aspects of a sea (fluid) and some aspects of a lattice.

Ex. 11-8   Would you expect that the ease of deformation and stiffness of metals caused by bending would be lessened if the metals were heated before bending and bent while hot? Explain.

11-16   INTERSTITIAL SOLID SOLUTIONS

The discussion of bonding in metals and its relation to physical properties has been based on the situation in a single metal crystal. By careful control of temperature in the proper environment, it is possible to grow single crystals of considerable size from molten metals or directly from metal vapors. When the surface of a metal other than a single crystal is examined under a microscope, what may have appeared to the unaided eye to be a smooth homogeneous surface will be seen to consist of a mosaic of granular crystals of irregular shape. A single crystal has a lattice very close to the perfect geometrical pattern, whereas an ordinary piece of metal contains empty spaces or imperfections due to the irregular joining of lattices at the grain boundaries. The tensile strength and electric conductivity will thus be less in polycrystalline metal samples than in single crystals. On the other hand, a single crystal of a metal is easier to deform than is a polycrystalline piece, because the atoms move more easily past each other in what are called glide planes when the crystals have a regularly ordered structure (Fig. 11-13) than when there are irregular gaps in the structure.

One characteristic feature of metals is the fact that in many cases a few tenths of 1 percent of a second substance will often produce a great change in properties. Thus copper containing a few tenths of 1 percent of arsenic is so hard and brittle that forming wire from the copper is quite difficult and even impossible. Since arsenic is often associated with copper in ores, the removal of traces of arsenic is an essential part of the preparation of copper for electrical and other uses. This large effect on many metals, produced by small amounts of material, is quite in contrast to the behavior of covalent materials. For example, adding a tenth of 1 percent of ammonia to water produces only quite small changes in most of the properties of water.

The introduction of a small number of foreign atoms into the lattice of a metal is often possible simply because the foreign atoms fit into small holes already present between the atoms of the crystal. If the foreign atoms are smaller than the atoms of the metal, the presence of the foreign atoms does not alter the original lattice. Up to the point where every hole is filled with a foreign atom, any number of foreign

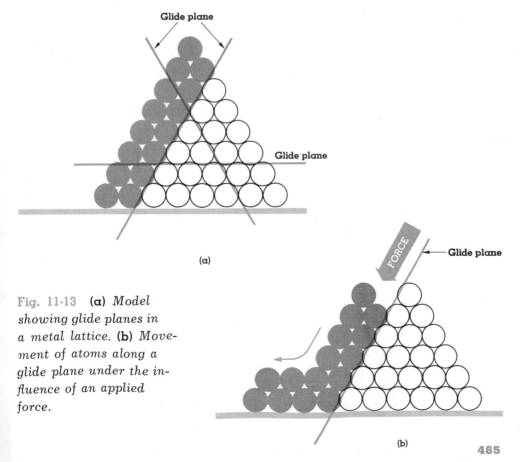

Fig. 11-13 (a) Model showing glide planes in a metal lattice. (b) Movement of atoms along a glide plane under the influence of an applied force.

485

TABLE 11-7   SOME INTERSTITIAL SOLID SOLUTIONS: NITRIDES, CARBIDES, BORIDES

Formula	Ratio of Atomic Radius of N, C, or B to Atomic Radius of Metal	Density, g/ml	Melting Point, °C	Hardness (Diamond = 10)
TiN	0.49	5.2	2927	8–9
ZrN	0.45	6.9	2952	8+
VN	0.53	5.6	2027	9–10
TaN			3067	8+
TiC	0.53	4.2	3127	8+
ZrC	0.48		3492	8–9
VC	0.58	5.4	2770	9–10
WC	0.55	16.7	2867	9+
TaC	0.53		3827	9+
TiB_2		4.0		9+
ZrB_2		5.6		
VB_2		5.3		8
WB			2925	
WB_2		10.8		9+
TaB_2		11.0		9+

atoms can be fitted into the crystal. A metal crystal which contains a variable amount of a second smaller atom scattered around in holes between atoms of the crystal is called an *interstitial solid solution.*

In some structures (close-packed), not all the interstitial holes are of the same size, so that only certain holes are large enough to accept a particular foreign atom. When all the holes which can be filled are filled, there is a definite ratio between the number of interstitial atoms and the number of metal atoms. One might call such systems saturated solutions, but it is customary to refer to them as compounds. Consequently, an interstitial compound is sometimes given a chemical formula. Cementite, Fe_3C, found in some steels, is an interstitial compound. Interstitial compounds are hard, have high melting points, and have low electric conductivities, as would be expected from their irregular structures (Table 11-7).

Consideration of the structure of a metal suggests why many interstitial solid solutions are harder than pure metals. Suppose that in an array of uniform spheres some smaller foreign spheres are placed in holes between the larger ones as in Fig. 11-14. Any attempt to push the

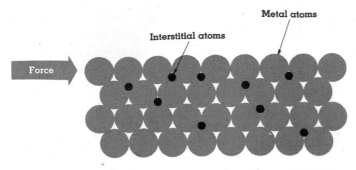

Fig. 11-14 *Interstitial atoms in a metal crystal lattice interfere with the displacement of atoms when a force is applied to the crystal.*

upper layer of spheres over the bottom layer will now encounter the small interstitial sphere as an obstacle. In a metallic substance in which the added atoms occupy small holes between large atoms, the interstitial atoms, even though relatively small in size and small in number, will interfere with the orderly displacement of the atoms in the original crystal. This provides an explanation for the observation that the addition of only a few tenths of 1 percent of a second substance will greatly increase hardness and decrease malleability and ductibility of a metal.

Ex. 11-9   Why are Cu-Be alloys sometimes used in electric switches where circuits are closed and opened frequently, instead of copper metal, which is a much better electric conductor than the Cu-Be alloy?

11-17   MIXTURES OF MOLTEN METALS

Most pairs of metals form solutions when they are melted together. This fact is understandable in terms of the delocalized-electron model for metals. Melting a pure metal (Section 11-6) does not appreciably change the environment of the metal ions. The ions are in the same sort of environment in all metals. Hence no unusual change in environment is involved when one metal is added to another and the mixture melted. The metals will tend to be mutually soluble in the melt.

Thallium and lead are examples of the small group of metals that do not form solutions with most other metals. Liquid thallium or liquid lead simply forms a second liquid phase when either metal is mixed with another metal in the liquid phase. This property of lead is used in purifying lead ore. When lead is first prepared, it is contaminated with other metals such as silver and gold, which are soluble in lead. Zinc, however, is not soluble in lead. Since silver and gold are more soluble in zinc than in lead, purification of the lead can be carried out by stirring molten zinc with the molten impure lead. The impurity metals (silver and gold) dissolve in the zinc, and when stirring is stopped, the zinc solution of silver and gold floats on top of the molten lead. After the floating layer has been separated from the lead, the zinc can be distilled away, leaving the silver and gold.

11-18 METAL CRYSTALS FROM MOLTEN SOLUTION

More commonly, a pair of molten metals forms a solution instead of a two-phase mixture. If a homogeneous melt is cooled, solid crystals form. The first solid to appear from a two-component melt will be one of three types of material: (1) a pure metal (or in special cases, a mixture of the two pure metals), (2) an intermetallic compound, or (3) a substitutional solid solution.

The temperature at which crystals begin to form when a molten homogeneous mixture of cadmium (Cd) and bismuth (Bi) is cooled is shown by the curve in Fig. 11-15. When the temperature and composition of a cadmium–bismuth mixture corresponds to any point above the curve in Fig. 11-15, the mixture will be in the liquid phase. If a mixture at a temperature corresponding to any point A above the curve in Fig. 11-15 is cooled, crystals will begin to form when the temperature reaches point B on the curve. If the mixture has a composition corresponding to point B, or any other mole ratio of Cd to Bi less than 55:45, crystals of pure bismuth appear first. If the mole ratio is more than 55:45 (point C, for example), crystals of pure cadmium appear first. The lowest temperature for which this pair of metals can exist in liquid form is about 140°C (point D). At point D the mixture has the composition 55 moles of Cd to 45 moles of Bi. The solid which

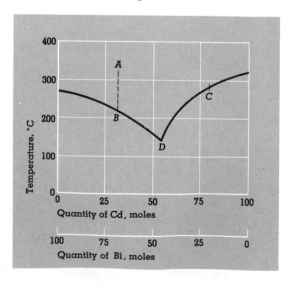

Fig. 11-15 *Temperature-composition diagram showing phase changes in systems of cadmium and bismuth.*

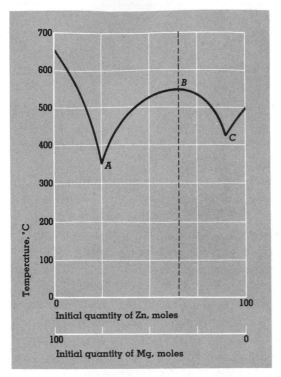

Fig. 11-16 *Temperature-com-position diagram showing phase changes in systems of zinc and magnesium.*

separates from a melt of the composition represented by point D will be a heterogeneous mixture of crystals of pure cadmium and pure bismuth, but in exactly the same ratio as the metals in the melt. The temperature and composition of a liquid mixture from which crystals of two solids form so that solid and liquid both have the same composition is called the **eutectic point.** The solid **eutectic mixture** (the mixture of cadmium and bismuth corresponding to point D in Fig. 11-15) that separates from the melt at the eutectic point is an example of the solid formed from a mixture of pure metals. Figure 11-15 illustrates a type of temperature-composition graph called a **phase diagram.**

11-19 INTERMETALLIC COMPOUNDS FROM MOLTEN SOLUTIONS

The phase diagram in Fig. 11-16 corresponds to a mixture that has two eutectic points. The two eutectic points of a mixture of magnesium and zinc are at 350°C and at 420°C. To the left of eutectic point A, the solid that separates from a melt being cooled is magnesium. To the right of eutectic point C, the solid formed is zinc. Systems with compositions between the two eutectic points give a solid containing both magnesium and zinc. If a molten mixture of Zn and Mg with a composition corresponding to a mole ratio of 67 moles of Zn to 33 moles of

TABLE 11-8   FORMULAS OF SOME INTERMETALLIC COMPOUNDS

$AgZn$	$NaSn_2$	Na_3Hg
$AuZn$	$MgZn_2$	Mg_4Ca_3
KHg	KHg_2	Cu_5Sn
$BaHg$	Mg_2Sn	Ag_5Zn_8

Mg is cooled to point B, the solid which appears is a homogeneous material made up of one type of crystal. The composition of each crystal is the same as the composition of the liquid phase. In this way, a mixture of Zn and Mg is different from a mixture of Cd and Bi. A mixture of Cd and Bi forms a solid made either of cadmium alone or of bismuth alone or of crystals of both mixed together. When a melt with any composition between those of the two eutectic mixtures A and C is cooled, the solid which first separates has the same composition as the system at point B, that is, a Zn/Mg mole ratio of 67:33.

The behavior of the zinc–magnesium systems is similar to that of the copper–sulfur systems discussed in Section 2-10. The behavior of the copper–sulfur systems was interpreted to mean that many different initial compositions result in a final product which always has the same composition. With the zinc–magnesium systems there is also a wide range of initial compositions for which the solid that first separates from the liquid has a mole ratio of 67:33. It is reasonable to conclude, then, that zinc and magnesium form a compound as we concluded for the copper–sulfur systems.

The melting point of the compound (point B) is 540°C. The mole ratio of zinc to magnesium in the compound corresponds to a 2:1 atomic ratio, and the composition of the compound can be represented by the formula $MgZn_2$. The compound with formula $MgZn_2$ is one example of a group of substances called intermetallic compounds. The formulas for some intermetallic compounds that are listed in Table 11-8 illustrate the variety of compounds formed.

11-20   SOLID SOLUTIONS FROM MOLTEN SOLUTIONS

In many cases, cooling a molten metal solution does not result in the formation of crystals of pure metal or in the formation of an intermetallic compound. Figure 11-17 is a phase diagram for systems of copper and nickel. For example, if a molten solution of composition A is cooled, the first crystals appear at the temperature indicated by point B and the composition of the crystals is given by point C. The crystals are homogeneous, but for different compositions of the initial liquid, they can have any composition between pure copper and pure nickel. A homogeneous solid formed by two or more components and having

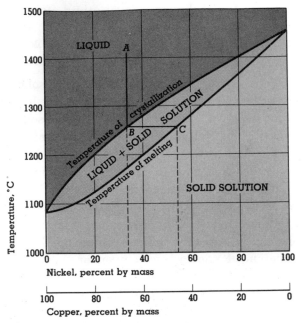

Fig. 11-17 *Temperature-composition diagram showing the temperatures at which phase changes occur in systems of nickel and copper which form solid solutions.*

a composition that falls anywhere within a wide range of possible compositions is called a **solid solution.** Solid solutions and liquid solutions have a number of characteristics in common. In both types of solutions, particles of one component are distributed at random among the particles of the other component. A liquid solution is, of course, a fluid; a solid solution is rigid. In liquid solutions the particles move about at random, whereas in solid solutions the particles can only vibrate about fixed positions.

Interstitial solid solutions are discussed in Section 11-16. A **substitutional solid solution** (Fig. 11-18) results when atoms of one metal are replaced in their lattice positions by atoms of another metal. In a true

Fig. 11-18 *Model for a substitutional solid solution. An atom of one metal takes the place of an atom of another metal in the crystal lattice.*

substitutional solid solution, the replacement of atoms of one metal by atoms of another metal is at random. In other words, there is no order such as replacement of every second atom or every third atom.

11-21 FACTORS INFLUENCING SUBSTITUTION IN SOLID SOLUTIONS

Whether or not a pair of metals will form substitutional solid solutions appears to depend upon three factors. The first of these has to do with the relative sizes of the atoms. To form a substitutional solid solution, an atom of one metal must take the place of an atom of another metal (Fig. 11-18). If the atom of the solute metal were too large, the lattice of the solvent metal would have to expand to accommodate it; if the atom were too small, the regularity of the lattice would have to be distorted. In either case, there is a limit to the amount of expansion or distortion that a lattice can undergo. Only atoms whose radii fall within a certain range can be expected to be accommodated in a particular lattice. Examination of known two-component solid solutions indicates that the radii of the two atoms never differ by more than 15 percent. This does not mean that solid solutions are always formed if the atoms of the metals differ in size by less than 15 percent; there are apparently other factors which may prevent formation of a solid solution. However, if the sizes of the atoms differ by more than 15 percent, this alone is sufficient to prevent the formation of substitutional solid solutions.

The second factor is the chemical nature of the metal. If a melted mixture of two metals with widely different first ionization energies is cooled, crystals of a compound of the metals often form instead of a solid solution. The formation of an intermetallic compound of zinc and magnesium discussed in Section 11-19 is an example of this type of behavior. First ionization energies for zinc and magnesium are 218 and 178 kcal/mole, respectively. The zinc–magnesium compound has a definite composition, has a definite melting point, and forms a single set of crystals from the melt—just as potassium chloride, for example, forms crystals from its solution in water as the solution is cooled below the limit of solubility of potassium chloride. There is evidence that intermetallic compounds are in fact similar to compounds like potassium chloride which have ionic bonds. The crystal structures of the compounds in which two atoms of one metal are combined with one atom of the other (for example, Mg_2Sn or $MgZn_2$) are like that of calcium fluoride, CaF_2, a typical compound with ionic bonds.

The third factor which influences the formation of substitutional solid solutions is the ratio of the number of electrons in the outer orbitals of the two types of atoms to the number of atoms in the mixture. Consider, for example, a solid solution in which 12 percent of the atoms are silicon and 88 percent are copper. The silicon atom has four outer electrons, whereas copper has one. For every 100 atoms of the alloy, the number of electrons contributed by silicon is 12×4 and the number of electrons contributed by copper is 88×1. Therefore, the electron/atom ratio is

$$\frac{12 \times 4 + 88 \times 1}{100} = 1.36$$

If the atoms of the two elements in a solid solution are of approximately the same size (1.17 A for Si and 1.28 A for Cu) and if the elements have similar first ionization energies (189 kcal/mole for Si and 178 kcal/mole for Cu), the electron/atom ratio appears to be the property which determines the maximum quantity of one element that will dissolve in another.

In Table 11-9 the compositions of some saturated solutions are listed with the corresponding electron/atom ratios. In computing the electron/atom ratios listed in Table 11-9, it was assumed that each copper or silver atom presents one electron to the lattice; each zinc or cadmium atom two; each gallium, aluminum, or indium atom three; and each silicon atom four. All the ratios listed in Table 11-9 are close to 1.4:1.

This suggests that the composition of saturated solid solutions is limited in some way by the number of electrons in the lattice. This could be interpreted to mean that there is a certain number of energy levels per atom to be filled by electrons, that the metal structure is indifferent to the source of these electrons, and that the lattice is unable

TABLE 11-9 COMPOSITION OF SATURATED SOLID SOLUTIONS (Approximate)

Components	Solubility (Atoms of the first element per 100 atoms of solid solution)	Electron/Atom Ratio[a]
Zinc in copper	39	1.39:1
Cadmium in silver	43	1.43:1
Gallium in copper	21	1.42:1
Indium in silver	20	1.40:1
Aluminum in copper	21	1.42:1
Aluminum in silver	21	1.42:1
Silicon in copper	12	1.36:1

[a] Ratio of the number of electrons in the outer orbitals of the atoms to the number of atoms.

to accommodate more than 1.4 delocalized electrons, on the average, for each atom. In the crystals of the solid solutions listed in Table 11-9, the atoms are arranged in a face-centered cubic structure. The electron/atom ratio of 1.4:1 seems to be the maximum that can occur in the face-centered cubic lattice. For each metal crystal lattice there is a characteristic electron/atom ratio that corresponds to a saturated solid solution.

Ex. 11-10 a. What type of alloy might be formed when metal A, atomic radius 1.40 A, is melted with metal B, atomic radius 1.33 A? Why?

b. What type of alloy might be formed when element C, atomic radius 0.77 A, is melted with metal D, atomic radius 1.58 A? Why?

c. Contrast the alloys that would be formed in the systems described in parts a and b with respect to hardness and melting point.

11-22 METALS OF COMMERCE

Most of the metallic substances found in articles of commerce are not pure metals but are mixtures, solutions, or compounds of metals

TABLE 11-10 SOME COMMON ALLOYS

Composition, % by Mass	Trade Name	Melting Point, °C	Density, g/ml	Use
75 Cu, 25 Ni	Coin nickel	1205	8.9	Nickel coins
50 Bi, 25 Pb, 12.5 Sn, 12.5 Cd	Wood's metal	70–72	9.7	Melting point baths
60 Ni, 33 Cu, 7 Fe	Monel	1360	8.9	Table tops (restaurants)
90 Ag, 10 Cu	Coin silver	890	10.3	Silver coins
92.5 Ag, 7.5 Cu	Sterling silver	920		Tableware and jewelry
67 Pb, 33 Sn	Plumber's solder	275	9.4	Plumbing joints
99.8 Pb, 0.2 As	Shot metal		10.9	Shot
82 Pb, 15 Sb, 3 Sn	Type metal			Printers type
84.3 Fe, 14.5 Si, 0.85 C, 0.35 Mn	Duriron	1265	7.0	Laboratory plumbing
90 Au, 10 Pd	White gold	1265		Jewelry

called *alloys.* Table 11-10 lists some important alloys and their uses. The metallurgist selects mixtures of metals that have whatever property he desires for a particular use.

A class of materials called cermets combines properties of metallic and ceramic materials for corrosion-resistant or high-temperature-resistant materials. One of the components of a cermet mixture is an interstitial solid solution. Cermets are used in nuclear engineering equipment, gas-turbine parts, and jet engine components. Examples are TiB_2 + Fe, Ni, or Co; ZrB_2 + Ni; TiN + Ni; and WC + Co.

The number of possible alloys is enormous because mixtures containing any number of metals can be prepared. The relation of the properties of alloys to their composition is not well understood, and much additional investigation is still necessary.

11-23 RELATION OF METALS AND NONMETALS

The structure and properties of metals have been described and interpreted in terms of the delocalized-electron model for the metallic bond. This model is based on the interaction between electrons and nuclei. The interaction between electrons and nuclei is also the basis for the models used for understanding the structure and properties of the nonmetallic elements and the compounds which they form.

Along any one row of the periodic table, there is a more or less regular change from metallic character on the left to nonmetallic character on the right. Similarly, within one family there is a fairly regular change from nonmetallic character for the elements of small atomic number to metallic character for the elements of large atomic number.

In Fig. 11-1 the elements with predominantly metallic properties are separated by a diagonal zone from the elements with predominantly nonmetallic properties. Within this diagonal zone, several of the elements are somewhat difficult to classify on the basis of properties as either metals or nonmetals. Four of these elements and some of their properties are listed in Table 11-11.

These elements and others near them in the periodic table are sometimes referred to as *metalloids.* The implication is that they resemble metals in some characteristics and resemble nonmetals in others. The four metalloids in Table 11-11 are solids at room temperature, but none are electric conductors. Their crystal lattices are not close-packed structures. Thus, silicon forms crystals in which each atom has only four nearest neighbors.

Carbon in the form of diamond crystals is an excellent electric insulator. Its transparency also suggests that it is a nonmetal. On the other hand, carbon in the form of graphite is opaque and is a fair conductor of electricity; that is, graphite is somewhat metallic. In Section

TABLE 11-11. PROPERTIES OF METALLOID ELEMENTS

Element	First Ionization Energy, kcal/mole	Melting Point, °C	Boiling Point, °C	Liquid Range, °C	Heat of Vaporization, kcal/mole
Boron	191	2040	3900	1860	75
Silicon	189	1410	2600	1190	41
Arsenic	244		610[a]	0	8
Tellurium	209	450	987	537	12

[a] Arsenic sublimes at 1 atmosphere pressure.

10-23 the structure of graphite is discussed in terms of delocalized electrons and the structure of diamond is discussed in terms of atoms held together by sp^3 hybrid bonds involving localized electrons. Carbon in its two allotropic forms indicates as well as any single element that a single set of ideas for interpreting different substances is not effective.

11-24 SUMMARY

According to the atomic orbital model, metals are composed of atoms which have several outer or available orbitals of nearly the same energy level but only a small number of electrons to occupy these available orbitals. In terms of the charge cloud model, the ratio of available space to electron charge clouds around the kernel of metal atom is high. Either model leads to the conclusion that a few electrons in the outer orbitals or a few electron charge clouds of a metal atom can spread out to lower the potential energy and the kinetic energy of the system. These mobile electrons are said to be delocalized.

The spreading out of the delocalized electrons in a metal crystal then results in some of the electrons becoming identified not with one or two atoms but with a large number of atoms. One consequence of low potential energy and low kinetic energy is a powerful force of attraction holding all the atoms together. Metallic properties are therefore associated with pieces of material and not with individual isolated atoms.

The idea of delocalized electrons can, at least qualitatively, account for high boiling temperatures and extended liquid range of metals. Electric conductivity fits in with the idea of delocalized electrons since the delocalization permits the electrons to shift easily in response to electric potential differences. Delocalized electrons can also transfer their energy easily to the atomic kernels and thereby transfer heat rapidly through a metal in response to temperature differences. The fact that solid metals can be deformed without breaking also fits in with the delocalized-electron model.

In most cases metal crystals consist of atoms arranged so that each atom is surrounded by 12 other atoms. Structures of this kind are called close-packed arrangements. Many of the essential features of metal crystals can be duplicated by packing sets of identical spheres together. A few metals have crystal lattices in which atoms have a coordination number of 8.

A radius for a metal atom can be calculated from density data for crystals by making three assumptions. (1) The atoms are hard, uniform spheres. (2) The centers of the atoms are arranged in a lattice with a regular pattern. (3) The atoms in the crystal are in contact with nearest neighbors.

The fact that there are so few nonmetals (about 20) and yet nearly four times as many metals also fits into the general picture. According to the delocalized-electron model, a metal atom has a kernel surrounded by a few electrons in wide open spaces (many orbitals) so that the electrons can go more places to do more things. Electrons can be delocalized as long as the number of orbitals in an atom exceeds the number of electrons. Metals consist of atoms in which there are many wide open spaces (available orbitals) into which electrons can move or can spread around the kernels of the atoms. Nonmetals consist of atoms in which there are few unfilled orbitals into which electrons can fit. Among the elements in one period, the elements with atoms in which there are many places to put a few electrons are the metallic elements. The elements with atoms in which there are few ways to fit a large number of electrons around the kernels are the nonmetals. Therefore, only a few elements can be nonmetals, but many elements can be metals.

As an analogy, a nonmetal atom can be likened to a pair of hands neatly covered with a pair of gloves, and a metal atom to a pair of hands covered with a pair of baggy mittens. There are many ways to put a pair of mittens on many different hands. Indeed, the mittens might be transferred around the family among persons that have hands of quite different sizes. The gloves may fit just a few hands, and care must be taken to get the right glove on the right hand. This situation is analogous to the case with electrons which fit into nonmetal atoms in only a few ways, whereas electrons fit around metal atoms in many ways.

Different metals may interact in several ways. Most molten metals will form liquid solutions of one metal in another. Molten mixtures of metals can, on cooling, form solid phases in which atoms of one metal are substituted for atoms of a second metal in the crystal lattice. A basic requirement is that there be less than 15 percent difference between the radii of the two types of atoms. Since the substitution process permits considerable variation in the ratios of different atoms present, such materials are solid solutions rather than compounds.

Small foreign metal atoms can often fit into the spaces left between atoms in a close-packed arrangement of metal atoms. Materials with structures of this type are called interstitial solid solutions. The properties of these solutions are markedly different from those of the original metal even when only a small amount of material has been added.

Two metals that differ markedly in ionization energy may react to form compounds of fixed composition. Many intermetallic compounds are known, but little is understood about what factors determine their compositions.

Although the properties of metals are quite different from the properties of nonmetals, the same principles of the interaction of electrons and nuclei can be used to interpret the structure and properties of both metals and nonmetals. These principles include the ideas that (1) electrons may be considered either as standing waves or as charge clouds, (2) kinetic energy of electrons will be low in a stable system, (3) the Pauli exclusion principle limits the number of electrons in any given orbital, and (4) electrons and nuclei interact to give a system of low potential energy.

Ex. 11-11 In terms of nearest neighbors and next nearest neighbors, explain why the coordination number of body-centered cubic crystals is often said to be 14 instead of 8.

Ex. 11-12 When building up layers of spheres in a model for a close-packed arrangement, how does the position of the third layer define whether the system is face-centered cubic close packed or hexagonal close packed?

Ex. 11-13 Element A is an excellent conductor of electricity, and element B is an electric insulator; both element A and element B are solids. Predict which element most probably:

a. Has the higher boiling point.

b. Has the greater ductility.

c. Is colored or transparent.

d. Has the lower heat of vaporization.

e. Would shatter if hit by a hammer.

f. Is the better conductor of heat.

g. Has the lower ionization energy.

h. Forms polyatomic molecules in the gas phase.

i. Has the greater ratio of outer electrons to available orbitals.

j. Has localized outer electrons.

k. Exists in close-packed structures.

l. Can be polished to a mirror surface.

Ex. 11-14 At temperatures above 18°C, the stable form of tin (white tin) is a silvery white solid with a density of 7.3 g/ml. At temperatures below 18°C, the stable form of tin (gray tin) is a gray powder with a density of 5.8 g/ml. Which form of tin:

a. Is the better conductor of electricity?

b. Has the smaller atomic volume?

c. Is more malleable?

Ex. 11-15 Answer the following questions with respect to the tin–lead phase diagram.

a. What is the melting point of lead? of tin?

b. What is the melting point of the eutectic mixture of tin and lead?

c. Which area represents the molten mixture of tin and lead?

d. At what temperature (approximately) does a 1:1 molar mixture of tin and lead begin to solidify?

e. What is the mole ratio of tin to lead at the eutectic point?

f. What is the mass ratio of tin to lead at the eutectic point? at the 1:1 molar ratio?

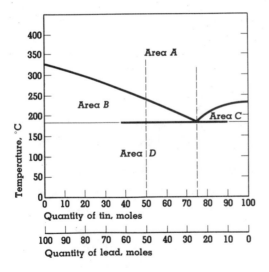

Ex. 11-16 a. What are the electron/available orbital ratios for the eight elements in the second period of the periodic table? for the five elements in the carbon family?

b. What is the number of filled orbitals for each of the eight elements in the second period? for each of the five elements in the carbon family?

c. Which members of the second period are classified as metals? Which members of the carbon family are classified as metals? Why?

Ex. 11-17 A sample of a very carefully treated copper wire had the following history. Explain the density changes described for the sample.

a. The density of the copper wire which had been heated to 970°C in a vacuum for 12 hours was 8.92420 g/ml at 25°C.

b. When the wire was drawn out to 32 percent of the original cross-sectional area, the density of the copper wire was 8.90525 g/ml at 25°C.

c. When the wire sample described in b was reheated to 995°C in a vacuum for 12 hours, the density was 8.92438 g/ml at 25°C.

Ex. 11-18 a. Compare the first ionization energies, liquid ranges, electric conductivities, and electronic configurations for the eight elements in the third period. (Use a handbook of chemistry as a source of data.)

b. On the basis of electric conductivity only, which of the elements in the third period are metals?

c. On the basis of liquid range only, which of the elements in the third period are metals?

d. Explain why decisions as to whether an element is a metal or a nonmetal must be based on determinations of more than one characteristic property.

Ex. 11-19 Predict whether a solid solution, an interstitial solid solution, or an intermetallic compound results upon the cooling of each of the following melts containing pairs of metallic elements (A and B).

	Metallic Pair		Mole Ratio	Number of Outer Electrons		Atomic Radius, angstroms		First Ionization Energy, kcal	
	A	B	A/B	A	B	A	B	A	B
(a)	Li	Pb	5:2	1	2	1.23	1.50	124	171
(b)	Mo	C	2:1	1	4	1.30	0.77	163	260
(c)	Cu	Sn	5:1	1	2	1.18	1.42	178	169
(d)	In	Ag	1:4	3	1	1.42	1.34	138	175

Hint: Determine electron/atom ratio, ratio of atomic radii, and difference between ionization energies of the metals in each of these pairs of metals.

Ex. 11-20 Bronze is a mixture of copper and tin. Definite compounds are formed when the percentage by mass of tin is (a) 27.20 percent, (b) 32.53 percent, and (c) 38.37 percent. What are the formulas of the three compounds?

IONIC SOLIDS 12

SEVENTY ELEMENTS have been classified as metals. In addition many compounds can be made by combining two or more metals. Many of these compounds have properties that are characteristic of metals and can, therefore, be referred to as metallic substances. Most of the elements which do not have properties similar to metals are called nonmetals.

12-1 CLASSIFICATION OF SUBSTANCES

Each substance has a set of properties which distinguishes it from every other substance. In Table 12-1 some substances and their properties are listed. On the basis of electric conductivity, these substances have been divided into three sets, and within each set the listing is in order of increasing boiling point. For the first set both solid and liquid forms of each substance have electric conductivities less than one-millionth of those of the substances in the other two sets. The heats of vaporization and the boiling points are lower for the substances in the first set than for the substances in the other two sets.

Three of the substances listed in the first set (chlorine, hydrogen, and phosphorus) are elements, whereas the others are compounds. Every substance in the first set consists of molecules in which atoms are joined by covalent bonds. Compounds with properties similar to those of the members of the first set in Table 12-1 are called *covalent*

TABLE 12-1 PROPERTIES OF SOME SUBSTANCES

Substance	Formula	Boiling Point, °C	Melting Point, °C	ΔH_v,[a] kcal/mole	Light Transmission	Electric Conductivity		Solubility	
						Solid	Liquid	H_2O	CCl_4
Set 1									
Hydrogen	H_2	−252.8	−259.2	0.22	Clear	−	−	−	−
Methane	CH_4	−161.5	−182.5	2.0	Clear	−	−	−	+
Hydrogen chloride	HCl	−85.0	−114.2	3.9	Clear	−	−	+	+
Acetylene	C_2H_2	−84.0	(sublimes)	5.1	Clear	−	−	−	+
Chlorine	Cl_2	−34.1	−101.0	4.9	Clear	−	−	+	+
Ammonia	NH_3	−33.4	−77.8	5.6	Clear	−	−	+	−
Methanol	CH_3OH	64.7	−97.9	8.4	Clear	−	−	+	+
Carbon tetrachloride	CCl_4	76.7	−22.9	7.2	Clear	−	−	−	+
n-Octane	C_8H_{18}	125.7	−56.8		Clear	−	−	−	+
Naphthalene	$C_{10}H_8$	218.0	80.2		Clear	−	−	−	+
Phosphorus (white)	P_4	280.	44.2	3.0	Translucent	−	−	−	+
Set 2									
Potassium	K	757	63		Opaque	+	+	(reacts)	(reacts)
Sodium	Na	889	98		Opaque	+	+	(reacts)	(reacts)
Magnesium	Mg	1120	650	31.5	Opaque	+	+	−	−
Calcium	Ca	1490	850	44.0	Opaque	+	+	(reacts)	−
Silver	Ag	2193	961	60.7	Opaque	+	+	−	−
Copper	Cu	2582	1083	72.8	Opaque	+	+	−	−

Iron	Fe	2800	1535	106.5	Opaque	+	+	−	−
Titanium	Ti	>3000	1812		Opaque	+	+	−	−
Zirconium	Zr	4375	1852		Opaque	+	+	−	−
Set 3									
Sodium carbonate	Na₂CO₃	(decomposes)	854		Clear	−	+	+	
Calcium sulfate	CaSO₄	(decomposes)	1400		Clear	−	+	+	−
Zinc chloride	ZnCl₂	756	275	30.9	Clear	−	+	+	−
Lead iodide	PbI₂	872	412	24.8	Clear, yellow	−	+	−	−
Cobalt chloride	CoCl₂	1049	724	27.2	Clear, blue	−	+	+	−
Potassium iodide	KI	1324	685	34.7	Clear	−	+	+	−
Potassium chloride	KCl	1407	772	38.8	Clear	−	+	+	−
Sodium chloride	NaCl	1465	808	40.8	Clear	−	+	+	−
Barium fluoride	BaF₂	1799	1320	83.	Clear	−	+	−	−
Magnesium oxide	MgO	3600	2800		Clear	−	+	−	−

SOURCE: Data are taken from *National Bureau of Standards Bulletin 500* and from N. A. Lange, *Handbook of Chemistry*, 10th ed., McGraw-Hill Book Company, Inc., New York, 1961.

[a] The heats of vaporization ΔH_v are given for converting the liquid to vapor where the molecules of vapor have the formulas indicated in the second column.

compounds. The substances in the second set are metals; their properties differ markedly from those of the covalent compounds in the first set.

Each substance in the third set in Table 12-1 has one distinctive property. The liquid phase of each is many times better an electric conductor than the solid phase. Boiling points and melting points, however, are in the same range as those found for metals. The solid phases of most metals are hard, tough, and malleable; whereas the solid phases of covalent compounds are soft and easily crushed. The solid phases of the substances in the third set are hard and brittle crystals.

One characteristic property of the substances in the third set is the electric conductivity of their solutions in water. Each of the substances, dissolved in water, forms a solution with a higher electric conductivity than either water or the undissolved solid substance. This is true even for those substances in the third set which are only slightly soluble in water. A few of the substances in the first set form solutions in water that have higher electric conductivity than water or the undissolved substance.

Solutions which conduct electricity are called ionic solutions (Section 4-17). A property common to ionic solutions is the reaction that occurs at the electrodes where charge enters and leaves the solution during electrolysis. Compounds which have high melting and boiling points and also produce ionic solutions in water are commonly called **ionic compounds.** Sodium chloride is an ionic compound. Ionic compounds are also referred to as **salts.**

Ionic compounds are crystalline substances that have high melting points, high boiling points, long liquid ranges, and hard, brittle crystals and which give solutions in water that conduct electricity. Crystals of most salts are transparent.

12-2 MOLTEN IONIC COMPOUNDS

Not only do ionic compounds produce water solutions that conduct electricity, but in most cases molten ionic compounds also conduct electricity. Why are the solid phases of ionic compounds, in contrast to the solid phases of metals, poor conductors of electricity? How is the conduction of electricity in molten ionic compounds related to conduction of electricity in metals?

Sodium chloride melts at 808°C to form a transparent liquid and forms crystals again when the liquid is cooled. There is no evidence that either melting or boiling produces any chemical change in sodium chloride.

Charge will flow between electrodes immersed in molten sodium chloride when the electrodes are connected to a source of electricity.

As charge flows, chemical reactions occur at each electrode. Chlorine gas is evolved at the positive electrode, and liquid sodium accumulates at the negative electrode. The overall chemical reaction is represented by

$$2NaCl \ (l) \rightarrow 2Na \ (l) + Cl_2 \ (g) \qquad (Eq. \ 12\text{-}1)$$

Just as the flow of charge through water leads to the decomposition of water according to the chemical equation,

$$2H_2O \ (l) \rightarrow 2H_2 \ (g) + O_2 \ (g) \qquad (Eq. \ 12\text{-}2)$$

so the flow of charge through molten sodium chloride leads to the decomposition of sodium chloride. In each case the quantity of material that decomposes is proportional to the quantity of charge that flows. Equations 12-1 and 12-2 exemplify and represent decompositions by electricity (Section 3-2).

The electrolysis of sodium chloride results in the production of 1 mole of sodium and $\frac{1}{2}$ mole of chlorine for each faraday of charge transferred (96,500 coulombs). Because a faraday of charge represents 1 mole of electrons, one electron is just sufficient for the production of one sodium atom or one chlorine atom.

To account for phenomena observed in the electrolysis of solutions, charged chemical species called ions have already been proposed (Section 5-6). The existence of ions is consistent with the observations described for molten sodium chloride. The simplest assumption is that molten sodium chloride contains sodium ions, Na^+, and chloride ions, Cl^-. If these ions are assumed to be present in the molten sodium chloride, the reactions at each electrode during the electrolysis can be represented by equations which show an electron as e^-, carrying one negative charge. At the negative electrode,

$$Na^+ + e^- \rightarrow Na \qquad (Eq. \ 12\text{-}3)$$

At the positive electrode,

$$Cl^- \rightarrow \tfrac{1}{2}Cl_2 + e^- \qquad (Eq. \ 12\text{-}4)$$

The addition of Equations 12-3 and 12-4 results in Equation 12-1.

The electrolysis of molten sodium chloride is the process used to manufacture sodium metal and chlorine gas in large quantities. One type of electrolysis apparatus for industrial use, called a Downs cell, is shown in Fig. 12-1.

Magnesium metal is produced by the electrolysis of molten magnesium chloride, $MgCl_2$. Two faradays of charge is transferred for each mole of magnesium produced. This leads to the assumption that

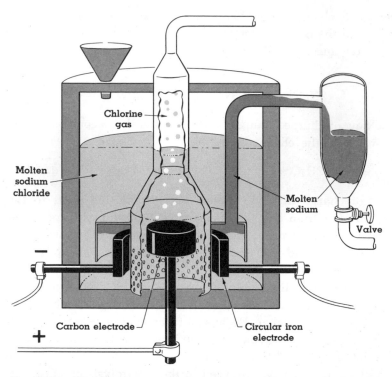

*Diagram in cross section of a Downs cell for the pro-
duction of sodium metal and chlorine.*

a magnesium ion has a positive charge twice that of sodium ion. Thus
the magnesium ion can be expressed as Mg^{++}.

Ex. 12-1 Aluminum metal is produced by the electrolysis of a solution of Al_2O_3 in
molten cryolite, Na_3AlF_6. The container for electrolysis is lined with carbon
as the negative electrode. Several carbon blocks are used as positive electrodes. At the carbon electrodes, aluminum and oxygen are liberated, although some of the oxygen reacts with the carbon to form CO_2.

a. Write the electrode reactions for the electrolysis of Al_2O_3.

b. How many faradays of charge are transferred for each mole of aluminum
produced?

c. How many moles of oxygen are produced for each mole of aluminum
produced?

12-3 CRYSTALLINE SALTS

At room temperature ionic compounds are crystalline solids. Molten
ionic compounds are good conductors of electricity, and solid ionic
compounds are extremely poor conductors of electricity; whereas both
liquid metals and solid metals are excellent conductors. If ions are
assumed to be present in molten ionic compounds, what is the nature

of crystalline salts? Can the properties of ionic compounds be explained in terms of a model based on the presence of ions in the solid phase?

Table 12-2 lists the names and properties of the chlorides formed by the elements in groups I and II of the periodic table. The elements in these two groups are referred to as the alkali metals and the alkaline-earth metals. Their chlorides are called the alkali chlorides and the alkaline-earth chlorides. In many ways their properties are representative of all salts.

Each of the compounds listed in Table 12-2 can be formed by the direct combination of the appropriate metal and chlorine. The various reactions can be represented in a general way by two equations where M is the symbol for any one of the metals.

For the alkali metals Li, Na, K, Rb, and Cs, the appropriate equation is

$$2M \ (s) \ + \ Cl_2 \ (g) \ \to \ 2MCl \ (s) \qquad (Eq. \ 12\text{-}5)$$

For the alkaline-earth metals Be, Mg, Ca, Sr, Ba, and Ra, the appropriate equation is

$$M \ (s) \ + \ Cl_2 \ (g) \ \to \ MCl_2 \ (s) \qquad (Eq. \ 12\text{-}6)$$

Crystals of the chlorides listed in Table 12-2 are colorless and trans-

TABLE 12-2 ENTHALPIES OF FUSION (ΔH_m), VAPORIZATION (ΔH_v), AND FORMATION (ΔH_f) FOR ALKALI AND ALKALINE-EARTH CHLORIDES

Compound	Melting Point, °C	Boiling Point, °C	ΔH_m, kcal/mole	ΔH_v, kcal/mole	ΔH_f, kcal/mole
Alkali metal chlorides:					
LiCl	610	1382	3.2	36.0	−97.7
NaCl	808	1465	6.8	40.8	−98.2
KCl	772	1407	6.1	38.8	−104.2
RbCl	717	1381	4.4	36.9	−102.9
CsCl	645	1300	3.6	35.7	−103.5
Alkaline-earth metal chlorides:					
BeCl$_2$	440	547		25.	−122.3
MgCl$_2$	714	1418	10.3	32.7	−153.4
CaCl$_2$	782	1600	6.8		−190.0
SrCl$_2$	875		4.1		−198.0
BaCl$_2$	962	1189[a]	5.4	57.	−205.6

[a] Boiling point at a pressure of 6.3 mm.

parent. In powdered form they are white. In this respect they resemble typical covalent compounds and differ from metals. Covalent compounds are usually transparent, and the bonds are formed by localized electrons. The opacity of metal crystals is correlated with the model for metal crystals based on the idea of delocalized electrons.

On the other hand, the high melting points, the high boiling points, the long liquid ranges, and the high enthalpies of fusion and vaporization of ionic compounds are more characteristic of metals than of covalent compounds. The model for metals consists of positive ions in a sea of delocalized electrons. Large forces of attraction between the positive ions and the negative sea hold the ions in a three-dimensional structure which corresponds to the crystal of the metal. Melting of metals requires only a small change in the arrangement of ions and electrons, but even though the change is small, melting occurs only at rather high temperatures. Since vaporization requires large quantities of energy to effect complete separation of the atoms from each other, metals boil at high temperatures.

Salts and most metals have high melting and boiling points, suggesting that large forces of attraction exist in salts. Salt crystals are similar to metal crystals (Fig. 12-2). Nonetheless, solid salts do not conduct electricity appreciably, so solid salts must not contain delocalized electrons. It is reasonable to assume that salts are composed of positive ions and negative ions rather than positive ions and delocalized electrons. In the solid ionic compound these negative ions cannot move as readily as can the delocalized electrons in metals. This accounts for the difference in conductivity.

Thus, in a crystal of sodium chloride there are sodium ions (Na^+) and chloride ions (Cl^-), consistent with the experimental evidence in the electrolysis of molten sodium chloride (Equation 12-1). For simplicity each ion can be assumed to be spherical, and the charge on the ion can be assumed to be located at the center of the sphere.

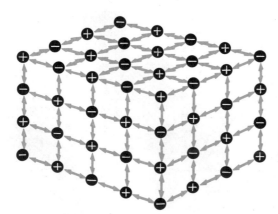

Fig. 12-2 *Attractive forces among ions in an ionic crystal.*

(a)   (b)

Fig. 12-3 *Calcium fluoride crystals. (a) Natural cubic crystal showing a cleavage plane A. (b) Natural crystal that has been split along several cleavage planes to give a crystal of approximately octahedral shape. The edges of the dark portion show the natural growth faces in relation to the cleavage planes.*

12-4 EVIDENCE FOR IONS IN CRYSTALS

If positive and negative ions could be arranged so that ions of opposite charge are close together but ions of like charge are far apart, a structure of low energy could be produced. To break up the low-energy structure and separate the ions from each other would require large amounts of energy. A model that includes these features could explain the high melting and boiling points of the salts in Table 12-2. What sort of arrangement of positive and negative ions could account for the observed properties of salts?

The alkali metal chlorides and alkaline-earth metal chlorides are hard, brittle solids. In this respect they differ from both the soft, easily crushed covalent solids and the tough but malleable metals. Examination of the fragments of a crushed crystal of an ionic solid shows that for each fragment the angles between adjacent surfaces are always the same and are characteristic of the substance. The surfaces formed when an ionic crystal breaks or splits are generally planes—referred to as **cleavage planes.** Figure 12-3 shows the relation between the faces of the crystal and the cleavage planes in calcium fluoride. The dark portion of the crystal is due to the incorporation of a colored impurity in the crystal during its growth.

An effective way of studying the structure of metal and ionic crystals is the use of x-ray interference measurements (Section 11-10). X-ray interference measurements provide information about the number of electrons per atom or ion in metal or ionic crystals. X-ray interference measurements cannot provide information about the relative masses or the nuclear charges of atoms in crystals.

A crystal made up of potassium atoms ($_{19}$K) and chlorine atoms ($_{17}$Cl) should therefore give x-ray interference patterns which suggest that not all the planes of atoms are alike. A plane of chlorine

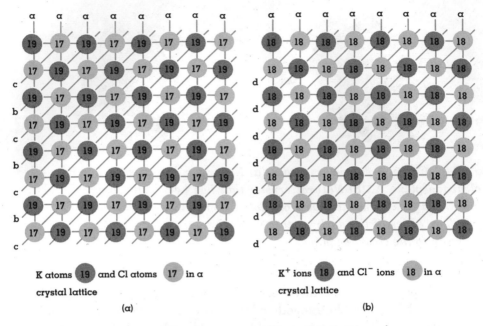

K atoms ⑲ and Cl atoms ⑰ in α
crystal lattice

(a)

K^+ ions ⑱ and Cl^- ions ⑱ in α
crystal lattice

(b)

Fig. 12-4 *Schematic representation of alternative lattices for*
potassium chloride. (a) Atomic. (b) Ionic. The numbers in the
circles are the numbers of electrons in the atoms and ions.

atoms would have only 17 electrons per atom, while a plane of potassium atoms would have 19 electrons per atom. The difference in
planes is shown schematically in Fig. 12-4a. The b planes differ from
the c planes, although all the a planes are alike.

Data obtained from x-ray measurements on potassium chloride crystals can only be interpreted to mean, however, that all planes in the
crystal are alike. That is, all the structural units have the same number of electrons. This means that b planes and c planes are not made
up of neutral atoms.

Crystals of potassium chloride must therefore consist of the ions
K^+ and Cl^-, each with 18 electrons in their orbitals. The formation of
potassium chloride could be explained by the transfer of one electron
from the 4s orbital of a $_{19}K$ atom to a 3p orbital of a $_{17}Cl$ atom. This
will account for the formation of crystals of KCl made up of ions each
one of which contains 18 electrons.

Transfer of electrons from one atom to another does not imply a
direction of motion, but rather it implies which atom controls the electrons. The molar volume of a liquid or solid is a reflection of the distances separating electrons and nuclei. For potassium metal the molar
volume is given by

$$\frac{39.1 \text{ g/mole of K}}{0.86 \text{ g/ml of K}} = 45.5 \text{ ml/mole of K}$$

This can be compared with the molar volume of potassium chloride which is given by

$$\frac{74.6 \text{ g/mole of KCl}}{1.99 \text{ g/ml of KCl}} = 37.5 \text{ ml/mole of KCl}$$

But 1 mole of potassium chloride contains within it 36 moles of electrons, of which 19 moles are furnished by the potassium. We can only conclude that 36 moles of electrons somehow occupy less volume in potassium chloride than do 19 moles of electrons in potassium metal. It must be that the electrons are packed more tightly around the potassium nuclei when these nuclei are in potassium chloride than when they are in potassium metal. So even though the 4s electron in a potassium atom has been transferred to a 3p orbital in a chlorine atom, the electron has not moved away from the potassium nucleus.

The symbol of a potassium ion ($_{19}K^+$) represents the assumption that a potassium nucleus controls 18 electrons, and similarly the symbol of a chloride ion ($_{17}Cl^-$) represents the assumption that a chlorine nucleus controls 18 electrons in KCl. Although the electrons are packed tightly around potassium nuclei in potassium chloride, the evidence indicates that each potassium nucleus controls only 18 of the 36 electrons and that each chlorine nucleus controls the other 18 electrons.

In Fig. 12-5, the planes labeled b contain only potassium nuclei while the planes labeled c contain only chlorine nuclei. So far as nuclei are concerned, the two planes b and c in Fig. 12-5 correspond to the b and and c planes in Fig. 12-4a. However, the x-ray measurements show that in a crystal of KCl, represented in Fig. 12-5, both the b and c

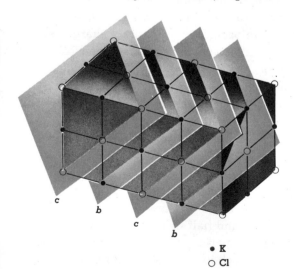

c
b

c
b

● K
○ Cl

Fig. 12-5 *Diagram of a potassium chloride crystal lattice showing b and c planes.*

planes contain ions with the same number of electrons (18) per nucleus. So far as electrons are concerned, the two planes b and c in Fig. 12-5 are identical and correspond to the d planes in Fig. 12-4b. The assumption that ions are present in ionic solids effectively accounts for the x-ray interference patterns observed in crystals of potassium chloride.

In the ionic compounds sodium fluoride and rubidium bromide, the positive ions (called **cations**) and the negative ions (called **anions**) contain the same number of electrons. X-ray interference measurements indicate that solid NaF, solid RbBr, and also solid LiH are each made up of structural units containing identical numbers of electrons. Except for the compound BeF_2, all the alkali metal halides and all the alkaline-earth halides have properties similar to those of the alkali metal chlorides and alkaline-earth metal chlorides. Hence it is reasonable to call them ionic compounds.

Ex. 12-2   *a.* Compare the molar volume of sodium metal (density = 0.97 g/ml) with the molar volume of sodium fluoride (density = 2.47 g/ml).

b. Compare the electron density (number of electrons per milliliter) for sodium metal and for sodium fluoride crystals.

12-5 PACKING OF IONS IN CRYSTALS

Because the structural units in ionic compounds are electrically charged, one of the major factors to be considered in devising a model for the arrangement of ions in ionic crystals is the electrostatic force described by Coulomb's law. A vast collection of spherical ions is difficult to analyze. To simplify the consideration of Coulomb's law, it is reasonable to assume that the packing of oppositely charged spherical ions will be determined exclusively by the attractions of unlike charges and the repulsions of like charges. Within a crystal, all the ions of each type are assumed to have the same size. Furthermore, the charge on each ion can be considered to be located at the center of the sphere. The arrangement of ions which will yield the lowest total energy is the most stable. The total assembly of ions must be electrically neutral. In other words, the total positive charge on all the positive ions must equal the total negative charge on all the negative ions. The simplest system which satisfies this requirement is one in which the charges on the ions are all of the same magnitude, with half of the spheres positively charged and half of them negatively charged.

The total energy consists of two parts, a kinetic energy and a potential energy. The assumption that each ion is a sphere of fixed size means that the kinetic energy is the same in all arrangements. Only the potential energy will be different in the different arrangements of ions.

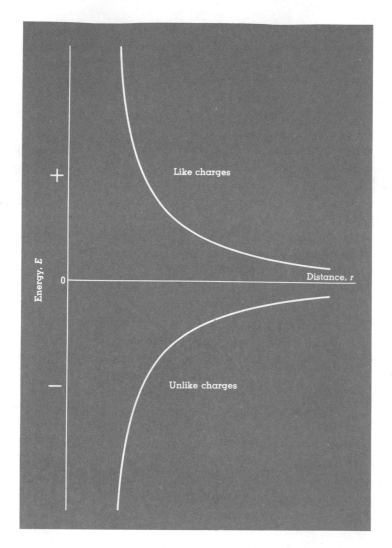

Fig. 12-6   *Relation of electric potential energy to distance of separation of like and unlike charges.*

The most stable of all possible arrangements will be the one with the lowest potential energy.

The potential energy of an assembly of charged spheres is proportional to the sum of the potential energies for pairs of charges. Arrangements in which unlike charges are close together have low potential energy, whereas arrangements in which like charges are close together have high potential energy (Fig. 12-6). Thus in arrangements with low potential energy, each ion will have nearest neighbors of the opposite charge. Does this mean that closest-packed structures of ions will give structures with lowest energy?

12-6 CESIUM CHLORIDE CRYSTAL STRUCTURE

In closest-packed structures, the coordination number is 12. Is it possible to produce a model for ionic crystals in which equal numbers of positive and negative ions are arranged in a close-packed structure with a coordination number of 12 and in which all the nearest neighbors are ions of opposite charge? Figure 12-7 shows a positively charged central ion surrounded by 12 negatively charged ions. The central positive ion is effectively prevented from ever touching another positive ion by its immediate contact with 12 negative ions. However, in this type of structure, each one of the negative ions is in contact with four other negatively charged ions. The lowering of energy by having each ion surrounded by 12 ions of opposite charge is offset by the increase in energy caused by placing ions of like charge in contact. A closest-packed arrangement of equal numbers of oppositely charged ions, then, is not likely to be a stable structure. No salts have ever been found with crystals corresponding to a closest-packed arrangement.

Metals form crystals with body-centered cubic lattices as well as closest-packed lattices. If the body-centered cubic lattice is applied to a system of ions, a positive ion can be surrounded by eight negatively charged nearest neighbors arranged as shown in Fig. 12-8. This model can be extended into a three-dimensional structure. Not only is each positively charged ion surrounded by eight negatively charged ions, but also each negatively charged ion is surrounded by eight positively charged ions. In the body-centered cubic crystal, each type of charged ion is separated from the other type so the electric potential energy of such an arrangement is low. Therefore, the body-centered cubic lattice appears to be a possible low-energy pattern in which to arrange equal numbers of oppositely charged ions.

X-ray interference measurements indicate that a number of ionic

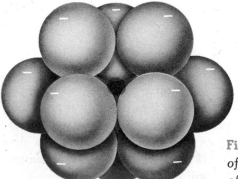

Fig. 12-7 *An improbable way of arranging ions in a crystal of a compound such as cesium chloride.*

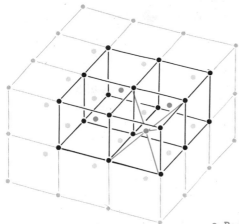

Fig. 12-8 *Cesium chloride lattice. Each ion has eight oppositely charged nearest neighbors.*

● Positive ion

Negative ion

compounds do, in fact, form crystals with body-centered cubic lattices. Cesium chloride is one of these compounds. A crystal that has a body-centered cubic lattice in which there are equal numbers of positive and negative ions is said to have a cesium chloride lattice. Table 12-3 lists some compounds that form crystals with the cesium chloride lattice.

12-7 SODIUM CHLORIDE CRYSTAL STRUCTURE

The first step in setting up another possible arrangement of equal numbers of oppositely charged ions is to start with a row of alternating positive and negative ions (Fig. 12-9a). This linear arrangement guarantees the separation of ions having charges of the same type. Extension of this linear arrangement in two dimensions results in a planar arrangement as shown in Fig. 12-9b. Stacking a number of planar arrangements of ions so that the nearest neighbors of each ion have the opposite electric charge produces the arrangement shown in Fig. 12-9c. Because sodium chloride forms crystals with a lattice like that shown in Fig. 12-9c, this lattice is called the sodium chloride lattice.

In the crystal lattice of sodium chloride, each ion has six nearest neighbors of opposite electric charge. These nearest-neighbor ions lie at the six corners of a regular octahedron which encloses a central ion (an octahedron has eight faces but six vertices). This octahedral ar-

TABLE 12-3 COMPOUNDS WITH CESIUM CHLORIDE LATTICES

CsCl	TlCl
CsBr	TlBr
CsI	TlI

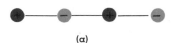

(a)

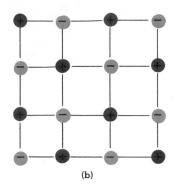

(b)

Fig. 12-9 *Sodium chloride crystal lattice. A row of alternating ions are shown in (a), one layer of the lattice in (b), and the three-dimensional lattice in (c). In (c), each ion is surrounded by six ions of opposite charge arranged in an octahedral pattern.*

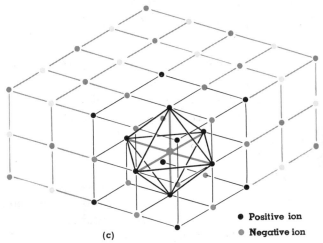

● Positive ion
● Negative ion

(c)

rangement is shown in Fig. 12-9c. The number of nearest neighbors (coordination number) of the central ion in the sodium chloride lattice is 6. On the other hand, the coordination number of the cesium chloride lattice is 8. Table 12-4 lists some compounds which form crystals with the sodium chloride lattice.

Two crystal lattices, one characteristic of sodium chloride and the other of cesium chloride, describe the crystals of all the alkali metal halides. In addition the sodium chloride lattice describes the crystals of all the alkaline-earth oxides and sulfides.

TABLE 12-4 COMPOUNDS WITH SODIUM CHLORIDE LATTICES

LiH	NaF	KF	RbF	AgF	MgO	MgS
LiF	NaCl	KCl	RbCl	AgCl	CaO	CaS
LiCl	NaBr	KBr	RbBr	AgBr	SrO	SrS
LiBr	NaI	KI	RbI		BaO	BaS
LiI			CsF		CdO	PbS

12-8 CLEAVAGE IN AN IONIC CRYSTAL

Does the model for the sodium chloride lattice provide a useful basis for interpreting the observation that salts are hard and brittle?

The ions making up an ionic crystal are held together by strong attractive forces that run through the entire crystal. This explains why an ionic crystal resists deformation. If the force exerted on a crystal becomes sufficiently large, one part of the crystal will shift relative to another part along a plane as shown in Fig. 12-10. If one part of the crystal moves far enough to place ions of like charge type opposite one another all along that plane, the crystal will break. Since there is no evidence that the electrons in ionic crystals are delocalized, a redistribution of electrons to relieve the repulsion between the two shifted parts of the crystal, as in the case of metal crystals, is impossible. Consequently, the crystal breaks or cleaves because of repulsion between like charges. Thus the models for metal crystals and ionic crystals can be used to explain the observed differences in the responses of metals and ionic compounds to deformation.

The planes in which a crystal cleaves intersect at angles characteristic of each type of crystal lattice. This implies that a crystal cleaves more easily along some planes than along others. On the basis of electrostatic principles, it is reasonable to expect cleavage to occur in such a way that separation of crystal fragments would not result in separation of electric charge. In other words cleavage is unlikely to occur so

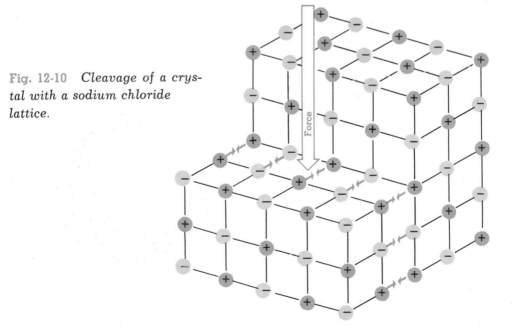

Fig. 12-10   *Cleavage of a crystal with a sodium chloride lattice.*

that it separates planes of opposite charge type, for example, the b and c planes as shown in Fig. 12-5. It is more likely that cleavage will occur so that the face of each fragment is neutral. Consequently, the two new faces formed by cleavage planes should be composed of a pattern of alternating positive and negative ions as in Fig. 12-9b instead of two faces of unlike charge—one made up of only positive ions and the other made up of negative ions.

12-9 UNIT CELLS IN AN IONIC CRYSTAL

Unit cells can be defined for the lattice arrangements of ions in ionic crystals. Figure 12-11a shows a diagram of the unit cell in the sodium chloride lattice, and Fig. 12-11b shows the unit cell in the cesium chloride lattice. There is a similarity between the unit cell of the

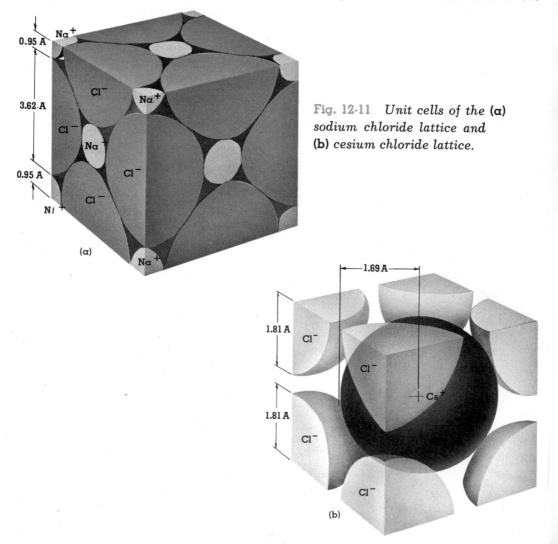

Fig. 12-11   Unit cells of the (a) sodium chloride lattice and (b) cesium chloride lattice.

sodium chloride lattice and the unit cell of the face-centered cubic lattice for metal crystals. The visible difference between Figs. 11-8a and 12-11a is that in metal crystals all structural units are identical whereas in ionic crystals there are two types of structural units. The sodium chloride lattice can be viewed as a structure made up of two interlocking face-centered cubic lattices. If only the Na^+ ions are considered in the diagram in Fig. 12-11a, their arrangement in a face-centered cubic structure is apparent. A similar diagram can be drawn, showing the Cl^- ions at the corners of a unit cell.

The unit cell of the cesium chloride lattice is similar to the unit cell of the body-centered cubic lattice for metals. In Fig. 12-11b, the cesium ion may be imagined as the body-centered atom caged in by eight chloride ions.

The sodium chloride and cesium chloride lattices are suitable models only for ionic compounds in which there are equal numbers of ions. The fact that crystalline ionic compounds with formulas such as $MgCl_2$ and $CaCl_2$ exist indicates that there are stable lattices in which unequal numbers of oppositely charged ions can be arranged. The geometrical and electrostatic features of the lattices of compounds such as $MgCl_2$ and $CaCl_2$ are more complex than are those of the sodium chloride or cesium chloride lattices.

Ex. 12-3 Refer to Fig. 12-11a and b. How many ions of each type make up the unit cell in the sodium chloride lattice? the unit cell in the cesium chloride lattice?

Ex. 12-4 What is the coordination number for an ion in the NaCl lattice? in the CsCl lattice? in most metallic crystal lattices?

12-10 IONIC CHARGES

In the ionic compounds formed by the alkali metals (group I) and alkaline-earth metals (group II) with the halogens (group VII), all the elements in a single group form ions with the same electric charge.

$$2K + Br_2 \rightarrow 2K^+Br^- \qquad \text{(Eq. 12-7)}$$

$$Mg + Cl_2 \rightarrow Mg^{++}(Cl^-)_2 \qquad \text{(Eq. 12-8)}$$

The superscript $+$ and $-$ signs indicate the type and magnitude of charge on the ions.

The compounds formed when magnesium combines with oxygen or with sulfur have the formulas MgO and MgS, respectively. Each of these compounds forms crystals with the sodium chloride crystal lattice (Table 12-4). If a magnesium ion has twice the charge of a potassium ion, then oxygen and sulfur must form ions with twice the charge of the chloride ion. The oxide ion is written as O^{--} and the sulfide ion as S^{--}.

A possible generalization then is that group I elements give ions with charge 1+, group II elements give ions with charge 2+, group VII elements give ions with charge 1−, and group VI elements give ions with charge 2−. On the basis of these generalizations, the reactions described by Equations 12-9 and 12-10 would be predicted.

$$2Sr + O_2 \rightarrow 2Sr^{++}O^{--} \qquad\qquad (Eq.\ 12\text{-}9)$$

$$2Na + S \rightarrow (Na^+)_2S^{--} \qquad\qquad (Eq.\ 12\text{-}10)$$

Compounds that have the formulas SrO and Na_2S have, in fact, been isolated. Thus, from a knowledge of the periodic table and of the compositions of some compounds, it is possible to predict the compositions of other compounds by assuming that all elements in a group always form ions of the same charge. Predictions based on the periodic table must be verified by experiment, however, before reliance is placed on them. Why do the charges on ions seem to be related to the position of the elements in the periodic table?

The formulas of ionic compounds give the relative numbers of ions in crystals of the compounds. Because compounds are electrically neutral, the formulas also give the relative magnitudes of the charges on the ions in the compound. For example, the ratio of the charges on the ions is 1:1 in CsCl, 2:1 in $CaCl_2$, and 1:2 in Na_2S. The formula does not give the magnitudes of the charges on the individual ions since it gives the same charge ratio for MgO as for CsCl, 1:1.

An isolated halogen atom has seven outer electrons. According to the charge cloud model, a halogen atom has three two-electron charge clouds and one one-electron charge cloud with the four clouds arranged around a kernel. According to the orbital model, a halogen atom has an outer electronic configuration of $s^2p_x^2p_y^2p_z^1$. If one more electron is transferred to a halogen atom, the resulting ion has eight outer electrons. In the charge cloud model the outer electrons in the chloride ion are represented by four two-electron clouds, and in the atomic orbital model by the electronic configuration of $s^2p_x^2p_y^2p_z^2$. This electronic configuration is identical with that of atoms of the elements in the noble gas family. The noble gases are quite unreactive, which implies that they have little tendency to attract more electrons from other elements (Section 10-15). It is unlikely, therefore, that the halide ion with one less proton than the nucleus of the neighboring noble gas would be able to attract additional electrons. If one electron is added to a chlorine atom to make a chloride ion, the charge on a chloride ion (Cl^-) is equal to the charge of one electron, or 1.60×10^{-19} coulomb.

The charge on an alkali metal ion in an alkali halide crystal must be positive, but equal in magnitude to the charge of one electron, 1.60×10^{-19} coulomb. A single positive charge for the potassium ion is consistent with predictions based on the charge cloud models for the atoms of each of the alkali metals. Each alkali metal atom has a one-electron charge cloud outside the kernel of the atom. In the atomic orbital model, the single outer electron of an alkali metal atom would be designated s^1. Loss of this electron by an atom forms an ion with a positive charge of 1.60×10^{-19} coulomb. The alkali metal ions also have the electronic configuration of a noble gas. Thus the sodium ion (Na^+) has the same electronic configuration as neon, $1s^2 2s^2 2p^6$. Since noble gas atoms have little tendency to lose electrons to other elements, and since the nuclear charge of an alkali metal atom is larger than on the neighboring noble gas, it is not reasonable to expect that an alkali metal atom would lose more than one electron.

Ionization energies for the elements are based on the energy required to form ions by the removal of electrons. In Fig. 12-12 ionization energies are plotted for some of the elements in groups I, II, and VII. These ionization energies show that relatively little energy is required to remove a single electron from an atom of the elements of group I, whereas much more energy is required to remove the second electron to form an ion with 2+ charge. Similarly two electrons can be removed readily from atoms of group II elements, but much more energy is required to remove a third electron. For elements in group VII the atoms actually go to a lower energy when one electron is transferred to each atom to form a negative ion, and the atoms must absorb considerable energy to ionize and form positive ions.

Ionic charges are periodic properties of the elements. Ionic charges are related to electronic configurations and to ionization energies of the elements. In each element the ionic charge represents the gain or loss of a single electron by an atom. The charge of an electron, then, is the unit of charge on ions. Thus the chloride ion has a charge of one negative unit, the sodium ion a charge of one positive unit, and the sulfide ion a charge of two negative units. The corresponding ionic formulas are Cl^-, Na^+, and S^{--}. Table 12-5 lists the formulas of some ionic compounds.

TABLE 12-5 FORMULAS OF SOME IONIC COMPOUNDS

$AgCl$	ZnF_2	PbF_4
$AgBr$	$SrBr_2$	Mg_3N_2
ZnO	Na_2S	Ca_3P_2
CdS	PbO_2	BaI_2

ENTHALPY DIAGRAM

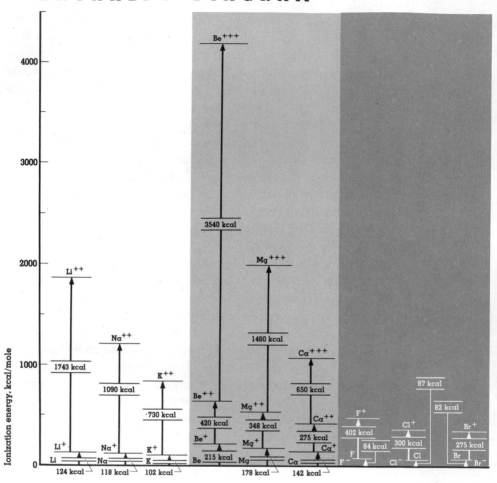

Fig. 12-12 *Ionization energies for some atoms and ions.*

Ex. 12-5 Write equations representing the reactions between the following pairs of elements: barium and oxygen, lithium and oxygen, beryllium and fluorine. Indicate the charges of the ions in the products.

12-11 ELECTRONEGATIVITY

The model for the structure of solid ionic compounds is based on the assumption that one or more electrons are transferred from one atom to another. On the other hand, the models for the structure of the hydrogen molecule are based on the assumption that two hydrogen nuclei each exert equal attractive forces on the pair of electrons in the covalent bond of the hydrogen molecule. Between complete electron transfer in an ionic bond and equal sharing of electrons in a covalent bond, there is a range of bond character in which the electrons are shared unequally by two nuclei. In other words, partial but not complete transfer of one or more electrons sometimes occurs. A situation in which electrons are shared unequally by two atoms can be explained on the basis that atoms of different elements differ in their tendency to attract electrons. A measure of the tendency for an atom of an element in a compound to attract electrons to itself is called the **electronegativity** of the element.

To form a qualitative picture of the meaning of electronegativity, suppose that we consider a pair of atoms, A and B, which do form a bond when they are situated a bond length apart and when two electrons (a single bond) are between them. There are three different possible positions for the two electrons.

$$A^+ \quad :B^- \qquad\qquad A \ : \ B \qquad\qquad A : B$$

$$1 \qquad\qquad\qquad\qquad 2 \qquad\qquad\qquad\qquad 3$$

1. Both electrons might be in an orbital of atom B to form a negative ion B^- and a positive ion A^+. This position of the electrons implies that B has a greater attraction for electrons than does A. The bond between A and B is an **ionic bond.** In this case, the electronegativity of element B is greater than the electronegativity of element A.

2. The two electrons might be halfway between the nuclei of the two atoms. This position of the electrons implies that A and B exert equal attraction for electrons. The bond between A and B is a **nonpolar covalent bond.** In this case, the electronegativities of A and B are equal.

3. The two electrons might be somewhat closer to A than to B. This position of the electrons implies that A has a somewhat greater attraction for electrons than does B. However, the difference is not sufficient to form negative and positive ions. The bond between A and B is a **polar covalent bond.** In this case, the electronegativity of element A is somewhat greater than that of element B, but the difference is not so great as in case 1.

These three cases suggest that ionization energies might be related to electronegativities. Ionization energies are a measure of the energy absorbed when an electron is removed from an isolated atom. The ion formed by the loss of an electron must have an attraction for an electron which is equal to the ionization energy. Electronegativity is not the same as ionization energy. Electronegativity describes the attraction for electrons exerted by a neutral atom in a compound, whereas ionization energy describes the attraction for electrons of an isolated ion.

For a single family in the periodic table, atoms with a small number of occupied orbitals will attract electrons more strongly than atoms with a large number of occupied orbitals. On this basis, small atoms have larger electronegativities than large atoms. Similarly, the magnitudes of the electronegativities of atoms of about the same size (for example, carbon and nitrogen) should be related to the nuclear charges of the atoms. Chlorine, in group VII, will have a higher electronegativity than sulfur, in group VI, in the same row of the periodic table. In other words, atoms with small radii have high electronegativities, and atoms of about the same size with larger nuclear charge have higher electronegativities. Since the atomic radius is a periodic property of the elements, it is reasonable to expect that electronegativity is a periodic property also. The dependence of electronegativity on atomic radius and nuclear charge leads to the prediction that the electronegativities of the elements will be higher in the upper right of the periodic table than in the lower left.

An approximate measure of the electronegativity of an atom in a compound would be an average of the quantity of energy required to remove one electron from an isolated atom (ionization energy) and the quantity of energy required to add an electron (called the **electron affinity**) to the isolated atom. Unfortunately, the electron affinities of elements are difficult to determine experimentally. Therefore, the averaging of ionization energies and electron affinities has not been very useful. Enthalpies of formation can be used to calculate a consistent set of numerical values for relative electronegativities of the elements (Fig. 12-13).

As an example of the reasoning used in calculating electronegativities, hydrogen iodide and hydrogen chloride can be compared. Data on enthalpies of formation can be used to calculate bond energies in HI and HCl. Because the atomic radii and nuclear charges of identical atoms are equal, it is assumed that bonds in hydrogen molecules and iodine molecules are nonpolar covalent. Therefore, if the bond in the hydrogen iodide molecule is also nonpolar covalent, the bond energy for HI should be the average of the bond energies for H_2 and I_2.

In the case of HI, the bond energy (71.4 kcal/mole) is almost identical with the average of the bond energies for H_2 (104.2 kcal/mole) and I_2 (36.1 kcal/mole); that is, $(104.2 + 36.1)/2 = 70.1$. This suggests that there is little difference between the electronegativities of hydrogen and iodine. In the case of HCl, the bond energy (103.0 kcal/mole) is found not to be the average of the bond energies of H_2 (104.2 kcal/mole) and Cl_2 (57.8 kcal/mole); that is, $(104.2 + 57.8)/2 = 81$. The difference between the bond energy of HCl and the average of the bond energies of H_2 and Cl_2 is used in the calculation of the difference between the electronegativities of H and Cl. The larger the difference in

Fig. 12-13   Periodic relationships for the electronegativities of elements.

the two bond energies, the greater will be the difference in electro-negativities. The fact that the bond in hydrogen chloride is polar co-valent (that is, the electrons in the bond are closer to the Cl atom than to the H atom) is consistent with the conclusion in Section 8-17 that hydrogen chloride molecules are dipoles.

For convenience, differences in electronegativities have been ex-pressed as numbers between 0 and 4. Hydrogen, chosen as the refer-ence standard, is assigned an electronegativity of 2.1. Calculations show that hydrogen and fluorine differ in electronegativity by 1.9. Ex-perimental evidence indicates that fluorine has a greater attraction for electrons than does hydrogen. Thus, the electronegativity of fluorine becomes $2.1 + 1.9 = 4.0$.

Electronegativities for most of the elements were first worked out by Linus Pauling. In Fig. 12-13 the electronegativities are arranged on a periodic table pattern to show the periodicity of electronegativity.

Electronegativities can be used to estimate how the electrons in a bond are shared between two atoms in a molecule. Zero difference between the electronegativities of two elements in a compound implies that the electrons will be attracted equally by the two atoms to form a nonpolar covalent bond. If the difference between electronegativities is not zero, this means that the electrons are not attracted equally by the two atoms. This gives a polar covalent bond.

In Fig. 12-14 compounds have been plotted on a graph to show the difference between the electronegativities of the two elements in each compound. Six different classes of compounds have been included in the graph: fluorides, oxides, chlorides, bromides, iodides, and hydrides. These six classes of compounds are arranged in order of increasing difference in electronegativity along the horizontal axis of the graph. The compounds listed in the light green area of Fig. 12-14 have boiling points above 400°C, while the compounds listed in the dark green area have boiling points below 400°C.

If high boiling point is taken as one indication of the presence of ionic bonds in a compound, Fig. 12-14 indicates how the difference be-tween the electronegativities of two elements in a compound is related to the ionic character of the compound. A difference of about 1.7 in the electronegativities of two elements is often suggested as the divi-sion between the formation of covalent and ionic bonds when the two elements are in a compound. For chlorides and bromides the difference of 1.7 is in reasonable agreement with observed properties, but for hydrides and fluorides, 1.7 is not satisfactory.

Figure 12-14 suggests that electronegativity by itself is not an ade-quate criterion for predicting the bond type and properties of com-pounds. In most of the compounds which have low boiling points and

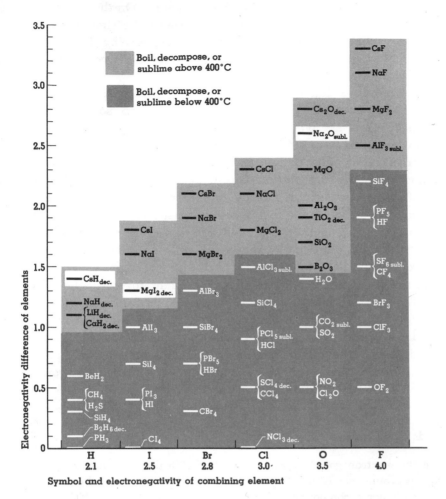

Fig. 12-14 *Formulas of various compounds arranged by electronega-tivity differences of the component elements. Substances that sublime or decompose instead of boil are indicated by* subl. *or* dec. *Data for the phase transformations of CsH, MgI₂, and Na₂O are not available.*

which are listed in Fig. 12-14, several atoms are joined to one central atom.

For the two compounds sodium iodide (NaI) and sulfur hexafluoride (SF₆), the differences between the electronegativities of the component elements are nearly the same. These differences are 1.6 for sodium and iodine and 1.5 for sulfur and fluorine. Sodium iodide is soluble in water, gives an ionic solution, and boils at 1300°C; whereas sulfur hexafluoride is insoluble in water and sublimes at −63.7°C. In terms of properties, therefore, sodium iodide is an ionic compound while sulfur hexafluoride is a covalent compound. On the other hand, electronegativities suggest that the bonds should be similar in character in sodium iodide and in sulfur hexafluoride. Why do classification by properties and classification by electronegativity come to different conclusions?

In the sodium iodide crystal, each sodium ion is surrounded by six iodide ions and each iodide ion is surrounded by six sodium ions. If an octahedron of six iodide ions around one sodium ion is considered, the cluster would have a net charge of 5— and consequently a powerful attraction for other sodium ions. In sulfur hexafluoride, however, six fluorine atoms surround one sulfur atom to form a neutral molecule. The zero net charge and the symmetry of the octahedral SF_6 molecule together with the high electron density of the fluorine atoms make interaction slight between sulfur atoms in different molecules. These structural differences can account for the difference between the properties of NaI and SF_6.

When sodium and iodine atoms are brought together, they form ions. The ions attract each other to form crystals. Sulfur and fluorine atoms may also form ionic bonds within SF_6 molecules, but whether they do or not, neutral and geometrically symmetrical molecules are formed which have little attraction for each other. It appears that geometrical and electrical symmetry is more important than electronegativity in determining the properties of the SF_6 molecule.

Ex. 12-6 Assuming ionic bonding, assign charges to each ion in each of the compounds listed in Table 12-5.

Ex. 12-7 From the electronegativities in Fig. 12-13, divide the following compounds into two groups, one of predominantly covalent compounds and one of predominantly ionic compounds: $CaCl_2$, PCl_3, RbF, CCl_4, BCl_3, MgO, BeH_2, H_2O, and HBr.

Ex. 12-8 What electronegativity corresponds to the point of separation of the elements into a metallic group and a nonmetallic group?

Ex. 12-9 Compare the experimentally determined bond energies of the compounds HF, HCl, HBr, and HI with the average of the bond energies calculated from the elements which form these compounds. On the basis of the differences between these two bond energies, list the elements fluorine, chlorine, bromine, and iodine in order of increasing electronegativity. Use the following bond energies: H—F 134.6 kcal, H—Cl 103.0 kcal, H—Br 87.4 kcal, H—I 71.4 kcal, F—F 36.6 kcal, Cl—Cl 57.8 kcal, Br—Br 46.1 kcal, I—I 36.1 kcal, H—H 104.2 kcal.

12-12 ATOMIC, IONIC, AND COVALENT RADII

Ionic crystals contain not only metal atoms which have lost one or more electrons but also other atoms which have an excess of electrons and which are therefore negatively charged. The positive metal ion cannot be the same size as the neutral metal atom, from which it comes (Section 12-4). If the atoms of metals are assumed to be spherical (Section 11-14), a radius can be calculated for each atom in the metallic crystal by knowing the density of the metal, the nature of the unit cell, and the number of atoms in the unit cell. Numerical values for radii calculated in this way show a periodicity similar to that observed for other properties of the elements (Fig. 11-9). The computation of radii for metals is based on the fact that only one kind of atom is present in a crystal and on the fact that the metals form closest-packed structures.

In ionic crystals, in which there are at least two different elements, a closest-packed structure is not likely because of the charges on the ions. Therefore, the calculation of a set of consistent radii for the ions in an ionic compound is more difficult than the calculation of a radius for an atom in a set of identical atoms. X-ray interference measurements provide the distances between the nuclei of adjacent ions. For example, the internuclear distance in a KBr crystal is 3.29 A. There is no direct experimental way of establishing how much of this distance should be assigned to the radius of the potassium ion and how much to the radius of the bromide ion.

Suppose that the distance between the nuclei of adjacent ions could be divided properly between the two ions to calculate a radius for a potassium ion in potassium bromide, for example. Would it be possible to assume that the radius of the potassium is the same in all potassium compounds? Does a potassium ion have a radius that is independent of the nature of other ions present? The question may be answered by comparing data for several potassium halides with data for the corresponding compounds of sodium (Table 12-6). The difference between

TABLE 12-6   INTERNUCLEAR DISTANCES IN SOME COMPOUNDS OF POTASSIUM AND SODIUM

Compound	Internuclear Distance, A	Difference between Internuclear Distances, A
KF	2.67	0.36
NaF	2.31	
KCl	3.14	0.33
NaCl	2.81	
KBr	3.29	0.31
NaBr	2.98	

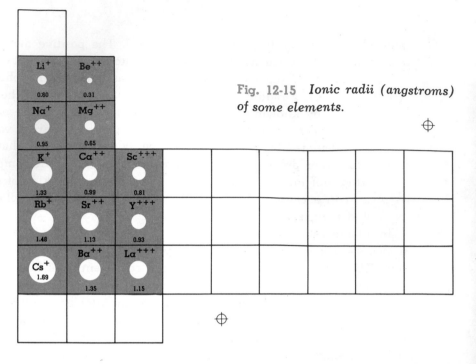

Fig. 12-15 *Ionic radii (angstroms) of some elements.*

the internuclear distance in KF and NaF is nearly the same as the corresponding difference between KCl and NaCl. This indicates that the difference between the radii of the potassium ion and the sodium ion is nearly the same whether the positive ions are associated with fluoride or chloride ions. Other similar comparisons suggest that the radius of an ion is nearly, although not exactly, the same from compound to compound.

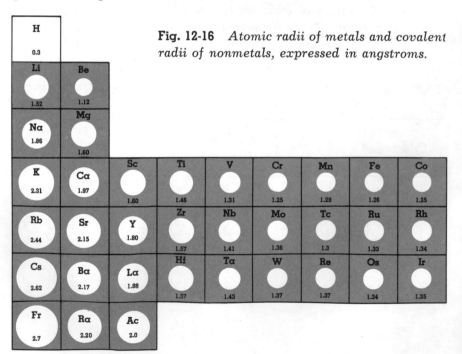

Fig. 12-16 *Atomic radii of metals and covalent radii of nonmetals, expressed in angstroms.*

						O⁻⁻ 1.40	F⁻ 1.36	
			Al⁺⁺⁺ 0.50			S⁻⁻ 1.84	Cl⁻ 1.81	
	Cu⁺ 0.96	Zn⁺⁺ 0.74	Ga⁺⁺⁺ 0.62	Ge⁺⁺⁺⁺ 0.53		Se⁻⁻ 1.98	Br⁻ 1.95	
	Ag⁺ 1.26	Cd⁺⁺ 0.97	In⁺⁺⁺ 0.81	Sn⁺⁺⁺⁺ 0.71		Te⁻⁻ 2.21	I⁻ 2.16	
	Au⁺ 1.37	Hg⁺⁺ 1.10	Tl⁺⁺⁺ 0.95	Pb⁺⁺⁺⁺ 0.84				

Several calculations of ionic radii have been made. Linus Pauling has used a theory of atomic structure to compute the ionic radii of sodium and fluoride ions in sodium fluoride. He calculated a radius of 0.95 A for the sodium ion and 1.36 A for the fluoride ion. On the basis that these two radii are established by the theory, other ionic radii can be calculated from measured distances between nuclei. Figure 12-15 lists ionic radii calculated for some positive and negative ions.

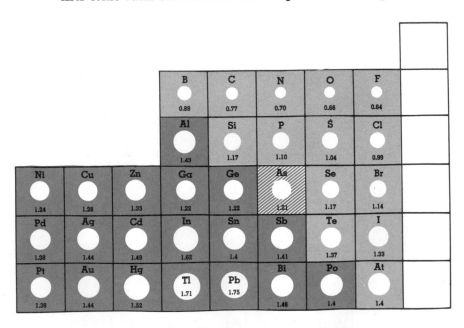

 Atomic radii   Covalent radii

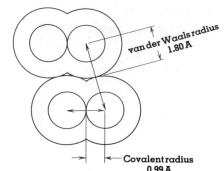

Fig. 12-17 *Comparison of covalent radius with van der Waals, or collision, radius for chlorine.*

A measure of the distance between two identical nuclei can be used to calculate radii for the atoms whose nuclei are involved. In a diatomic molecule the internuclear distance is called the bond length (Section 7-21). Thus in a hydrogen molecule the bond length is 0.74 A. If this bond length is divided by 2, the result (0.37) can be considered to be the radius of a hydrogen atom. The two hydrogen atoms in a hydrogen molecule are joined by a covalent bond so that the radius of 0.37 A just calculated is called the covalent radius for hydrogen. For any covalently bonded diatomic molecule consisting of identical atoms, the internuclear distance divided by 2 is called the **covalent radius.** Covalent radii of the atoms of the nonmetals are listed in Fig. 12-16. Covalent radii for two different atoms joined by a covalent bond can be added to give internuclear distances that agree fairly well with experimentally determined bond lengths. If the covalent radius of hydro-

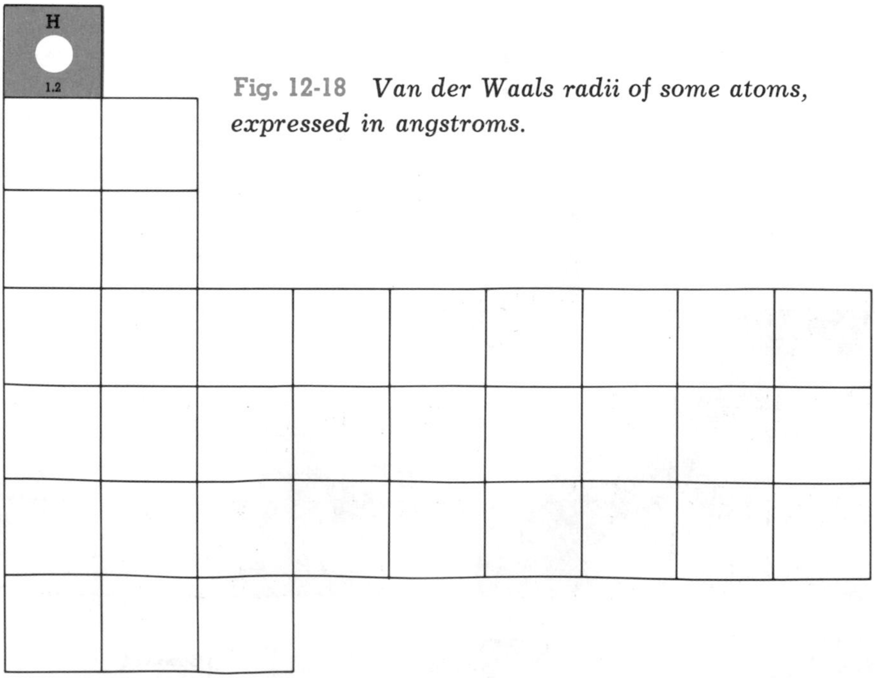

Fig. 12-18 *Van der Waals radii of some atoms, expressed in angstroms.*

gen (0.37 A) is added to the covalent radius of chlorine (0.99 A), the result is 1.36 A, which compares roughly with the experimentally measured bond length of 1.27 A for the hydrogen–chlorine bond in HCl. In carbon compounds, the addition of covalent radii gives bond lengths that agree with measured internuclear distances to within a few hundredths of an angstrom. Atomic radii calculated from data on metal crystals as described in Section 11-14 are also listed in Fig. 12-16.

Calculations show that a chloride ion has an ionic radius of 1.81 A in comparison with the covalent radius of 0.99 A for a chlorine atom. A sodium atom has an atomic radius of 1.86 A, and a sodium ion has an ionic radius of 0.95 A. Each radius reflects the particular definition used as a basis for calculations.

One other radius may be defined for interpreting the closest distance of approach of two molecules. It is sometimes called the collision radius. Two chlorine atoms joined in a molecule are separated by an internuclear distance of 1.98 A, or twice the covalent radius of a chlorine atom. But two chlorine atoms, each in different molecules, cannot approach each other nearly as closely because all the outer orbitals of the chlorine atoms are filled with electrons (Fig. 12-17). When two chlorine molecules are in contact, the distance between nuclei of atoms in separate molecules is 3.60 A. For atoms in contact but not joined by bonds, one-half the internuclear distance is called the *van der Waals radius* (or *collision radius*). A chlorine atom has a van der Waals radius of 1.80 A. The van der Waals radius for a chlorine atom is nearly the same as the radius for a chloride ion. Van der Waals radii for some atoms are listed in Fig. 12-18. Some covalent

					He
			N 1.5	O 1.4	F 1.35	Ne 1.60
			P 1.9	S 1.85	Cl 1.80	Ar 1.92
			As 2.0	Se 2.0	Br 1.95	Kr 1.97
			Sb 2.2	Te 2.2	I 2.15	Xe 2.17
						Rn

TABLE 12-7 **COVALENT AND VAN DER WAALS RADII OF SOME ATOMS**

Atom	Covalent Radius, A	Van der Waals Radius, A
H	0.37	1.2
He		0.93
O	0.66	1.40
F	0.64	1.35
Ne		1.60
S	1.04	1.85
Cl	0.99	1.80
Br	1.11	1.95
I	1.28	2.15

and van der Waals radii are compared in Table 12-7. The covalent radii for helium and neon are omitted from Table 12-7 since covalent radius has no meaning for the elements that do not form di- or poly-atomic molecules.

Ex. 12-10 Using the data in Fig. 12–16, calculate the bond lengths for the bonds in the following compounds: CCl_4, SiO_2, NCl_3, PBr_3, CH_4, and H_2S.

12-13 COMPARISON OF RADII

Four different kinds of radii have been defined: atomic, ionic, covalent, and van der Waals. The definitions of and numerical values for the different kinds of radii of some ions and atoms have been discussed in the previous section. But why does an atom not have a radius with a single value rather than several different radii?

Each different kind of radius for an atom has a numerical value that is calculated from experimental data as interpreted by the definition of the particular kind of radius. Thus the atomic radius of sodium (1.86 A) is taken as one-half the internuclear distance for sodium atoms in a crystal of sodium metal with the assumption that the sodium atoms are in contact. On the other hand, the ionic radius of sodium (0.95 A) is calculated from the internuclear distance in a crystal of sodium chloride on the basis of Pauling's theory. A positive ion has fewer electrons than a neutral atom and is always found to have a shorter radius than the neutral atom from which it is derived.

The covalent radius of a chlorine atom (0.99 A) is calculated from measurements of the internuclear distance in a diatomic molecule of chlorine. Within the molecule it is assumed that the atoms overlap so that two electrons are shared by two atoms. A van der Waals radius

LINUS PAULING 1901–

*An American chemist born in Portland, Oregon. Pauling received his B.S.
degree from Oregon State College in 1922 and his Ph.D. from the California Institute of Technology in 1925. He has been associated with the
latter institution since 1922, becoming professor of chemistry in 1931.*

*A longtime friend of G. N. Lewis, Pauling had an interest in the properties
of the chemical bond from the time he read Lewis's 1916 paper
on the concept of the chemical bond as a pair of shared electrons. The
title of one of Pauling's books,* The Nature of the Chemical Bond, *aptly
describes the central focus of almost all his research. He has determined crystal structures by x-ray diffraction and the structures of gas
molecules by electron diffraction. He has studied the magnetic properties
of substances, including hemoglobin, and the role of abnormal hemoglobin molecules in causing human disease. His theoretical studies have
dealt with the application of quantum mechanics to the structure of
molecules and to the nature of chemical bonds, the development of the
concepts of electronegativity and of hybrid bonds, and the determination of
sets of consistent atomic, ionic, and covalent radii. He extended the
theory of the covalent bond to include metals and intermetallic compounds. He proposed a detailed helical structure for some protein molecules, such as those present in hair and muscle, and recently has devoted
much of his work to the application of chemical concepts to biological
and medical problems, including the causes and nature of mental deficiency.*

*Linus Pauling has for many years sought to mobilize scientists all over
the world in the cause of ending nuclear bomb tests and the nuclear
arms race. The recipient of numerous honors, Pauling was president of the
American Chemical Society in 1949 and received the Nobel Prize in 1954
for his research into the nature of the chemical bond and its application
to the elucidation of the structures of complex substances. In 1963,
Pauling received the Nobel Peace Prize.*

---

for chlorine (1.80 A) is calculated from the internuclear distance for
chlorine with two molecules in contact but not overlapping. A van der
Waals radius for an atom is always longer than a covalent radius for
the same atom.

For chlorine an ionic radius (1.81 A) can also be calculated from
internuclear distances in ionic crystals such as a sodium chloride
crystal. A chloride ion is assumed to have 18 electrons and to be in
contact with sodium ions but not overlapping. An ionic radius and a
van der Waals radius therefore are somewhat similar since both are
defined for atoms in contact but not overlapping.

The ionic radii given in Fig. 12-15 show that the radii of the ions of the elements in the alkali metal family increase from Li^+ to Cs^+. This increase would be predicted on the basis of the corresponding increase in the number of filled orbitals in the ions. A similar increase in ion size is noted in the other families of elements, corresponding to the increase in the number of filled orbitals in the ions. The atomic radii of the atoms of the elements in the alkali and alkaline-earth families are longer than the ionic radii of the corresponding ions. For example, the radius of the sodium ion is scarcely half that of the sodium atom, and the radius of the magnesium ion is less than half that of the magnesium atom.

$$
\begin{array}{lll}
& \text{Metal} & \text{Ion} \\
& Na \rightarrow & Na^+ + e^- \\
\text{Radii, A} & 1.86 & 0.95
\end{array}
\qquad (Eq.\ 12\text{-}11)
$$

$$
\begin{array}{lll}
& Mg \rightarrow & Mg^{++} + 2e^- \\
\text{Radii, A} & 1.60 & 0.65
\end{array}
\qquad (Eq.\ 12\text{-}12)
$$

The atomic radii decrease steadily from left to right for the elements in one row of the periodic table because of the increase in nuclear charge. Ionic radii of positive ions decrease across the periodic table from left to right. For negative ions the same trend occurs also. In general the negative ions in any period are considerably larger than any positive ions in the same period.

A consistent set of ionic radii makes it possible to look for correspondence between ionic sizes and lattice arrangement. For instance, is the fact that some ionic solids form crystals with the cesium chloride lattice whereas other salts form crystals with the sodium chloride lattice related to the radii of the ions involved?

When the ionic radii listed in Fig. 12-15 are studied for all the substances with a cesium chloride lattice (Table 12-3), it is evident that a large positive ion is characteristic of the compounds having the cesium chloride lattice. Cesium fluoride, unlike cesium chloride, forms crystals with the sodium chloride lattice. The presence of a large positive ion, then, is not sufficient information upon which to base a prediction that a substance will form crystals with a cesium chloride lattice.

Although the size of the positive ion by itself does not provide a sufficient basis for predicting the crystal lattice of a compound, the relative sizes of the two ions in the crystal do seem to be significant. For most of the ionic compounds which form crystals with the sodium chloride lattice, the positive ion is considerably smaller than the negative ion. For cesium chloride, however, the two ions are of approximately the same size (Cs^+, 1.69 A and Cl^-, 1.81 A), and cesium chloride with a radius ratio of 1.69/1.81 forms the cesium chloride type of crystal lattice. In the case of cesium fluoride the sizes of the two ions are markedly different. The radius ratio of 1.69/1.36 is considerably larger than that of CsCl, and cesium fluoride forms crystals having the sodium chloride lattice. This suggests that the radius ratio of the two ions in a crystal may be sufficient information on which to base a prediction of the lattice in which a particular compound forms crystals. If the radius ratio has a numerical value of about 1, the cesium chloride lattice provides the better packing; whereas if the radius ratio differs markedly from 1, the sodium chloride lattice provides better packing.

Ex. 12-11 From the charge cloud model for lithium, would you expect a lithium ion, Li^+, to be larger or smaller than a lithium atom, Li? Would you expect a fluoride ion, F^-, to be larger or smaller than a fluorine atom, F?

Ex. 12-12 On the basis of the atomic radius and the ionic radius for sodium, what fraction of the total volume of the sodium atom is available for the 3s electron? What fraction of the total volume for the magnesium atom is available for the two 3s electrons of magnesium?

12-15 CRYSTAL ENERGY

The model for the structure of ionic compounds has been developed to account for the characteristic melting points, boiling points, and crystal structures of ionic compounds. Can enthalpy of formation data for ionic compounds be successfully related to the structural model? Certainly any model of ionic crystals must be consistent with data for enthalpies of formation.

The change in enthalpy accompanying the formation of 1 mole of solid NaCl from sodium metal and gaseous chlorine is −98.2 kcal/mole.

$$Na\ (s) + \tfrac{1}{2}Cl_2\ (g) \rightarrow NaCl\ (s) \quad \Delta H = -98.2\ \text{kcal/mole} \quad (Exp.\ 12\text{-}13)$$

This numerical value is obtained by direct calorimetric measurement. Two different pathways might be postulated as alternative routes for the reaction of sodium metal and chlorine gas to form sodium chloride. In one, isolated gaseous atoms are first formed from the elements. In the other, isolated ions are first formed. Either set of isolated particles may then be considered to come together to form solid sodium chloride. Expressions 12-14 and 12-15 represent the two pathways.

$$Na\ (s) + \tfrac{1}{2}Cl_2\ (g) \rightarrow Na\ (g) + Cl\ (g) \rightarrow NaCl\ (s) \quad (Exp.\ 12\text{-}14)$$

$$Na\ (s) + \tfrac{1}{2}Cl_2\ (g) \rightarrow Na^+\ (g) + Cl^-\ (g) \rightarrow NaCl\ (s) \quad (Exp.\ 12\text{-}15)$$

For either pathway the total change in enthalpy when the composition of the system changes from reactants to product must be the same according to Hess's law; that is, $\Delta H = -98.2$ kcal/mole.

For the first of the two imaginary reaction pathways (Expression 12-14), the change in enthalpy for the reaction of gaseous sodium atoms with gaseous chlorine atoms can be calculated from the change in enthalpy accompanying the formation of the gaseous atoms from the elements. The enthalpy change for the conversion of sodium metal into gaseous sodium vapor is listed in Table 11-2. This enthalpy change is the sum of the heat of fusion and the heat of vaporization of sodium and corresponds to a heat of sublimation (Expression 12-16).

$$Na(s) \rightarrow Na(g) \qquad \Delta H = 26.0 \text{ kcal/mole of Na} \qquad (Exp.\ 12\text{-}16)$$

For chlorine, the enthalpy change accompanying the formation of 1 mole of gaseous atoms is the energy required to dissociate $\frac{1}{2}$ mole of Cl_2 molecules. In other words, it is one-half the enthalpy of dissociation listed for chlorine in Table 11-2.

$$\tfrac{1}{2}Cl_2(g) \rightarrow Cl(g) \qquad \Delta H = 28.9 \text{ kcal/mole of Cl} \qquad (Exp.\ 12\text{-}17)$$

To represent the production of solid sodium and of molecular chlorine from gaseous atoms, the two equations of Expressions 12-16 and 12-17 can be reversed and the algebraic sign changed for each enthalpy change. These operations give Expressions 12-18 and 12-19. These two expressions can now be added to Expression 12-13 for the formation of solid sodium chloride from the elements in their standard states.

$$Na(g) \rightarrow Na(s) \quad \Delta H = -26.0 \text{ kcal} \qquad (Exp.\ 12\text{-}18)$$

$$Cl(g) \rightarrow \tfrac{1}{2}Cl_2(g) \quad \Delta H = -28.9 \text{ kcal} \qquad (Exp.\ 12\text{-}19)$$

$$Na(s) + \tfrac{1}{2}Cl_2(g) \rightarrow NaCl(s) \quad \Delta H = -98.2 \text{ kcal} \qquad (Exp.\ 12\text{-}13)$$

$$\overline{Na(g) + Cl(g) \rightarrow NaCl(s) \quad \Delta H = -153.1 \text{ kcal} \qquad (Exp.\ 12\text{-}20)}$$

When 1 mole of gaseous sodium atoms reacts with 1 mole of chlorine atoms to form 1 mole of solid sodium chloride, the enthalpy change (heat evolved) is -153.1 kcal (Expression 12-20). The calculation of the result shown in Expression 12-20 is summarized in Fig. 12-19.

Expression 12-20 represents the formation of solid NaCl from its isolated atoms. The second pathway involving the formation of ions and their aggregation into solid sodium chloride offers a test of the ionic model. The second step of this pathway (Expression 12-15) is the formation of 1 mole of sodium chloride crystals from 1 mole of sodium ions and 1 mole of chloride ions.

Knowing the charges of two ions and their distance of separation, it is possible to calculate from Coulomb's law the electric potential energy of a pair of ions in the crystal relative to the electric potential energy when they are infinitely separated. A further calculation can be made to give the change in electric potential energy when the

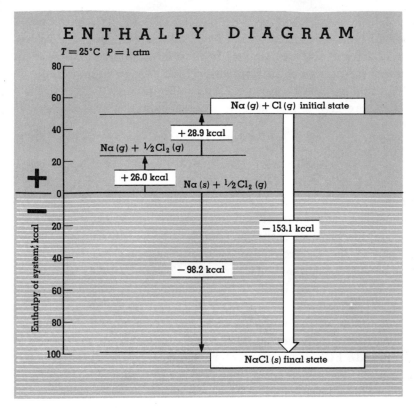

ENTHALPY DIAGRAM

$T = 25°C \quad P = 1 \text{ atm}$

Enthalpy of system, kcal

Na (g) + Cl (g) initial state

+28.9 kcal

Na (g) + ½ Cl₂ (g)

+26.0 kcal

Na (s) + ½ Cl₂ (g)

−153.1 kcal

−98.2 kcal

NaCl (s) final state

Fig. 12-19 *Enthalpy change for the formation of solid NaCl from Na (g) and Cl (g).*

gaseous ions form a crystal lattice in a mole of crystalline sodium chloride (Expression 12-21).

$$Na^+ (g) + Cl^- (g) \rightarrow NaCl (s) \quad \Delta H = -183.8 \text{ kcal/mole of NaCl}$$
$$(Exp. \ 12\text{-}21)$$

Does this decrease in electric potential energy determined from Coulomb's law and the crystal lattice agree with the decrease in enthalpy for the reaction of gaseous sodium ions and gaseous chloride ions calculated from calorimetric data? It is convenient to define the **crystal energy** or **lattice energy** as the energy needed to transform 1 mole of compound from the solid state to gaseous ions infinitely separated (Expression 12-22).

$$\text{Compound AB } (s) \rightarrow \text{ion } A^+ (g) + \text{ion } B^- (g)$$
$$\Delta H = \text{crystal energy} \quad (Exp. \ 12\text{-}22)$$

The question can then be phrased to ask whether experimental data do give a crystal energy for sodium chloride of 183.8 kcal/mole of NaCl.

A numerical value for the crystal energy of sodium chloride can be calculated from available data for related reactions. The enthalpy of formation of gaseous sodium atoms from solid sodium is given in Expression 12-16, and the enthalpy of formation of chlorine atoms from chlorine molecules is given in Expression 12-17. A determination of the change in enthalpy for the two reactions of Equations 12-23 and 12-24 should therefore give the remaining necessary data.

$$\text{Na } (g) \rightarrow \text{Na}^+ (g) + e^- \qquad (Eq.\ 12\text{-}23)$$

$$\text{Cl } (g) + e^- \rightarrow \text{Cl}^- (g) \qquad (Eq.\ 12\text{-}24)$$

The change in enthalpy for the reaction in Equation 12-23 is the first ionization energy of sodium. It is numerically equal to 118.0 kcal/mole (Expression 12-25). The enthalpy change involved in Equation 12-24 corresponds to the electron affinity of chlorine and has been determined to be -87.3 kcal/mole (Expression 12-26). Transfer of an electron to a chlorine atom leads to a lowering of the enthalpy of the system.

This knowledge of the enthalpy changes accompanying the formation of ions from atoms can be used to calculate the crystal energy of sodium chloride by the pathway of Expression 12-15. By adding Expressions 12-25, 12-26, and 12-27 (the reverse of Expression 12-20), we obtain Expression 12-28 which represents the crystal energy of sodium chloride.

$$\text{Na } (g) \rightarrow \text{Na}^+ (g) + e^- \quad \Delta H = 118.0 \text{ kcal} \qquad (Exp.\ 12\text{-}25)$$

$$\text{Cl } (g) + e^- \rightarrow \text{Cl}^- (g) \quad \Delta H = -87.3 \text{ kcal} \qquad (Exp.\ 12\text{-}26)$$

$$\underline{\text{NaCl } (s) \rightarrow \text{Na } (g) + \text{Cl } (g) \quad \Delta H = 153.1 \text{ kcal} \qquad (Exp.\ 12\text{-}27)}$$

$$\text{NaCl } (s) \rightarrow \text{Na}^+ (g) + \text{Cl}^- (g) \quad \Delta H = 183.8 \text{ kcal} \quad (Exp.\ 12\text{-}28)$$

Figure 12-20 is an enthalpy diagram which compares the two pathways for forming sodium chloride crystals as stated in Expressions 12-14 and 12-15. By either pathway the enthalpy of formation of NaCl has to be the experimental value of -98.2 kcal/mole of NaCl. In Fig. 12-20 the value of -183.8 kcal is the negative of the crystal energy given in Expression 12-28.

Direct measurement of the energy required to convert solid sodium chloride into gaseous ions would also yield an experimental value for the crystal energy. It has not proved possible, however, to vaporize sodium chloride to give only sodium ions and chloride ions. Because of the electric charges on the ions, they tend to stick together in aggregates containing several ions. To vaporize sodium chloride in such a way that the crystal energy can be obtained, it is necessary to know the identity and concentrations of all the gaseous species formed when sodium chloride is heated. Measurements have been made, in spite of the difficulties, to give a change in enthalpy of 181 kcal/mole of NaCl, within 2 percent of the numerical value of 183.8 kcal/mole of NaCl that was calculated in Expression 12-28.

In establishing this consistency between the ionic structural model and observed energy changes, Hess's law has been used. The reactions and associated enthalpy changes by which the crystal energy of an ionic crystal is calculated from experimental enthalpy data is called a Born-Haber cycle. The cycle for sodium chloride can be represented

Fig. 12-20 *Enthalpy change for formation of NaCl (s) from Na⁺ (g) and Cl⁻ (g).*

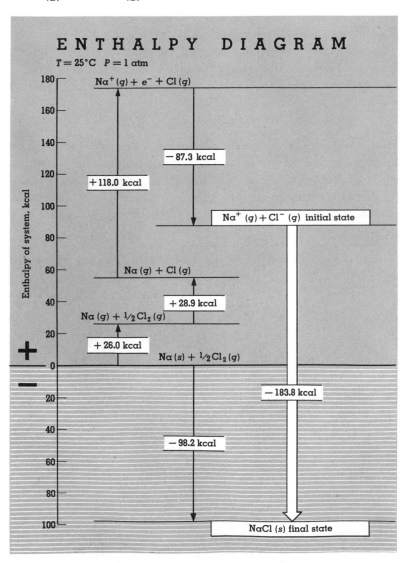

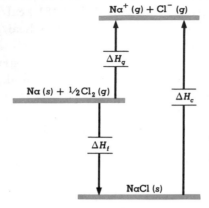

Na$^+$ (g) + Cl$^-$ (g)

ΔH_g

Na (s) + ½Cl$_2$ (g)

ΔH_c

ΔH_f

NaCl (s)

Fig. 12-21 *Born-Haber cycle diagram for the crystal energy of sodium chloride.*

by Fig. 12-21 as a diagram where ΔH_f is the enthalpy of formation, ΔH_g is the enthalpy change for forming gaseous ions from the elements, and ΔH_c is the crystal energy for converting solid sodium chloride to gaseous ions. The enthalpy changes in the Born-Haber cycle are related by

$$\Delta H_c = \Delta H_g - \Delta H_f$$

The Born-Haber cycle calculations have been carried out for all the alkali halides as well as for some other compounds. The agreement between experiment and theory for the alkali halides is comparable to that obtained for sodium chloride. Thus the ionic model is a reasonable and useful description of the nature of the bonding in these substances.

Ex. 12-13 Examine the reactions listed below with their accompanying changes in enthalpy.

Sublimation: Li (s) → Li (g) $\Delta H = 37.1$ kcal

Dissociation: ½F$_2$ (g) → F (g) $\Delta H = 18.3$ kcal

Ionization: Li (g) → Li$^+$ (g) + e$^-$ $\Delta H = 124$ kcal

Electron affinity: F (g) + e$^-$ → F$^-$ (g) $\Delta H = -84$ kcal

Crystal energy: Li$^+$ (g) + F$^-$ (g) → LiF (s) $\Delta H = -246.6$ kcal

a. What is the change in enthalpy for the following reaction?

$$\text{Li (s)} + \tfrac{1}{2}\text{F}_2 \text{ (g)} \rightarrow \text{LiF (s)}$$

Prepare a Born-Haber cycle diagram for the reaction of Li (s) and F$_2$ (g) to produce LiF (s).

b. From the enthalpy data, is the reaction given below exothermic? Explain.

$$\text{Li (s)} + \tfrac{1}{2}\text{F}_2 \text{ (g)} \rightarrow \text{Li}^+ \text{ (g)} + \text{F}^- \text{ (g)}$$

12-16 SUMMARY

Crystalline solids of high melting point include not only metals and intermetallic substances but also ionic compounds. Unlike the opaque and conducting metallic solids, ionic compounds are transparent and nonconducting solids. Many salts dissolve in water to form solutions that are electrically conducting.

Metal atoms pack like spheres into lattices generally giving coordination numbers of 12 and 8 (or 8 + 6). Ions of opposite charge arranged in lattices cannot have coordination numbers as high as 12, but coordination numbers of 8 or 6 are commonly found (Sections 12-6 and 12-7). The type of crystal lattice formed by a salt is determined by the relative sizes of the ions and the ratio of their charges (Section 12-9).

Since ions appear to pack tightly together, it is possible to compute the sizes of ions from x-ray interference measurements of internuclear distances in crystals. Most positive ions are relatively small in relation to negative ions of elements in the same period. For any one family of the periodic table, ion size increases as atomic number increases. The atomic radius for a metal atom is much larger than the radius of an ion of the same element.

The ions in a crystal are held together because each ion is surrounded with ions of opposite charge type. This arrangement, with ions of opposite charge close together, gives a low electric potential energy. When the crystal is broken up by adding enough thermal energy to give separated ions in the gas phase, the enthalpy increase is called the crystal energy. It is difficult to measure crystal energies experimentally.

A crystal energy can be calculated from the geometry of the lattice and Coulomb's law. Enthalpy measurements can also be made for the formation of either the crystal or the ions from the elements. A Born-Haber cycle combines experimental enthalpy data to give a crystal energy. When the crystal energies for the alkali halides and the alkaline-earth halides calculated from theory are compared with experimental data, the two energies are found to be in agreement to within a few percent. This agreement is interpreted to support the idea that salts consist of ions.

The idea that one atom should combine with another atom to form two ions is related to the attraction an atom has for electrons. To describe the attraction for electrons exerted by an atom in a compound, a scale of electronegativities has been devised. This scale is based on bond energy data and covers a range of values from the least electronegative, cesium (0.7), to the most electronegative, fluorine (4.0). Two atoms whose electronegativities differ by about 1.7 will form a compound about halfway between being completely ionic and completely covalent. How the ionic or covalent character of the bond between atoms in a compound is related to the properties of the compound is determined by the structural arrangement of the atoms in the compound. Although electronegativities give only a rough guide, they are often useful in distinguishing between ionic and covalent substances in the absence of other data.

Ex. 12-14 The noble gases have low melting points, low boiling points, and short liquid ranges. Based on these criteria, with what kind of substances would the noble gases be classified? Explain why this classification would not be valid.

Ex. 12-15 A student interpreted the formula $CaCl_2$ to mean that calcium chloride contained one molecule of chlorine for each atom of calcium. What can be said about this interpretation?

Ex. 12-16 Compare the electric conductivities of methane, silver, and calcium bromide at 25°C and at 800°C.

Ex. 12-17 Classify each of the substances described below as metallic, ionic, or covalent. Give reasons for your answer in each case.

a. Substance A
   Color: solid, bright yellow; liquid, clear yellow
   Melting point: 113°C
   Conducts electricity: solid, no; liquid, no

b. Substance B
   Color: solid, silver white; liquid, silver
   Melting point: 660°C
   Conducts electricity: solid, yes; liquid, yes

c. Substance C
   Color: powder, white; liquid, transparent
   Melting point: 680°C
   Conducts electricity: solid, no; liquid, yes

d. Substance D
   Color: liquid, red; gas, red-brown
   Melting point: −7.2°C
   Conducts electricity: solid, no; liquid, no

Ex. 12-18 Plot the enthalpies of fusion (ΔH_m) for the alkali metal chlorides (Table 12-2) against the number of the row in which each alkali metal appears in the periodic table. Draw the best straight line through the points corresponding to NaCl, KCl, RbCl, and CsCl. Using the radius-ratio concept developed in Experiment 16 and Section 12-14, give possible reasons why the enthalpy of fusion for LiCl does not fall on the straight line.

Ex. 12-19 On the basis of electronegativities, divide the following compounds into two groups, one in which each compound will conduct electricity as a liquid at temperatures above its melting point, and one in which each compound will not conduct electricity as a liquid at temperatures above its melting point: $BeCl_2$, $MgCl_2$, $AlCl_3$, CCl_4, BCl_3, BeH_2, NaF, and $CaBr_2$.

Ex. 12-20 At 25°C a water solution of sulfuric acid conducts electric charge many times better than either water or sulfuric acid. What statement can be made concerning the type of bonds in water and sulfuric acid?

Ex. 12-21 Consider copper metal, lithium fluoride, and phosphorus pentoxide. Predict which one of these three substances:

    a. Has the lowest melting point.

    b. Has the longest liquid range.

    c. Is the most malleable.

    d. Is the best electric conductor at 25°C.

    e. Has definite cleavage planes in crystalline form.

    f. Conducts electricity only in its liquid phase.

Ex. 12-22 *a.* What noble gas is isoelectronic with the ions that make up the NaF crystal? the RbBr, CaS, and CsI crystals?

    b. What is the net charge (in coulombs) on the Be^{++} ion, on the S^{--} ion, and on the Cl^- ion?

    c. Examine the periodic table and write the symbol for and predict the most probable charge on the following ions: lithium, boron, oxide (oxygen ion), bromide, calcium, iodide, hydrogen, sulfide, phosphide, barium, cesium, fluoride, hydride.

Ex. 12-23 *a.* Explain why the close-packed lattices characteristic of metal crystals are not probable arrangements for ionic crystals.

    b. Describe the CsCl crystal structure, and explain how it is a reasonable structure for equal numbers of oppositely charged ions.

Ex. 12-24 The covalent radii of the halogen atoms and the ionic radii of the negatively charged halogen ions are compared with the van der Waals radii of the neutral halogen atoms in the table. What reasons can you suggest to explain the similarities or differences in the three types of radii for each halogen atom?

Atom	Covalent Radius, A	Ion	Ionic Radius, A	Atom	Van der Waals Radius, A
F	0.64	F⁻	1.36	F	1.35
Cl	0.99	Cl⁻	1.81	Cl	1.80
Br	1.11	Br⁻	1.95	Br	1.95
I	1.28	I⁻	2.16	I	2.15

Ex. 12-25 Show by means of a graph that electronegativity is a periodic property for at least the first 20 elements.

Ex. 12-26 *a.* What single energy requirement must be applied to the packing of charged ions in crystals?

    b. What single electrical requirement must be applied to charged ions in crystals?

Arrangement A   Arrangement B

c. Which of the arrangements of ions above gives the lowest potential energy? Why?

Ex. 12-27 Determine the enthalpy of reaction represented by the equation Na (g) + F (g) → NaF (s) from the information in Exercise 12-13 and from the information given in Section 12-15. The enthalpy of formation of NaF (s) is $\Delta H = -136$ kcal.

Ex. 12-28 From the data in Table 9-5, show that the difference between the electronegativities of H and Br should be less than the corresponding difference for H and Cl.

Ex. 12-29 a. What are the products formed at each electrode when charge flows through molten LiCl?

b. Is solid $CaCl_2$ an electric conductor? Why or why not?

c. Write the electrode reactions for the electrolysis of molten $MgCl_2$. Will the magnesium produced be solid, liquid, or gas?

d. What is the least amount of $MgCl_2$ required to produce 1 ton of Mg metal by electrolysis?

Ex. 12-30 a. Make a table listing the five alkali metal (group I) fluorides, chlorides, bromides, and iodides. List the ionic radius of each ion.

b. Draw a line through your table separating salts that form crystals with the NaCl arrangement from the salts that form crystals with the CsCl arrangement. Use Tables 12-3 and 12-4.)

c. Determine which alkali metal salt with a CsCl structure has the lowest radius ratio for positive ion to negative ion. Determine which salt with the NaCl structure has the highest radius ratio.

IONS IN SOLUTION

13

ON THE BASIS of x-ray interference measurements (Section 12-4), potassium chloride crystals are assumed to be an arrangement of positive and negative ions each with one unit of charge. Water and potassium chloride can form solutions which conduct electricity at least a million times better than does either water or solid potassium chloride separately. Electric conduction in solution (Section 4-17) is accounted for by the presence of ions in solution. Are the ions in a crystal of potassium chloride related to the ions in a water solution of potassium chloride?

13-1 IONIC CHARGE IN SOLUTION

In Experiment 11 of *Investigating Chemical Systems* a method was developed for determining the number of electrons transferred from one electrode to another per atom of lead deposited during the electrolysis of lead nitrate solution. Presumably, there is a relationship between the number of electrons transferred per lead atom and the charge on a lead ion in solution (Section 12-10).

The demonstration of the existence of ions in a crystal of potassium chloride (Section 12-4) was possible only because the ions are arranged in a regular pattern in the crystal. In solution, the evidence indicates that there is no such regular arrangement of ions.

547

Two properties of an ion need to be determined: (1) the type of charge, positive or negative, and (2) the magnitude of the charge. Can experimental data on solutions be interpreted so as to give information about both properties?

The type of charge possessed by any object determines whether the object is attracted or repelled by other charged objects. When electrodes are placed in an ionic solution so that charge flows through the solution, material moves through the solution (Experiment 11). Presumably the material that moves must be in the form of ions. So the identification of what is moving toward or away from a particular electrode should give a clue as to the type of ionic charge present.

For example, in a solution of copper chloride in water, the presence of copper and chloride ions can be demonstrated qualitatively. Copper ions in solutions are always associated with a characteristic blue color. The blue color of copper chloride solution shows that copper ion is present. Chloride ions can be detected in the solution by the immediate formation of a precipitate of silver chloride when silver nitrate solution is added to a small portion of the solution.

An apparatus such as that indicated in Fig. 13-1 can be used in making observations on the migration of ions during electrolysis. At the beginning of the experiment, the concentration of the copper chloride solution placed in the apparatus is uniform throughout. The initial concentration should be known, but the magnitude of the concentration is not important.

Electrolysis of the copper chloride is carried out using two silver

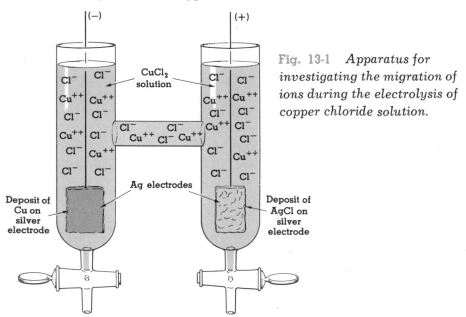

Fig. 13-1 *Apparatus for investigating the migration of ions during the electrolysis of copper chloride solution.*

electrodes. In the absence of charge flow, no reaction takes place at either electrode. After electricity has passed through the solution for some time, the solution around the positive electrode can be analyzed to see if the copper chloride concentration has changed. The copper ion concentration can be determined by measuring the intensity of the blue color. The chloride ion concentration can be determined by measuring the mass of silver chloride precipitated from a known quantity of solution. Analysis shows that the concentration of copper chloride has decreased near the positive electrode. Visual inspection of the positive electrode indicates that a deposit of silver chloride has formed on the electrode but that no copper has deposited. What do these changes indicate?

The decrease in copper ion concentration around the positive electrode must mean that copper ions move away from the positive electrode. This implies that the copper ion in solution is a positive ion. Chloride ion, on the other hand, must have moved to the positive electrode, which implies that the chloride ion is a negative ion. How do these results and conclusions correspond to the situation around the negative electrode?

Analysis of the solution around the negative electrode shows that here, too, the concentration of copper chloride has decreased. Examination of the negative electrode surface reveals a deposit on the electrode consisting only of copper metal. No chloride ion or chlorine in any other form is found in the deposit. The decrease in copper chloride concentration must mean that chloride ions have moved away from the negative electrode while copper ions moved toward it. Observations of changes at both electrodes lead to the same conclusion—that the copper ion is positive and the chloride ion is negative. What is now needed to determine the charge on each ion?

In Section 4-24 it was found that a faraday of charge (96,500 coulombs) or some integral multiple of this charge is transferred through a solution for each mole of material reacting at an electrode. The number of coulombs transferred during the electrolysis of the copper chloride solution can be measured by the procedure used in Experiment 11. Each faraday of charge transferred from one electrode to the other represents a mole of electrons. In the electrolysis of copper chloride solution, the measured increase in mass of the negative electrode indicates that 1 mole of copper is deposited on the negative electrode when 2 faradays of charge is transferred. The increase in mass of the positive electrode indicates that when 2 faradays of charge is transferred, 2 moles of chloride ion is deposited as silver chloride.

The charge/mass ratio for the reactions at the electrodes can be accounted for by assigning two positive charges to each copper ion and one negative charge to each chloride ion. The magnitude of each charge equals the charge on the electron. The formulas for copper ion and chloride ion in solution are represented as follows.

$$Cu^{++} \ (aq) \qquad Cl^- \ (aq)$$
$$\text{Copper ion} \qquad \text{Chloride ion}$$

Solid copper chloride has been shown by analysis to have the formula $CuCl_2$ (s), and the solid has the properties of an ionic crystal. Thus, both solid copper chloride and dissolved copper chloride behave in a manner consistent with the presence of ions. The overall reaction in the electrolysis can be represented by

$$2Ag \ (s) + Cu^{++} \ (aq) + 2Cl^- \ (aq) \rightarrow 2AgCl \ (s) + Cu \ (s)$$
$$(Eq. \ 13\text{-}1)$$

Electrolysis of potassium chloride solutions in the apparatus shown in Fig. 13-1 gives observations which indicate that ions are present in the solution. The chloride ion behaves as it does in the electrolysis of copper chloride, but hydrogen gas rather than potassium is produced at the negative electrode. The concentration of potassium ions increases around the negative electrode. This increase suggests that potassium ions are positively charged. Electrolysis gives no direct indication as to the magnitude of the positive charge on the potassium ion in solution.

The composition of solid potassium chloride is represented by the formula KCl. In solution, therefore, there cannot be more than one potassium ion for each chloride ion. Since the chloride ion has one negative charge, the potassium ion must have one positive charge whether it is in a solid (Section 12-4) or in a solution. Hence, a solution of potassium chloride contains the ions K^+ (aq) and Cl^- (aq).

Hydrogen gas is produced at the negative electrode in the electrolysis of a number of salt solutions. Water solutions of hydrogen chloride and sulfuric acid, and solutions of most substances called acids, not only give hydrogen gas when electrolyzed but also react with such metals as magnesium, iron, and zinc to produce hydrogen gas. Acids dissolved in water form conducting, and hence ionic, solutions. Solutions of hydrogen chloride (HCl) in water are referred to as hydrochloric acid. In hydrochloric acid, chloride ion can be shown to be present just as it can in potassium chloride solutions. The positive ion in hydrochloric acid and in other acid solutions is called hydrogen ion which has the formula H^+ (aq). It is the hydrogen ion from which hydrogen gas is produced by electrolysis of ionic solutions or by reaction of acid solutions with metals.

The results from the electrolysis of solutions of ionic compounds and the study of ionic solids have been used to demonstrate the existence of a considerable number of ions in solution. Table 13-1 lists some ions that exist in water solutions of various salts.

TABLE 13-1 SOME IONS FOUND IN AQUEOUS SOLUTION

Name of Ion	Formula	Name of Ion	Formula
Hydrogen	H^+	Fluoride	F^-
Lithium	Li^+	Chloride	Cl^-
Sodium	Na^+	Bromide	Br^-
Potassium	K^+	Iodide	I^-
Ammonium	NH_4^+	Hydroxide	OH^-
Silver	Ag^+	Nitrate	NO_3^-
Magnesium	Mg^{++}	Chlorate	ClO_3^-
Calcium	Ca^{++}	Perchlorate	ClO_4^-
Barium	Ba^{++}	Sulfide	S^{--}
Copper	Cu^{++}	Carbonate	CO_3^{--}
Zinc	Zn^{++}	Sulfite	SO_3^{--}
Lead	Pb^{++}	Sulfate	SO_4^{--}
Aluminum	Al^{+++}	Phosphate	PO_4^{---}

The formulas of ions listed in Table 13-1 as well as formulas of a number of other ions can be arranged in the form of a periodic table, according to the element from which each ion is formed (Fig. 13-2).

Ex. 13-1   *a.* If a sodium iodide–water solution is placed in an apparatus similar to that shown in Fig. 13-1, what would happen to the initially homogeneous solution of Na^+ (aq) and I^- (aq) during electrolysis?

b. If silver iodide is formed at the positive electrode, what substance is formed at the negative electrode?

c. What is the molar ratio of the electrode products?

d. How many coulombs of electric charge are transferred during the formation of 2.35 g of AgI?

e. Write an equation describing the overall reaction during electrolysis.

13-2 POLYATOMIC IONS

Several of the ions listed in Table 13-1 and in Fig. 13-2 contain more than one atom per ion. The discussion of ionic compounds in Chapter 12 and this chapter has been limited to salts which are made from just two elements and which contain monatomic ions.

Many ionic compounds are formed from more than two elements. Thus there is a set of compounds whose compositions are represented by the formulas NH_4F, NH_4Cl, NH_4Br, and NH_4I. Each of these salts forms crystals with the sodium chloride lattice, and each has chemical properties quite similar to those of the corresponding alkali metal halides. In other words, these compounds appear to contain a negative halide ion in each case. The positive ion, called the ammonium ion, has

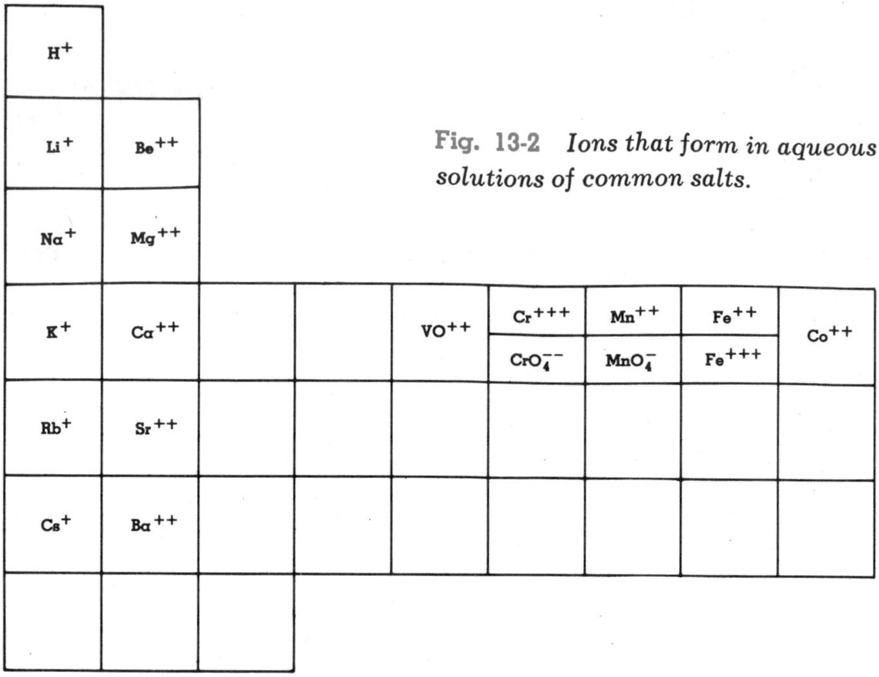

Fig. 13-2 Ions that form in aqueous solutions of common salts.

the formula NH_4^+. The ammonium ion is one example of a large class of ions containing more than one kind of atom and referred to as **polyatomic ions.**

Each of the alkali metals forms a compound containing chlorine and oxygen. The formulas of these compounds are $LiClO_4$, $NaClO_4$, $KClO_4$, $RbClO_4$, and $CsClO_4$. In each compound the alkali metal is a positive ion, and the chlorine and oxygen act together as a unit called the perchlorate ion (ClO_4^-).

Isoelectronic with the perchlorate ion, which has 50 electrons, are two other polyatomic ions, sulfate (SO_4^{--}) and phosphate (PO_4^{---}). Another isoelectronic pair of ions consists of nitrate (NO_3^-) and carbonate (CO_3^{--}). Closely related to the 10-electron molecules discussed in Section 7-17 are the isoelectronic ions fluoride (F^-), hydroxide (OH^-), amide (NH_2^-), oxide (O^{--}), and nitride (N^{---}). Neither oxide nor nitride ions can be detected in solution, but they are found in solid compounds such as magnesium oxide (MgO) and calcium nitride (Ca_3N_2). In the 10-electron series of ions, of course, only hydroxide and amide are polyatomic ions.

Structural studies of the isoelectronic ions PO_4^{---}, SO_4^{--}, and ClO_4^- have shown that the oxygen atoms are arranged tetrahedrally around the central atom which is less electronegative. The central atom forms sp^3 hybrid bonds with the oxygen atoms.

What is the structure and geometry of the isoelectronic CO_3^{--} and NO_3^- ions? Each of these ions has a flat planar structure with three oxygen atoms surrounding the central atom. In CO_3^{--}, the experi-

			BF_4^-	HCO_3^-; CO_3^{--}	α NH_4^+; NO_3^-	OH^-	F^-
			Al^{+++}		b $H_2PO_4^-$; PO_4^{---}	c S^{--}; SO_4^{--}	d Cl^-; ClO_4^-
Ni^{++}	Cu^{++}	Zn^{++}; $Zn(OH)_4^{--}$			AsO_3^{---}; AsO_4^{---}	Se^{--}	Br^-; BrO_3^-
Pd^{++}	Ag^+	Cd^{++}		Sn^{++}; $Sn(OH)_6^{--}$		Te^{--}	e I^-; IO_3^-
		Hg_2^{++}; Hg^{++}	Tl^+	Pb^{++}; $Pb(OH)_6^{--}$			

Footnote to table
a. also NO_2^-
b. also HPO_4^{--}
c. also HS^- and SO_3^{--}
d. also ClO^-, ClO_2^-, and ClO_3^-
e. also IO_4^-

mentally measured bond lengths of the three C—O distances are equal and considerably shorter (1.30 A) than that calculated by adding the covalent radii (Fig. 12-16) of carbon (0.77 A) and oxygen (0.66 A). The calculated bond length is 1.43 A. The bond angles are 120°. How can these facts be explained in terms of charge cloud or atomic orbital models? In the planar molecule of ethylene, C_2H_4, the bond length for the carbon–carbon bond is 1.33 A, whereas for ethane, C_2H_6, the carbon–carbon bond is 1.54 A. Ethylene is pictured by the atomic orbital model as involving three sp^2 hybrid orbitals from each carbon atom oriented in a plane at bond angles of 120° (Section 10-23).

Hybrid orbitals of this type would be in accord with the observed flat planar structure of CO_3^{--}. If a carbon atom is bonded in the hybridized state as shown by the underline,

$$\text{Hybridized state, C} \quad 1s^2 2\underline{s^1 2p_x^1 2p_y^1 2p_z^1}$$
$$\text{Ground state, O} \quad 1s^2 2s^2 2p_x^2 2p_y^1 2p_z^1$$

one p orbital would be left half-filled. A sigma bond (sp^2-p) to each oxygen atom would also leave one p orbital on each oxygen atom half-filled. If the carbon atom and oxygen atoms are close enough together, sidewise overlap of election waves can occur to form a pi bond. The carbon–oxygen bond length should be shorter than that calculated from covalent radii for a single covalent bond. The fact that the bond length in carbonate ion is shorter (1.30 A) than that calculated (1.43 A) for a carbon–oxygen single bond indicates pi bonding, but the bond must be of a different character from that formed in ethylene. If the C—O internuclear distances are equal, the sidewise overlap of electron

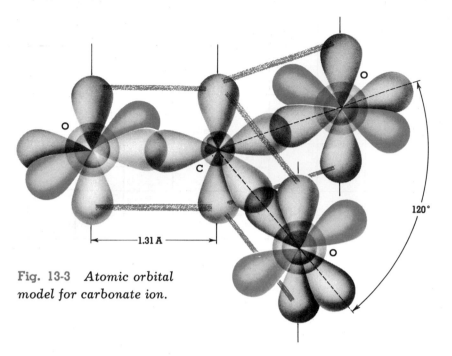

Fig. 13-3 *Atomic orbital model for carbonate ion.*

waves in a pi bond must be smeared out over four kernels (one C and three O's) to increase electron density equally in three directions (Fig. 13-3). In a sense, the carbon atom and each oxygen atom are joined by one sigma bond and one-third of a pi bond. The pi bond is delocalized, smeared out among four atoms (three bonds), rather than localized between two atoms as in ethylene.

A satisfactory Lewis structure cannot be written for the CO_3^{--} ion since Lewis structures provide only for pairs of electrons to be shared between two kernels. Lewis structures cannot be written to show electrons shared between several kernels. The usual solution is to write three equivalent Lewis structures that show the four electrons outside the carbon kernel, six electrons outside each oxygen kernel, and the two that were transferred from the cation (24 electrons in all). The carbonate ion structure is assumed to have the electrons arranged in a way that is intermediate between the three equivalent structures shown, as if $1\frac{1}{3}$ bonds join each oxygen atom to the central carbon atom.

Ex. 13-2 Write Lewis structures for the following polyatomic ions: ClO_4^-, NH_4^+, NO_3^-. What geometric shape would you expect for each of these ions?

Ex. 13-3 What positive ions are isoelectronic with OH^- and F^-? with S^{--} and Cl^-?

13-3 INDEPENDENCE OF IONS IN SOLUTION

Experiments show that in electrolytic conduction positive and negative ions move independently in opposite directions when there is an electric potential difference between the electrodes (Section 13-1). Is there any evidence that ions behave independently in solution even when no charge is flowing through the solution? The question can be stated in a different form. To what extent do the positive and negative ions (for example, potassium and chloride ions) in an aqueous solution interact with each other? Is there evidence to indicate that the ions are actually independent of each other and that their properties are additive, in spite of the fact that positive and negative ions attract each other?

Experimental evidence that many ions interact with each other appreciably in solution is already available to us. For instance, in Experiment 5 of *Investigating Chemical Systems* a solution of silver nitrate was added to a solution of sodium chloride to produce white solid silver chloride as a precipitate.

In an extension of this experiment, solutions of magnesium chloride ($MgCl_2$) and of barium chloride ($BaCl_2$) reacted with a solution of silver nitrate. The precipitate formed in each case is the same substance, solid silver chloride. Since one of the reactants (silver nitrate) and the observed product (silver chloride) are the same in these reactions, it is reasonable to suppose that there is a common ion in solutions of sodium chloride, magnesium chloride, and barium chloride. If a solution of silver nitrate is added to a solution of sodium chlorate ($NaClO_3$), no silver chloride is formed, even though sodium chlorate is known to contain chlorine. The tentative deduction is that the chlorine in the three chlorides is an independent ion and that chloride ion reacts with silver ion to form a precipitate of silver chloride, but that chlorine in chlorate is not an independent ion. In other words, the chlorate ion is a polyatomic ion that reacts as a unit.

Further information about the possible interaction of ions can be obtained from a quantitative study of the reaction of silver nitrate with a series of solutions each of which contain two ionic chlorides. The solutions differ from each other in terms of the mole ratio of the two ionic chlorides. Data obtained in a continuous variation study of such systems are presented in Fig. 13-4.

The property measured in these systems was the number of moles

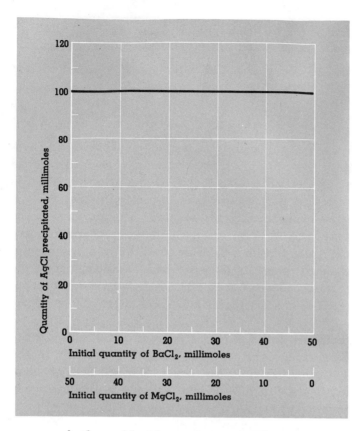

Fig. 13-4 *Quantity
of AgCl precipitated
when AgNO$_3$ solu-
tion is added to
solutions containing
both BaCl$_2$ and
MgCl$_2$.*

of silver chloride precipitated. The purpose of the experiment was to
relate this quantity to the number of moles of barium chloride and magnesium chloride initially present. The initial components of these systems were solutions containing barium chloride and magnesium chloride. The solutions were prepared so that different mole ratios of the
two chlorides were present but so that the total quantity of solute was
kept constant at 50. millimoles (1 millimole $= 10^{-3}$ mole). In each
case, a solution containing 120 millimoles of silver nitrate was used.
Figure 13-4 indicates that the quantity of precipitate remains constant
no matter what mole ratio of the two chlorides is present as initial components. A single straight line in the continuous variation method is evidence that the properties of initial components are additive. For the
systems considered here, the property being examined is the quantity
of silver chloride precipitated when silver nitrate is added to each
initial component or to mixtures of the initial components. Therefore,
Fig. 13-4 indicates that magnesium chloride and barium chloride each
separately and independently react with silver nitrate to precipitate
silver chloride. The fact that all the chloride ion in a solution containing both magnesium chloride and barium chloride precipitates as silver
chloride implies that there is no interaction between MgCl$_2$ and BaCl$_2$.

In Fig. 13-5 are plotted the data obtained when solutions containing magnesium chloride and sodium chloride are investigated by the same technique. Instead of a horizontal straight line, a sloping straight line fits the data.

When only sodium chloride is present, 50 millimoles of silver chloride is precipitated. When only magnesium chloride is present, 100 millimoles of silver chloride is precipitated. For mixtures of sodium chloride and magnesium chloride, the quantity of silver chloride precipitated is indicated by the straight line in Fig. 13-5.

Since the total number of moles of sodium chloride and magnesium chloride was kept constant, the total number of moles of chloride ion initially present is not constant for the set of systems described by Fig. 13-5. In each system the quantity of precipitate is determined simply by the sum of the chloride ion from $MgCl_2$ and the chloride ion from $NaCl$. Neither magnesium ion nor sodium ion plays any role in altering the quantity of precipitate formed.

Do these results imply that magnesium chloride and sodium chloride interact? Here again the answer is "No." The data shown in Fig. 13-5 can be interpreted by considering that 1 mole of magnesium chloride

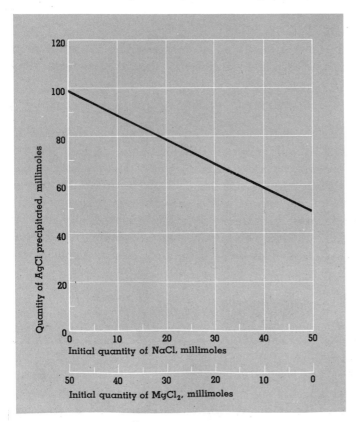

Fig. 13-5 *Quantity of AgCl precipitated when AgNO$_3$ solution is added to solutions containing both NaCl and MgCl$_2$.*

contributes 2 moles of chloride ion to the solution and that 1 mole of sodium chloride contributes 1 mole of chloride ion to the solution.

Three conclusions can be drawn from a comparison of the data summarized in Figs. 13-4 and 13-5. (1) Chloride ion must be present in a solution in order for silver chloride to precipitate when silver nitrate is added. (2) The quantity of chloride ion present determines the quantity of silver chloride precipitated. (3) The presence of magnesium, barium, or sodium ion or a mixture of the ions does not affect the quantity of silver chloride formed.

Ex. 13-4 What systems of magnesium chloride and sodium chloride (Fig. 13-5) could be used to obtain a horizontal line in a graph as was found for systems of magnesium chloride and barium chloride in Fig. 13-4?

Ex. 13-5 For each of the reactions in each of the following systems, write the net ionic equation and predict the quantity of precipitate formed in millimoles.

a. 100 millimoles of Ag^+ (aq) plus 200 millimoles of Cl^- (aq)

b. 20 millimoles of Ba^{++} (aq) plus 10 millimoles of CO_3^{--} (aq)

c. 120 millimoles of $AgNO_3$ dissolved in 100 ml of water plus 100 millimoles of $CaCl_2$ dissolved in 100 ml of water

13-4 NET IONIC EQUATIONS

If chloride ion (Cl^-) is assumed to be present in all solutions of chlorides no matter what cation is present, then the reaction which forms solid silver chloride might be written in the form

$$Ag^+ \ (aq) + Cl^- \ (aq) \rightarrow AgCl \ (s) \qquad (Eq. \ 13\text{-}2)$$

Experiments similar to those just described can be performed by using a single ionic chloride, such as potassium chloride, to precipitate silver chloride from solutions of various silver-containing compounds. The experiments show that the reaction of the silver ion, Ag^+, present in these solutions is independent of the anion present. Silver ion, like chloride ion, precipitates silver chloride quite independently of other ions present in the solution. When solutions of sodium chloride and silver nitrate in a system in its initial state are mixed, the change that occurs is described by

$$Na^+ \ (aq) + Cl^- \ (aq) + Ag^+ \ (aq) + NO_3^- \ (aq) \rightarrow$$
$$Na^+ \ (aq) + NO_3^- \ (aq) + AgCl \ (s) \qquad (Eq. \ 13\text{-}3)$$

However, Equation 13-2 accurately expresses the net change that takes place in the system.

Since Na^+ (aq) and NO_3^- (aq) are present in the system in its initial and final states and since no evidence suggests that they are involved in the reaction, they are sometimes referred to as **spectator ions.** It is their lack of effect on the change which occurs in the system

TABLE 13-2 IONS IN AQUEOUS SOLUTIONS OF SEVERAL COMPOUNDS

Compound	Formula	Ions in Solution
Silver nitrate	$AgNO_3$	Ag^+ (aq) + NO_3^- (aq)
Sodium chloride	$NaCl$	Na^+ (aq) + Cl^- (aq)
Magnesium chloride	$MgCl_2$	Mg^{++} (aq) + $2Cl^-$ (aq)
Barium chloride	$BaCl_2$	Ba^{++} (aq) + $2Cl^-$ (aq)
Sodium chlorate	$NaClO_3$	Na^+ (aq) + ClO_3^- (aq)

that justifies omitting the spectator ions from Equation 13-2. When magnesium chloride solution reacts with silver nitrate solution, the change is described by

$$Mg^{++} \ (aq) + 2Cl^- \ (aq) + 2Ag^+ \ (aq) + 2NO_3^- \ (aq) \rightarrow$$
$$Mg^{++} \ (aq) + 2NO_3^- \ (aq) + 2AgCl \ (s) \qquad (Eq. \ 13\text{-}4)$$

However, Mg^{++} (aq) and $2NO_3^-$ (aq) are spectator ions. Omitting them leaves

$$2Cl^- \ (aq) + 2Ag^+ \ (aq) \rightarrow 2AgCl \ (s) \qquad (Eq. \ 13\text{-}5)$$

which can be simplified by dividing all coefficients by 2 to give Equation 13-2. Equations which show only those ions and compounds that are assumed to take part in a reaction and which omit spectator ions are called **net ionic equations.**

Sodium chlorate ($NaClO_3$) is composed of sodium, oxygen, and chlorine. Solutions of silver nitrate and sodium chlorate do not react to produce a precipitate of silver chloride. From the fact that sodium chlorate solutions conduct electricity and from freezing point data such as those collected in Experiment 13, one concludes that sodium chlorate solutions contain the ions Na^+ and ClO_3^-. However, the polyatomic ion ClO_3^- has properties different from those of chloride, Cl^-. Reaction with Ag^+ to form a precipitate is not one of the properties of ClO_3^-.

The compounds discussed in Section 13-3 form conducting solutions which support the idea that the compounds exist in solution in the form of ions. The types and relative numbers of ions that each compound forms in a water solution are indicated in Table 13-2. Crystal data, electrolytic data, and behavior in solution all indicate that sodium chlorate is made up of sodium ions (Na^+) and chlorate ions (ClO_3^-).

Ex. 13-6 Which of the following compounds, in water solution, will react with Ag^+ (aq) ions to form a precipitate of AgCl: $NaCl$, $KClO_3$, $MgCl_2$?

An ionic solution obviously contains both ions and solvent. Even though many ions are able to act independently of each other, it is possible that the ions in an ionic solution may interact with water.

In Experiment 13 a study was made of the freezing points of solutions in relation to the freezing point of the solvent. Solutions of methanol in water as well as sodium chloride in water gave lower freezing points than did water alone.

Figure 13-6 is a graph of freezing points for the two systems, methanol–water and aqueous sodium chloride–water. The data plotted are over a wider range of concentrations than those studied in Experiment 13. The graph is the form used for continuous variation studies. When water solutions of either methanol or sodium chloride with concentrations shown in Fig. 13-6 are cooled, the only solid that separates as the solution begins to freeze is ice.

The freezing points of solutions decrease as the concentration of the solute increases. The two systems shown in Fig. 13-6 appear to differ only in that the freezing point of a sodium chloride solution is lower than that of a methanol solution with the same mole ratio of solute to water. Ethanol–water systems and other solutions that do not conduct

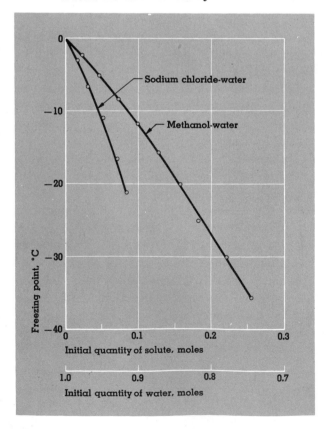

Fig. 13-6 *Freezing points of sodium chloride–water systems and methanol–water systems.*

TABLE 13-3 VOLUME INCREASE IN SOLUTIONS OF METHANOL AND SODIUM CHLORIDE IN 100.00 ml OF WATER AT 25°C

Property of System	*NaCl*	*CH_3OH*
Initial number of moles of solute	0.0362	0.0315
Initial volume of solute, ml	0.98	1.27
Final volume of solution, ml	100.64	101.19
Volume increase, ml	0.64	1.19
Volume increase per mole, ml	17.7	37.8

electricity show the same relation between freezing points and solution concentration that is shown by methanol–water systems. On the other hand, the graph shows that sodium chloride gives a lower freezing point than does methanol for a given molar concentration. In general the freezing points of salt solutions follow the pattern of sodium chloride–water systems and not the pattern of methanol–water systems. Although freezing point data suggest that there is some interaction between water and salts, which indicates a difference between ionic solutions and other solutions, the nature and the extent of the interaction is not clear from the type of data given in Fig. 13-6.

Measurements of volume changes were used in Chapter 2 to get information about interaction in systems. Four systems were discussed: sodium bromide–sucrose, methanol–ethanol, ethanol–water, and potassium chloride–water. Sodium sulfate solutions were studied in Experiment 4 by determining densities and computing volume changes. It was found that a solution of sodium sulfate in water has a smaller volume than the sum of the volumes of the unmixed sodium sulfate and water.

Interaction in methanol solutions and in sodium chloride solutions can be compared on the basis of volume measurements. Data for this comparison are given in Table 13-3. The volume increase is the difference between the volume of the solution and the volume of the water used. For each example, the volume increase per mole is calculated by dividing the volume increase by the number of moles of solute used. Solid sodium chloride has a molar volume of 27.0 ml/mole of NaCl, and liquid methanol has a molar volume of 40.5 ml/mole of CH_3OH. On a molar volume basis, more than 9 ml of space occupied by sodium chloride (27.0 − 17.7) seems to disappear when a solution of NaCl is formed, whereas less than 3 ml of space occupied by methanol (40.5 − 37.8) disappears when methanol forms a solution in water. At lower concentrations, an even larger fraction of the molar volume of NaCl disappears, but a smaller fraction of the molar volume of methanol disappears. Other salts are similar to sodium chloride.

The data on the volumes of solutes in solution are interpreted to mean that in a sodium chloride–water system there is more interaction between the solute and the water than there is in a methanol–water system. This interaction results in the systems' shrinking when the solutions are formed. The loss in volume produced by the dissolving of sodium chloride is typical of other ionic compounds. On the other hand, substances like methanol, which are not ionic in character, give solutions whose final volumes are very nearly equal to the sum of the volumes of the separate components.

13-6 INTERACTION OF IONS

In Section 13-3, evidence was presented to show the independence of certain ions, such as Ag^+ and NO_3^-, in aqueous solution. Each ion contributes its own properties to a silver nitrate solution. However, in the presence of chloride ion, silver chloride precipitates. This must mean that interaction takes place between silver ion and chloride ion when they are brought together in solution.

The degree to which one ion interacts with another to produce a precipitate can be examined in the lead nitrate–potassium iodide system used in Experiment 6. Data are plotted in Fig. 13-7 for this system, using the continuous variation method. The intersection of the two solid lines corresponds very nearly to a mole ratio of 1:2 for the relative quantities of lead nitrate and potassium iodide. This mole ratio is consistent with a formula of PbI_2 for lead iodide. Within the experimental error, the quantity of PbI_2 formed represents complete reac-

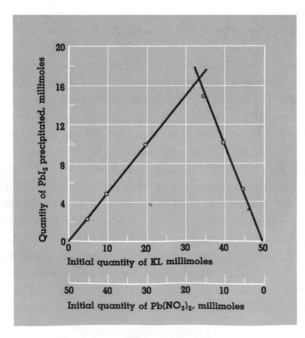

Fig. 13-7 *Quantity of PbI₂ precipitated from systems of KI and Pb(NO₃)₂.*

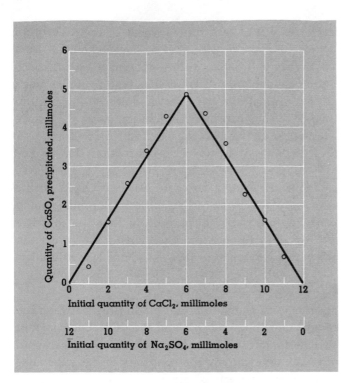

Fig. 13-8 *Quantity of CaSO₄ precipitated from systems of Na₂SO₄ and CaCl₂ in a total volume of 12 ml.*

tion of lead ion and iodide ion to form PbI_2. The net ionic equation for the reaction is

$$Pb^{++} \ (aq) + 2I^- \ (aq) \rightarrow PbI_2 \ (s) \qquad (Eq. \ 13\text{-}6)$$

Systems containing calcium ion and sulfate ion are represented by the data plotted in Fig. 13-8. A maximum quantity of precipitate is obtained when the mole ratio of the reactants, calcium chloride ($CaCl_2$) and sodium sulfate (Na_2SO_4), is very nearly 1:1. The precipitation reaction can then be represented by the net ionic equation

$$Ca^{++} \ (aq) + SO_4^{--} \ (aq) \rightarrow CaSO_4 \ (s) \qquad (Eq. \ 13\text{-}7)$$

At the intersection of the two lines in the graph, 6 millimoles of calcium chloride and 6 millimoles of sodium sulfate were used, and yet only 5 millimoles of solid calcium sulfate was recovered from the system. In the calcium chloride–sodium sulfate system which gives maximum precipitation, there must still be about 1 millimole each of calcium ions and sulfate ions remaining in solution. The presence of sulfate ion can be demonstrated by the formation of a precipitate of barium sulfate when a solution containing barium ion is added to a sample of the filtrate from the calcium sulfate precipitation. The presence of calcium ion can be demonstrated by the formation of a precipitate of calcium carbonate when a solution containing carbonate ion is added to a sample of the filtrate.

Potassium iodide and lead nitrate solutions react so that nearly all the lead ions and iodide ions are precipitated as lead iodide. Calcium chloride and sodium sulfate solutions, on the other hand, react much less completely to form calcium sulfate. These observations must mean that calcium sulfate is more soluble than lead iodide. The maximum concentration that a pair of ions can have in solution gives a measure of the extent of interaction of the two ions to form a precipitate. A high concentration of the ions indicates less interaction than a low concentration.

Three aspects of ionic solutions can be usefully summarized. In the first place, ions interact with water to form solutions. Secondly, many ions exhibit properties in solutions which indicate that the ions are essentially unaffected by the presence of other ions. Finally, certain pairs of ions interact with each other to form solids of low solubility.

13-7 SOLUBILITY OF SALTS IN WATER

The results of Experiment 12 indicate some relationship between the solubility of a given substance in a solvent and the dielectric constant of the solvent. This suggests that the characters of both the solvent and the solute are important in determining the solubility of one substance in another. This relationship is particularly evident with ionic substances which generally are soluble only in liquids of high dielectric constant. Unfortunately, neither this generalization nor the models for the structure of matter permit the prediction of the solubility of a particular substance in a given solvent.

You might well ask, "What's wrong with our theory of matter if it can't be used to make predictions?" The answer is that the theory of matter needs to be developed in more detail, but it is not clear what changes should be made. Interpretations based on these ideas may enable a chemist to come up with three or four good reasons why a given ionic solid should be soluble in water. Unfortunately, he might also find reasons why it should be insoluble!

For laboratory work, practical general rules are helpful to summarize what is known. There will be some exceptions to these generalizations about solubility, but the rules are useful nonetheless. Some simple rules are given below and summarized in Fig. 13-9. The rules are in agreement with the data in Table 13-4 for compounds of the elements in groups I and II of the periodic table. The data in Table 13-4 give an idea of the ranges of solubility encountered for some salts.

1. All salts of ammonium (NH_4^+) and of the alkali metals Li^+, Na^+, K^+, Rb^+, and Cs^+ are soluble in water.

2. All nitrates (NO_3^-) and perchlorates (ClO_4^-) are soluble in water.

TABLE 13-4
TABLE 13-4 SOLUBILITIES OF SALTS OF GROUPS I AND II, MOLES PER LITER OF WATER AT 25°C[a]

	Fluoride	Chloride	Bromide	Nitrate	Sulfate
Group I and ammonium ions:					
Li^+	0.05	20.0	21.2	12.0	3.1
Na^+	0.99	6.2	9.2	10.8	2.0
K^+	17.5	4.8	5.8	3.7	0.69
NH_4^+		7.3	8.0	26.1	5.8
Rb^+	28.8	7.8	7.0	4.4	1.9
Cs^+	38.6	11.4	5.5	1.4	5.0
Group II ions:					
Be^{++}	∞	9.3		8.0[b]	4.0
Mg^{++}	0.001	6.0	5.5	4.9	3.0
Ca^{++}	0.0002	7.5	7.7	8.4	0.015
Sr^{++}	0.001	3.5	4.2	3.8	6×10^{-4}
Ba^{++}	0.007	1.8	3.5	0.39	9.6×10^{-6}
$Ra^{++}{}^b$		0.82	1.8	0.40	6.5×10^{-8}

[a] Substances are usually considered to be insoluble if the concentration of a saturated solution is less than 0.01 M.
[b] Solubilities at 20°C.

3. Most halides (F^-, Cl^-, Br^-, and I^-) are soluble in water except those of Ag^+, Hg^+, and Pb^{++}. Note, however, that AgF is soluble and that fluorides of Mg^{++}, Ca^{++}, Sr^{++}, and Ba^{++} are insoluble.

4. All sulfates (SO_4^{--}) are soluble except those of Ba^{++}, Sr^{++}, Ra^{++}, and Pb^{++}. The solubility of $CaSO_4$ is borderline, 0.015 molar.

5. All hydroxides, oxides, carbonates, and phosphates are insoluble, except those of the alkali metals and NH_4^+. $Ba(OH)_2$ and BaO give solutions of about 0.15 molar.

6. All sulfides are insoluble except those of the alkali metals and NH_4^+ as well as those of Ca^{++}, Mg^{++}, Sr^{++}, and Ba^{++}.

Ex. 13-7 Arrange the following compounds in order of increasing molar solubility in water at 25°C on the basis of the data listed in Table 13-4: LiCl, KBr, NH_4NO_3, Na_2SO_4, $MgCl_2$, $BaBr_2$, $CsNO_3$.

13-8 SEPARATION AND IDENTIFICATION OF IONS

In the case of covalent substances the chemical properties to be expected are properties of the whole molecule and not those of the individual components, that is, the atoms. But in Section 13-3, evidence was given for the view that the properties of a solution containing several ions are the sums of the properties of the individual ions.

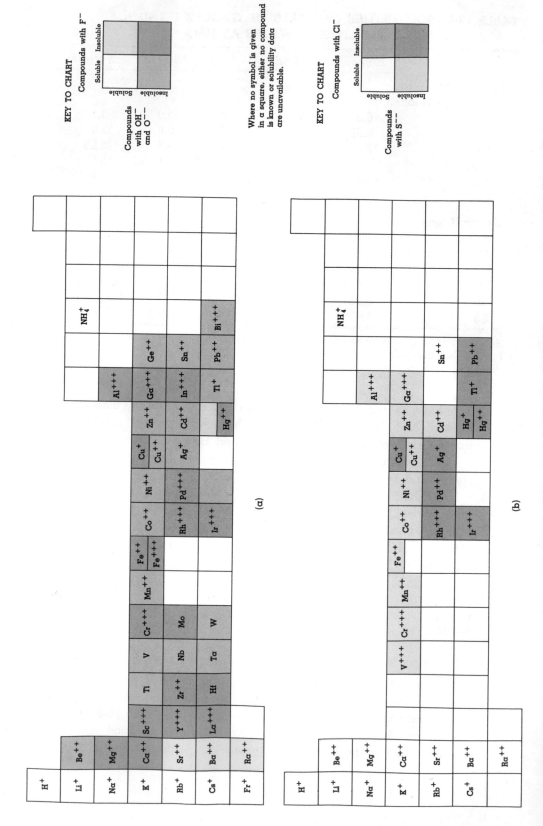

KEY TO CHART

Compounds with F⁻

	Soluble	Insoluble
Insoluble		
Soluble		

Compounds with OH⁻ and O⁻⁻

Where no symbol is given in a square, either no compound is known or solubility data are unavailable.

KEY TO CHART

Compounds with Cl⁻

	Soluble	Insoluble
Insoluble		
Soluble		

Compounds with S⁻⁻

(a)

(b)

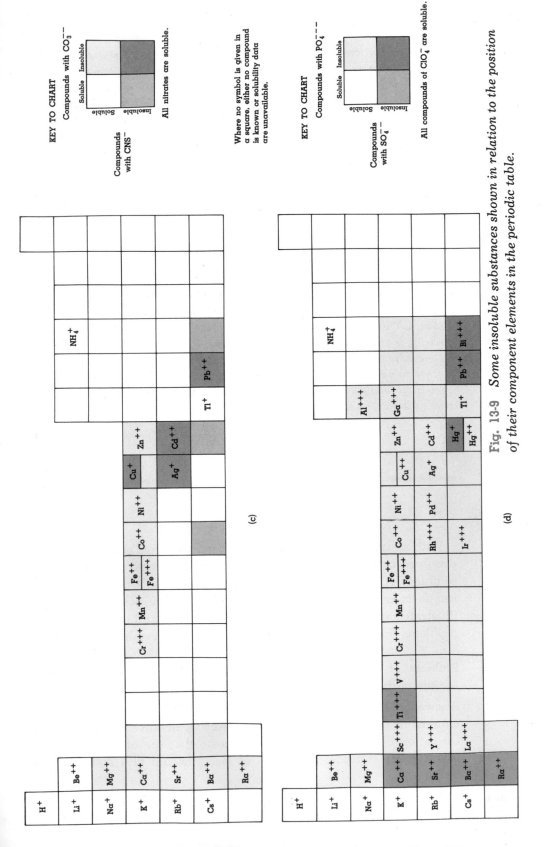

Fig. 13-9 Some insoluble substances shown in relation to the position of their component elements in the periodic table.

PETER JOSEPH WILLEM DEBYE *1884–*

A Dutch-American physical chemist. Debye was born in Holland and he trained first as an electrical engineer in Aachen, Germany, then as a physicist in Munich where he received his Ph.D. in 1910. He was appointed professor of theoretical physics at the University of Zürich in 1911, and later he held teaching positions at Utrecht, Göttingen, Zürich, and Leipzig. In 1935, he became director of the Kaiser Wilhelm Institute of Physics in Berlin. He escaped to the United States in 1940 and accepted a post as professor and chairman of the chemistry department at Cornell University.

Debye derived a general law for the specific heat of crystal lattices at low temperatures. The Debye-Hückel theory describes the properties of ionic solutions in terms of the coulombic interactions between ions. In collaboration with P. Scherrer, he showed how x-rays reflected by powdered crystals can give patterns from which the crystal structure can be deduced.

Part of Debye's work has been in the study of polar molecules through dielectric constant measurements from which the dipole moment can be deduced. The dipole moment, which measures the magnitude of a molecule's polarity, is expressed in terms of Debye units. In his most recent work, Debye is investigating the scattering of light by molecules in solutions as a method to determine their sizes and interactions. The Nobel Prize in chemistry for 1936 was awarded to Debye for his studies of molecular structure and the atomic distances within the molecule.

With an understanding that the properties of ionic compounds, when dissolved in water, are the properties of their ions, and using a few solubility rules (Section 13-7), a surprisingly large number of chemical facts can be fitted into a single picture. The possibilities can be illustrated with a few problems in ion separation and ion identification, problems that can be solved by application of the solubility rules.

Problem 1: A substance is known to be either sodium chloride or sodium sulfate. How could you tell which one it is?

Answer: Dissolve it in water, and add a solution containing a small amount of silver ions (for example, $AgNO_3$ dissolved in water). The formation of a precipitate would indicate that the original substance was sodium chloride. (Addition of Ba^{++} would also make the distinction.)

$$Ag^+ \ (aq) + Cl^- \ (aq) \rightarrow AgCl \ (s) \qquad (Eq. \ 13\text{-}8)$$

$Ag^+ \ (aq) + SO_4^{--} \ (aq) \rightarrow$
  no reaction unless a large amount of Ag^+ is used (*Exp. 13-9*)

Problem 2: What would happen if you mixed aqueous solutions of strontium nitrate, $Sr(NO_3)_2$, and magnesium sulfate, $MgSO_4$?

Answer: Four ions are present: $Sr^{++} \ (aq)$, $NO_3^- \ (aq)$, $Mg^{++} \ (aq)$, and $SO_4^{--} \ (aq)$. All nitrates are soluble in water (Rule 2). Similarly, magnesium sulfate ($MgSO_4$) is soluble, but the sulfate of Sr^{++} is insoluble (Rule 4). Therefore, a precipitate of strontium sulfate ($SrSO_4$) will form.

$$Sr^{++} \ (aq) + SO_4^{--} \ (aq) \rightarrow SrSO_4 \ (s) \qquad (Eq. \ 13\text{-}10)$$

Problem 3: What would happen in each of the following cases if water solutions of the indicated chemicals were mixed?

a. $NaCl + Pb(NO_3)_2$

b. $(NH_4)_2S + FeBr_2$

c. $MgSO_4 + MnCl_2$

Answer: The answers can best be given in the form of net ionic equations.

a. $2Cl^- + Pb^{++} \rightarrow PbCl_2 \ (s)$ (Rule 3)   (*Eq. 13-11*)

b. $Fe^{++} + S^{--} \rightarrow FeS \ (s)$ (Rule 6)   (*Eq. 13-12*)

c. No precipitate is formed (Rules 3 and 4)

Problem 4: How would you separate the ions of Ag^+, Pb^{++}, and Hg^+? The following information is to be used. $AgCl$ is soluble in ammonia solution, and $PbCl_2$ is appreciably soluble in hot water (33.4 g/liter of water at $100°C$ compared with 6.7 g/liter of water at $0°C$).

Answer: An extension of solubility rules can be used to devise a procedure for separating the ions of Ag^+, Pb^{++}, and Hg^+. The three ions are precipitated as the chlorides $AgCl$, $PbCl_2$, and $HgCl$ by the addition of cold dilute hydrochloric acid. The precipitates are collected by filtration and treated with ammonia solution to dissolve the silver chloride. A second filtration, and treatment with hot water, separates the lead chloride, leaving only mercury chloride precipitated.

Solubility relationships for ions are widely used in the interpretation of laboratory observations. Several experiments in *Investigating Chemical Systems* make use of these rules. For example, in Experiment 26 the reactions among six different solutions are studied.

Ex. 13-8 Explain how a student could confirm the presence of each of the two indicated ions in the presence of the other ion.

Solution A: Cu^{++} (aq), Mg^{++} (aq)

Solution B: Cl^- (aq), SO_4^{--} (aq)

Solution C: F^- (aq), Cl^- (aq)

Solution D: Ag^+ (aq), Pb^{++} (aq)

Ex. 13-9 a. Write net ionic equations for possible interactions between the ions in each pair: Mg^{++} (aq) and F^- (aq); Na^+ (aq) and NO_3^- (aq); Ag^+ (aq) and I^- (aq).

b. What reaction will occur when solutions of the following pairs of compounds are mixed: $CaBr_2$ and NaF; $BaCl_2$ and $AgNO_3$; $Pb(NO_3)_2$ and $MgSO_4$; $CuCl_2$ and Na_2S?

13-9 THE FORMATION OF SOLUTIONS CONTAINING IONS

The ions in some ionic solids interact with water to form ionic solutions. On the other hand, when certain sets of ions come together in solution, a precipitate is formed. The formation of a precipitate, such as lead iodide in Experiment 6, suggests that at least some ions interact with each other.

In Chapter 9 the transfer of energy was related quantitatively to changes in structure in a chemical system. In Experiment 8 when aqueous hydrochloric acid was diluted with water, the mixture was found to have a higher temperature than the reactants. This temperature-changing capacity of the components of the initial state was interpreted as an enthalpy lowering in Chapter 9. Dissolving ammonium chloride in water (Experiment 22) causes the enthalpy of the system to rise. In Section 9-14 enthalpy changes produced when solutions were formed or diluted were interpreted as evidence for interaction between solute and solvent. In general, the dissolving of a substance in water at constant temperature is accompanied by a change in enthalpy (Section 9-16). The enthalpy may be raised or lowered.

Why do solutions form, and how can we account for the great differences in the solubilities of ionic compounds?

When any ionic substance is dissolved, the ions must separate. But, since ions of opposite electric charge have a low potential energy when they are close together in a crystal, energy is required to separate the ions. In terms of ionic crystal energy (Section 12-15), energy will have to be supplied to perform the work of separating the charged ions against the attractive forces operating to hold the ions and, thus, the crystal together. For example, for sodium chloride.

$$NaCl\,(s) \rightarrow Na^+\,(g) + Cl^-\,(g) \qquad \Delta H = 183.8 \text{ kcal/mole of NaCl}$$
$$(Exp.\ 13\text{-}13)$$

Since a solution is homogeneous, it is reasonable to assume that a small quantity of salt dissolved in a large quantity of water results in the ions spreading out from the crystal into all parts of the solution. In other words the formation of an ionic solution is a process in which ions are separated. For the dissolving of sodium chloride in water, experiment indicates that the enthalpy change is 0.93 kcal/mole of NaCl. Enthalpy changes for the formation of other solutions are rarely larger than 20 kcal/mole. But the crystal energy for sodium chloride is 183.8 kcal/mole of NaCl. Why does the formation of separated ions in water require so much less energy than the formation of separated gaseous ions?

Interaction between ions and water could provide a way of raising the energy of the ions without absorbing energy from outside the system and therefore without much of an enthalpy change. An understanding of the nature of the interaction of ions and water must take into account the forces that hold ions together in crystals. An interpretation of the interaction of ions and water must include an explanation of how these forces can be overcome.

The force of attraction between two charged particles is given by

$$F = \frac{Kq^+q^-}{Dr^2}$$

where q^+ and q^- are the charges separated by a distance r in a substance that has dielectric constant D. If any substance is present between two unlike charges, the force of attraction between the charges is less than it is when the same charges are separated by a vacuum or by air. When water is between the charges, the force is one-eightieth of the force in a vacuum. Since a vacuum is assigned a dielectric constant of 1, the dielectric constant D for water is 80. On the other hand, the dielectric constant for most other substances is low. Carbon tetrachloride, for instance, has a dielectric constant of about 2.

No one has yet been able to measure the dielectric constant of the space between ions in a crystal lattice, but we can be fairly certain that the dielectric constant is low, much lower than that of water. For want of any direct evidence, the dielectric constant in the space between the ions in an ionic crystal is assumed to be equal to that of a vacuum, 1. Therefore, if water could be inserted between the ions in a salt lattice while maintaining the same distance of separation r, the attractive forces between the ions would be greatly reduced. Consequently, much less energy would be necessary to separate the ions when water is between the ions than when there is no water.

For a water molecule to get between the ions of a crystal, sufficient space must be available. The space required is determined by the size of a water molecule. A water molecule is about the size of an oxygen atom. If no covalent bonds are formed between a water molecule and

Fig. 13-10 *Charge cloud model of a water molecule.*

an ion, the van der Waals radius is the best measure of the size of the water molecule. An oxygen atom has a van der Waals radius of 1.40 A (Table 12-7), and presumably the radius of a water molecule is near this value. A chloride ion (1.81 A) is a little larger and a sodium ion (0.95 A) is a little smaller than a water molecule. Before water molecules can get between the ions of a sodium chloride crystal, it is necessary for the ions to separate by a small amount. The energy of the ions will have to be raised for this initial separation.

Interaction of water molecules and ions in the crystal can be considered as a means of raising the energy of the ions. The charge cloud model of a water molecule consists of four outer two-electron clouds arranged tetrahedrally about the oxygen kernel. The negative charge of the electron clouds is distributed nearly symmetrically about the oxygen nucleus. A proton in each of two of the outer charge clouds completes the charge cloud model for water. The result is a molecule in which the center of positive charge and the center of negative charge do not coincide (Fig. 13-10). This unsymmetrical distribution of positive and negative charge produces a dipole as shown in Fig. 13-11 (Section 8-16). Molecules such as the water molecule, which are dipoles and which contain polar covalent bonds, are referred to as **polar molecules.** It would be reasonable to predict that the water molecule is a polar molecule on the basis of the difference of 1.4 between the electronegativities of hydrogen and oxygen (Section 12-11). The polar character of the water molecule is also evident in the atomic orbital model (Fig. 13-12).

The overlapping of the *s* orbital of each of two hydrogen atoms with

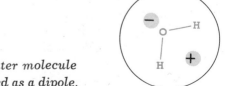

Fig. 13-11 *A water molecule can be represented as a dipole.*

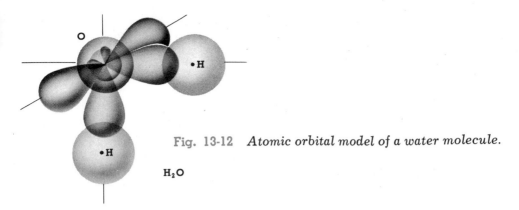

Fig. 13-12 *Atomic orbital model of a water molecule.*

H_2O

two p orbitals of an oxygen atom, followed by repulsion of the protons by the oxygen nucleus, leads to a molecular structure that is positively charged near the hydrogen nuclei and negatively charged near the electrons in the unshared orbitals of the oxygen atom.

When a crystal of sodium chloride is placed in water, the water molecules not only bombard the ions but also exert attractive forces on the sodium and chloride ions. The attraction between the ions and the water molecules tends to separate the ions so that other water molecules can get in between as shown schematically in Fig. 13-13. Once water molecules have moved between the ions of an ionic solid, the process of ion separation becomes easier since the high dielectric constant reduces the attractive forces between the ions.

The argument based exclusively on dielectric constants and dipoles is inadequate, as is illustrated by the relative insolubility of NaCl in liquid hydrogen cyanide, HCN. Hydrogen cyanide has a dielectric

Fig. 13-13 *Water molecules (dipoles) exert attractive forces on the ions at the surface of a crystal and surround the ions that are separated from the crystal.*

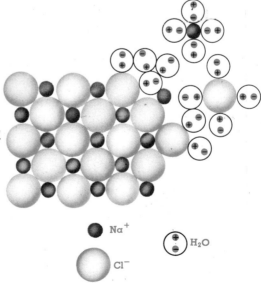

Na$^+$

Cl$^-$

H_2O

constant of 115 at 20°C, which is higher than the dielectric constant of water. Hydrogen cyanide is even more polar than water, yet it does not dissolve sodium chloride as effectively as does water. The HCN molecule is linear, whereas the water molecule is V-shaped. Whether the V-shape is advantageous in getting the first ions loose is not clear. A hydrogen cyanide molecule has a radius of about 1.9 A compared to about 1.4 A for water, and this difference in size may account in part for the difference between the solvent character of water and hydrogen cyanide. Many aspects of the solution process for ionic solids remain unexplained.

The reaction for dissolving sodium chloride is described by

$$NaCl \ (s) \ + \ (y + z) \, H_2O \rightarrow Na^+ \ (H_2O)_y + Cl^- \, (H_2O)_z$$
$$\Delta H = 0.93 \ \text{kcal/mole of NaCl} \quad (Exp. \ 13\text{-}14)$$

The numerical values of y and z, however, are not known with certainty, although y is often considered to be 6. At room temperature no stable compound of sodium chloride and water has been isolated. For this reason, formulas such as Na^+ (aq) and Cl^- (aq) are normally used to represent ions in solution.

In a qualitative way, the solution process represents competition between the interaction of ions of unlike charge and the interaction of solvent with ions. The solution process can be discussed quantitatively in terms of energy data.

13-10 ENTHALPY CHANGES IN THE FORMATION OF A SOLUTION

Table 13-5 lists the enthalpies of solution for the halides of the alkali metals and the alkaline-earth metals.

In Chapter 12 the Born-Haber cycle was introduced as a means of interpreting the enthalpy changes associated with the formation of an ionic solid from its component elements. The same technique can be applied to enthalpy changes associated with the solution process.

TABLE 13-5 ENTHALPIES OF SOLUTION (kcal/mole) FOR ALKALI METAL HALIDES AND ALKALINE-EARTH METAL HALIDES AT 25°C

LiCl	—8.88	$BeCl_2$	—41.6	KF	—4.24
NaCl	+0.93	$MgCl_2$	—37.06	KBr	+4.79
KCl	+4.12	$CaCl_2$	—19.8	KI	+4.90
RbCl	+4.0	$SrCl_2$	—12.4	BaF_2	+0.9
CsCl	+4.3	$BaCl_2$	—3.16	$BaBr_2$	—6.1

SOURCE: Calculated from data in *National Bureau of Standards Bulletin 500.*

The enthalpies of solution for ionic solids given in Table 13-5 are quantitative measures of the heat transfer in the reactions described by

$$MX \ (s) \rightarrow M^+ \ (aq) + X^- \ (aq) \qquad (Eq. \ 13\text{-}15)$$

A two-step process describes how a solution is formed from an ionic solid: (1) separation of the ions, which raises the enthalpy of the system (Equation 13-16); and (2) interaction of the ions with water, which lowers the enthalpy of the system (Equation 13-17).

$$MX \ (s) \rightarrow M^+ \ (g) + X^- \ (g) \qquad (Eq. \ 13\text{-}16)$$

$$M^+ \ (g) + X^- \ (g) \rightarrow M^+ \ (aq) + X^- \ (aq) \qquad (Eq. \ 13\text{-}17)$$

The enthalpy change for the reaction in Equation 13-16 is the crystal energy (Section 12-15). The enthalpy change, for example, when separated gaseous Na^+ and Cl^- ions are formed from solid sodium chloride is 183.8 kcal/mole of NaCl.

$$NaCl \ (s) \rightarrow Na^+ \ (g) + Cl^- \ (g) \qquad \Delta H = 183.8 \text{ kcal/mole of NaCl}$$
$$(Exp. \ 13\text{-}18)$$

The overall solution process described in Equations 13-16 and 13-17 corresponds to the process for which the enthalpy of solution is listed in Table 13-5. The enthalpy of solution for sodium chloride is 0.93 kcal/mole of NaCl or about 1 kcal/mole. From the enthalpy changes for the reactions shown in Expression 13-18 and in Equation 13-15, the enthalpy change for the reaction shown in Equation 13-17 can be calculated.

The enthalpy change calculated for the interaction of Na^+ (g) and Cl^- (g) ions with water is

$$Na^+ \ (g) + Cl^- \ (g) \rightarrow Na^+ \ (aq) + Cl^- \ (aq)$$
$$\Delta H = -182.9 \text{ kcal/mole of NaCl}$$

The interaction of gaseous ions with water is called **hydration,** and the accompanying enthalpy change is called the **hydration energy.** The enthalpy changes for the solution of sodium chloride are indicated by the enthalpy diagram in Fig. 13-14.

The enthalpy of solution of lithium chloride is the greatest of the alkali metal chlorides (Table 13-5). But the lithium ion is also the smallest of the ions of the five alkali metals. The hydration energy for Li^+ (radius = 0.60 A) is expected to be large compared with the hydration energy of Na^+ (radius = 0.95 A) because the water dipoles are farther away from the center of the sodium ion, whereas the net ionic charge is the same in both cases. Therefore, water molecules are held less strongly around the sodium ion than around the lithium ion.

Sodium chloride and lithium chloride have hydration energies of −182.9 kcal/mole and −211 kcal/mole, respectively, or a difference of

29 kcal/mole. However, the crystal energies differ by only 19 kcal/mole. The fact that sodium chloride dissolves with absorption of heat and lithium chloride with evolution of heat must be due to some difference between lithium ion and sodium ion. The enthalpy data in Figs. 13-14 and 13-15 suggest that the interaction of lithium ion with water produces a larger enthalpy change than the interaction of the lithium ion with chloride ion, whereas the interaction of sodium ion with either water or chloride ion produces about equal enthalpy changes.

The same trend toward less negative and hence more positive enthalpies of solution with increased ionic size is manifest in the alkaline-earth metal chlorides, except that the enthalpies of solution are all negative and larger than those of the alkali metal chlorides. This difference between the properties of the alkali metal halides and the alkaline-earth metal halides is related to the fact that the positive charge

Fig. 13-14 *Crystal energy, hydration energy, and enthalpy of solution of sodium chloride.*

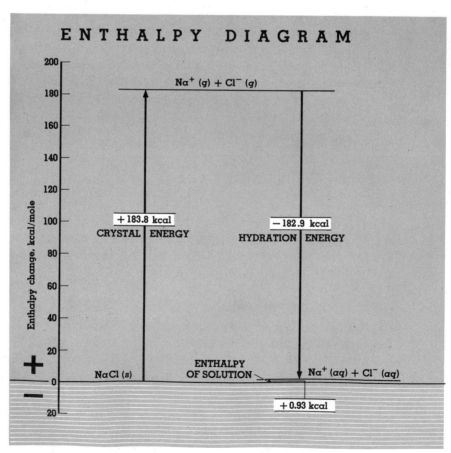

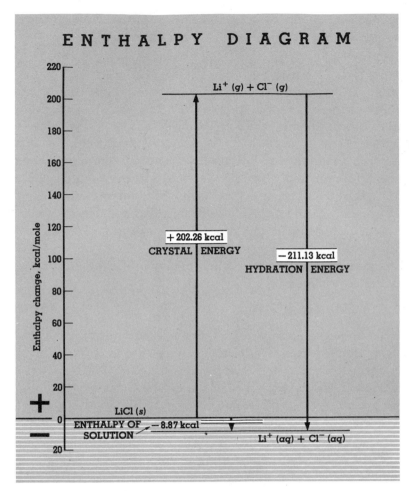

ENTHALPY DIAGRAM

Enthalpy change, kcal/mole

$Li^+ (g) + Cl^- (g)$

$+202.26 \text{ kcal}$
CRYSTAL ENERGY

-211.13 kcal
HYDRATION ENERGY

LiCl (s)

ENTHALPY OF SOLUTION -8.87 kcal

$Li^+ (aq) + Cl^- (aq)$

Fig. 13-15 *Crystal energy, hydration energy, and enthalpy of solution of lithium chloride.*

on an alkaline-earth metal ion is twice that on an alkali metal ion. A larger charge on an ion should result in there being greater interaction between the ion and the polar water molecule.

13-11 OXIDATION NUMBERS

The reaction of sodium metal and chlorine molecules (Section 12-15) is summarized by

$$2Na \ (s) + Cl_2 \ (g) \rightarrow 2Na^+Cl^- \ (s) \qquad (Eq. \ 13\text{-}19)$$

The sodium atom is described by the charge cloud model as containing a single one-electron cloud outside the kernel. Seven two-electron clouds and two kernels make up the chlorine molecule. The resulting sodium and chloride ions may each be considered to have a tetrahedral arrangement of four two-electron clouds outside a kernel. Lewis structures for the reactants and products are illustrated in

$$2Na\cdot + :\ddot{C}l:\ddot{C}l: \rightarrow 2Na^+ + 2:\ddot{C}l:^- \qquad (Eq.\ 13\text{-}20)$$

Examination of the equation shows that one electron has been transferred from each sodium atom to give Na^+ and that two electrons (total) have been gained by a chlorine molecule to give two chloride ions. Equation 13-20 is somewhat misleading in that it implies that sodium has lost an electron in a transfer to chlorine. Actually volume measurements demonstrate that the electron is closer to the sodium nucleus in the sodium chloride crystal than it is to the sodium nucleus in metallic sodium (Section 12-4). The change is in the degree of control. In sodium chloride the chlorine nucleus exerts greater control over the electron than does the sodium nucleus.

The formation of magnesium ions and oxide ions in the burning of magnesium is represented by

$$2Mg\ (s) + O_2\ (g) \rightarrow 2Mg^{++}O^{--}\ (s) \qquad (Eq.\ 13\text{-}21)$$

According to the atomic orbital model, the $3s$ electrons of magnesium have been transferred to the $2p$ orbitals in oxygen to give O^{--}. In the two reactions represented by Equations 13-19 and 13-21, electrons originally in the metal become part of the nonmetal ions.

For over a century the combination of oxygen with another element has been known as **oxidation.** In the reaction of magnesium with oxygen to form magnesium oxide, the magnesium atoms are said to be oxidized. When magnesium atoms react with chlorine molecules to form magnesium chloride, Mg^{++} ions are formed which are in every way identical with the magnesium ions present in magnesium oxide.

$$Mg + Cl_2 \rightarrow Mg^{++} + 2Cl^- \qquad (Eq.\ 13\text{-}22)$$

Recognition of the fact that magnesium ions are formed from magnesium atoms in both reactions has led chemists to call the reaction of chlorine and magnesium an oxidation reaction also.

Reactions other than those that form ions can also be considered to be oxidation reactions. Thus hydrogen molecules react with oxygen molecules to form water molecules, and the burning of hydrogen (Equation 13-23) is certainly an oxidation of the hydrogen in the same sense that the burning of magnesium (Equation 13-21) is an oxidation.

$$2H_2\ (g) + O_2\ (g) \rightarrow 2H_2O\ (l) \qquad (Eq.\ 13\text{-}23)$$

If Equation 13-23 is compared with the equation for the reaction of hydrogen molecules with chlorine molecules, the similarity between the two reactions is apparent.

$$H_2\ (g) + Cl_2\ (g) \rightarrow 2HCl\ (g) \qquad (Eq.\ 13\text{-}24)$$

In both reactions each hydrogen atom forms a covalent bond with an atom other than hydrogen. If Equation 13-23 represents an oxidation of hydrogen, then also Equation 13-24 represents an oxidation of hydrogen.

However, when the oxidation reactions of hydrogen are compared with the oxidation reactions of magnesium in another way, the two cases appear to be quite different. In the oxidation of hydrogen (Equations 13-23 and 13-24), covalent compounds are formed; in the oxidation of magnesium (Equations 13-21 and 13-22), ionic compounds are formed. To apply the same term, oxidation, to all four reactions might seem to be unwise, but a general term which includes all four types of reaction is both useful and convenient. Hence, chemists have invented a definition of oxidation which applies to the four reactions represented by Equations 13-21 to 13-24 and which includes other reactions in addition to those between elements. The definition is based upon a concept known as the oxidation number.

The **oxidation number** of an element in a compound is the charge, positive or negative, which would be assigned to the atoms of that element in the compound, if all the bonds were ionic bonds. We know perfectly well that not all the bonds are ionic; some bonds are ionic, but others are not. It is arbitrary, and merely for convenience in computing oxidation numbers, that all compounds are treated as if they were ionic. To obtain a set of consistent, though arbitrary, oxidation numbers, it is necessary only to design a set of rules.

For deciding the type of charge, positive $(+)$ or negative $(-)$, of an atom, the electronegativity scale (Fig. 12-13) is used. The less electronegative element of a pair is arbitrarily given a positive oxidation number, and the more electronegative is given a negative oxidation number.

Of all the elements, fluorine has the highest electronegativity. In all its compounds, then, fluorine is assigned a negative oxidation number. Oxygen is second only to fluorine in electronegativity and is therefore assigned a negative oxidation number in all its compounds, except in oxygen–fluorine compounds, for example, the oxide of fluorine, F_2O. The alkali metals are similar to each other, and all have low electronegativity. Therefore, these elements will have positive oxidation numbers in compounds.

In all their compounds, the alkali metals behave as do ions with a single positive charge or exist in polar molecules with positive charge on the metal atom. Therefore each of the alkali metals is assigned an oxidation number of $+1$. In combination with fluorine the atomic ratio of alkali metal and fluorine is always 1:1, and the fluorine behaves as an ion of charge $1-$. Fluorine is therefore assigned an oxidation number of -1.

Hydrogen and fluorine form a compound which is a gas at room temperature and hence does not appear to be made up of ions. Fluorine is more electronegative than hydrogen. If fluorine is assigned an oxidation number of −1, then hydrogen is assigned an oxidation number of +1. Hydrogen also combines with oxygen to form water in which the atomic ratio is 2:1. If hydrogen is assigned a +1 oxidation number, oxygen will have an oxidation number of −2.

The examples discussed so far fit into the following general rules for the assignment of oxidation numbers.

1. The algebraic sum of the oxidation numbers of all the atoms in a compound must be zero (Fig. 13-16). In any ion the algebraic sum must equal the charge on the ion. Thus, the sum of the oxidation numbers of one sulfur atom and four oxygen atoms in the sulfate ion (SO_4^{--}) must equal −2.

2. The atoms in molecules (for example, F_2, O_2, N_2, H_2, S_8) or crystals (for example, Li, Ca, Au, U) of elements are bonded to atoms of identical electronegativity and are therefore assigned oxidation numbers of zero.

3. In all compounds except peroxides (such as H_2O_2) and F_2O, oxygen has an oxidation number of −2. In peroxides the oxidation number of oxygen is −1 because hydrogen has an oxidation number of +1, and in F_2O it is +2 because fluorine is more electronegative than oxygen.

Fig. 13-16 . *The algebraic sum of the oxidation numbers in a compound must be zero.*

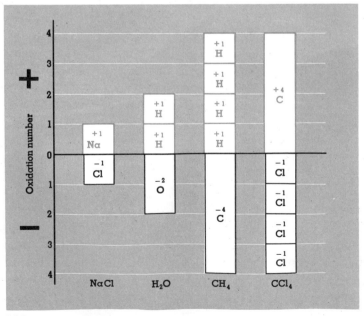

4. In all compounds except the metal hydrides (for example, LiH and $LiAlH_4$), the oxidation number of hydrogen is $+1$; in the metal hydrides it is -1.

5. In all compounds, the alkali metals have oxidation numbers of $+1$ and the alkaline-earth metals have oxidation numbers of $+2$. Boron and aluminum ordinarily have oxidation numbers of $+3$.

6. In halogen compounds containing only one other element, the oxidation numbers of the halogen elements are -1.

7. In a compound not covered by the above rules, the element of high electronegativity has a negative oxidation number and the element of low electronegativity has a positive oxidation number.

13-12 APPLICATION OF RULES FOR OXIDATION NUMBERS

On the basis of the seven rules, the oxidation numbers of elements in compounds can be calculated from the formulas of the compounds.

Example 1: The formula of carbon dioxide is CO_2. Hence the oxidation number of carbon in this compound is $+4$ since that of oxygen is -2 (Rule 3). The oxidation number of carbon in CO is $+2$.

Example 2: The formula of carbon tetrachloride is CCl_4. Hence the oxidation number of carbon in this compound is $+4$ since that of chlorine is -1 (Rule 6).

Example 3: The formula of methane is CH_4. Hence the oxidation number of carbon in this compound is -4 if hydrogen is $+1$ (Rule 4).

This method of classifying compounds by the magnitude of the oxidation number of the central element is used in a naming system devised in 1920 by a German chemist, Alfred Stock. The detailed rules for naming compounds according to this system are given in the Appendix.

The most common usage of the Stock nomenclature system is for designating the oxidation number of the metallic component of compounds. In copper (II) sulfate, the Roman numeral II indicates the oxidation number of the copper in the compound. This oxidation-number designation is often helpful in distinguishing two compounds containing the same elements but differing in the oxidation number of one of the elements. For example, copper forms copper (I) chloride, CuCl, and copper (II) chloride, $CuCl_2$; iron can form iron (II) chloride, $FeCl_2$, and iron (III) chloride, $FeCl_3$. Some elements form compounds with only a single oxidation number for the element. Examples of this group are the alkali metals, the alkaline-earth metals, and zinc. The names of compounds formed from elements in this group ordinarily do not include the oxidation numbers.

Older names of compounds were frequently based on inadequate concepts of what compounds could or could not be prepared. The Stock system, on the other hand, presents a systematic way of establishing the name of a compound. Universal usage of the Stock system has not been obtained so that it is still necessary to recognize the older names.

Ex. 13-10 Using Stock nomenclature, name the following compounds: $AuCl$, $AuCl_3$; Tl_2O, $TlBr_3$; FeO, Fe_2O_3; $CrCl_2$, $CrCl_3$; CuI, CuO; $MnSO_4$, MnF_3, $MnCl_4$.

13-13 OXIDATION NUMBERS IN COMPOUNDS OF THREE ELEMENTS

If three or more elements are combined in a compound whose formula is known, the oxidation number of any one of the elements may be calculated if the oxidation numbers of all the other elements are assigned. For example, from the oxidation number for hydrogen, $+1$, and for oxygen, -2, the oxidation number of sulfur in sulfuric acid, H_2SO_4, is calculated to be $+6$.

The sulfur in both sulfuric acid and sulfur trioxide (SO_3) has an oxidation number of $+6$. The two compounds are related chemically, since sulfuric acid is formed by reaction of sulfur trioxide with water.

$$SO_3 + H_2O \rightarrow H_2SO_4 \qquad (Eq.\ 13\text{-}25)$$

In this reaction there is no change in oxidation number for any of the elements involved.

Similarly, sulfur has the same oxidation number ($+4$) in sulfur dioxide, SO_2, as in sulfurous acid, H_2SO_3, and these two compounds are chemically related in the reaction of sulfur dioxide with water.

$$SO_2 + H_2O \rightarrow H_2SO_3 \qquad (Eq.\ 13\text{-}26)$$

In $KClO_4$, potassium has an oxidation number of $+1$ (Rule 5). Then, if oxygen is -2, Cl in $KClO_4$ must be $+7$. The common name for $KClO_4$ is potassium perchlorate, but according to the Stock system, the name is potassium chlorate (VII).

Ex. 13-11 *a.* What is the sum of the oxidation numbers corresponding to the formula of a chemical compound?

b. Calculate the oxidation number of the element whose symbol is underlined in each of the following formulas: $Na\underline{Cl}O_4$, $Na\underline{Cl}O_3$, $Na\underline{Cl}O_2$, $Na\underline{Cl}O$, $Na\underline{Cl}$, $K_2\underline{Cr}_2O_7$, $H_2\underline{C}O_3$, $\underline{Sb}_2O_5$, $\underline{Ti}Cl_4$, $Ca\underline{H}_2$, $\underline{N}_2O_5$, $\underline{N}_2O_4$, $\underline{N}_2O_3$, $\underline{N}O$, $\underline{N}_2O$, $\underline{N}H_3$, $\underline{P}H_3$, $Na\underline{H}_2PO_4$, $Na_2\underline{HP}O_3$, $Ba\underline{O}_2$, $O\underline{F}_2$.

13-14 USES OF OXIDATION NUMBERS

The Stock system of nomenclature is completely dependent on the concept of oxidation number. Oxidation numbers can also be used as a classification scheme for types of reagents, or reactants. For example, in the listed carbon compounds, the conversion of methane, CH_4, to CO_2 or CCl_4 by reaction with O_2 and Cl_2, respectively, increases the oxidation number of carbon.

Compound	Oxidation Number of Carbon
CH_4	-4
CH_3Cl	-2
CH_2Cl_2	0
$CHCl_3$	$+2$
CCl_4	$+4$
CO_2	$+4$

Reagents, such as oxygen or chlorine, which can increase the oxidation number of an element are called **oxidizing agents.** An oxidizing agent is needed to convert SO_2 to SO_3 since the oxidation number of sulfur is raised. Similarly, a reagent which lowers the oxidation number of an element in a compound is called a **reducing agent.**

13-15 OXIDATION-REDUCTION REACTIONS

The most useful thing that comes from the concept of the oxidation number is a simplified system for writing chemical equations. Equations 13-21 to 13-24 show that the increases in oxidation numbers for magnesium and hydrogen are accompanied by equivalent decreases in oxidation numbers for oxygen and chlorine.

$$2Mg + O_2 \rightarrow 2Mg^{++} + 2O^{--} \qquad (Eq.\ 13\text{-}21)$$

$$Mg + Cl_2 \rightarrow Mg^{++} + 2Cl^- \qquad (Eq.\ 13\text{-}22)$$

$$2H_2 + O_2 \rightarrow 2H_2O \qquad (Eq.\ 13\text{-}23)$$

$$H_2 + Cl_2 \rightarrow 2HCl \qquad (Eq.\ 13\text{-}24)$$

In Equations 13-21 and 13-23 the oxidation number of oxygen changes from zero to -2, and that of chlorine in Equations 13-22 and 13-24 from zero to -1. A decrease in oxidation number of an element is called **reduction. Oxidation** is defined analogously as an increase in oxidation number. Magnesium is oxidized when it is changed in oxidation number from zero in the element to $+2$ in the compound. In discussing both oxidation and reduction, the algebraic sign of the oxidation number must be considered. Thus, a change of oxidation number from -4 to -2 (for example, the carbon in the process $CH_4 \rightarrow CH_3Cl$) is an increase in oxidation number and, hence, is an oxidation just as a change from $+2$ to $+4$ (for example, the nitrogen in the process NO $\rightarrow NO_2$) would be. The relation of oxidation and reduction to change in oxidation number can be shown schematically (page 584).

$$\text{Oxidation: an increase in oxidation number}$$

$$\ldots \quad -4 \quad -3 \quad -2 \quad -1 \quad 0 \quad +1 \quad +2 \quad +3 \quad +4 \quad \ldots$$

$$\text{Reduction: a decrease in oxidation number}$$

Oxidation and reduction are always found to occur together during a reaction. Whenever one element is oxidized, another is reduced at the same time. Reactions in which this occurs are called oxidation-reduction reactions.

The idea that some reactions are oxidations and reductions and others are not is, like the concept of oxidation numbers, a rather arbitrary view of reactions. There is no single operational definition of an oxidation-reduction reaction. This means that there is no purely experimental test by which oxidation-reduction processes can be identified without consideration of oxidation numbers. With few exceptions, every reaction in which one or more substances are elements will be an oxidation-reduction reaction. Reactions in electrochemical cells are considered to be oxidation-reduction reactions. On the other hand, proton-transfer reactions are not usually considered to be examples of oxidation-reduction. The description of a reaction as oxidation-reduction is often convenient for classification purposes. It does not, however, give any clue as to why a reaction occurs or does not occur.

13-16 BOOKKEEPING IN OXIDATION-REDUCTION REACTIONS

In an equation for an oxidation-reduction reaction, the total increase in oxidation number is always equal to the total decrease in oxidation number. Thus, in the reaction of magnesium with chlorine, the total increase in oxidation number is 2 (from 0 to +2 for one magnesium atom) and the total decrease in oxidation number is 2 (from 0 to −1 for each chlorine atom). Similarly in the reaction of magnesium and oxygen, the total increase is 4 (0 to +2 for each of the two magnesium atoms) and the total decrease is 4 (0 to −2 for each of the two oxygen atoms).

An equation for an oxidation-reduction reaction can be written by adjusting coefficients for the formulas of the reactants and products in such a way that the total increase in oxidation number equals the total decrease in oxidation number. This procedure is possible because of the first rule for oxidation numbers (Section 13-11) that all compounds have a total oxidation number of zero and that all ions have a total oxidation number equal to the ionic charge. This means that the sum of oxidation numbers for the products in a reaction must be identical with the sum of oxidation numbers for the reactants.

In writing equations for oxidation-reduction reactions, just as for other reactions, the compositions and formulas must be known for the substances that react and for the products that are formed. In the following scheme for writing oxidation-reduction equations, Steps 3 to 5 take into account conservation of oxidation numbers, conservation of electric charges, and conservation of atoms, respectively.

Step 1. Write correct formulas for each reactant and product.

Step 2. Determine which atoms undergo change in oxidation number in the reaction by assigning oxidation numbers to all elements in the reaction.

Step 3. Determine the increase in oxidation number for the reaction of 1 mole of the reducing agent and the decrease in oxidation number for the reaction of 1 mole of the oxidizing agent. Make the increase equal the decrease by inserting suitable coefficients for each of the reactants. (This establishes the molar ratio of oxidizing agent to reducing agent, and the ratio cannot be changed for the remainder of the equation-writing process. If you find that two substances are reduced and that nothing is oxidized, or vice-versa, something is wrong. Either the formulas of reactants or products are in error or the oxidation numbers have not been assigned properly.)

Step 4. If ions in water solution are involved in the reaction, add H^+ or OH^- ions to the expression on the appropriate side of the arrow so that the total ionic charges of reactants and products are equal. If the reaction is carried out in acidic solution, use H^+ ions in the equation; if in basic solution, use OH^- ions.

Step 5. Make the number of hydrogen atoms in the expression on the two sides of the arrow equal by adding H_2O molecules to the reactants or products. Check by counting oxygen atoms. If there are the same number of oxygen atoms in the reactants and products, the equation then represents the reaction.

The following examples illustrate the procedure just outlined. The (aq) symbols and spectator ions are omitted. The numbered steps correspond to the steps just described.

Example 1: Write a net ionic equation for the reaction of potassium manganate (VII), $KMnO_4$, with sodium stannate (II), Na_2SnO_2, in basic solution to give manganese (IV) oxide, MnO_2, and the stannate (IV) ion SnO_3^{--}.

Step 1. $$MnO_4^- + SnO_2^{--} \rightarrow MnO_2 + SnO_3^{--}$$

Step 2. Assume that the oxidation number of oxygen remains unchanged, and assign oxidation numbers to manganese and tin.

$$\overset{+7}{MnO_4^-} + \overset{+2}{SnO_2^{--}} \rightarrow \overset{+4}{MnO_2} + \overset{+4}{SnO_3^{--}}$$

Step 3. Calculate the increase and decrease of oxidation number.

Mn decreases 3 in oxidation number

$$\overset{+7}{MnO_4^-} + \overset{+2}{SnO_2^{--}} \rightarrow \overset{+4}{MnO_2} + \overset{+4}{SnO_3^{--}}$$

Sn increases 2 in oxidation number

Make the increase in oxidation number equal the decrease.

decrease of 2 × 3 for Mn

$$2MnO_4^- + 3SnO_2^{--} \rightarrow 2MnO_2 + 3SnO_3^{--}$$

increase of 3 × 2 for Sn

Step 4. Because the reaction mixture is basic and because the ionic charges are not equal on the two sides of the expression, add OH^- to the right-hand side and make the OH^- coefficient 2 in order to have equal ionic charges. Each side now shows a total charge of 8—.

$$2MnO_4^- + 3SnO_2^{--} \rightarrow 2MnO_2 + 3SnO_3^{--} + \mathbf{2OH^-}$$

Step 5. Since there are two hydrogen atoms on the right and none on left, this means that H_2O will have to be added to the left side.

$$2MnO_4^- + 3SnO_2^{--} + \mathbf{H_2O} \rightarrow 2MnO_2 + 3SnO_3^{--} + 2OH^-$$

Check by counting oxygen atoms on each side (15). The equation now represents a chemical reaction.

Example 2:   Write the net ionic equation for the reaction of potassium dichromate (VI), $K_2Cr_2O_7$, with sodium sulfate (IV), Na_2SO_3, in acid solution to give chromium (III) ion and the sulfate (VI) ion.

Step 1. $$Cr_2O_7^{--} + SO_3^{--} \rightarrow Cr^{+++} + SO_4^{--}$$

Step 2. Assign oxidation numbers for Cr and S.

$$\overset{2(+6)}{Cr_2O_7^{--}} + \overset{+4}{SO_3^{--}} \rightarrow \overset{+3}{Cr^{+++}} + \overset{+6}{SO_4^{--}}$$

In $Cr_2O_7^{--}$, with seven oxygen atoms and an ionic charge of 2—, the two Cr atoms must together account for an oxidation number of +12 $[-2 \times 7 - (-2) = -12]$. Each Cr atom on the left therefore has an oxidation number of +6.

Step 3. Calculate the increase and decrease of oxidation number, and make the increase equal the decrease.

decrease of 2 × 3 for 2Cr

$$\overset{2(+6)}{Cr_2O_7^{--}} + \overset{+4}{3SO_3^{--}} \rightarrow \overset{2(+3)}{2Cr^{+++}} + \overset{+6}{3SO_4^{--}}$$

increase of 3 × 2 for S

Step 4. Because the reaction mixture is acidic and because the ionic charges are not balanced, add 8H$^+$ on the left to make ionic charges equal.

$$Cr_2O_7^{--} + 3SO_3^{--} + \mathbf{8H^+} \rightarrow 2Cr^{+++} + 3SO_4^{--}$$

Step 5. Finally, count the hydrogen atoms, and add 4H$_2$O on the right.

$$Cr_2O_7^{--} + 3SO_3^{--} + 8H^+ \rightarrow 2Cr^{+++} + 3SO_4^{--} + \mathbf{4H_2O}$$

Count the oxygen atoms on each side (16). The equation now represents a chemical reaction.

Example 3: Write the equation for the reaction of Fe$_3$O$_4$ with aluminum to give iron and aluminum oxide.

Step 1.
$$Fe_3O_4 + Al \rightarrow Fe + Al_2O_3$$

Step 2. Assign oxidation numbers to iron and aluminum.

$$\overset{3(+8/3)}{Fe_3O_4} + \overset{0}{Al} \rightarrow \overset{0}{Fe} + \overset{2(+3)}{Al_2O_3}$$

decrease of 3(8/3) for 3Fe

$$\overset{3(+8/3)}{Fe_3O_4} + \overset{0}{2Al} \rightarrow \overset{0}{3Fe} + \overset{2(+3)}{Al_2O_3}$$

increase of 2 × 3 for 2Al

Step 3. To make the increase in oxidation number equal the decrease in oxidation number, calculate the lowest common multiple of 8 and 6, which is 24. Set coefficients so that there will be an increase of 24 in oxidation number for Al and a decrease of 24 in oxidation number for Fe. Hence

$$3Fe_3O_4 + 8Al \rightarrow 9Fe + 4Al_2O_3$$

Only the first three steps in the equation-writing process are needed in this example, since no electric charges on ions are involved. Note the occurrence of a fractional oxidation number in this example, a manifest impossibility in terms of charges on atoms, and yet through the use of fractional oxidation numbers, an equation can be written. This emphasizes the usefulness of the purely formal bookkeeping system for oxidation numbers. By applying a set of consistent rules in the proper order, it is possible to write the equation without detailed information concerning the actual structure of the substance involved. In a crystal of Fe$_3$O$_4$, one-third of the iron ions have a charge of 2+

and two-thirds have a charge of 3+. For this reason, the equation could have been written using $Fe_2O_3 \cdot FeO$ in place of Fe_3O_4.

Example 4: Sometimes the same substance undergoes both oxidation and reduction in a chemical change. Chlorine reacts to give chloride ion and chlorate (V) ion in basic solution.

Step 1.
$$Cl_2 \rightarrow Cl^- + ClO_3^-$$

Step 2. As a further bookkeeping aid in these circumstances, the formula for the substance that is both oxidized and reduced may be written twice.

$$\overset{0}{Cl_2} + \overset{0}{Cl_2} \rightarrow \overset{-1}{Cl^-} + \overset{+5}{ClO_3^-}$$

decrease of 1 for Cl

$$\overset{0}{Cl_2} + \overset{0}{Cl_2} \rightarrow \overset{-1}{2Cl^-} + \overset{+5}{2ClO_3^-}$$

increase of 5 for Cl

Step 3. There will have to be five times as many Cl_2 molecules reduced (decrease in oxidation number) as are oxidized.

$$Cl_2 + 5Cl_2 \rightarrow 10Cl^- + 2ClO_3^-$$

Step 4. Because the reaction mixture is basic, add $12OH^-$ to the left side to make the ionic charges equal.

$$Cl_2 + 5Cl_2 + 12OH^- \rightarrow 10Cl^- + 2ClO_3^-$$

Step 5. Now that Step 4 has been completed, the coefficients for Cl_2 can be combined. Finally, $6H_2O$ molecules are necessary on the right-hand side to provide for the 12 hydrogen atoms on the left.

$$6Cl_2 + 12OH^- \rightarrow 10Cl^- + 2ClO_3^- + 6H_2O$$

Because it is customary to use the smallest integers possible, all the coefficients should be divided by 2.

$$3Cl_2 + 6OH^- \rightarrow 5Cl^- + ClO_3^- + 3H_2O$$

Check by counting oxygen atoms on each side (6).

Oxidation numbers provide a scheme for classifying the different compounds of a given element and a basis for a systematic nomenclature of chemical compounds. For systems which involve more than about five reactants and products, oxidation numbers usually provide a way of simplifying the bookkeeping necessary for writing an equation for the reaction.

13-17 SUMMARY

The idea that some substances contain ions has been applied to gases, to solids, and now to solutions. The idea of ions makes it possible to account for electric conductivity of solutions and to provide a rather systematic picture of a variety of chemical reactions.

Electric charge can be assigned to ions in solution by a study of the quantitative relation between charge flow through a solution and the extent of reaction at the electrodes. Changes in the concentration of solute in solutions through which charge is flowing can be used to establish the chemical identity of ions. In Section 13-3 this was applied to the determination of the charge type and the magnitude of charge on ions.

Ions of opposite charge interact to form solids with low electric potential energy. The separation of ions normally raises their potential energy. The energy can be provided through interaction between solvent molecules and ions. By virtue of the solvent-ion interaction, the enthalpy of solution is either slightly endothermic or even exothermic as the ions dissolve. Water molecules with their unsymmetrical distribution of charge are particularly effective for lowering the potential energy of separated ions. Small size and high charge for the ions also favors interaction with water.

The competition between solvent-ion interaction and ion-ion interaction in the crystal provides a qualitative picture for the dissolving of an ionic solid in water. It also provides a basis for working out enthalpy relations. Using this idea of competitive interaction, it is possible to interpret the enthalpy of solution as the difference between two large enthalpy changes—crystal energy (ion-ion interaction) and hydration energy (solvent-ion interaction).

The idea that some atoms exist as charged species in solution or in solids can be extended arbitrarily to all atoms in compounds. Direct experimental data do not justify this extension, but it is nonetheless useful as a bookkeeping device. This extended notion of ionic charge is called oxidation number. Oxidation numbers are assigned in accordance with a consistent set of rules. In many reactions the oxidation numbers of elements do not change, but in many others the oxidation numbers do change. A decrease in oxidation number is called reduction, and an increase is called oxidation. Oxidation numbers are useful in writing equations for oxidation-reduction reactions.

Ex. 13-12 List the characteristic properties which might be used to identify an ion.

Ex. 13-13 Write formulas for the following compounds.

a. Nickel(II) sulfide   c. Tin(II) chloride

b. Titanium(IV) oxide   d. Thallium(I) sulfate

e. Sodium manganate(VII)   g. Iron(II) carbonate

f. Lead(IV) oxide   h. Nitrogen(IV) oxide

Ex. 13-14 The charges on the ions in a salt can be indicated in an ionic formula. For example, the formula for sodium chloride can be written as Na^+Cl^-. Indicate the charges on the ions in each of the following salts.

a. Silver chlorate(VII)   f. Aluminum sulfate

b. Lead sulfate(VI)   g. Ammonium iodide

c. Ammonium carbonate   h. Sodium sulfate(IV)

d. Zinc bromide   i. Calcium carbonate

e. Magnesium hydroxide   j. Potassium nitrate(V)

Ex. 13-15 The list shows the number of electrons in some isoelectronic negative ions.

Number of Electrons	Ion
50	ClO_4^-, SO_4^{--}, PO_4^{---}
32	NO_3^-, CO_3^{--}
18	Cl^-, S^{--}

a. What general statement can be made concerning the relative solubilities of the salts for a set of isoelectronic negative ions?

b. Does the general statement apply equally well to a set of isoelectronic positive ions?

Ex. 13-16 For each of the following reactions write an equation.

a. Water is decomposed by electrolysis to produce hydrogen gas and oxygen gas.

b. Zinc metal reacts with a solution of sulfuric acid, H_2SO_4 (aq), to produce hydrogen gas, aqueous zinc(II) ions, and aqueous sulfate ions.

c. Chlorine gas reacts with an aqueous solution containing bromide ions to produce bromine (Br_2) and chloride ions.

d. Iron(II) ions react with manganate(VII) ions in an acid solution to produce iron(III) ions, manganese(II) ions, and water.

Ex. 13-17 What two primary changes in energy are considered to occur when an ionic solid dissolves in water?

Ex. 13-18 Why does the temperature rise for some solutions as additional solute is dissolved, whereas the temperature falls for other solutions as additional solute is dissolved?

Ex. 13-19 Change the following expressions to equations.

a. $Cr_2O_7^{--} + SO_2 + H^+ \rightarrow Cr^{+++} + HSO_4^- + H_2O$

b. Cu (s) $+ NO_3^- \rightarrow Cu^{++} + NO$ (g) (acid solution)

c. NH_3 (g) $+ O_2$ (g) $\rightarrow NO_2$ (g) $+ H_2O$ (g)

d. NF_3 (g) $+ H_2O \rightarrow HF$ (aq) $+ NO$ (g) $+ NO_2$ (g)

e. $BrO_3^- + Br^- \rightarrow Br_2$ (l) $+ H_2O$ (acid solution)

f. $I_2 + Cl_2 + H_2O \rightarrow HIO_3 + HCl$

PART FOUR: BONDS IN CHEMICAL SYSTEMS

Chapters 11, 12, and 13

SUBSTANCES have been classified into three major groups: covalent, metallic, and ionic. These groupings have in turn been tied to the type of bond between atoms in each substance. In Chapters 7 and 10, the bond formed by sharing of electrons between pairs of nuclei was called a covalent bond. In Chapter 11 the bond formed by sharing of electrons among many nuclei was called a metallic bond. The formation of structures made up of charged atoms or molecules (called ions) led to ionic bonds as described in Chapter 12. Many ionic substances dissolve in water to give solutions as described in Chapter 13.

As a summary of these bond types, let us consider a specific chemical system in terms of the relation of the properties of the substances and ideas about bonds. Potassium chloride was considered briefly in Sections 12-4 and 13-1. Potassium chloride can be formed from the reaction of potassium and chlorine. The properties of these three substances lead to the classification of chlorine as covalent, potassium as metallic, and potassium chloride as ionic. At 25°C the standard enthalpy of formation for solid potassium chloride is —104.2 kcal/mole of KCl. The energy of potassium chloride is therefore lower than the energy of the elements from which it is formed. A lower energy implies that electrons and nuclei are closer together.

Volume is perhaps the most readily observable property that is immediately connected with the structure and bonding characteristic of a substance. For potassium, chlorine, and potassium chloride, the molar volumes at 25°C and 1 atmosphere pressure are 45.5 ml/mole of K, 24.5 liters/mole of Cl_2, and 37.5 ml/mole of KCl. Since chlorine is a gas, it is not surprising that there should be an enormous shrinkage of the potassium–chlorine system to form a solid product. However, even a comparison of potassium and chlorine with potassium chloride shows more shrinkage than can be accounted for by change of chlorine from the gas phase to the solid phase. Thus the molar volume of potassium chloride is 8.0 ml less than the volume of the quantity of potassium from which it is formed. The chlorine seems to contribute "negative volume" to the potassium chloride produced. Similar changes are characteristic of the formation of many other salts. For example, magnesium oxide (MgO) has a molar volume that is 2.9 ml less than the molar volume of magnesium, whereas sodium chloride (NaCl) has a molar volume that is 3.3 ml larger than the molar volume of sodium.

In potassium chloride the distance between nearest potassium nuclei can be computed from the ionic radii of potassium and chloride ions. The computed internuclear distance for adjacent potassium nuclei is 4.44 A. In potassium metal the internuclear distance is 4.54 A. Thus the formation of potassium chloride is a change in which potassium nuclei move closer together than they were in potassium metal.

Atoms are arranged in solid potassium chloride so that each one has six nearest neighbors. Similarly in potassium metal each atom has eight nearest neighbors as well as six other neighbors only slightly more distant. Chlorine gas at 1 atmosphere pressure, however, behaves as a substance in which each atom has just one nearest neighbor with an internuclear distance of 1.99 A (Fig. 12-16). Thus, the formation of potassium chloride can be considered to be a change in which chlorine atoms increase their number of nearest neighbors from one to six while potassium atoms decrease their number of nearest neighbors from eight to six.

Internuclear distances, number of nearest neighbors, enthalpy change, and volume change all point to the conclusion that the formation of potassium chloride is a process in which electrons and nuclei are packed together more tightly in the product than in the reactants. How do bond types help our understanding of the formation of potassium chloride?

Potassium metal crystals are considered to be made up of atoms in which delocalized electrons are shared among the atoms. The delocalized electrons spread uniformly around every atom kernel so that the packing of atoms around each other tends to approach the maximum possible number of twelve. This maximum number twelve is a geometrical limitation on the packing of uniform spheres. Electric conductivity, opacity, and flexibility are characteristic of metal crystals since the charge on the atom kernel is not high enough to hold the outer electrons firmly in place.

Chlorine gas consists of diatomic molecules. Each chlorine kernel is surrounded by eight electrons. Electrons in the molecules are localized, with one pair of electrons forming a covalent bond between two atoms in each molecule. Electrons are then packed together as tightly as possible to form a system of low potential energy. Geometrical limitations on the packing of electrons and the Pauli exclusion principle, which prevents the presence of more than two electrons in a charge cloud or an orbital, account for the fact that chlorine atoms join only in pairs.

Chlorine atoms and potassium atoms together in the same system arrange themselves in a manner quite different from the arrangements of the atoms of the separate elements. The kernel of a potassium atom in solid KCl is surrounded by electrons in six chlorine atoms to give a low potential energy. Similarly each chlorine kernel surrounded by six potassium atoms gives a low potential energy. But this arrangement of six nearest neighbors has a geometry which can be repeated endlessly to form a large crystal. All that is required for the KCl structure is an equal number of potassium atoms and chlorine atoms. It is this type of structure with two or more different atoms endlessly repeated that is characteristic of many ionic substances.

Potassium chloride mixed with a large amount of water forms a solution. When 1 mole of KCl is dissolved in water to form a dilute solution, the volume of the solution is 26.8 ml greater than the volume of the water. This is 10.7 ml less than the molar volume of solid KCl. Water solution provides therefore still another way of arranging electrons and nuclei compactly. In water solution, potassium behaves as a positive ion and chloride as a negative ion. It is probable that the potassium ion is surrounded by at least one layer of water molecules so that each K^+ ion and the surrounding water molecules move as a unit. Like the potassium ions in KCl, which are surrounded by the electrons in chloride ions, potassium ions in water solution are surrounded by the electrons in water molecules. Chloride ions are also surrounded by water molecules but not as compactly as in the case of potassium ions.

Covalent, metallic, and ionic bonds prove to be a useful way of regarding the structures of many substances. These three types of bonds symbolize three different arrangements of atoms to give structures characteristic of particular substances. The underlying principles for the three types of bonds, however, are based on electrostatics in each type. Each substance represents a system of low energy consistent with the limitations imposed by the Pauli exclusion principle and geometrical relations of the electrons and nuclei which are more fundamental units of structure than are atoms.

With the same underlying principles common to all structures, it is not surprising that not all substances can be neatly classified into one of three possible types. The situation can be symbolized by a trigonal diagram. The vertices of the triangle represent the three extreme bond types. Along each edge of the triangle are represented bond types characteristic of the many substances which do not have extreme bond types.

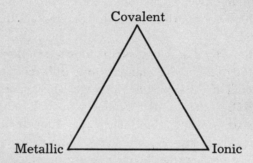

14

FREE ENERGY AND ELECTRON TRANSFER

ELECTRICITY AND CHEMICAL CHANGE are closely connected. The arrangement of zinc and copper sulfate in a Daniell cell can be used to produce electricity, or the two chemicals can react chemically without producing electricity. The entire concept of the nature of matter presupposes that electrical structures are the best way to think about matter and chemical change.

The idea of bonds between atoms in molecules and in crystals led to the development of bond energies. Yet these bond energies are based not on electric energy but on thermal energy. Is this justified? Can measurements of electric energy transferred during chemical change be correlated with measurements of thermal energy transferred during chemical change?

14-1 ELECTRON-TRANSFER REACTIONS

When zinc metal is immersed in copper (II) sulfate solution, the net reaction involves the conversion of zinc metal and hydrated copper ions to hydrated zinc ions and copper metal.

$$\text{Zn } (s) + \text{Cu}^{++} (aq) \rightarrow \text{Zn}^{++} (aq) + \text{Cu } (s) \qquad (Eq.\ 14\text{-}1)$$

During the reaction, electrons are transferred from zinc atoms to copper ions (Fig. 14-1a).

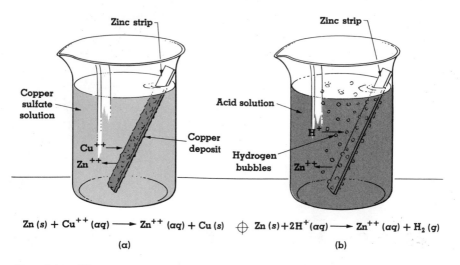

$$Zn\ (s) + Cu^{++}\ (aq) \longrightarrow Zn^{++}\ (aq) + Cu\ (s) \quad \oplus \quad Zn\ (s) + 2H^+(aq) \longrightarrow Zn^{++}\ (aq) + H_2\ (g)$$

(a)   (b)

Fig. 14-1 *The reactions of Zn* (s) *with* (a) *Cu*$^{++}$ (aq) *and* (b) *H*$^+$ (aq) *are electron-transfer reactions.*

Similarly, the reaction of metals such as iron, magnesium, and zinc with acid solutions (for example, hydrochloric acid or sulfuric acid) results in the production of positively charged metal ions and neutral hydrogen molecules. Thus for the reaction of zinc metal in acid solution, the net equation is

$$Zn\ (s) + 2H^+\ (aq) \rightarrow Zn^{++}\ (aq) + H_2\ (g) \qquad (Eq.\ 14\text{-}2)$$

The reaction in the zinc–hydrogen ion system, like that in the zinc–copper ion system, can be viewed as the transfer of two electrons from a zinc atom to two hydrogen ions to form one molecule of hydrogen gas (Fig. 14-1b).

Hydrogen gas can be produced from an acid solution not only by reaction with zinc but also by electrolysis. When electrodes made of a metal such as platinum, which does not react with the solution, are used, passage of charge through the solution results in the evolution of hydrogen gas at the negative electrode. This reaction can be represented by

$$2H^+\ (aq) + 2e^- \rightarrow H_2\ (g) \qquad (Eq.\ 14\text{-}3)$$

If platinum electrodes are placed in a copper (II) sulfate solution, an electric current in the system leads to the formation of metallic copper on the negative electrode. The deposition of solid copper is represented by

$$Cu^{++}\ (aq) + 2e^- \rightarrow Cu\ (s) \qquad (Eq.\ 14\text{-}4)$$

Copper can be formed from a solution of copper ion or hydrogen gas can be formed from a solution of hydrogen ion either by reaction with a metal such as zinc or by the action of an electric current. In either case the reaction is interpreted to proceed as the result of electron transfer.

Ex. 14-1 Complete the following expressions to make equations, and then indicate the electron transfer implied by each equation.

a. $Mg\ (s) + H^+\ (aq)$ c. $Br_2\ (l) + I^-\ (aq)$

b. $Zn\ (s) + Ag^+\ (aq)$ d. $Mg\ (s) + Cu^{++}\ (aq)$

14-2 DANIELL CELL REACTION

The Daniell cell described in Section 4-4 consists of a copper electrode in a copper (II) sulfate solution and a zinc electrode in an ionic solution which does not contain copper ion. The solution around the zinc electrode contained sodium chloride, but zinc sulfate can be used instead of sodium chloride. With zinc sulfate, the number of substances involved is kept to the smallest possible number. Sulfate ion is present around both electrodes. Any zinc ion produced at the zinc electrode does not constitute a new species in solution.

From the discussion in Section 4-4 and the subsequent development of net ionic equations, it is possible to write a net ionic equation describing the reaction in the Daniell cell. Equation 14-1 describes, therefore, not only the reaction occurring when zinc metal is placed in copper (II) sulfate solution, but also the reaction which takes place in a Daniell cell when the cell is being used as a source of electricity. When the zinc–copper ion system undergoes a change in state, either its temperature is raised or its energy is lowered (Sections 3-19 and 9-1). At constant temperature, the reaction is accompanied by an enthalpy change of -52.1 kcal/mole of Zn. This represents thermal energy transferred out of the system as the reaction proceeds.

The Daniell cell can be used to produce charge flow in a circuit. The flow of charge through a resistance in a circuit causes a temperature change which results in energy transfer. Can the same quantity of energy be produced when zinc and copper (II) sulfate react to produce thermal energy as when they react in a Daniell cell to produce electric energy (Section 4-4)?

The electric energy which a cell delivers is measured by the product of the quantity of charge transferred and the potential difference between the cell terminals. In Section 14-1, evidence was presented to indicate that each zinc atom transfers two electrons to one copper ion. For 1 mole of zinc atoms, the amount of charge transferred is 2 moles of electrons or 2 faradays ($2 \times 96,500$ coulombs). The charge is transferred through the wires of the external circuit. Within the cell the charged ions move toward the electrodes and thus provide for charge flow inside the cell. Throughout the entire circuit, charge flows. Transfer of energy comes only as the charge moves from the high potential of one electrode to the low potential of the other electrode.

The potential difference between the terminals of a cell is fairly easily measured with a voltmeter (Fig. 14-2). Measurements show, however, that different voltages are obtained for different currents in a circuit. The smaller the current, the larger the voltage. When the concentrations of the copper (II) sulfate solution and the zinc sulfate solution in the Daniell cell are each 1 molar (1 M), the largest voltage that can be measured is 1.10 volts at 25°C. The current is nearly zero when this voltage is measured.

For the reaction of 1 mole of zinc, the energy that can be obtained from the Daniell cell is

$$2 \times 96,500 \times 1.10 = 2.12 \times 10^5 \text{ joules/mole of Zn}$$

Since 1 kilocalorie is equivalent to 4,186 joules, the energy can be expressed as

$$\frac{2.12 \times 10^5 \text{ joules/mole of Zn}}{4,186 \text{ joules/kcal}} = 50.7 \text{ kcal/mole of Zn}$$

No attempt to obtain any higher potential difference than 1.10 volts has been successful. Therefore, the calculated energy of 50.7 kcal/mole of Zn must be the maximum available. In fact, when the Daniell cell produces large currents, the measured voltage decreases, and therefore, the quantity of electric energy per unit of charge decreases. If the terminals of the cell are connected with a piece of low-resistance copper wire, no electric energy is produced at all. Instead of electric energy in the external circuit, thermal energy is produced within the cell.

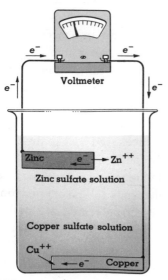

Fig. 14-2 *The electric potential difference between the zinc and copper electrodes in a Daniell cell is a measure of the tendency of the electron-transfer reaction to proceed.*

The reaction

$$Zn\ (s) + Cu^{++}\ (aq) \rightarrow Zn^{++}\ (aq) + Cu\ (s) \quad (Eq.\ 14\text{-}1)$$

will produce either thermal energy equivalent to -52.1 kcal/mole of Zn or a maximum electric energy of -50.7 kcal/mole of Zn. Therefore, it is not possible to produce the same quantities of thermal energy and electric energy.

Why is it not possible to obtain the same quantity of energy from a reaction conducted in two different ways? What happens, for example, if voltages higher than 1.10 volts are sought from a Daniell cell? An answer to this question can be obtained by deliberately connecting a Daniell cell to an external source of potential difference.

Experiments with the Daniell cell have shown that the reproducibility of the voltage measurements is improved if the metal electrodes are coated with mercury. A number of metals, including copper and zinc, dissolve in mercury to form solutions called amalgams. The Daniell cells discussed in the remainder of the text will be equipped with amalgam electrodes.

Ex. 14-2 A Daniell cell transfers 4,825 coulombs of electric charge through an external circuit when the potential difference between the terminals is 1 volt.

a. How many moles of zinc will be changed to zinc ion?

b. What is the quantity of electric energy (kilocalories) transferred per mole of zinc?

c. Compare the quantity of electric energy transferred per mole of zinc in this case with the maximum quantity of electric energy that can be transferred by a Daniell cell.

14-3 REVERSIBLE CELL REACTIONS

Two identical Daniell cells may be connected as shown in Fig. 14-3a. When the copper amalgam electrodes of two cells are connected and the zinc amalgam electrodes are also connected, nothing is observed to happen. No chemical change takes place in either cell. With three cells connected as shown in Fig. 14-3b, reactions do occur and charge flows, but the chemical change in cell A is

$$Cu\ (s) + Zn^{++}\ (aq) \rightarrow Cu^{++}\ (aq) + Zn\ (s) \quad (Eq.\ 14\text{-}5)$$

Compared to the reaction of zinc metal with copper ion (Equation 14-1), the reaction described by Equation 14-5 is just the reverse, since zinc is deposited on the zinc electrode and copper ions are formed at the copper electrode.

An additional electric circuit makes it possible to provide a source of variable potential difference to connect to the Daniell cell. In the

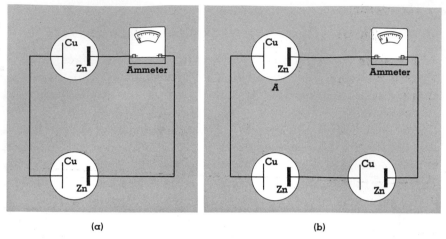

(a)   (b)

Fig. 14-3 (a) *Two identical Daniell cells connected so that the copper electrodes are joined and the two zinc electrodes are joined.* (b) *Three Daniell cells arranged so that the electrodes of two cells are connected in series and then to the electrodes of a third Daniell cell.*

arrangement shown in Fig. 14-4, two cells are connected together in series and then to a resistance R. One end of the resistance is connected to one terminal of a voltmeter. A contact free to slide along the resistance is connected to the other terminal of the voltmeter. As the sliding contact is moved along the resistance, the voltage indicated by the voltmeter changes. With the sliding contact at the upper end of the resistance, the indicated voltage is zero. At the lower end, the indicated voltage is about equal to the sum of the potential differences of the two cells or nearly 2.2 volts. The arrangement of resistance and a sliding contact is called a **potentiometer.**

The potentiometer can be adjusted so that any potential difference

Fig. 14-4 *Two Daniell cells in series connected to a potentiometer (resistance and sliding contact) are a source of variable potential difference.*

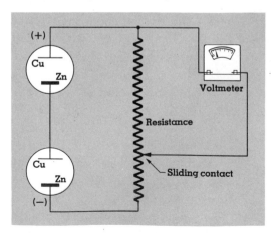

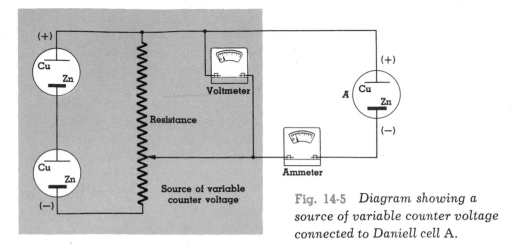

Fig. 14-5 *Diagram showing a source of variable counter voltage connected to Daniell cell A.*

between 0 and 2.2 volts is established on the two wires connected to the voltmeter. In the circuit arrangement sketched in Fig. 14-5, the potentiometer is connected so that it is possible to supply a voltage opposed to that of Daniell cell *A*. A voltage opposed to the voltage of a cell is called a **counter voltage.** The counter voltage can be greater than, less than, or equal to the voltage of the cell.

As the voltage is varied, the current indicated by the ammeter in the circuit varies. When the voltage is zero, the current is large; whereas increased counter voltages reduce the current. Figure 14-6 shows

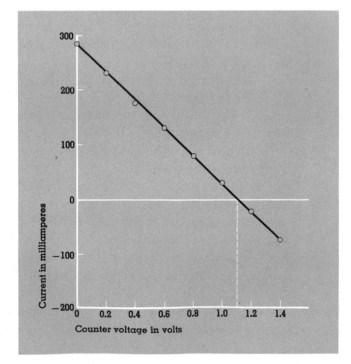

Fig. 14-6 *Relationship between current and counter voltage in a potentiometer circuit.*

the relationship between current and counter voltage. The current in the circuit is said to be positive when the counter voltage is zero. The current decreases, becomes zero, and then becomes negative (that is, charge flows in the opposite direction) as the counter voltage is increased. For positive current, the cell reaction is described by Equation 14-1 where zinc reacts with copper ion. For negative current, the reaction is described by Equation 14-5 where copper reacts with zinc ion. Zero current is found if the counter voltage is 1.10 volts.

Because the Daniell cell reaction can result in the reaction or formation of either the reactants or the products, it is said to be reversible. In other words, the reaction can go in either of two directions. The forward reaction is shown by Equation 14-1, and the reverse reaction is shown by Equation 14-5. At zero current, the tendency of the reaction to proceed is just balanced by the counter voltage. Again this indicates that, for the reaction of zinc metal with copper, the voltage at zero current represents the maximum obtainable electric energy per unit of charge transferred. An attempt to obtain more energy per unit of charge by applying a counter voltage above 1.10 volts only results in the reaction shown in Equation 14-5.

A chemical reaction provides the energy necessary to cause charge to flow from one terminal to another of an electrochemical cell. A counter voltage can be used to determine the potential difference for which a charge does not flow. The magnitude of a counter voltage can therefore provide two things: (1) a measure of the tendency for charge to flow between the terminals of an electrochemical cell, and (2) a measure of the tendency for a chemical reaction to occur within an electrochemical cell.

A measurement of the potential difference between the electrodes of a cell is a quantitative measure of the tendency of a reaction to occur. Such a method of measurement is most useful if it provides a way of comparing the tendencies of different reactions to occur.

Electrochemical cell reactions have one feature which distinguishes them from other chemical reactions. The reactants are not in contact; that is, two separated electrodes are involved. Thus, in the Daniell cell the conversion of zinc to zinc ion occurs at one electrode, while the conversion of copper ion to copper occurs at the other electrode even though the two electrodes are separated by solution. In fact, it is perfectly possible to have the electrodes as far apart as 10 ft so long as a column of some solution connects them.

Ex. 14-3 The maximum voltage of the nickel–lead cell is 0.124 volt.

a. What counter voltage would be required to reverse this reaction?

$$Ni\ (s) + Pb^{++}\ (1\ M) \rightarrow Ni^{++}\ (1\ M) + Pb\ (s)$$

b. What is the maximum quantity of electric energy per mole of Ni available from the nickel–lead cell described?

14-4 HALF REACTIONS

Since an electrochemical cell always contains two electrodes with a different reaction characteristic of each one, it is often advantageous to consider each electrode reaction separately. In the Daniell cell the reaction at the zinc electrode can be written as

$$Zn\ (s) \rightarrow Zn^{++}\ (aq) + 2e^- \qquad (Eq.\ 14\text{-}6)$$

At the copper electrode the reaction is described by

$$Cu^{++}\ (aq) + 2e^- \rightarrow Cu\ (s) \qquad (Eq.\ 14\text{-}4)$$

Written in this way the two electrode reactions can be added together to give the overall reaction for the cell.

$$Zn\ (s) + Cu^{++}\ (aq) \rightarrow Zn^{++}\ (aq) + Cu\ (s) \quad (Eq.\ 14\text{-}1)$$

An equation for a reaction at a single electrode of an electrochemical cell is called a **half reaction.** It is possible both experimentally and conceptually to confine one reaction to the compartment in which a single electrode is placed. It has never been possible, however, to separate two half reactions in time so that just one takes place without the other. An equation for a half reaction represents the reaction imagined to occur at an electrode.

Because a different reaction occurs at each of the two electrodes and because the electric potential difference between the electrodes can be measured, it is possible to determine quantitatively the ability of one electrode to transfer electrons to another electrode in a cell. In fact, on the basis of the tendencies of a number of different electrodes to transfer electrons to a single selected electrode, different electrodes can be arranged in order of their abilities to transfer electrons. This argument, of course, is based on the assumption that the selected reference electrode always has the same ability to transfer electrons. When this can be assured or assumed, the chosen reference is called a **standard electrode.** An electrode and the surrounding solution in the electrode compartment is called a **half cell.** The chemical change in a half cell is described by a half reaction. It is often necessary to describe the nature of a particular half cell. Thus, the half cell for hydrogen ion, hydrogen gas, and a metal electrode is referred to as either a hydrogen half cell or, more commonly, a hydrogen electrode.

Ex. 14-4 Write the half reactions for the two electrodes of the nickel–lead cell described in Exercise 14-3.

14-5 A STANDARD ELECTRODE

For some years a hydrogen electrode has been the standard used for comparison with other electrodes. The half reaction at the hydrogen electrode is described by

$$H^+ \ (aq) + e^- \rightarrow \tfrac{1}{2}H_2 \ (g) \qquad\qquad (Eq. \ 14\text{-}7)$$

This half cell, then, includes hydrogen ion in solution, hydrogen gas, and a piece of metal whose surface makes contact with both the hydrogen gas and the solution. The metal must be one which does not itself react with the solution but which does provide a conducting path for electron transfer. Platinum is most commonly used as the metal in a hydrogen electrode.

A *standard hydrogen electrode* consists of a platinum plate immersed in a solution containing $H^+ \ (aq)$ at a concentration of $1 \ M$ with hydrogen gas bubbled over the surface of the metal as shown in Fig. 14-7 at a pressure of 1 atmosphere and 25°C. The hydrogen gas is supplied from some source outside the electrode system. A complete electrochemical cell could be made from two hydrogen–hydrogen ion half cells connected by a solution. The solution used to connect the two half cells is usually placed in an inverted U-tube. A concentrated solution of potassium chloride in water is most frequently used. The U-tube and the potassium chloride solution it contains is called a *salt bridge.* Two hydrogen–hydrogen ion half cells can be constructed in such a way that there is zero potential difference between them (Fig. 14-8). It is necessary that the solution around each electrode have the same concentration of hydrogen ion and that the pressure of H_2 gas be the same at each electrode. The temperature (generally 25°C) in both

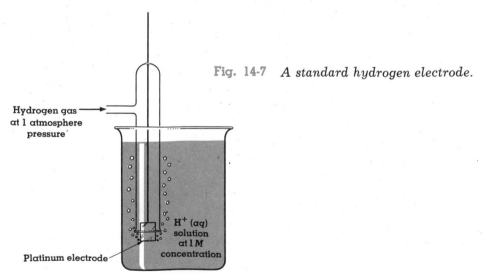

Fig. 14-7   *A standard hydrogen electrode.*

Hydrogen gas
at 1 atmosphere
pressure

Platinum electrode

$H^+ \ (aq)$
solution
at $1 \ M$
concentration

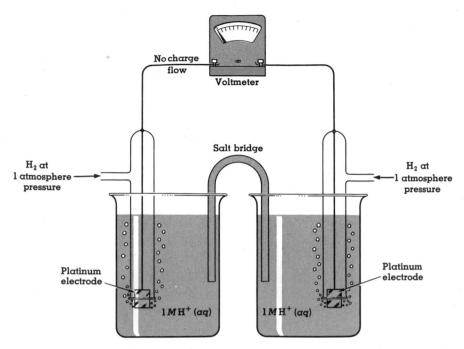

Fig. 14-8 *There is zero potential difference between two hydrogen electrodes arranged as shown.*

half cells must also be the same so that there will be no transfer of heat. The nature of the electrode surface also plays a minor role in determining the potential of an electrode. A rough electrode surface having a large surface area is prepared by depositing finely divided platinum on a smooth platinum surface.

To measure the potential difference between the two hydrogen electrodes, it is necessary to establish a complete electric circuit through which charge can flow. Such a complete circuit includes a voltmeter as shown in Fig. 14-8. Any tendency for one hydrogen electrode to transfer charge to the other hydrogen electrode can be measured by the voltmeter. With both half cells prepared in the same way, the voltmeter reading is zero, indicating that the two half cells have identical tendencies to transfer electrons.

14-6 DISSIMILAR ELECTRODES

What is the potential difference between two half cells when one of the half cells involves substances other than hydrogen ions and hydrogen gas?

For the cell illustrated in Fig. 14-9, one half cell A is a standard hydrogen electrode with H_2 gas at 1 atmosphere and hydrogen ion at 1 M concentration. The other half cell B is metallic copper immersed in a 1 M solution of Cu^{++} (aq). The measured potential difference

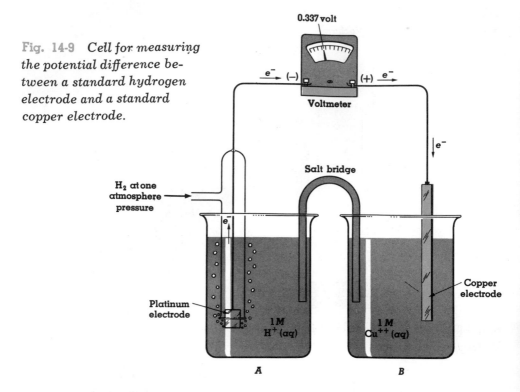

between the electrodes of this cell is 0.337 volt (Fig. 14-9). This potential difference corresponds to the reaction of Equation 14-8.

$$\tfrac{1}{2}Cu^{++} \ (1 \ M) + \tfrac{1}{2}H_2 \ (1 \ atm) \rightarrow \tfrac{1}{2}Cu \ (s) + H^+ \ (1 \ M)$$

$$(Eq. \ 14\text{-}8)$$

The cell reaction can be thought of as consisting of two half reactions,

$$\tfrac{1}{2}Cu^{++} \ (1 \ M) + e^- \rightarrow \tfrac{1}{2}Cu \ (s) \qquad (Eq. \ 14\text{-}9)$$

and $$\qquad \tfrac{1}{2}H_2 \ (1 \ atm) \rightarrow H^+ \ (1 \ M) + e^- \qquad (Eq. \ 14\text{-}10)$$

For components of electrochemical cells involved in electrode reactions, the **standard state** is chosen as 1 atmosphere pressure for gases and 1 M concentration for solutions in the electrode compartment. Metallic electrodes and insoluble components such as silver chloride do not change in concentration in electrochemical cells, and as long as any amount is present, each insoluble component is considered to be in its standard state. In addition, the standard hydrogen electrode is arbitrarily assigned zero potential when hydrogen ion concentration is 1 M and the pressure of hydrogen gas is 1 atmosphere.

$$\tfrac{1}{2}H_2 \ (1 \ atm) \rightarrow H^+ \ (1 \ M) + e^- \quad \varepsilon° = 0.000 \quad (Eq. \ 14\text{-}11)$$

For electrochemical cells, chemists use the symbol ε (read as script ee) to indicate the potential difference rather than the symbol ΔV that was used in Chapter 4 for potential difference in electric circuits. The symbol ε° (read as script ee zero) represents the potential of a half cell in which each of the reactants and products is in a standard state. When a second dissimilar half cell in its standard state is coupled to a standard hydrogen electrode so as to form a cell, the measured potential difference of the cell is defined as the **standard electrode potential** for the second electrode.

In the hydrogen–copper cell (Equation 14-8), a potential difference of 0.337 volt is measured with all reactants and products in their standard states. The standard copper electrode therefore differs in potential from the standard hydrogen electrode by 0.337 volt, and this potential difference is the standard electrode potential for the copper electrode.

$$\tfrac{1}{2}Cu^{++}\ (1\ M) + e^- \rightarrow \tfrac{1}{2}Cu\ (s) \quad \varepsilon^\circ = 0.337 \quad (Eq.\ 14\text{-}12)$$

14-7 SPONTANEOUS REACTION

When zinc is placed in a solution containing copper ion, a reaction takes place; that is, reaction occurs when the reactants are Zn (s) and Cu^{++} (aq). On the other hand, if copper is placed in a solution of zinc ion, no reaction takes place; that is, no reaction occurs when the reactants are Zn^{++} (aq) and Cu (s).

$$Cu\ (s) + Zn^{++}\ (aq) \rightarrow \text{no reaction}$$

The difference between the two cases is described by saying that spontaneous change occurs in the first system but not in the second system.

For the copper–hydrogen system considered in Section 14-6, spontaneous change occurs when the change in state of the system is described by Equation 14-8. A reaction between solid copper and hydrogen ion does not occur spontaneously.

$$Cu\ (s) + H^+\ (1\ M) \rightarrow \text{no reaction}$$

Certain states of a system change without any accompanying change in the surroundings of the system. A change in state that can occur without external effects of any kind is called a spontaneous change.

A characteristic of every spontaneous change in state is that the reverse change in state is always accompanied by a change in the surroundings of the system. A ball, initially at rest, can spontaneously roll downhill without a change in anything else, but a ball, initially at rest, rolls uphill only when someone or something pushes on the ball. Energy must be expended in pushing the ball uphill.

A sample of water at a temperature below 0°C (−40°C, for example) sooner or later turns partially or completely to ice. This change from liquid to solid occurs even though the system is carefully isolated from all connection with its surroundings. No one has ever observed ice at or below 0°C to melt spontaneously. To change ice, initially at or below 0°C, to water, some change in the surroundings always occurs. Thus, the surroundings might be at a higher temperature so that heat is transferred to the ice. As heat is transferred, the surroundings decrease in temperature. In terms of the kinetic-molecular theory and the concept of heat capacity, this decrease in temperature of the surroundings is both predictable and unavoidable.

An electrochemical cell may transfer electric energy to its surroundings when a spontaneous reaction takes place within the cell at constant temperature and pressure. Alternatively, the cell reaction can be

TABLE 14-1 STANDARD ELECTRODE POTENTIALS ε° AND STANDARD FREE ENERGY CHANGES ΔG° FOR SOME HALF REACTIONS AT 25°C

Half Reaction	$\varepsilon°$, volts	$\Delta G°$, kcal for the Half Reaction as Written
$Ba\ (s) \rightarrow Ba^{++}\ (aq) + 2e^-$	+2.90	−133.7
$Na\ (s) \rightarrow Na^+\ (aq) + e^-$	+2.714	−62.6
$Mg\ (s) \rightarrow Mg^{++}\ (aq) + 2e^-$	+2.37	−109.3
$Al\ (s) \rightarrow Al^{+++}\ (aq) + 3e^-$	+1.66	−114.9
$Mn\ (s) \rightarrow Mn^{++}\ (aq) + 2e^-$	+1.18	−54.4
$Zn\ (s) \rightarrow Zn^{++}\ (aq) + 2e^-$	+0.763	−35.2
$Fe\ (s) \rightarrow Fe^{++}\ (aq) + 2e^-$	+0.440	−20.3
$Ni\ (s) \rightarrow Ni^{++}\ (aq) + 2e^-$	+0.250	−11.5
$Sn\ (s) \rightarrow Sn^{++}\ (aq) + 2e^-$	+0.136	−6.3
$Pb\ (s) \rightarrow Pb^{++}\ (aq) + 2e^-$	+0.126	−5.8
$Fe\ (s) \rightarrow Fe^{+++}\ (aq) + 3e^-$	+0.036	−2.5
$H_2\ (g) \rightarrow 2H^+\ (aq) + 2e^-$	0.000	0.00
$Sn^{++}\ (aq) \rightarrow Sn^{++++}\ (aq) + 2e^-$	−0.15	+6.9
$Ag\ (s) + Cl^-\ (aq) \rightarrow AgCl\ (s) + e^-$	−0.223	+5.1
$Cu\ (s) \rightarrow Cu^{++}\ (aq) + 2e^-$	−0.337	+15.5
$Cu\ (s) \rightarrow Cu^+\ (aq) + e^-$	−0.521	+12.0
$2I^-\ (aq) \rightarrow I_2\ (s) + 2e^-$	−0.536	+24.7
$Fe^{++}\ (aq) \rightarrow Fe^{+++}\ (aq) + e^-$	−0.771	+17.8
$Hg\ (l) \rightarrow Hg^+\ (aq) + e^-$	−0.789	+18.2
$Ag\ (s) \rightarrow Ag^+\ (aq) + e^-$	−0.799	+18.4
$Hg\ (l) \rightarrow Hg^{++}\ (aq) + 2e^-$	−0.854	+38.8
$2Br^-\ (aq) \rightarrow Br_2\ (l) + 2e^-$	−1.087	+50.1
$2H_2O\ (l) \rightarrow O_2\ (g) + 4H^+\ (aq) + 4e^-$	−1.229	+113.3
$2Cl^-\ (aq) \rightarrow Cl_2\ (g) + 2e^-$	−1.360	+62.7
$2F^-\ (aq) \rightarrow F_2\ (g) + 2e^-$	−2.87	+132.3

made to take place in the reverse direction by connecting a source of sufficiently large potential difference to the cell terminals. It is convenient, therefore, to record the potential difference for the spontaneous reaction that would occur in the cell.

For the electrochemical cell reaction of the copper–hydrogen system, the positive sign written in front of the numerical value for $\varepsilon°$ indicates that the chemical equation describes the spontaneous reaction.

$$\tfrac{1}{2}H_2 \; (g) + \tfrac{1}{2}Cu^{++} \; (1 \; M) \rightarrow H^+ \; (1 \; M) + \tfrac{1}{2}Cu \; (s) \qquad \varepsilon° = +0.337 \text{ volt}$$

The negative sign in front of the numerical value for $\varepsilon°$ accompanying the chemical equation for the reverse reaction indicates that the reverse reaction is not spontaneous.

$$H^+ \; (1 \; M) + \tfrac{1}{2}Cu \; (s) \rightarrow \tfrac{1}{2}H_2 \; (g) + \tfrac{1}{2}Cu^{++} \; (1 \; M) \qquad \varepsilon° = -0.337 \text{ volt}$$

Table 14-1 lists some electrochemical cell half reactions and the corresponding standard electrode potentials. The standard free energy changes listed in Table 14-1 are defined and related to the standard electrode potentials in Section 14-8. For each listing in the table, it is assumed that the complete electrochemical cell includes the standard hydrogen electrode. Thus for the first entry in Table 14-1, the complete chemical equation is given by combining the listed half reaction with the half reaction for the hydrogen electrode. The positive sign for $\varepsilon°$ indicates that the chemical equation represents a spontaneous change.

$$
\begin{array}{lll}
Ba \; (s) \rightarrow Ba^{++} \; (aq) + 2e^- & \varepsilon° = & +2.90 \text{ volts} \\
2e^- + 2H^+ \; (aq) \rightarrow H_2 \; (g) & \varepsilon° = & 0.00 \text{ volts} \\
\hline
Ba \; (s) + 2H^+ \; (aq) \rightarrow Ba^{++} \; (aq) + H_2 \; (g) & \varepsilon° = & +2.90 \text{ volts}
\end{array}
$$

Any pair of half reactions listed in Table 14-1 can be combined to give the complete reaction for a cell whose potential difference can be calculated by adding appropriate potentials (Fig. 14-10). For example,

$$
\begin{array}{lll}
Fe \; (s) \rightarrow Fe^{++} \; (aq) + 2e^- & \varepsilon° = & +0.440 \text{ volt} \\
2e^- + 2Ag^+ \; (aq) \rightarrow 2Ag \; (s) & \varepsilon° = & +0.799 \text{ volt} \\
\hline
2Ag^+ \; (aq) + Fe \; (s) \rightarrow 2Ag \; (s) + Fe^{++} \; (aq) & \varepsilon° = & +1.239 \text{ volts}
\end{array}
$$

In this example the silver–silver ion half reaction listed in the table has been reversed and coefficients doubled to balance the number of electrons transferred. Reversal of the direction of writing the equation reverses the sign of the corresponding electrode potential. Doubling the number of electrons transferred does not change the electrode potential at which they are transferred, however, so $\varepsilon°$ for the silver electrode changes only from -0.799 to $+0.799$. A positive value for the sum of the standard electrode potentials in a cell indicates that the reaction as written describes a spontaneous reaction. When iron is

CELL POTENTIAL DIAGRAM

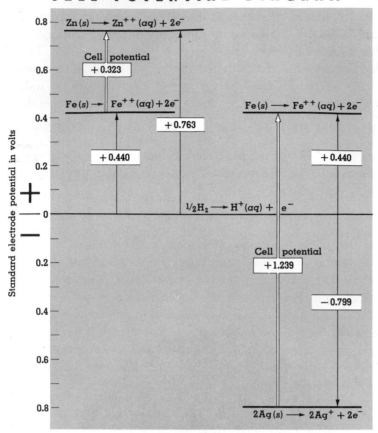

Fig. 14-10 *Cell potentials can be calculated by adding algebraically the standard electrode potentials of the electrodes in the cell.*

placed in a 1 M solution of Ag^+, Ag is observed to form spontaneously.

Table 14-1 can be considered to summarize spontaneous reactions. Chemical equations can be written that will represent spontaneous reactions if they are obtained by taking a half reaction from the table and adding it to any half reaction below it in Table 14-1, but with the second half reaction written in reverse.

Ex. 14-5   Write the overall equations for the spontaneous reactions, and calculate $\varepsilon°$ for the cells described below.

a. The standard aluminum–aluminum (III) half cell and the standard iron–iron (III) half cell

b. The standard copper–copper (II) half cell and the standard chlorine–chloride half cell

An electrochemical cell always has an electric potential difference between the electrodes. The magnitude of the potential difference is related to the composition of the two half cells. Measured in volts, the potential difference is a measure of the energy that can be obtained from the cell when 1 coulomb of charge is transferred from one electrode to the other.

The electrochemical unit of charge is the faraday (96,500 coulombs = 1 faraday) where 1 faraday is the charge on 1 mole of electrons. A potential difference measured in volts can therefore represent the energy which a cell delivers when 1 faraday of charge is transferred between the electrodes. Chemists are in the habit of using the kilocalorie as an energy unit, and a potential difference of 1 volt corresponds to 23.05 kcal/faraday of charge transferred between electrodes. This energy is supplied by the chemical system which makes up the cell.

A Daniell cell has a potential difference of 1.10 volts at 25°C. For the cell reaction written

$$Zn\ (s) + Cu^{++}\ (1\ M) \rightarrow Zn^{++}\ (1\ M) + Cu\ (s)$$

the transfer of 2 faradays of charge is equivalent to the reaction of 1 mole of zinc with 1 mole of copper ion. For the transfer of 2 faradays of charge between electrodes which differ in potential by 1.10 volts, the energy transfer will be $2 \times 1.10 \times 23.05 = 50.7$ kcal.

When zinc is placed in contact with a solution of copper ion, the reaction of 1 mole of zinc results in the transfer of 52.1 kcal of thermal energy. The electric energy and the thermal energy differ in quantity for the same system of reagents. A difference between thermal and electric energy is found for all electrochemical systems.

All forms of energy transferred out of a system can be converted completely into heat without any other changes taking place in the system or in its surroundings. The conversion of heat into work or into potential energy is always accompanied by the transfer of some of the heat to the surroundings. In other words, only a portion of a quantity of available heat can be converted to work or potential energy.

For chemical reactions each system is always studied at a uniform temperature. So long as the temperature of a system is kept constant, any heat transferred into or out of the system can only be transferred one way. This is a consequence of the fact that heat is transferred only from a system of high temperature to a system of low temperature. To transfer heat in the reverse direction some work must be transferred. Consequently, any isolated chemical system which reacts at constant temperature so that heat is transferred to some cooler surroundings cannot return to its initial state by itself. For the system to return to its initial state, heat would have to be transferred from surroundings which are cooler than the system—an impossibility. The only way the system can possibly acquire the energy needed to return to its initial state is with some outside assistance in the form of work.

The spontaneous reaction of zinc and copper ion illustrates the relationship of heat transfer to change in the state of a chemical system. Whenever zinc and copper ion react at constant temperature, some heat will be transferred out of the system. The maximum amount of heat which is transferred at a constant pressure and a constant temperature of 25°C is the enthalpy change, $\Delta H = -52.1$ kcal/mole of Zn.

After zinc and copper ion have reacted, the system will not return to zinc and copper ion by itself. In Section 14-3, however, the point was made that electric energy can be used to form zinc and copper ion from zinc ion and copper. If only electric energy is used, the amount of energy required at constant temperature is $\Delta H = 52.1$ kcal/mole of Zn for the reaction of Equation 14-5.

$$Cu\ (s)\ +\ Zn^{++}\ (aq)\ \rightarrow\ Cu^{++}\ (aq)\ +\ Zn\ (s)\quad (Eq.\ 14\text{-}5)$$

But when the Daniell cell is used as a source of electric energy, the most energy that can be obtained is 50.7 kcal/mole of Zn. So the reaction

$$Zn\ (s)\ +\ Cu^{++}\ (aq)\ \rightarrow\ Zn^{++}\ (aq)\ +\ Cu\ (s)\quad (Eq.\ 14\text{-}1)$$

can provide either 52.1 kcal of heat or 50.7 kcal of electric energy. Along with the 50.7 kcal of electric energy, 1.4 kcal of heat is also transferred if the system is maintained at constant temperature. Thus, the law of conservation of energy correctly describes the energy change in the system.

For the reaction represented by Equation 14-1 at constant temperature, either heat (52.1 kcal) or any combination of electric energy and heat which adds up to 52.1 kcal can be transferred out of the system as the change in state of the system takes place. The only restriction on the combination of electric energy and heat is that no more than 50.7 kcal of electric energy can be obtained, but any amount less than this is possible. On the other hand, for the reaction represented by Equation 14-5 to take place at constant temperature, 50.7 kcal of electric energy plus 1.4 kcal of either heat or work must be transferred into the system and heat cannot be substituted for any portion of the electric energy. Electric energy can be used to cause some otherwise nonspontaneous reactions to take place at constant temperature. By contrast, thermal energy cannot be used to cause any nonspontaneous reactions to take place at constant temperature. The capacity of a system to produce electric energy is defined as the *free energy* of the system. Any spontaneous change in the state of a system is accompanied by a decrease in free energy. Thus, as a system of zinc and copper (II) sulfate solution changes in state, its free energy goes down.

Electric potential difference between the electrodes in an electrochemical cell represents not only potential energy due to charge separation but a free energy difference (ΔG) between the initial and final states of the cell. The relation between free energy change and electric potential difference is given by

$$\Delta G = -nF\varepsilon \qquad (Eq.\ 14\text{-}13)$$

where ε is the potential difference in volts, F is the faraday in coulombs per mole of electrons, and n is the number of moles of electrons transferred per mole of reactant. This definition of free energy change will be in units of joules per mole. To obtain ΔG in kilocalories per mole,

$$\Delta G = - \frac{nF\varepsilon}{4,186\ \text{joules/kcal}} = -23.05n\varepsilon \qquad (Eq.\ 14\text{-}14)$$

The assignment of zero potential to the standard hydrogen electrode means that a free energy change of zero is assigned to the reaction at the standard hydrogen electrode, also. Other electrodes can be combined with the hydrogen electrode to form cells which have potential differences between the electrodes. These potential differences can be used to calculate the change in free energy accompanying the reaction of 1 mole of each of the reactants. When each electrode is in its standard state, the free energy change is called the **standard free energy change** and is designated by the symbol $\Delta G°$. Table 14-1 lists the standard free energy changes for some half reactions.

Ex. 14-6   *a.* What is $\Delta G°$ for the magnesium–iodine cell in this reaction?

$$\text{Mg} + \text{I}_2 \rightarrow \text{Mg}^{++}\ (1\ M) + 2\text{I}^-\ (1\ M)$$

b. How many moles of electrons are transferred for each mole of magnesium that reacts?

c. What is the electric potential difference for the magnesium–iodine cell?

14-9   USE OF STANDARD FREE ENERGIES

Use of the data in Table 14-1 can perhaps best be made clear by examples. The first entry for the table is shown in Expression 14-15.

$$\text{Ba (s)} \rightarrow \text{Ba}^{++}\ (aq) + 2e^- \qquad \Delta G° = -133.7\ \text{kcal} \qquad (Exp.\ 14\text{-}15)$$

This means that in the reaction represented by

$$\text{Ba (s)} + 2\text{H}^+\ (1\ M) \rightarrow \text{Ba}^{++}\ (1\ M) + \text{H}_2\ (1\ \text{atm}) \qquad (Eq.\ 14\text{-}16)$$

the free energy of the products is lower than the free energy of the reactants by 133.7 kcal/mole of Ba when each component is in its standard state. A free energy decrease (a negative $\Delta G°$) means that the reaction may proceed spontaneously as written.

Farther down the table is the entry

$$Cu \ (s) \rightarrow Cu^{++} \ (aq) + 2e^- \quad \Delta G° = +15.5 \ \text{kcal} \quad (Exp. \ 14\text{-}17)$$

This refers to the reaction described by

$$Cu \ (s) + 2H^+ \ (1 \ M) \rightarrow Cu^{++} \ (1 \ M) + H_2 \ (1 \ \text{atm})$$
$$\Delta G° = 15.5 \ \text{kcal} \quad (Exp. \ 14\text{-}18)$$

for which the free energy of the products is higher than that of the reactants by 15.5 kcal/mole of Cu. The reaction will not proceed spontaneously as written. The reverse reaction (Expression 14-19) will be spontaneous since the $\Delta G°$ for the reverse reaction will have a negative sign.

$$Cu^{++} \ (1 \ M) + H_2 \ (1 \ \text{atm}) \rightarrow Cu \ (s) + 2H^+ \ (1 \ M)$$
$$\Delta G° = -15.5 \ \text{kcal} \quad (Exp. \ 14\text{-}19)$$

The same calculation procedures can be applied to free energy changes that are used for calculating enthalpy changes. This fact enhances the utility of tabulated free energy data. Consider a possible reaction between Cu metal, Zn metal, Cu^{++} ion, and Zn^{++} ion. Expression 14-20 can be written from data in Table 14-1.

$$Zn \ (s) + 2H^+ \ (1 \ M) \rightarrow Zn^{++} \ (1 \ M) + H_2 \ (1 \ \text{atm})$$
$$\Delta G° = -35.2 \ \text{kcal} \quad (Exp. \ 14\text{-}20)$$

Expression 14-19 can be added to Expression 14-20 to obtain

$$Zn \ (s) + Cu^{++} \ (1 \ M) \rightarrow Zn^{++} \ (1 \ M) + Cu \ (s)$$
$$\Delta G° = -50.7 \ \text{kcal} \quad (Exp. \ 14\text{-}21)$$

The large negative $\Delta G°$ indicates that at the conditions specified [25°C, Cu^{++} (aq) at 1 M concentration, and Zn^{++} (aq) ion at 1 M concentration], metallic zinc will dissolve to increase the Zn^{++} (aq) concentration above 1 M and copper will precipitate to reduce the concentration of Cu^{++} (aq) below 1 M. A strip of zinc metal placed in copper ion solution does in fact precipitate metallic copper.

The relation shown for copper and zinc in Expression 14-21 from data in Table 14-1 can be generalized to include all the reactions represented in the table. Any equation in Table 14-1 can be added to the reverse of an equation appearing below it in the table to give an equation which describes a reaction that can occur spontaneously in the laboratory. The free energies associated with these equations may also be treated algebraically.

14-10 TWO HYDROGEN ELECTRODES

If all conditions in the cell are kept the same except the concentration of H^+ (aq) for one of the half cells, the effect of the H^+ (aq) concentration on the tendency of the hydrogen–hydrogen ion half cell to transfer electrons can be investigated. When the concentration of H^+ (aq) for one half cell is 1 M and that for the other half cell is different from 1 M, the voltmeter reading is not zero. In fact, the voltmeter reading can be interpreted to mean that there is a tendency for electrons to flow through the external circuit from the electrode surrounded by the more dilute solution of H^+ (aq) to the electrode surrounded by the more concentrated solution of H^+ (aq). In other words, the hydrogen–hydrogen ion half cell becomes more negatively charged as the concentration of H^+ (aq) is reduced. This effect is diagramed in Fig. 14-11 where electrode A is immersed in a solution with $[H^+] = 0.1 \ M$ and electrode B is immersed in a solution with $[H^+] = 1 \ M$. The symbol $[H^+]$ is read "molar concentration of hydrogen ion."

The flow of electrons between the terminals of an electrochemical cell requires that a chemical reaction take place at each electrode. What chemical reaction is associated with the two hydrogen electrodes in this cell? At electrode A with a hydrogen ion concentration that is

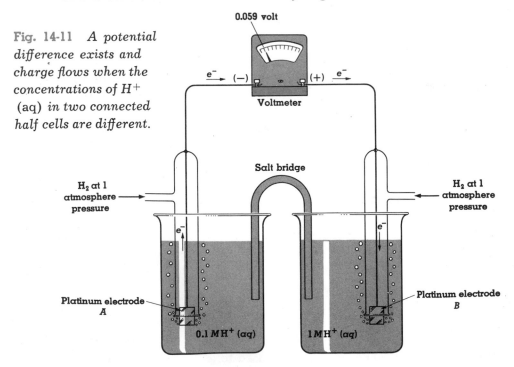

Fig. 14-11 *A potential difference exists and charge flows when the concentrations of H^+ (aq) in two connected half cells are different.*

0.059 volt

Voltmeter

Salt bridge

H_2 at 1 atmosphere pressure

H_2 at 1 atmosphere pressure

Platinum electrode A

Platinum electrode B

$0.1 \ M H^+$ (aq)

$1 M H^+$ (aq)

0.1 M, there is a greater tendency to transfer electrons from hydrogen gas to the external circuit than at electrode B with $[H^+] = 1\ M$. The reaction at electrode A is given by

$$\tfrac{1}{2}H_2\ (g) \rightarrow H^+\ (aq) + e^- \text{ (transferred to the external circuit)}$$
$$(Eq.\ 14\text{-}22)$$

The reaction occurring at electrode B with $[H^+] = 1\ M$ involves the transfer of electrons from the external circuit to hydrogen ions (Equation 14-23).

$$H^+\ (aq) + e^- \text{ (transferred from the external circuit)} \rightarrow \tfrac{1}{2}H_2\ (g)$$
$$(Eq.\ 14\text{-}23)$$

The reaction at electrode B is, then, the reverse of the reaction occurring at electrode A.

At electrode A hydrogen ion is formed from hydrogen gas, thereby tending to increase the concentration of H^+ (aq) around electrode A. At electrode B hydrogen gas is formed from hydrogen ion. The hydrogen gas leaves the solution, thereby decreasing the concentration of H^+ (aq) around electrode B. The reaction proceeds from left to right.

$$\tfrac{1}{2}H_2\ (1\ \text{atm})_A + H^+\ (1\ M)_B \rightarrow H^+\ (0.1\ M)_A + \tfrac{1}{2}H_2\ (1\ \text{atm})_B$$
$$(Eq.\ 14\text{-}24)$$

The number of hydrogen ions generated at electrode A must be equal to the number of hydrogen ions converted to H_2 (g) at electrode B. Each electrode is maintained at 1 atmosphere of hydrogen gas. The net change in the solutions in compartments A and B, then, is equivalent to the transfer of H^+ (aq) from the more concentrated solution to the less concentrated solution. The net change in each electrode compartment tends to bring the solutions in compartments A and B closer to the same concentration.

The potential difference between two hydrogen–hydrogen ion half cells can be measured for cases in which $[H^+]$ around electrode A is varied while $[H^+]$ at electrode B is constant at $1\ M$. The potential difference increases as the difference between the concentrations of H^+ (aq) around the two electrodes becomes greater. Data for the observed potential differences are tabulated in Table 14-2.

A plot of potential difference against the concentration of H^+ (aq) in solution A does not give a straight line. However, the ratio of the hydrogen ion concentrations for the two half cells can be plotted on a scale for which each tenfold change in ratio is assigned the same scale distance on the graph. The resulting graph is a straight line. This graph is shown in Fig. 14-12. The potential difference is not proportional to the hydrogen ion concentration but is proportional to the power to which 10 must be raised to express the ratio of the hydrogen

TABLE 14-2   POTENTIAL DIFFERENCES BETWEEN TWO HYDROGEN
ELECTRODES FOR DIFFERENT CONCENTRATIONS
OF H^+ (aq) AT 25°C

Concentration of H^+ (aq) at Electrode A, mole/liter	Concentration of H^+ (aq) at Electrode B, mole/liter	Potential Difference Between Electrodes A and B, volt
1.00	1.00	0.000
1.00×10^{-1}	1.00	0.059
1.00×10^{-2}	1.00	0.118
1.00×10^{-3}	1.00	0.177
1.00×10^{-4}	1.00	0.236

ion concentrations for the two half cells. You may recognize that the
power to which 10 must be raised to express a certain number is
known as the **logarithm** of that number to the base 10. For example,
for the base 10,

$$100 = 10^2 \qquad \text{logarithm of} \qquad 100 = 2$$
$$10 = 10^1 \qquad \text{logarithm of} \qquad 10 = 1$$
$$1 = 10^0 \qquad \text{logarithm of} \qquad 1 = 0$$
$$1/10 = 10^{-1} \qquad \text{logarithm of} \qquad 1/10 = -1$$
$$1/100 = 10^{-2} \qquad \text{logarithm of} \qquad 1/100 = -2$$
$$1/1,000 = 10^{-3} \qquad \text{logarithm of} \quad 1/1,000 = -3$$

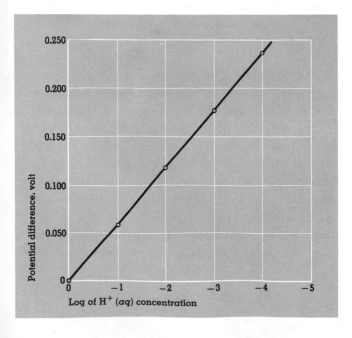

Fig. 14-12 *Potential
difference between a
hydrogen electrode in
1 M H^+ (aq) and a
hydrogen electrode in
solutions of different
concentrations of H^+
(aq) plotted against
log $[H^+]$.*

A graph of the potential difference between the two electrodes A and B against the logarithm of the ratio of H^+ (aq) concentrations for the two half cells is a straight line. Therefore, the measured potential difference between the electrodes is proportional to the logarithm of the ratio of hydrogen ion concentrations around the two electrodes.

$$\text{Potential difference} = \varepsilon = -K \log \frac{[H^+] \text{ electrode } A}{[H^+] \text{ electrode } B} \qquad (Eq.\ 14\text{-}25)$$

The slope of the curve is numerically equal to the proportionality constant K. K is 0.059 when the potential difference ε is expressed in volts and when the temperature is 25°C.

$$\varepsilon = -0.059 \log \frac{[H^+]_A}{[H^+]_B} \qquad (Eq.\ 14\text{-}26)$$

If Equation 14-26 is applied to the last item of data in Table 14-2, the calculated potential difference is equal to the experimentally determined potential difference recorded in the table.

$$\varepsilon = -0.059 \log \frac{0.000100}{1.00} = -0.059 \log 10^{-4}$$

$$= -0.059 \times -4 = 0.236$$

Ex. 14-7   a. What is the maximum electric potential difference between two hydrogen half cells with the following description?

Half cell A: H_2 (1 atm) | H^+ (1 M)

Half cell B: H_2 (1 atm) | H^+ (10^{-8} M)

b. If the two half cells described in part a are connected so that charge is transferred for a long time interval, what will eventually happen to the hydrogen ion concentration in the two cells?

14-11 CONCENTRATION AND CELL POTENTIAL

What is the potential of a cell when the electrodes are prepared from components not in their standard states? The potential of a half cell is dependent upon the concentration of the ions in solution. The observed potential difference ε for the copper–hydrogen cell represents the sum of two terms: (1) the potential difference calculated by adding the standard electrode potentials $\varepsilon°$, and (2) a potential difference determined by the ratio of the concentration of the ions in the electrode compartment to the concentration of the ions (1 M) in the standard electrode compartment. Each half reaction is written so as to represent the transfer of one electron. For the cell described by Equation 14-27, $[H^+] = 1$, and $[Cu^{++}]$ is not equal to 1.

$$\tfrac{1}{2}Cu^{++} \ (x \ M) + \tfrac{1}{2}H_2 \ (g) \ (1 \text{ atm}) \rightarrow \tfrac{1}{2}Cu \ (s) + H^+ \ (1 \ M)$$

$$(Eq.\ 14\text{-}27)$$

$$\varepsilon = \varepsilon° - 0.059 \log \frac{1}{[\text{Cu}^{++}]^{\frac{1}{2}}} \qquad (Eq.\ 14\text{-}28)$$

If [H$^+$] also differs from 1, the observed potential difference will be given by

$$\varepsilon = \varepsilon° - 0.059 \log \frac{[\text{H}^+]}{[\text{Cu}^{++}]^{\frac{1}{2}}} \qquad (Eq.\ 14\text{-}29)$$

Each dissolved substance or ion in the chemical equation for the cell contributes to the cell potential in terms of the molar concentration of the substance or the ion raised to a power which is identical with the coefficient used for that substance in the chemical equation. Thus, since the chemical equation (Equation 14-27) uses a coefficient of $\frac{1}{2}$ for Cu^{++}, the square root of the copper ion concentration, that is, $[\text{Cu}^{++}]^{\frac{1}{2}}$, is used in Equations 14-28 and 14-29.

The equation developed for calculating the potential difference for a cell containing a copper electrode and a hydrogen electrode can be generalized to fit other electrochemical cells. In each case the chemical equation for the cell reaction is associated with the equation for calculating the potential difference for a cell.

A reaction for a possible electrochemical cell can be written in general terms; for example,

$$\tfrac{1}{x}\text{A }(s) + \tfrac{1}{y}\text{B}^{y+} \ (aq) \rightarrow \tfrac{1}{x}\text{A}^{x+} \ (aq) + \tfrac{1}{y}\text{B }(s) \qquad (Eq.\ 14\text{-}30)$$

where the two half reactions are

$$\tfrac{1}{x}\text{A }(s) \rightarrow \tfrac{1}{x}\text{A}^{x+} \ (aq) + e^- \qquad (Eq.\ 14\text{-}31)$$

and

$$e^- + \tfrac{1}{y}\text{B}^{y+} \ (aq) \rightarrow \tfrac{1}{y}\text{B }(s) \qquad (Eq.\ 14\text{-}32)$$

The equation that relates the potential difference for the cell to the concentration of the ions in the reaction is

$$\varepsilon = \varepsilon° - K \log \frac{[\text{A}^{x+}]^{1/x}}{[\text{B}^{y+}]^{1/y}} \qquad (Eq.\ 14\text{-}33)$$

At 25°C, K is 0.059; at other temperatures K will be different.

14-12 MEASUREMENT OF ION CONCENTRATION

Because the electric potential difference developed between two electrodes depends upon the concentrations of ions around the electrodes, cell potentials can be used to determine ion concentrations in solution. The procedure can be used with any ion which is involved in an electrode half reaction. By way of illustration, the situation for hydrogen ion will be discussed, but the technique can be applied to other ions equally well.

In Section 14-10, the cell potential for a cell consisting of two hydrogen electrodes depended upon the hydrogen ion concentration according to Equation 14-34.

$$\varepsilon = -0.059 \log \frac{[H^+]_A}{[H^+]_B} \qquad (Eq.\ 14\text{-}34)$$

Here $[H^+]$ represents the concentration of H^+ (aq) in the electrode compartments, and the constant 0.059 is used since the measurement is made at 25°C. Dividing Equation 14-34 by -0.059 gives

$$\log \frac{[H^+]_A}{[H^+]_B} = - \frac{\varepsilon}{0.059} \qquad (Eq.\ 14\text{-}35)$$

If electrode B is prepared with $[H^+]_B = 1$ mole/liter, the expression becomes

$$\log [H^+]_A = - \frac{\varepsilon}{0.059} \qquad (Eq.\ 14\text{-}36)$$

where $[H^+]_A$ is in units of moles per liter. Since ε can be measured, the logarithm of the concentration of H^+ (aq) can be calculated and, from this, the concentration of H^+ (aq).

For example, if a hydrogen electrode is placed in a container of water free of other dissolved materials, the potential difference between this electrode and the standard hydrogen electrode, in which $[H^+]$ is 1 M, is 0.413 volt. The logarithm of the hydrogen ion concentration in water is calculated in Equation 14-37.

$$\log [H^+]_A = - \frac{0.413}{0.059} = -7.0 \qquad (Eq.\ 14\text{-}37)$$

This means that the hydrogen ion concentration in water as indicated by the potential difference between the two electrodes is equal to 1×10^{-7} mole/liter.

It is often convenient to use the measured potential difference directly rather than the calculated hydrogen ion concentration. This is usually done by taking not ε itself but $\varepsilon/0.059$ and calling this quotient the potential for hydrogen.

$$\frac{\varepsilon}{0.059} = \text{potential for hydrogen} \qquad (Eq.\ 14\text{-}38)$$

The phrase potential for hydrogen is generally abbreviated to pH. The term pH is then equal to the negative logarithm of the hydrogen ion concentration in moles per liter since

$$pH = \frac{\varepsilon}{0.059} = -\log [H^+] = \log \frac{1}{[H^+]} \qquad (Eq.\ 14\text{-}39)$$

For water the pH is 7.0. A solution whose hydrogen ion concentration is greater than that for water is called an **acidic solution.** The pH of an acidic solution is less than 7. Conversely, a solution whose hydrogen ion concentration is less than that for water is called a **basic solution.** The pH of a basic solution is greater than 7.

Hydrogen electrode measurements indicate that hydrogen ions are present in water. Is it reasonable from any other evidence that water contains ions? If ions are present in water, then water should conduct electricity.

Because water solutions of ionic substances conduct electricity much better than water itself, water is described as a nonconductor. When sufficiently sensitive instruments are used to detect charge flow, however, water is found to conduct electricity slightly. In fact, every material conducts electricity to some slight extent. All attempts to separate dissolved ionic substances from water always result in a final product water that has a small but measurable conductance. The magnitude of this conductance for water is consistent with a hydrogen ion concentration of 10^{-7} mole/liter. Hydrogen electrode measurements and conductance measurements are therefore in agreement. Some further consequences of the presence of hydrogen ions in water are discussed in Chapter 16.

The ability to measure concentrations of ions by means of electrode potentials is not peculiar to hydrogen ions. The potential difference between the electrodes of a cell depends upon the concentration of ions involved in the electrode reaction. Thus, the methods outlined here with the hydrogen electrode can be applied to other electrode systems. The problem which has to be faced is the experimental difficulty of constructing an appropriate electrode system.

Ex. 14-8 *a.* Calculate the hydrogen ion concentration of a hydrogen electrode for which the electrode potential is $\varepsilon = 0.708$ volt and of a hydrogen electrode for which $\varepsilon = 0.295$ volt.

b. Which solution in part *a* is basic? Which is acidic?

14-13 SUMMARY

An electrochemical cell is interpreted as a device in which electrons are transferred between two electrodes. As the electrons are transferred, a chemical reaction occurs at each electrode. For the cell system, a chemical equation can be written to describe the change that takes place as electrons are transferred through the circuit.

The chemical change which takes place within an electrochemical cell can, in many cases, be duplicated without the use of electrodes at all. Thus zinc and copper (II) sulfate solution will react either in an electrochemical cell without being in direct contact or by simply mixing the two materials in a beaker. In the latter case, electron transfer is assumed to take place even though it cannot be demonstrated by any direct measurement.

A potential difference between the electrodes of an electrochemical cell can be measured with a voltmeter. If the measured potential difference is zero, no reaction takes place in the cell. When the potential difference is not zero, a reaction does occur. The tendency for a chemical reaction to proceed can be determined by a measurement of electrode potential differences.

The potential difference between two electrodes is related to differences in concentration of the solutions around the two electrodes. The standard hydrogen electrode is defined as one for which the concentration of H^+ (aq) in the electrode compartment is 1 M and the pressure of hydrogen gas is 1 atm. The standard hydrogen electrode is assigned a potential of zero. Every other concentration of hydrogen ion gives a half cell with a potential which is not zero. The relation between concentration and potential is described by the equation

$$\varepsilon = -0.059 \log \frac{[H^+]_A}{[H^+]_B}$$

where $[H^+]_B$ means concentration of hydrogen ion at electrode B and $[H^+]_A$ has a corresponding meaning. The temperature is 25°C.

Since an electrochemical cell has both a potential difference and an ability to transfer charge, the chemical system within the cell has an energy which can be calculated from electrical measurements. The product of potential difference and charge transferred gives the energy change for the chemical system when the chemical reaction takes place. This calculated energy change is called the free energy change.

Free energy gives a measure of the tendency of a reaction to proceed. Every chemical system that reacts spontaneously undergoes a decrease in free energy. No system can, alone, increase in free energy. Measured free energy changes in a system are usually found to differ from measured enthalpy changes in the same system. The significance of the difference between free energy and enthalpy is discussed in Chapter 15.

An electrochemical cell gives a potential difference related to the concentration of ions involved in the electrode reactions. This fact provides an experimental basis for measuring the concentration of individual ions in solution. In Chapter 15, the relation of ion concentration to chemical change is considered.

Ex. 14-9 Do the half-cell reactions as written in Table 14-1 correspond to oxidation or reduction? In Equation 14-2 what is the oxidizing agent? the reducing agent?

Ex. 14-10 Compare the electronegativity of an element and its position in Table 14-1. How is electronegativity related to oxidation and reduction?

Ex. 14-11 Iron placed in hydrochloric acid reacts to produce hydrogen gas, but copper placed in hydrochloric acid does not react to produce hydrogen gas. How are these facts related to the free energy data in Table 14-1?

Ex. 14-12 Write the overall equation for the reaction involved in each of the cells described below, and predict the electric potential difference. Use Table 14-1.

a. Fe (s) | Fe^{+++} (1 M) || Fe^{++} (1 M) | Fe (s)

b. Pt (s) | Sn^{++} (1 M), Sn^{++++} (1 M) || Sn^{++} (1 M) | Sn (s)

c. Cu (s) | Cu^{++} (1 M) || Cl$^-$ (1 M) | Cl$_2$ (1 atm) | Pt (s)

Ex. 14-13 The graph represents the equation for the potential difference of a cell composed of two Ag | Ag$^+$ (aq) half cells, where

$$\varepsilon = -0.059 \log \frac{[Ag^+]_A}{[Ag^+]_B}$$

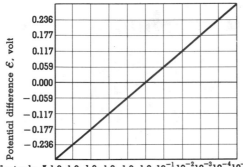

Potential difference ε, volt

| 0.236 |
| 0.177 |
| 0.117 |
| 0.059 |
| 0.000 |
| −0.059 |
| −0.117 |
| −0.177 |
| −0.236 |

Electrode A 1.0 1.0 1.0 1.0 1.0 1.0 $10^{-1}10^{-2}10^{-3}10^{-4}10^{-5}$
Electrode B $10^{-5}10^{-4}10^{-3}10^{-2}10^{-1}$1.0 1.0 1.0 1.0 1.0 1.0
Ag$^+$(aq) concentration, mole/liter

a. According to the graph, what electrode conditions exist when the potential difference between the connected half cells is zero?

b. What potential difference will exist between the electrodes if [Ag$^+$] at electrode A is one-tenth that at electrode B?

c. What is the potential difference between the connected half cells if [Ag$^+$]$_B$ = 10^{-4} M while [Ag$^+$]$_A$ = 1 M? In which direction will electrons flow in the external circuit under these conditions?

Ex. 14-14 The half-cell reactions for the discharging cycle of each lead storage cell in a car battery are

$$Pb \text{ (s)} + HSO_4^- \text{ (aq)} \rightarrow PbSO_4 \text{ (s)} + 2e^- + H^+$$

$$PbO_2 \text{ (s)} + HSO_4^- \text{ (aq)} + 3H^+ \text{ (aq)} + 2e^- \rightarrow PbSO_4 \text{ (s)} + 2H_2O \text{ (l)}$$

a. Write the overall equation for the cell reaction during discharging.

b. During the discharging cycle, at which electrode is oxidation occurring? at which electrode is reduction occurring?

c. Does the concentration of sulfuric acid increase or decrease during the discharging cycle? Why is it possible to use the density of the sulfuric acid solution as an indication of the amount of energy that can be obtained from a car battery?

d. What is the composition of each electrode when the cell is completely discharged?

e. The maximum electric potential difference of the lead cell is 2.03 volts at 25°C when the concentration of H$_2$SO$_4$ is 1 M. What electric energy, in kilocalories, can be delivered per gram of lead converted to PbSO$_4$ (s) at this potential difference?

f. If the standard electrode potential $\varepsilon°$ of the lead–lead sulfate electrode is +0.35 volt at 25°C, what is $\varepsilon°$ for the lead(IV) oxide–lead sulfate electrode?

CONCENTRATION AND CHEMICAL CHANGE

IN AN ELECTROCHEMICAL cell constructed so that spontaneous reaction is possible, there is a potential difference between the electrodes. Chemists are interested in determining the circumstances under which a reaction can proceed spontaneously. Can the ideas of electrode potential and free energy change be used to supply information of aid in determining how to predict those states of a chemical system for which spontaneous change is possible? Even for reactions that begin spontaneously, does the system undergo a continuous change in state until all the initial components have been transformed to products? Can the components of a system be selected so that a predetermined reaction will occur?

15-1 EXTENT OF A CHEMICAL CHANGE

To what extent are the reactants of a chemical system converted to products? Four different sets of systems will be studied to determine the extent of reaction in each. The components are a different one of the alkaline-earth metal chlorides, sodium sulfate, and water for each of the four sets. The experimental procedure is based on the method of continuous variation.

The chlorides of magnesium, calcium, strontium, and barium are mixed with sodium sulfate in water in 11 different mole ratios according to the continuous variation method. Precipitates form in the sys-

624

tems containing calcium, strontium, or barium chloride and sodium sulfate and water. No precipitate is formed in the systems containing magnesium chloride. The observed chemical reactions are described in Equations 15-1, 15-2, and 15-3.

$$MgCl_2 \ (aq) + Na_2SO_4 \ (aq) \rightarrow \text{no reaction}$$

$$CaCl_2 \ (aq) + Na_2SO_4 \ (aq) \rightarrow 2NaCl \ (aq) + CaSO_4 \ (s) \qquad (Eq. \ 15\text{-}1)$$

$$SrCl_2 \ (aq) + Na_2SO_4 \ (aq) \rightarrow 2NaCl \ (aq) + SrSO_4 \ (s) \qquad (Eq. \ 15\text{-}2)$$

$$BaCl_2 \ (aq) + Na_2SO_4 \ (aq) \rightarrow 2NaCl \ (aq) + BaSO_4 \ (s) \qquad (Eq. \ 15\text{-}3)$$

The net ionic equation for the chemical changes expressed in Equations 15-1, 15-2, and 15-3 can be stated in the general form

$$M^{++} \ (aq) + SO_4^{--} \ (aq) \rightarrow MSO_4 \ (s) \qquad (Eq. \ 15\text{-}4)$$

In Equation 15-4, M may be Ca, Sr, or Ba, and M^{++} represents any one of the alkaline-earth metal cations, Ca^{++}, Sr^{++}, or Ba^{++}. For example, the precipitation of barium sulfate is represented by

$$Ba^{++} \ (aq) + SO_4^{--} \ (aq) \rightarrow BaSO_4 \ (s) \qquad (Eq. \ 15\text{-}5)$$

In Fig. 15-1 are shown the quantities of precipitate formed for different mole ratios of reactants in the three systems. Each system was prepared by mixing a 1 M solution of sodium sulfate and a 1 M solution of one of the alkaline-earth metal chlorides. The total volume of each mixture was 12 ml. In each set the maximum quantity of precipitate formed from sodium sulfate and the alkaline-earth metal chloride is found when the mole ratio of alkaline-earth metal chloride and sodium sulfate is about 1:1. The quantity of precipitate formed was established by filtering, drying, and determining the mass of each precipitate. In all cases the points fall near two straight lines which intersect at the 1:1 mole ratio for the initial components. The three different sets of systems symbolized by Equation 15-4 all form insoluble sulfates of the same general formula, MSO_4. Are the systems comparable in other ways?

The data given in Fig. 15-1 suggest that the calcium sulfate system differs from the others in that the amount of precipitate is markedly less than in the systems where either $SrSO_4$ or $BaSO_4$ is a final component. Comparison of the maximum quantity of precipitate formed in each set of systems shows that there is but 4.8 millimoles of calcium sulfate precipitated compared to 6.0 millimoles of strontium sulfate and 6.0 millimoles of barium sulfate precipitated when each of the three systems contains 6.0 millimoles of alkaline-earth metal cation and 6.0 millimoles of sulfate ion.

From the quantities of reactants and the quantity of precipitate, it is possible to compute the ratio of number of moles of metal sulfate

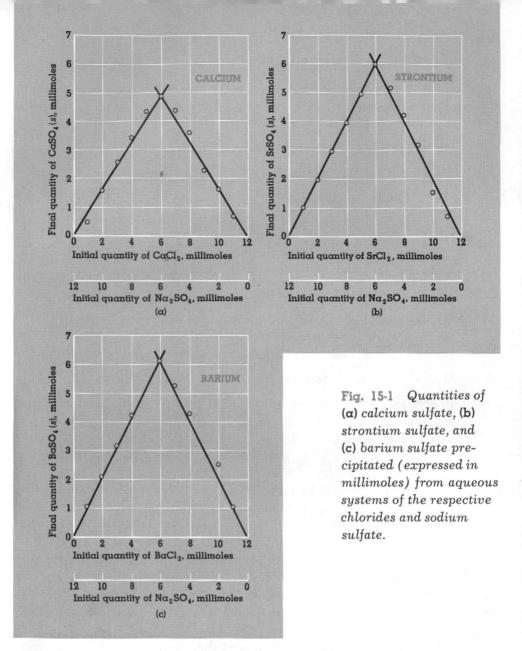

Fig. 15-1 *Quantities of* **(a)** *calcium sulfate,* **(b)** *strontium sulfate, and* **(c)** *barium sulfate precipitated (expressed in millimoles) from aqueous systems of the respective chlorides and sodium sulfate.*

precipitated to the initial number of moles of alkaline-earth metal chloride for each system of the set. An equivalent numerical ratio is obtained by dividing the number of moles of compound in the precipitate by the initial number of moles of alkaline-earth metal ion. The maximum possible quantity of precipitate would be obtained if every alkaline-earth metal ion initially present reacted to form the metal sulfate. For the systems described in Fig. 15-1 the decimal fraction of the alkaline-earth metal ion that has reacted to form the metal sulfate has been calculated to give the data in Table 15-1 and Fig. 15-2.

As an example of the calculation of the fraction precipitated, consider a system initially prepared from 4 ml of 1 M $CaCl_2$ and 8 ml of 1 M Na_2SO_4 (Fig. 15-1a). A precipitate of 3.38 millimoles of $CaSO_4$ (s) was obtained. Since 1 liter of 1 M $CaCl_2$ solution contains 1 mole of calcium ion, 4 ml of 1 M $CaCl_2$ solution must contain 4 millimoles of calcium ion. Complete reaction would precipitate 4 millimoles of $CaSO_4$ (s). Since only 3.38 millimoles of $CaSO_4$ (s) was obtained experimentally, the fraction precipitated for this particular system is $3.38/4 = 0.85$, which is the number plotted at point D on the graph in Fig. 15-2.

The fractions larger than 1 obtained for barium sulfate suggest that there is some experimental error or that the barium sulfate precipitate may contain a small amount of some material in addition to $BaSO_4$. For those systems in which the fraction of metal ion precipitated is essentially 1, there is initially one, or more than one, sulfate ion present in solution for each strontium or barium ion. Within the error of the experiments, the reaction between sulfate ion and either strontium ion or barium ion is complete in each system where the number of moles of sulfate ion equals or exceeds the number of moles of strontium ion or barium ion. However, the reaction between calcium ion and sulfate ion, as already mentioned in Section 13-6, is not complete

TABLE 15-1 FRACTION OF ALKALINE-EARTH METAL ION PRECIPITATED AS SULFATE FROM 12 ml OF AQUEOUS SOLUTION

Quantities of Initial Components, millimoles		Fraction of Metal Ion Precipitated		
M^{++}	SO_4^{--}	$\dfrac{CaSO_4\ (s)}{Ca^{++}}$	$\dfrac{SrSO_4\ (s)}{Sr^{++}}$	$\dfrac{BaSO_4\ (s)}{Ba^{++}}$
11.00	1.00	0.06	0.06	0.09
10.00	2.00	0.16	0.15	0.25
9.00	3.00	0.25	0.35	
8.00	4.00	0.46	0.52	0.53
7.00	5.00	0.62	0.73	0.74
6.00	6.00	0.81	0.99	
5.00	7.00	0.85	0.98	1.05
4.00	8.00	0.85	0.98	1.04
3.00	9.00	0.84	0.97	1.03
2.00	10.00	0.78	0.97	1.03
1.00	11.00	0.42	1.00	

for any mole ratio of calcium ion to sulfate ion. The fraction of calcium ion precipitated in any of the systems is never as large as 1.

However, Fig. 15-1a indicates that a maximum quantity of calcium sulfate is precipitated for a 1:1 mole ratio of calcium ion to sulfate ion. Although sufficient calcium ion and sulfate ion were present to form 6 millimoles of calcium sulfate, the maximum quantity precipitated was only 4.8 millimoles. For each of the calcium chloride–sodium sulfate–water systems shown in Fig. 15-2, the quantity of precipitate is less than the initial quantity of calcium ion. Some calcium ions and sulfate ions always remain in solution in the system in its final state. The change in state of each of the systems is described by saying that the reaction between calcium ion and sulfate ion is an example of an *incomplete reaction.*

Are there other systems in which reaction of initial components is not complete? For example, is the reaction in the copper–sulfur system presented in Chapters 2 and 3 complete or incomplete?

From the data for the copper–sulfur system in Tables 2-4 and 2-5 and the discussion in Section 3-18, the ratio of moles of Cu_9S_5 to moles of copper can be computed. In Fig. 15-3a, the number of moles of

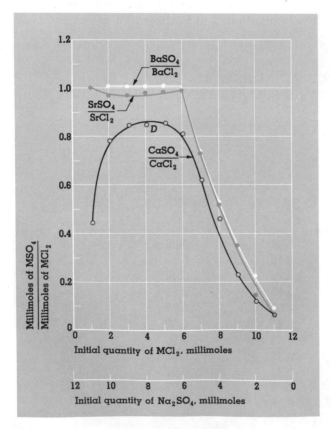

Fig. 15-2 *Graph of the ratios of the quantity of MSO_4 precipitated to the initial quantity of MCl_2 plotted against the quantity of MCl_2 initially present in aqueous systems of MCl_2 and Na_2SO_4.*

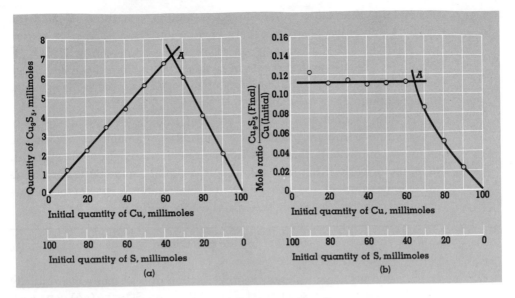

Fig. 15-3 (a) *Graph of quantity of Cu_9S_5 produced in copper–*
sulfur systems plotted against initial quantities of Cu and S.
(b) *Graph of the ratio of the quantity of Cu_9S_5 produced to the*
quantity of Cu initially present plotted against the initial
quantities of Cu and S. Based on data in Table 2-5.

Cu_9S_5 formed is plotted against the number of moles of copper initially present. In Fig. 15-3b, the mole ratio of Cu_9S_5/Cu is plotted against moles of copper initially present. Figure 15-3a shows the point of maximum yield of Cu_9S_5. The number of moles of Cu_9S_5 formed per mole of copper initially present remains nearly constant at about 0.11 when there is more sulfur initially present than is needed to react with all the copper present to form Cu_9S_5 (point A in Fig. 15-3b). Only for initial quantities of sulfur less than that represented by point A does the ratio fall below 0.11.

Since 9 moles of copper is needed to form 1 mole of Cu_9S_5, the calculated ratio of moles of Cu_9S_5 to moles of Cu is 0.11 if all the copper initially present in a system reacts to form Cu_9S_5. Since experiment shows that in the copper–sulfur systems the mole ratio is $\frac{1}{9}$ or 0.11 within experimental error, the reaction (Equation 15-6) is said to go to completion.

$$9Cu \ (s) + 5S \ (s) \rightarrow Cu_9S_5 \ (s) \qquad (Eq. \ 15\text{-}6)$$

The copper sulfide formation is like the strontium sulfate formation and barium sulfate formation in that, within experimental error, all three reactions are complete.

Other reactions, like the reaction of calcium ion and sulfate ion, are incomplete. Examples of incomplete reactions are those of lead ion (Pb^{++}) and chloride ion (Cl^-), of barium ion (Ba^{++}) and hydroxide ion (OH^-), and of hydrogen ion (H^+) and acetate ion ($CH_3CO_2^-$). Incomplete reactions also occur in systems other than those composed of ions. For example, the reaction of nitrogen gas and hydrogen gas to form ammonia is incomplete.

The final components of a system that undergoes incomplete reaction include a fraction of each of the initial components as well as one or more components that were not present initially. In some systems, then, factors other than the mixing of the initial components determine the composition of the system in its final state. What factors affect chemical reaction between the initial components of a system?

Ex. 15-1 a. Write the net ionic equation for the reaction in a system which initially consists of $CaSO_4$ (s) and water.

b. Write the net ionic equation for the reaction in a system which initially consists of an aqueous solution of Sr^{++} (aq) and SO_4^{--} (aq) ions each at 1 M concentration.

Ex. 15-2 According to Fig. 15-2 (the data in this figure are taken from Table 15-1), what fraction of the initial quantity of Ca^{++} (aq) is precipitated as $CaSO_4$ (s) if 2.5 ml of 1 M $CaCl_2$ solution is added to 9.5 ml of 1 M Na_2SO_4 solution? if 9.5 ml of 1 M $CaCl_2$ solution is added to 2.5 ml of 1 M Na_2SO_4 solution?

15-2 REVERSIBLE REACTIONS

Any liquid, water included, will turn to gas at any temperature provided space is available for the gas. For many substances the change from liquid phase to gas phase can be reversed so that a gas can be changed to a liquid. For a given change in phase, there is a pressure of the gas for which the reversal of the change in phase requires only a small change in temperature. Conditions can always be found for which phase changes are reversible, but are chemical changes ever reversible?

The calcium chloride–sodium sulfate–water system can be examined for reversibility. For the data plotted in Fig. 15-1, the maximum quantity of precipitated calcium sulfate is obtained when the mole ratio of initial components is 1:1. A system of this initial composition will, in its final state, consist of solid calcium sulfate and a solution containing calcium ion, sulfate ion, sodium ion, and chloride ion. For the systems for which data are shown in Fig. 15-1, the sodium ion and chloride ion will each be present in solution at a final concentration of 1 M when the initial mole ratio is 1:1.

Let us examine another system which is prepared by taking solid calcium sulfate and a 1 M solution of sodium chloride. When the

CaSO$_4$ solid and the sodium chloride solution are stirred together, some of the CaSO$_4$ dissolves at first, but after a while no further dissolving occurs even though solid CaSO$_4$ is still present. The liquid phase of the system in its final state is identical in every way with the liquid phase of the system described in the preceding paragraph. So long as any solid calcium sulfate is present in the system, the amount present is found to make no difference in the properties of the liquid phase of the system in its final state (Fig. 15-4).

The system whose composition corresponds to the point at which the maximum quantity of precipitate forms (Fig. 15-1) can be produced in either of two ways. One way starts with solutions of calcium chloride and sodium sulfate which react as described in Equation 15-1.

$$CaCl_2 \ (aq) + Na_2SO_4 \ (aq) \rightarrow 2NaCl \ (aq) + CaSO_4 \ (s) \quad (Eq. \ 15\text{-}1)$$

The other way starts with a solid calcium sulfate and a solution of sodium chloride which react as described in Equation 15-7.

$$2NaCl \ (aq) + CaSO_4 \ (s) \rightarrow CaCl_2 \ (aq) + Na_2SO_4 \ (aq) \quad (Eq. \ 15\text{-}7)$$

Beginning with either of two different initial states, the calcium chloride–sodium sulfate–water system undergoes changes in state to form final states in which the systems have the same composition. In one initial state the system contains calcium chloride and sodium sulfate solutions, and in the other initial state the system contains sodium chloride solution and solid calcium sulfate. A system is said to be capable of a **reversible change** in state (**reversible reaction**) when its final state can be reached from two or more initial states in which the system has different sets of initial components.

A great many systems are capable of reversible changes in state. Phase changes are reversible. The Daniell cell reaction is reversible. At temperatures of about 1000°C, the reaction in the hydrogen–oxygen–steam system is reversible. The reaction in the lead nitrate–potassium iodide system can be shown to be reversible if a sufficiently sensitive detector is available to determine the lead ion and iodide ion present in the system in its final state.

Many reactions have never been demonstrated to be reversible.

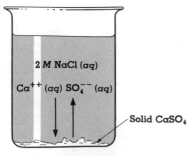

Fig. 15-4 *Diagram representing chemical equilibrium in a saturated solution of CaSO$_4$ in 2 M NaCl.*

2 M NaCl (aq)

Ca^{++} (aq) SO$_4^{--}$ (aq)

Solid CaSO$_4$

When potassium chlorate is heated, the reaction is described by Equation 15-8.

$$2KClO_3 \ (s) \rightarrow 2KCl \ (s) + 3O_2 \ (g) \qquad (Eq. \ 15\text{-}8)$$

All attempts have failed to demonstrate any reaction between oxygen gas and potassium chloride. The reaction proceeds until all the initial potassium chlorate has completely disappeared and the system contains only oxygen and potassium chloride. On the other hand, the decomposition of calcium carbonate (Equation 15-9) proceeds at about 800°C and is readily reversible. Reversible reactions are represented in equation form by a double arrow.

$$CaCO_3 \ (s) \rightleftarrows CaO \ (s) + CO_2 \ (g) \qquad (Eq. \ 15\text{-}9)$$

In its final state the calcium carbonate–calcium oxide–carbon dioxide system contains all three substances, if the carbon dioxide gas is not allowed to escape from the system.

Some reversible reactions that have been discussed are described by Equations 15-9 to 15-13.

$$Ca^{++} \ (aq) + SO_4{}^{--} \ (aq) \rightleftarrows CaSO_4 \ (s) \qquad (Eq. \ 15\text{-}10)$$

$$H_2O \ (l) \rightleftarrows H_2O \ (g) \qquad (Eq. \ 15\text{-}11)$$

$$Pb^{++} \ (aq) + 2I^- \ (aq) \rightleftarrows PbI_2 \ (s) \qquad (Eq. \ 15\text{-}12)$$

$$Zn \ (s) + Cu^{++} \ (aq) \rightleftarrows Cu \ (s) + Zn^{++} \ (aq) \qquad (Eq. \ 15\text{-}13)$$

Ex. 15-3 Compare the final states of the two systems whose initial compositions are described below.

System *A*:   1 mole of $Pb(NO_3)_2$, 2 moles of NaCl, 3 liters of water

System *B*:   1 mole of $PbCl_2$, 2 moles of $NaNO_3$, 3 liters of water

15-3 LE CHATELIER'S PRINCIPLE: EFFECT OF CONCENTRATION

When a concentrated solution of calcium chloride is added to a saturated solution of calcium sulfate, calcium sulfate precipitates. If calcium sulfate did not precipitate, the calcium ion concentration in the solution would be the sum of that due to the calcium sulfate and that due to the added calcium chloride in the solution. Instead, the concentration of calcium ion is always found to be less than this sum. Additional calcium sulfate precipitates if solid sodium sulfate is added to a saturated solution of calcium sulfate, also. In both cases interaction between calcium ion and sulfate ion results in the formation of additional calcium sulfate. The solubility of calcium sulfate is reduced whenever a substance containing either calcium ion or sulfate ion is added to a saturated solution of calcium sulfate. Experiments show that in the final solution the concentration of the added ion is greater than in the saturated solution of calcium sulfate. The concentration of the other ion is less than in the saturated solution of calcium sulfate.

The characteristic behavior of the calcium sulfate–water system can be described as follows. When calcium ions and sulfate ions are brought together in solution in sufficient and equal concentration, interaction between the ions occurs, causing some but not all of the calcium and sulfate ions to precipitate as calcium sulfate. Whether a precipitate forms or not depends on the concentrations of the ions present. The calcium ions and sulfate ions remaining in the saturated solution have concentrations which are characteristic for each temperature. The concentrations of the ions do not change by allowing further time to elapse. When solid calcium sulfate is shaken with water, some of it dissolves to form a saturated solution in which the calcium ions and sulfate ions also have constant concentrations in the solution. The reaction represented by Equation 15-10 is reversible.

The differences in the amount of solid calcium sulfate produced by adding either calcium ion or sulfate ion illustrate a general phenomenon. When an operation is performed on a system, any initial change produced in the system is called a **disturbance.** One example of a disturbance is the addition or removal of a component of a system so as to change the concentration of a solution in the system. The initial change in concentration is a disturbance. For a system that can undergo a reversible change in state, a disturbance of the concentration is followed by a further change in state. This further change always results in reducing the effect of the disturbance on the system. A schematic diagram of a disturbance and an accompanying change in state is shown in Fig. 15-5.

A disturbance in a system is illustrated by the addition of calcium ion to a saturated solution of calcium sulfate. Calcium sulfate dissolved in water gives a saturated solution whose concentration at 25°C is 6.2×10^{-3} M. The solution contains calcium ions and sulfate ions.

$$[Ca^{++}] = [SO_4^{--}] = 6.2 \times 10^{-3} \ M$$

The ions and the solid calcium sulfate form a reversible system described by Equation 15-10. What happens if the system is disturbed by adding calcium chloride to the saturated solution?

Suppose that 6.2×10^{-3} mole of $CaCl_2$ is added to 1 liter of the saturated solution of calcium sulfate. The initial change would be a doubling of the calcium ion concentration to give an initial concentration of calcium ion of 1.24×10^{-2} M. It is found, however, that some calcium sulfate precipitates so that the final concentration of calcium ion is found to be about 9.3×10^{-3} M. Instead of the disturbance

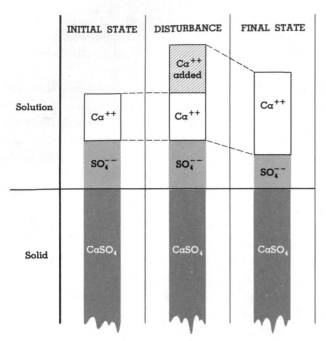

| | INITIAL STATE | DISTURBANCE | FINAL STATE |

Fig. 15-5 *Schematic diagram of the effect of a disturbance on the state of a system (Le Chatelier's principle).*

doubling the calcium ion concentration from 6.2×10^{-3} to 1.24×10^{-2} M, the observed change is only from 6.2×10^{-3} to 9.3×10^{-3} M.

Henri Le Chatelier, a French scientist, first pointed out in 1888 the generality of the effect of a disturbance on a system. In general, a disturbance in the concentration of a component of a system that can undergo a reversible change in state produces a change in state which reduces the amount by which the disturbance affects the concentration.

This general conclusion is known as Le Chatelier's principle. Experiments show that this principle has an application broader than to disturbances in concentration alone. Changes in volume and the transfer of energy as well as the addition or removal of components can act as disturbances to chemical systems that can undergo a reversible change in state.

15-4 LE CHATELIER'S PRINCIPLE: EFFECT OF VOLUME CHANGE

For systems that are composed of one or more gaseous components and that can undergo reversible changes in state, pressure is an important part of the description of the system. As a gas sample is compressed, the gas volume decreases and hence the gas concentration (moles per volume) increases. To the extent that the ideal gas law applies, gas pressure and gas concentration are directly proportional.

Carbon monoxide reacts incompletely with oxygen at temperatures around 1000°C to produce a system containing carbon dioxide, carbon monoxide, and oxygen. The same final state can be attained, starting either with carbon dioxide or with carbon monoxide and oxygen. Hence, the carbon monoxide–oxygen–carbon dioxide system is capable of reversible changes in state. A chemical equation for the reversible reaction in the system is therefore written

$$2CO + O_2 \rightleftarrows 2CO_2 \qquad\qquad (Eq.\ 15\text{-}14)$$

A disturbance of the system produced by compression or expansion is found to alter the state of the system. Compression of the system at 1000°C is accompanied by conversion of some carbon monoxide and oxygen to carbon dioxide. Conversely, any expansion of the system is accompanied by the conversion of carbon dioxide to carbon monoxide and oxygen.

During compression, two molecules of carbon monoxide and one molecule of oxygen react to produce two molecules of carbon dioxide. The reaction therefore transforms three molecules into two molecules. Compression of the system is accompanied by a reaction which, by decreasing the number of molecules in the system, reduces the pressure exerted by the system. Conversely, expansion of the system is accompanied by a reaction which, by increasing the number of molecules in the system, increases the pressure exerted by the system. Therefore, in the carbon monoxide–oxygen–carbon dioxide system, a disturbance which decreases the volume (increase in pressure) leads to a reaction which tends to decrease the pressure. An increase in volume (decrease in pressure) leads to a reaction which tends to increase the pressure. A volume disturbance in a system characterized by a reversible reaction always produces a smaller change in pressure than would have been the case if a reversible reaction were not characteristic of the system.

In the industrial synthesis of ammonia by the reaction of nitrogen and hydrogen, a system is established in which there is a reversible and incomplete reaction (Expression 15-15).

$$N_2\ (g) + 3H_2\ (g) \rightleftarrows 2NH_3\ (g) \qquad \Delta H = -22.0 \text{ kcal at } 25°C$$
$$(Exp.\ 15\text{-}15)$$

For the system to reach its final state in a reasonable time, the gases are allowed to react in the presence of iron oxides at a temperature of about 500°C. Exactly the same state can be reached in the absence of the iron oxides, but much more slowly. According to Expression 15-15, for every 2 volumes of gaseous ammonia formed, a total of 4 volumes of gaseous reagents (1 volume of nitrogen and 3 volumes of hydrogen) is needed. The synthesis of ammonia therefore involves a reduction in volume when all components are considered at the same temperature and pressure. If a mixture of hydrogen, nitrogen, and ammonia at 1 atmosphere is compressed so as to reduce the volume by a factor of 500, would this disturbance result in a pressure that is 500 atmospheres? The rearrangement of the atoms in three hydrogen molecules and one nitrogen molecule to form two ammonia molecules allows the system to exert a smaller pressure. A compression of the system will lead to a conversion of additional nitrogen and hydrogen into ammonia and hence a smaller number of molecules per unit volume. The commercial process for the manufacture of ammonia utilizes the fact that the hydrogen–nitrogen–ammonia system contains a higher percentage of ammonia at high pressure than at low pressure. The reaction is often carried out at a pressure close to 1,000 atmospheres so that the final concentration of ammonia is markedly increased over the concentration reached at 1 atmosphere pressure. Le Chatelier's principle applies therefore not only to concentration changes in liquid solutions but also to pressure or volume changes in gaseous reactions.

Ex. 15-4　In Section 15-2 it is stated that the reaction in the hydrogen–oxygen–steam system is reversible at 1000°C. If a hydrogen–oxygen–steam system in an equilibrium state is compressed at constant temperature, in which direction will the reaction go in order to reestablish equilibrium?

15-5　LE CHATELIER'S PRINCIPLE: EFFECT OF TEMPERATURE CHANGE

Concentration and pressure changes are not the only possible disturbances that can be applied to a chemical system. Thermal energy transferred into or out of a system usually results in a temperature change. Consider the case of the transfer of thermal energy to a saturated solution of barium hydroxide in contact with solid barium hydroxide. As temperature is increased (that is, as heat is transferred to the solution), the concentrations of barium ions and hydroxide ions in solution increase also, as shown in Fig. 15-6. Conversely, the removal of thermal energy (cooling) from a saturated solution of barium hydroxide is accompanied not only by a decrease in temperature but also by precipitation of solid barium hydroxide. The solid barium hydroxide separating from the saturated solution has the formula $Ba(OH)_2 \cdot 8H_2O$. If this substance is shaken with water, some of it dissolves to form barium ions and hydroxide ions. Barium hydroxide and water form a system which can undergo a reversible change in state.

The dissolving process at 25°C is accompanied by an enthalpy increase of 14.3 kcal/mole of hydrated barium hydroxide that goes into solution.

$$Ba(OH)_2 \cdot 8H_2O \ (s) \rightarrow Ba^{++} \ (aq) + 2OH^- \ (aq) + 8H_2O$$
$$\Delta H = 14.3 \text{ kcal} \quad (Exp. \ 15\text{-}16)$$

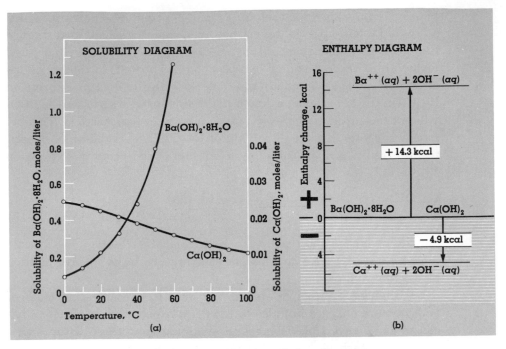

Fig. 15-6 (a) *Solubility diagram and* (b) *enthalpy diagram for interactions in the system of* H_2O *and* $\overset{\frown}{Ba}(OH)_2 \cdot 8H_2O$ *and in the* $Ca(OH)_2$ -H_2O *system.*

Heat is absorbed as barium hydroxide dissolves, and the process, as represented in Expression 15-16 read from left to right, is endothermic.

If 1 liter of saturated barium hydroxide solution is heated from 25 to 35°C while solid $Ba(OH)_2 \cdot 8H_2O$ is present at all times, the system absorbs 12.0 kcal of energy. The concentration of barium ions and hydroxide ions in solution increases as the temperature rises. A liter of saturated barium hydroxide solution, at 25°C but not in contact with solid barium hydroxide, will increase in temperature not by 10°C but by about 12°C when 12 kcal of energy is transferred into the system. Since no solid barium hydroxide is present in the second case, the barium hydroxide solution becomes unsaturated once the temperature rises above 25°C.

Viewed as a disturbance, the transfer of thermal energy to a system produces a temperature change. For a system such as the H_2O-$Ba(OH)_2$ system, the transfer of thermal energy produces a smaller temperature change if the system can change in state reversibly.

How the state of a system changes in response to a change in temperature is directly related to whether the change in state is exothermic or endothermic. For saturated solutions of barium hydroxide, $Ba(OH)_2 \cdot 8H_2O$, and calcium hydroxide, $Ca(OH)_2$, concentration and temperature data are given in Fig. 15-6a. Barium hydroxide forms an aqueous solution in which solubility increases with rise in temperature. Since a system that is reversible undergoes changes that reduce the effect of a disturbance, the increase in solubility with increased temperature is accompanied by absorption of heat. That the dissolving of $Ba(OH)_2 \cdot 8H_2O$ is endothermic agrees with the data in Expression 15-16. On the other hand, calcium hydroxide forms a saturated solution whose concentration decreases with increase in temperature. This behavior suggests that the dissolving of $Ca(OH)_2$ is exothermic. Experimental results give an enthalpy of solution as indicated in Expression 15-17.

$$Ca(OH)_2 \ (s) \rightarrow Ca^{++} \ (aq) + 2OH^- \ (aq)$$
$$\Delta H = -3.9 \text{ kcal} \quad (Exp. \ 15\text{-}17)$$

For the reverse of the reaction in Expression 15-17, $\Delta H = +3.9$ kcal/mole of $Ca(OH)_2$. An increase in temperature leads to precipitation of calcium hydroxide.

Le Chatelier's principle applies not only to concentration changes and pressure changes but also to temperature changes in systems that can undergo reversible changes in state. Concentration disturbances, pressure disturbances, and thermal disturbances may each be accompanied by changes in the state of the disturbed system that reduce the magnitude of the disturbance, provided only that the system is able to undergo a reversible change in state.

Ex. 15-5 For the reaction in the hydrogen–oxygen–steam system, how is the composition of the system affected when the temperature is increased above 1000°C? ($\Delta H_{25°C} = -57.8$ kcal/mole of H_2O.)

15-6 CHEMICAL EQUILIBRIUM

A chemical system that exhibits the following characteristic set of properties is said to be in an **equilibrium state.**

1. Stability: The state of the system does not change spontaneously.

2. Incomplete reaction: The system in its final state includes both reactants and products.

3. Reversible reaction: Two different sets of initial components can react to form a system with the same set of final components.

4. Le Chatelier's principle: Disturbances in concentration, pressure, or temperature may each be accompanied by changes in the state of the system which reduce the magnitude of the initial change in concentration, pressure, or temperature.

The possibility that a chemical change will occur in a chemical system is not determined solely by the presence of the reagents. Although the presence of appropriate reagents is essential for reaction to occur, it is also necessary that the reagents be present in sufficient concentration. A chemist can in fact alter the concentration of reagents in order to control the direction and the extent of a chemical reaction. Study of chemical equilibrium is primarily a study of the way in which concentration changes alter reactivity.

15-7 ELECTROCHEMICAL EQUILIBRIUM

The equilibrium states of a number of chemical systems can be studied in electrochemical cells. A cell convenient for experimental study can be assembled by taking two half cells. One half cell is made up of a platinum electrode in a beaker containing both an iron (II) salt and an iron (III) salt in solution. This half cell is connected by a salt bridge to a second half cell made up of a silver electrode in a beaker containing a solution of a silver salt (Fig. 15-7).

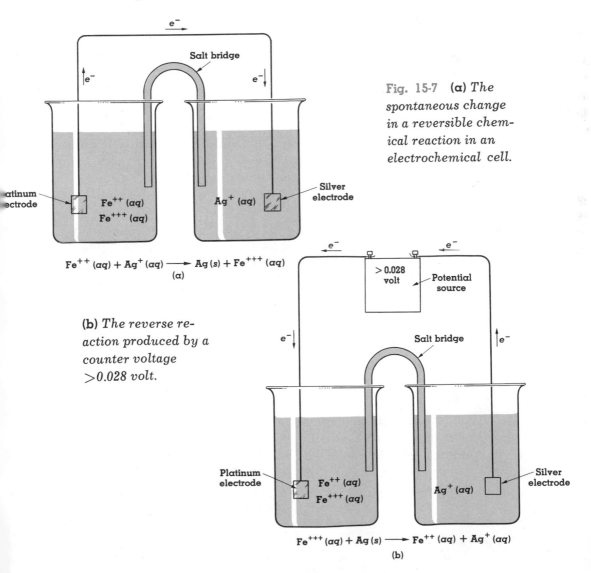

Fig. 15-7 (a) *The spontaneous change in a reversible chemical reaction in an electrochemical cell.*

(b) *The reverse reaction produced by a counter voltage >0.028 volt.*

Using a 1 M concentration of each ion, a reaction described by Equation 15-18 takes place when the electrodes are connected with a wire as shown in Fig. 15-7a.

$$Fe^{++} \ (1 \ M) + Ag^+ \ (1 \ M) \rightarrow Ag \ (s) + Fe^{+++} \ (1 \ M) \qquad (Eq. \ 15\text{-}18)$$

Metallic silver is deposited on the silver electrode during this reaction. If, instead of connecting the electrodes together, they are connected to an external source of electric potential of more than about 0.028 volt (Fig. 15-7b), the chemical reaction proceeds in the reverse direction as indicated by Equation 15-19, and silver from the silver electrode goes into solution as silver ion.

$$Fe^{+++} \ (1 \ M) + Ag \ (s) \rightarrow Fe^{++} \ (1 \ M) + Ag^+ \ (1 \ M) \qquad (Eq. \ 15\text{-}19)$$

The two reactions shown in Equations 15-18 and 15-19 indicate that a reversible reaction can occur in the electrochemical system.

At the silver electrode, the changes are represented by

$$Ag^+ \ (aq) + e^- \rightleftarrows Ag \ (s) \qquad (Eq. \ 15\text{-}20)$$

while at the platinum electrode the changes are given by

$$Fe^{++} \ (aq) \rightleftarrows Fe^{+++} \ (aq) + e^- \qquad (Eq. \ 15\text{-}21)$$

It is also possible to measure the electric potential difference produced in the silver–iron electrochemical cell when the ion concentrations are other than 1 M. The data obtained when $[Ag^+] = 1$ and when different ratios of Fe^{++} and Fe^{+++} concentrations are used are plotted in Fig. 15-8. In this example, the silver ion concentration is kept at 1 M for all measurements. Except for a single ratio of $[Fe^{++}]/[Fe^{+++}]$ at point B, indicated by the dotted vertical line (Fig. 15-8), an electric potential difference between the electrodes is always observed. The potential difference increases on either side of the composition represented by the dotted line. In other words, for all ratios of $[Fe^{++}]/[Fe^{+++}]$ other than the one indicated by point B, the potential difference differs from zero. At ratios of $[Fe^{++}]/[Fe^{+++}]$ less than the composition at point B, silver goes into solution as silver ion. At ratios greater than that at point B, the reaction proceeds in the opposite direction and silver is deposited on the electrode.

For the system in Fig. 15-8 represented by point B for which the potential difference is found to be zero, no change takes place when the electrodes are connected by an external conductor. Application of an external electric potential difference will cause one or the other of the reactions of Equations 15-18 and 15-19 to take place, depending upon which electrode, the platinum or the silver, is made the more positive.

Alternatively, a chemical change may be produced by changing the concentration of one of the reagents. Thus, an increase in either the

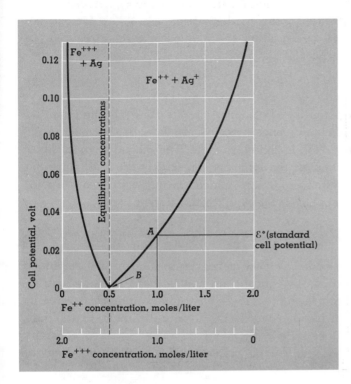

Fig. 15-8 *Potential difference plotted against iron(II) ion concentration for a cell made up of a silver–silver ion electrode and an iron(II) ion– iron(III) ion electrode. In the cell, [Ag+] = 1 and [Fe++] + [Fe+++] = 1. The dotted line represents the point at which connection between the counter voltage source and the cell terminals is reversed. To the left of the dotted line the spontaneous cell reaction is Fe+++ + Ag → Fe++ + Ag+, while to the right of the dotted line the spontaneous cell reaction is Fe++ + Ag+ → Fe+++ + Ag.*

Ag^+ concentration or the Fe^{++} concentration from the concentrations characteristic of the system when $\varepsilon = 0$ will cause the reaction of Equation 15-22 to proceed toward the deposition of metallic silver.

$$Fe^{++} \ (aq) + Ag^+ \ (aq) \rightleftarrows Fe^{+++} \ (aq) + Ag \ (s) \qquad (Eq. \ 15\text{-}22)$$

Conversely, an increase in the Fe^{+++} concentration or reduction in the Ag^+ concentration will lead to the reaction of some Fe^{+++} to form Fe^{++} and Ag^+. In both situations the quantity of added reagent is partially diminished by reaction of that reagent to form other products. The system therefore behaves according to Le Chatelier's principle.

A system in a state that is stable, that includes reactants and products, that is reversible, and that obeys Le Chatelier's principle is in an equilibrium state. The graph of Fig. 15-8 indicates that the iron–silver system shows no potential difference ($\varepsilon = 0$) at B. Therefore the system is at equilibrium when $[Fe^{++}] = 0.50 \ M$, $[Fe^{+++}] = 1.50 \ M$, and $[Ag^+] = 1.0 \ M$. As long as the silver electrode is present, changes in its size or mass are found not to influence the equilibrium state. This is true of all solid or liquid phases of components of a system in an equilibrium state. How are the solution concentrations related to the measured electric potential differences for this cell system?

In Chapter 14, an equation describing the relation between cell potential differences and concentrations of ions in solution was developed. When the chemical reaction for the iron–silver system can be described by Equation 15-22, the mathematical expression for the potential of the cell will be Equation 15-23, where ε is the measured potential difference of the cell at 25°C.

$$\varepsilon = \varepsilon^\circ - 0.059 \log \frac{[Fe^{+++}]}{[Fe^{++}][Ag^+]} \qquad (Eq.\ 15\text{-}23)$$

The standard cell potential ε° (point A in Fig. 15-8) is the potential of the cell when all ionic concentrations are 1 M so that each component of the system is in its standard state. The second term in Equation 15-23 is zero when all the ionic concentrations are 1 M, since the logarithm of 1 is zero, and so $\varepsilon = \varepsilon^\circ$. Since $\varepsilon = 0$ at equilibrium (point B), Equation 15-24 applies at the equilibrium state.

$$\varepsilon^\circ = 0.059 \log \frac{[Fe^{+++}]_{eq}}{[Fe^{++}]_{eq}[Ag^+]_{eq}} \qquad (Eq.\ 15\text{-}24)$$

The subscript eq is added to each concentration term as a reminder that only concentrations at equilibrium can be used in the equation. The right-hand side of Equation 15-24 has a fixed numerical value at a given temperature. In other words, in the equilibrium state, the quotient of concentrations $[Fe^{+++}]_{eq}/[Fe^{++}]_{eq}[Ag^+]_{eq}$ is a constant. This constant, represented by K_{eq}, is called the **equilibrium constant** for the reaction. Thus

$$K_{eq} = \frac{[Fe^{+++}]_{eq}}{[Fe^{++}]_{eq}[Ag^+]_{eq}} \qquad (Eq.\ 15\text{-}25)$$

If K_{eq} is now substituted into Equation 15-24, Equation 15-26 is obtained.

$$\varepsilon^\circ = 0.059 \log K_{eq} \qquad (Eq.\ 15\text{-}26)$$

In this way K_{eq} describes the relation of the concentrations actually present at equilibrium in an electrochemical cell since $\varepsilon = 0$.

With data from Fig. 15-8, the numerical value of K_{eq} can be calculated for the iron–silver system, since at equilibrium (point B) $[Fe^{+++}]_{eq} = 1.50$, $[Fe^{++}]_{eq} = 0.50$, and $[Ag^+]_{eq} = 1.0$. Therefore

$$K_{eq} = \frac{[Fe^{+++}]_{eq}}{[Fe^{++}]_{eq}[Ag^+]_{eq}} = \frac{1.50}{0.50 \times 1.0} = 3.0 \qquad (Eq.\ 15\text{-}27)$$

and

$$\varepsilon^\circ = 0.059 \log 3.0 = 0.028 \text{ volt} \qquad (Eq.\ 15\text{-}28)$$

for the reaction expressed by Equation 15-22.

Electric potential difference is related not only to concentration of ions but also to free energy change (Section 14-8).

$$\Delta G = -nF\varepsilon \qquad (Eq.\ 15\text{-}29)$$

and so if each term in Equation 15-23 is multiplied by $-nF$, the equation describing the free energy change ΔG is given in Equation 15-30.

$$\Delta G = -nF\varepsilon = -nF\varepsilon° + 0.059nF \log \frac{[Fe^{+++}]}{[Fe^{++}][Ag^+]} \quad (Eq.\ 15\text{-}30)$$

At equilibrium both the potential difference ε and the free energy difference ΔG are equal to zero, which changes Equation 15-30 to

$$0 = -nF\varepsilon° + 0.059nF \log \frac{[Fe^{+++}]_{eq}}{[Fe^{++}]_{eq}[Ag^+]_{eq}} \quad (Eq.\ 15\text{-}31)$$

Since the free energy change for a system in its standard state is given by $\Delta G° = -nF\varepsilon°$, Equation 15-31 implies a relation between the standard free energy change and the equilibrium constant as given in Equation 15-32a and b.

$$\Delta G° = -nF\varepsilon° = -0.059nF \log K_{eq} \quad (Eq.\ 15\text{-}32a)$$

where $\Delta G°$ is given in volt-coulombs. For $\Delta G°$ in kilocalories per mole of electrons transferred, the relation will be

$$\Delta G° = -1.36 \log K_{eq} \quad (Eq.\ 15\text{-}32b)$$

The equilibrium constant, which describes the system in its equilibrium state, is therefore related to the standard free energy change characteristic of the system in its standard state. In the laboratory, it is often possible to measure the concentration of each of the components in a system where the system is in its equilibrium state. When these equilibrium concentrations are substituted in an equation similar to Equation 15-25, a numerical value for the equilibrium constant is obtained. Substituting K_{eq} in Equation 15-32 allows the calculation of the standard free energy change $\Delta G°$; that is, the free energy change accompanying the reaction when each soluble component of the system is at $1\ M$ concentration. For the iron–silver system, the equilibrium constant K_{eq} was found to be 3.0 (Equation 15-27). The standard free energy change $\Delta G°$ at $25°C$ is therefore given by

$$\Delta G° = -1.36 \log 3.0 = -1.36 \times 0.48 = -0.65 \text{ kcal/mole of Ag}$$
$$(Eq.\ 15\text{-}33)$$

Just as experimentally determined enthalpy changes are additive in chemical systems and are used to compute enthalpy changes in other systems, so free energy change data are additive and can be used to compute free energy changes for other chemical systems.

Ex. 15-6 *a.* Show how the constant -1.36 in Equation 15-32b is derived from Equation 15-26.

b. What is $\Delta G°$ for a system if $K = 10$? if $K = 10^{-3}$?

15-8 FREE ENERGY AND EQUILIBRIUM

Because there is a direct relationship between the standard free energy change for a system and the equilibrium concentrations of components, the equilibrium state of a system can be specified equally well either by a standard free energy change or by an equilibrium constant. Can we be clear, however, as to the difference in meaning of these two quantities?

The equilibrium constant for the iron–silver system describes the concentration relationships for the components of the system in a state for which no spontaneous change occurs, the equilibrium state.

When the standard free energy change is given for the iron–silver system by Equation 15-31, what does it describe? For the reaction taking place under conditions where each component is in its standard state, the change in free energy is then the standard free energy change. Strictly speaking, all concentrations should remain at 1 M during the reaction of 1 mole of Fe^{++} with 1 mole of Ag^+ to form 1 mole of Fe^{+++} and 1 mole of Ag (s). This could occur only if the system contained an infinitely large volume of solution so that a change of 1 mole in the quantity of a component would result in insignificant changes in the concentrations of the components. But the standard free energy change is approximated in a finite system as long as the chemical change does not make the final state appreciably different from the initial state.

Whatever reaction takes place in a system will necessarily proceed in a direction that, sooner or later, brings the system to the equilibrium state. All nonequilibrium states tend to change so as to decrease their free energy and so as to alter the concentrations of the components of the system in the direction toward the equilibrium state. No further decrease in free energy is possible in a system in the equilibrium state. The decrease in free energy will occur whether the spontaneous change is exothermic or endothermic.

Knowledge of the equilibrium constant not only provides a way of determining a standard free energy change, but it also provides a way of relating the concentrations which can make up the system in its equilibrium state. Thus, the iron–silver system is described at 25°C by Equation 15-34.

$$K_{eq} = \frac{[Fe^{+++}]_{eq}}{[Fe^{++}]_{eq}[Ag^+]_{eq}} = 3.0 \qquad (Eq.\ 15\text{-}34)$$

So long as the temperature is 25°C, the equilibrium constant is equal to 3.0. Concentrations of the three ions may be varied provided only that they be related according to Equation 15-34 to give the constant 3.0. Two of the three ion concentrations may be chosen within the limits of solubility. The equilibrium concentration for the third ion is calculated from Equation 15-34.

Example 1: For $[Ag^+]_{eq} = 1\ M$, what concentrations are possible for $[Fe^{++}]_{eq}$ and $[Fe^{+++}]_{eq}$ at equilibrium at 25°C?

Answer:

$$\frac{[Fe^{+++}]_{eq}}{[Fe^{++}]_{eq}} = K_{eq}[Ag^+]_{eq} = 3.0 \times 1.0$$

Any concentrations attainable in the laboratory are possible for the two iron ions provided only that the ratio of their concentrations is 3.0.

Example 2: For $[Ag^+]_{eq} = 0.25\ M$ and $[Fe^{+++}]_{eq} = 0.50\ M$, what is the equilibrium concentration of Fe^{++}?

Answer:

$$K_{eq} = \frac{0.50}{[Fe^{++}]_{eq}0.25} = 3.0$$

$$[Fe^{++}]_{eq} = \frac{0.50}{3.0 \times 0.25} = 0.67\ M$$

Example 3: For $[Fe^{+++}]/[Fe^{++}] = 0.10$, what will be the silver ion concentration?

Answer:

$$K_{eq} = \frac{0.10}{[Ag^+]_{eq}} = 3.0$$

$$[Ag^+]_{eq} = \frac{0.10}{3.0} = 0.033\ M$$

Although the definition of an equilibrium constant has been developed through an analysis of electrochemical cells, experiments show that the concept of an equilibrium constant can be applied to any chemical system whether or not the system is arranged as an electrochemical system. The only requirement is that the state of the system be characterized by (1) stability, (2) incomplete reaction, (3) reversibility, and (4) Le Chatelier's principle. When these operational conditions are fulfilled, concentration measurements can be used to calculate the equilibrium constant.

In a qualitative way, the equilibrium constant expression describing the system in its final state is related to the chemical equation which describes the change from reactants to products. A general equation for a chemical reaction may be written

$$qQ + rR \rightleftarrows yY + zZ \qquad \text{(Eq. 15-35)}$$

Besides the meanings previously assigned to a chemical equation (Section 3-17), one more can be added: A **chemical equation** describes the decrease in number of moles of reactants and the increase in number of moles of products as the equilibrium state is approached. The equilibrium constant, on the other hand, describes the relationship of the concentrations of the components when the system is in its final and equilibrium state. The equilibrium constant expression includes only those components which are either gases or are dissolved in some solvent. The solvent and substances in separate solid or liquid phases are not included. The equilibrium constant expression for the system described by Equation 15-35, provided that Q, R, Y, and Z are all gases or solutes, is

$$K_{eq} = \frac{[Y]^y[Z]^z}{[Q]^q[R]^r} \qquad (Eq.\ 15\text{-}36)$$

where [Y], [Z], [Q], and [R] are the concentrations of the components of the equilibrium state and y, z, q, and r are the coefficients in the equation. The coefficients appear as exponents of the concentration in the equilibrium constant expression.

Equilibrium constant expressions are used extensively for representing and computing the composition of chemical systems. A few examples of the use of equilibrium constants are included here.

Example 1: The solubility of calcium sulfate in water at 25°C is 6.2 × 10^{-3} mole of $CaSO_4$ per liter. What is the equilibrium constant?

Answer: The chemical equation and the equilibrium constant for the dissolving of calcium sulfate are

$$CaSO_4\ (s) \rightarrow Ca^{++}\ (aq) + SO_4^{--}\ (aq)$$

and
$$K_{eq} = [Ca^{++}]_{eq}[SO_4^{--}]_{eq}$$

Since solid calcium sulfate is in its standard state, no concentration term for it is included in the expression for K_{eq}. For each mole of $CaSO_4$ that dissolves, 1 mole of Ca^{++} and 1 mole of SO_4^{--} are produced. Therefore,

$$[Ca^{++}]_{eq} = [SO_4^{--}]_{eq} = 6.2 \times 10^{-3}\ M$$

and hence,

$$K_{eq} = 6.2 \times 10^{-3} \times 6.2 \times 10^{-3} = 3.8 \times 10^{-5}$$

Example 2: What is the calcium ion concentration in a solution for which $[SO_4^{--}] = 0.0200\ M$ and the solution is in equilibrium with solid calcium sulfate at 25°C?

Answer:
$$K_{eq} = [Ca^{++}]_{eq}[SO_4^{--}]_{eq} = 3.8 \times 10^{-5}$$
$$[Ca^{++}]_{eq}\ 0.0200 = 3.8 \times 10^{-5}$$
$$[Ca^{++}]_{eq} = 1.9 \times 10^{-3}\ M$$

Example 3: A solution that is 0.100 M in $CaCl_2$ is mixed with an equal volume of a solution that is 0.020 M in $MgSO_4$. Will any precipitate of $CaSO_4$ be formed?

Answer: When equal volumes are mixed, each component is diluted by a factor of 2. For the two solutions mixed together, the initial concentration will therefore be

$$[Ca^{++}] = 0.050$$
$$[SO_4^{--}] = 0.010$$

The initial product of the concentrations is

$$[Ca^{++}][SO_4^{--}] = 5.0 \times 10^{-4}$$

However, with a saturated solution the maximum value for the final product of the concentrations at 25°C cannot be more than

$$K_{eq} = [Ca^{++}]_{eq}[SO_4^{--}]_{eq} = 3.8 \times 10^{-5}$$

Therefore, precipitation of $CaSO_4$ would occur since 5×10^{-4} is greater than K_{eq}.

This chapter began with a study of the precipitation of alkaline-earth metal sulfates by the reaction of solutions of alkaline-earth metal chlorides with sodium sulfate. The solubilities are given in Table 15-2 for the four alkaline-earth metal sulfates plus radium sulfate in water at 25°C. Since each of the saturated solutions of the alkaline-earth metal sulfates represents a system in an equilibrium state when it is in contact with the same sulfate in solid phase, an equilibrium constant K_{sp} is also included in Table 15-2 for all except magnesium sulfate. With its relatively high solubility a saturated solution of magnesium sulfate gives ionic concentrations so high that the application of an equilibrium constant expression does not give a constant numerical value.

The calculation of an equilibrium constant for one of the sulfates can be based on the solubility reaction

$$MSO_4 \ (s) \rightarrow M^{++} \ (aq) + SO_4^{--} \ (aq)$$

The equilibrium constant expression is called a **solubility product** K_{sp}.

$$K_{sp} = [M^{++}][SO_4^{--}]$$

TABLE 15-2 SOLUBILITY DATA FOR SOME COMPOUNDS AT 25°C

Compound	Solubility, moles/liter	Solubility Product, K_{sp}
$MgSO_4$	1.128	—
$CaSO_4$	6.2×10^{-3}	3.8×10^{-5}
$SrSO_4$	6.9×10^{-4}	4.8×10^{-7}
$BaSO_4$	3.6×10^{-5}	1.3×10^{-9}
$RaSO_4$	6.2×10^{-6}	3.8×10^{-11}

Ex. 15-7 The equilibrium constant at 25°C for the reaction

$$Zn\ (s) + Cu^{++}\ (aq) \rightarrow Cu\ (s) + Zn^{++}\ (aq)$$

is 1.5×10^{37}. What is the ratio of $[Zn^{++}]/[Cu^{++}]$ at equilibrium?

Ex. 15-8 *a.* What would happen if 0.02 mole of Na_2SO_4 (s) is added to 1 liter of a saturated solution of $CaSO_4$ at 25°C?

b. The solubility product constant for the reaction

$$AgCl\ (s) \rightarrow Ag^+\ (aq) + Cl^-\ (aq)$$

at 25°C is 1.56×10^{-10}. What is the solubility of AgCl (s) expressed in moles of AgCl per liter of solution?

15-9 HYDROGEN FLUORIDE–WATER EQUILIBRIUM

At room temperature the hydrogen fluoride–water system has an equilibrium state. For the proton-transfer reaction (Equation 15-37), the equilibrium constant expression is given by Equation 15-38.

$$HF\ (aq) + H_2O\ (l) \rightleftharpoons H_3O^+\ (aq) + F^-\ (aq) \qquad (Eq.\ 15\text{-}37)$$

$$K_{eq} = \frac{[H_3O^+]_{eq}[F^-]_{eq}}{[HF]_{eq}} \qquad (Eq.\ 15\text{-}38)$$

Since water is the solvent, each of the other three concentrations, $[H_3O^+]$, $[F^-]$, and $[HF]$, is described in terms of moles per liter of water. Water itself cannot have a concentration described in comparable terms. The solvent is considered to be in its standard state and is assigned unit concentration in the equilibrium constant expression.

In Experiment 14, hydrochloric acid is added to solid magnesium oxide suspended in water. As the acid is added, more and more of the magnesium oxide dissolves until, with care, one drop of acid is just enough to dissolve the last remaining trace of solid.

The process of adding successive portions of one reagent to a fixed amount of another reagent is called **titration.** Titration is used in Experiment 14 to determine how much acid is necessary to dissolve a given mass of magnesium oxide. The least amount of one reagent necessary to produce some change such as the dissolving of a second reagent determines the **end point** of the titration.

The total amount of hydrogen fluoride used to prepare a solution can be determined by titration of the solution with sodium hydroxide in the presence of a suitable indicator, such as litmus or phenolphthalein, which changes color at the end point. The electrode systems discussed in Chapter 14 can be used to measure ion concentrations. In particular, hydrogen ion concentrations are readily determined with a cell system including a hydrogen electrode.

The chemical equation indicates that each molecule of hydrogen fluoride that ionizes produces one hydrogen ion and one fluoride ion. Therefore, $[H_3O^+]_{eq} = [F^-]_{eq}$. A determination of hydrogen ion concentration thus provides the concentration for fluoride ion. At equilibrium some of the initial hydrogen fluoride will be present as ions and some as molecules. But, if all the hydrogen ion comes from hydrogen fluoride, it must be that

Final HF concentration = initial HF concentration − $[H_3O^+]$
and

Initial HF concentration = $[HF]_{eq} + [H_3O^+]_{eq}$

Table 15-3 lists some typical concentrations of the components of the hydrogen fluoride–water system as might be determined experimentally in aqueous solutions of hydrogen fluoride.

The calculated equilibrium constants for the two systems shown in Table 15-3 are nearly the same even though the concentrations of the components of the two systems differ by tenfold. At high concentrations of hydrogen fluoride, the equilibrium constants tend to deviate somewhat from equilibrium constants found at low concentration. Similar deviations are found in the equilibrium constants for all systems at equilibrium at higher concentrations. At low concentrations the equilibrium constant for the hydrogen fluoride–water system approaches the number 7.2×10^{-4}. Nonetheless, the idea of an equilibrium constant continues to be a most helpful method of describing equilibrium systems.

The data in Table 15-3 indicate that the reaction of hydrogen fluoride with water is incomplete. Thus, when 0.01 mole of HF per liter of solution is present initially, 0.0077 mole/liter remains finally at equilibrium as HF molecules, while the difference, or 0.0023 mole/liter, reacts to form hydrogen ion and fluoride ion. Less than one-quarter of the initial quantity of HF appears finally as hydrogen ion and fluoride ion. When the initial concentration of HF is 0.001 mole/liter, about

TABLE 15-3 EQUILIBRIUM DATA FOR THE HYDROGEN
FLUORIDE–WATER SYSTEM AT 25°C

Initial concentration of HF, mole/liter	0.01000	0.00100
Equilibrium concentration, mole/liter		
H_3O^+	0.0023	0.00056
F^-	0.0023	0.00056
HF	0.0077	0.00044
$K_{eq} = \dfrac{[H_3O^+][F^-]}{[HF]}$	6.9×10^{-4}	7.1×10^{-4}

one-half of the initial quantity of HF appears finally as hydrogen ion and fluoride ion. In contrast with the incomplete proton-transfer reaction in the case of the hydrogen fluoride–water system, the reaction of hydrogen fluoride and ammonia appears to result in essentially complete proton transfer. When equal numbers of moles of ammonia and hydrogen fluoride in the gas phase are brought together at room temperature, solid NH_4F is formed and the pressure of ammonia gas and hydrogen fluoride gas in equilibrium with solid NH_4F is less than 10^{-5} mm of mercury at 25°C. The reaction is

$$HF\ (g) + NH_3\ (g) \rightarrow NH_4{}^+F^-\ (s)$$

15-10 FREE ENERGY CHANGES

For any system which has an equilibrium state, there is an associated standard free energy change. Measurements of cell potential or equilibrium concentrations can provide data for calculating the free energy change. Calculated free energy changes are listed in Table 15-4 for several of the reactions discussed in this chapter.

A positive standard free energy change is always associated with an equilibrium constant of less than 1, while a negative free energy change is associated with an equilibrium constant greater than 1. For a negative free energy change, the system in its final state is at a lower free energy than in its initial state. A standard free energy change applies to a system in which each solute is at 1 M concentration, each gas is at 1 atmosphere pressure, and the solvent and each substance present as a separate solid or liquid are in their standard states. Those substances that are in their standard states appear in the equilibrium constant with the value of unity for each. When 1 mole of material reacts in a system in which all solutes and gases are at unit concentration or pressure, the free energy changes at a constant temperature and constant pressure are given as $\Delta G°$.

A decrease in free energy represents the maximum work that can be transferred by the system at constant temperature and pressure. In Chapter 9 we found that the enthalpy change of the system is meas-

TABLE 15-4 STANDARD FREE ENERGY CHANGES AT 25°C FOR SOME REACTIONS

Reaction	$\Delta G°$, kcal	K
$CaSO_4\ (s) \rightarrow Ca^{++}\ (aq) + SO_4{}^{--}\ (aq)$	6.0	3.8×10^{-5}
$HF\ (aq) + H_2O\ (l) \rightarrow H_3O^+\ (aq) + F^-\ (aq)$	4.3	7.2×10^{-4}
$Fe^{++}\ (aq) + Ag^+\ (aq) \rightarrow Fe^{+++}\ (aq) + Ag\ (s)$	—0.65	3.0
$Zn\ (s) + Cu^{++}\ (aq) \rightarrow Zn^{++}\ (aq) + Cu\ (s)$	—50.7	2×10^{37}
$2CO\ (g) + O_2\ (g) \rightarrow 2CO_2\ (g)$	—122.9	1×10^{90}

ured by the amount of heat that is transferred to or from a system at constant temperature and pressure. How are these two energy changes related to each other?

15-11 ENTHALPY CHANGES

Calorimetric measurements have been made on the systems listed in Table 15-4. The corresponding enthalpy changes have been calculated and are listed in Table 15-5. Since the enthalpy data apply to each system with each component in its standard state just as described for the free energy change, the enthalpy change is given the symbol $\Delta H°$.

Comparison of the five systems in Table 15-5 suggests that free energy changes and enthalpy changes are not closely related. The changes listed in the table are also plotted in Fig. 15-9. Included in the figure is a line representing $\Delta H° - \Delta G°$ for each system. In the next section this relationship will be discussed.

Whenever a chemical system changes in state at constant temperature and constant pressure, its enthalpy changes. When a reaction occurs in a calorimeter, the enthalpy change is measured by the heat transfer between the system at a constant temperature and the calorimeter. When a system undergoes a particular change in state, the enthalpy change is the same—no matter what route or sequence of changes is followed, and no matter whether the enthalpy change is accompanied by a transfer of heat or of a combination of work and heat. The system might just as well undergo a change in state not in a calorimeter but in some other device where work rather than heat is transferred. The electrochemical cell is one such device for transferring electric energy (work) between the system and its surroundings. The sum of work transferred and heat transferred at a constant temperature and a constant pressure is always equal to the enthalpy change.

For the second system listed in Table 15-5, $\Delta H°$ is negative but $\Delta G°$ is positive. The numbers in Table 15-5 mean that 4.3 kcal of work would have to be transferred into the system to have a mole of hydrogen fluoride ionize when all components are in the standard state. But the

TABLE 15-5 STANDARD FREE ENERGY CHANGES AND ENTHALPY CHANGES AT 25°C FOR SOME REACTIONS

Reaction	$\Delta G°$, kcal	$\Delta H°$, kcal
$CaSO_4 \ (s) \rightarrow Ca^{++} \ (aq) + SO_4^{--} \ (aq)$	+6.0	−4.4
$HF \ (aq) + H_2O \ (l) \rightarrow H_3O^+ \ (aq) + F^- \ (aq)$	+4.3	−3.0
$Fe^{++} \ (aq) + Ag^+ \ (aq) \rightarrow Fe^{+++} \ (aq) + Ag \ (s)$	−0.65	−17.4
$Zn \ (s) + Cu^{++} \ (aq) \rightarrow Zn^{++} \ (aq) + Cu \ (s)$	−50.7	−52.1
$2CO \ (g) + O_2 \ (g) \rightarrow 2CO_2 \ (g)$	−122.9	−135.4

ENTHALPY–FREE ENERGY DIAGRAM

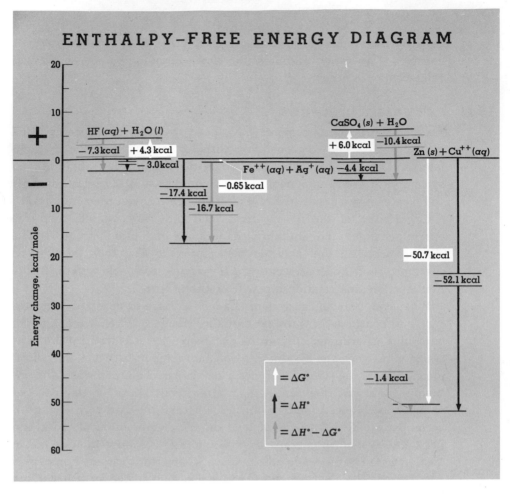

Fig. 15-9 *Comparison of free energy changes and enthalpy changes for four systems.*

ionization of hydrogen fluoride results in an enthalpy decrease of 3.0 kcal/mole. If 4.3 kcal of work (ΔG) could be added to the hydrogen fluoride system to cause ionization, 7.3 kcal (3.0 + 4.3) of heat would be evolved, corresponding to $\Delta H - \Delta G = -7.3$ kcal. Transferring 4.3 kcal of thermal energy into a hydrogen fluoride–water system would only raise the temperature of the system and would not be effective in producing ionization. Thermal energy cannot be substituted for work in the ionization reaction.

The ionization of hydrogen fluoride is an exothermic reaction ($\Delta H° = -3.0$ kcal/mole of HF). When hydrogen ions, fluoride ions, and hydrogen fluoride molecules are placed in solution each at 1 M concentration, the spontaneous reaction is endothermic. In this spontaneous endothermic reaction, hydrogen ions join with fluoride ions to form hydrogen fluoride molecules. Although the enthalpy of the system increases ($\Delta H° = +3.0$ kcal/mole of HF), the free energy decreases ($\Delta G° = -4.3$ kcal/mole of HF). In its initial state the system has a capacity to do work even though its enthalpy increases while the work is being done by the system.

Ex. 15-9   In order to ionize 1 mole of $CaSO_4$ (s) to ions in a solution for which $[Ca^{++}] = [SO_4^{--}] = 1$ M, what is the minimum amount of work which needs to be transferred into the system? What amount of heat would be evolved?

15-12   INTERPRETATION OF FREE ENERGY AND ENTHALPY DATA

One immediate question raised by the data of Table 15-5 is why $\Delta H°$ is not equal to $\Delta G°$. After all, they seem to be simply two ways of measuring the energy changes during a reaction.

The standard free energy changes and standard enthalpy changes shown in Fig. 15-9 are each to be read as part of a sentence that begins with "if." For example, the data on hydrogen fluoride ionization can be described in two ways.

1. If 1 mole of HF were to ionize completely under conditions of unit concentration of hydrogen fluoride, hydrogen ion, and fluoride ion, 4.3 kcal of work would have to be transferred into the system at 25°C. This statement is implied by the expression $\Delta G° = 4.3$ kcal/mole for the ionization of hydrogen fluoride. During this process, 7.3 kcal of heat would be transferred from the system.

2. If 1 mole of HF were to ionize completely but without any transfer of useful work into the system, enough heat would have to be transferred from the system to lower the enthalpy of the system by 3.0 kcal. This statement is implied by the enthalpy change for the system, $\Delta H° = -3.0$ kcal/mole.

But instead of "if" sentences, what actually does happen? Imagine that hydrogen fluoride is initially dissolved in water but in a system completely free of ions. Such a state is not the equilibrium state, and the system will undergo change in state until the final equilibrium state is achieved. As the state of the system changes from initial to final state, only about one molecule in each four molecules of HF actually ionizes. For this amount of ionization, the system will transfer $\frac{1}{4} \times 3.0$ kcal of thermal energy per mole of initial HF. So instead of 1 mole of hydrogen fluoride ionizing completely with the evolution of 3.0 kcal, the initial mole of hydrogen fluoride ionizes only partially and evolves 0.8 kcal of thermal energy. Why ionization proceeds in this way is discussed in Section 15-16.

The reaction for the ionization of hydrogen fluoride is represented by

$$HF \text{ } (aq) + H_2O \text{ } (l) \rightarrow H_3O^+ \text{ } (aq) + F^- \text{ } (aq)$$

This implies that the water is not only a solvent for the system but that water actually participates as a reagent.

The sequence of events during ionization of HF can be viewed in the following way. Water molecules are able to move about freely in liquid water although the forces of attraction are considerable. For the water molecules to be able to move about freely means that there are many possible ways in which the molecules might be arranged. For one or more water molecules to become tied to a proton or to a fluoride ion must limit severely the number of possible arrangements and must thereby restrict the freedom of the water molecules involved. In a sense, it is this loss of possible arrangements or of freedom which prevents the reaction from proceeding to completion unless work is done on the system. But how does freedom, or the lack of it, play a role in determining the direction and extent of a chemical change? What is there besides the availability of energy that may affect the completeness of the reaction?

Ex. 15-10 What is the actual change in enthalpy for a system that goes to an equilibrium state if the system initially consists of 1 mole of $CaSO_4$ (s) and 1 liter of water? (Hint: Only 6.2×10^{-3} mole of $CaSO_4$ (s) dissolves in 1 liter of water at 25°C.)

15-13 FREEDOM AND CHANGE

Consider the following analogy. Suppose you are playing a game in which the object is to toss a ball onto a shelf above your head (Fig. 15-10). To define success, a pail is placed on the shelf, and success in the game consists of tossing the ball into the pail. The pail is designed,

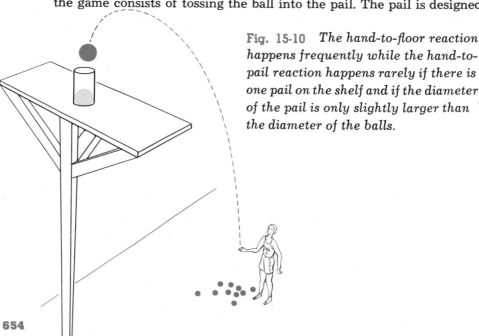

Fig. 15-10 *The hand-to-floor reaction happens frequently while the hand-to-pail reaction happens rarely if there is one pail on the shelf and if the diameter of the pail is only slightly larger than the diameter of the balls.*

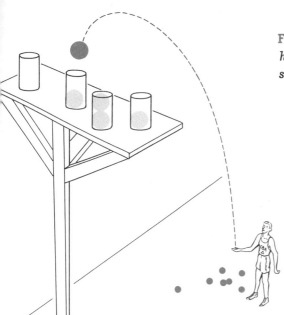

Fig. 15-11 *The hand-to-pail reaction happens more frequently if there are several pails on the shelf.*

however, so that its mouth is only slightly larger than the ball. The player makes a large number of tosses but is successful in getting only a few balls into the pail, while most of the balls end up on the floor. The desired reaction (hand to pail) is not very likely to happen. The difficulty arises in part because of the energy required to throw the balls upward and in part because of the narrow opening of the pail.

One way of improving the player's chances of transferring the ball to the basket is simply to put more pails on the shelf (Fig. 15-11). Now the desired change (hand to pail) for the ball occurs more frequently, and a smaller fraction of the balls end up on the floor. In fact, if a large number of pails are placed on the shelf, the game may reach the point of absurdity! Every ball thrown will fall in one of the pails almost without regard for how carelessly or precisely the ball is thrown (Fig. 15-12).

Of course, the game can always be made more difficult by raising the shelf higher above the player's head. Raising the shelf requires that more energy must be used for each throw. Within limits, however, the increased effort demanded of the thrower by raising the shelf can be counterbalanced by increasing the number of pails. Conversely, decreasing the number of pails will compensate for lowering the shelf. The process of transferring the ball from the player to the shelf is in part determined by the number of places the ball can be put on the shelf.

Another example can also illustrate the effect of the number of possible arrangements in a system. Imagine a box with a partition which divides the volume of the box into two halves. On one side of the partition the space is filled with neon gas, while on the other side

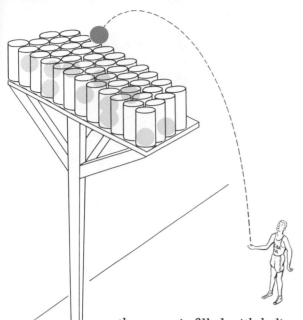

Fig. 15-12 *If the shelf is filled with pails, almost every ball thrown will fall into a pail.*

the space is filled with helium gas as in Fig. 15-13a. When the partition is removed as in (b), within a matter of minutes the two gases have mixed together. Why do the gases mix?

There is no measurable enthalpy change during the mixing of helium and neon so helium and neon must not interact with each other. Yet to separate the two gases requires the expenditure of considerable work. By mixing, each gas occupies a larger volume. At the instant the partition is removed and the available volume increased, the number of possible locations for each gas molecule is increased. The gases mix because of the random motion of the molecules. Once mixed, the gases cannot separate because to do so would involve a decrease in the number of possible arrangements. But a decrease in the number of possible arrangements implies a more orderly system. The random motion of molecules can never by itself produce a more

Fig. 15-13 *Change in patterns of arrangement when neon gas and helium gas mix.*

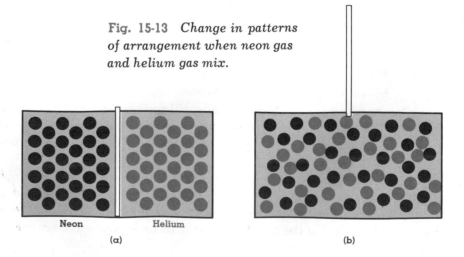

Neon   Helium

(a)   (b)

orderly system—only a less orderly system. It is in this way that we can understand why gases always mix and never separate spontaneously.

Systems of all kinds tend to change from a level of high energy to low energy. But a system also tends to change from a level of high order to one of low order. The two factors may tend to shift a chemical system in opposite directions. A system in a state with many possibilities is spoken of as having little organization. With the idea of states of high and low levels of organization, another formulation can be given of the conditions controlling change in a system.

A system tends to change from a state of high energy to a state of low energy. A system also tends to change from a state of high organization to a state of low organization. Sometimes one state of a system has low energy and high organization, while another state has high energy and low organization. What determines whether a system of this type will undergo a change in state? How important is the energy factor contrasted with the organization factor? In terms of the ball-and-pail analogy, which throw has greater chance of success, toward a high shelf with many pails or toward a low shelf with few pails?

There are examples of chemical change which can be interpreted in terms of organizational effects. Hydrogen gas is made up of diatomic molecules. The molecules come apart with difficulty since 1 mole of hydrogen absorbs 104.2 kcal of energy during dissociation. If hydrogen gas is blown through a high-temperature flame, the molecules do separate and hydrogen atoms are formed.

Why do the diatomic molecules separate when to do so means producing atoms in a system of higher energy than a system containing hydrogen molecules? The hydrogen atoms are free of each other when they are separated. A system of hydrogen atoms has less organization than a system of hydrogen molecules. Hydrogen found in interstellar space with lots of places to be is in the form of separate atoms, not molecules.

The terms low and high organization are being used with a special emphasis here. Low organization refers to a situation with many possibilities. Which alternative possibility (pail) is actually occupied then is not predetermined, and so the system is described as one in which freedom of action is high. High organization in the extreme case refers to a system or a game with only one possibility and hence no alternatives. There is no freedom of action in a system without alternatives.

In terms of energy, the measure of extent of change is given by the enthalpy change ΔH. For the organization factor, the measure of extent of change is given by the term $\Delta H - \Delta G$. In a thinly disguised form, this situation has occurred in systems already discussed. The case of the phase change of a solid or a liquid to gas discussed in Chapter 8 represents the tendency of a system to form a phase of low organization (gas) rather than a phase of low energy (liquid or solid).

15-14 ORGANIZATION AND TEMPERATURE

Why do liquids vaporize? Molecules exist in a liquid phase because of intermolecular attraction (van der Waals attraction). The closer the molecules in a system, the lower the energy arising from attraction (Section 8-16). Yet molecules do transfer from the liquid phase to the gas phase in spite of the fact that molecules in the gas phase must represent a high-energy arrangement.

In fact, the vaporizing process always results in the system's absorbing energy if the change takes place at constant temperature (Section 8-21). For example, water changing to steam is an endothermic reaction. Yet, at a particular temperature the only requirement, in addition to a source of energy to supply the heat of vaporization, for the formation of steam is space.

$$H_2O \ (l) \rightarrow H_2O \ (g) \quad \Delta H = 10.5 \text{ kcal} \quad (Exp. \ 15\text{-}37)$$

In a liquid–gas system at a fixed temperature, then, the molecules can be at low energy and small volume (liquid phase) or at high energy and large volume (gas phase). In a small volume the molecules are close together with relatively little freedom of movement. In a large volume, as in the gas phase, the same number of molecules are far apart and free to move for considerable distances.

We can say, then, that a gas represents a phase of high energy and low organization. On the other hand, a liquid represents a phase of low energy and high organization. But an increase in the temperature of a system, resulting from the transfer of energy to the system, also converts liquid to gas. How is temperature involved?

At high temperature a certain quantity of substance can exist in the gas phase in a relatively small volume at high pressure, while the same quantity of substance at low temperatures would condense to a liquid occupying a still smaller volume. Temperature, we have seen before, is proportional to the average kinetic energy of the molecules in random translational motion. The effect of temperature on the vaporizing process implies that organization may be decreased in a system by increased translational motion.

15-15 ENTROPY AND ORGANIZATION

Change in organization is represented by two factors, the absolute temperature T and a change in entropy ΔS. Their product is related to ΔH and ΔG by the equation

$$\Delta H - \Delta G = T \, \Delta S$$

Entropy is a measure of the disorder, or lack of organization, in a system. Entropy is defined so that the more disordered a system is, the higher its entropy. An increase in entropy during a change in the state of a system means that in its final state the system is more disordered than in its initial state.

At a constant temperature, a system tends to undergo a reaction so that in its final state it has lower energy and higher entropy than in its initial state.

Alternatively, disorganization may arise in a system as the result of a change to a state which provides more ways of arranging the structural units of the components of the system. One change that provides more possibilities of arrangement is an increase in volume. With more space a given number of atoms or molecules can be arranged in more patterns. In this way a gas is more disorderly than the liquid or solid from which it is produced, even though all phases are at the same temperature. Increase in the number of ways that the energy of a system can be distributed within a system is also an increase in disorder. Thus, the dissociation of a molecule into several fragments provides more pieces to share in the energy of the system and hence more disorder, even though no change in volume may occur.

15-16 ORDER, ENERGY, AND STRUCTURE

A system tends to change from a state of high energy to one of low energy. For chemical systems this energy change is described by ΔH. But systems are also found to change from a state of great order to a state of less order. For chemical systems this change in order is described by $T \Delta S$.

When both of these tendencies cannot be satisfied simultaneously, the balance reached in the actual change is described by

$$\Delta G = \Delta H - T \Delta S$$

Free energy change ΔG describes, then, the balance struck between energy change and entropy change. For a change to occur in a system, the free energy must undergo a decrease. Even though ΔH may be positive for the change, a sufficient increase in the entropy of the system will result in a negative free energy change. In other words, a system may change in state from a state of low energy to one of higher energy if the new state represents an increase in randomness (decrease in organization).

If a hydrogen fluoride–water system in its standard state at 25°C ionizes, there is an enthalpy decrease of 3.0 kcal/mole of HF, but there is also an increase in order measured by $T \Delta S = -7.3$. kcal. These two changes together $[-3.0 - (-7.3)]$ give a standard free energy change of $\Delta G° = +4.3$ kcal. The spontaneous change is for hydrogen ions and fluoride to join together in a hydrogen fluoride–water system in its standard state.

Once the system reaches equilibrium, no state of lower free energy is possible, and so ΔG must be positive for any slight change in either direction. At equilibrium the system is in a state where the tendency for its parts to develop an arrangement of lower energy (decrease in enthalpy) is just equal to the tendency of the parts to separate so as to become more disorganized (increase in entropy).

In an equilibrium state, $\Delta H - T \Delta S = 0$ for a system, since $\Delta G = 0$; on this basis $\Delta H = T \Delta S$. This means that the approach to equilibrium may be from either of two directions. From one direction the change in state results in lower energy and lower entropy, while from the other direction the change in state results in higher energy and higher entropy.

Equilibrium in chemical systems has led us to a way of understanding the tendency of a system to change in state. Each system has one state which best combines the tendency to low enthalpy (ΔH negative) and to low organization ($T \Delta S$ positive).

When a liquid evaporates, the enthalpy of the vapor is always higher than the enthalpy of the liquid. If the vapor is in equilibrium with the liquid, vaporization takes place without change in free energy so that $\Delta H_v = T \Delta S$. The evaporation can proceed only if energy is supplied to the liquid and if an increased volume is provided for the vapor. In its final state, the system is composed of a disorganized gas rather than an organized liquid. The heat of vaporization ΔH_v represents the energy absorbed by the system as the molecules of the liquid separate from each other against the attractive forces.

When the bonds in gas molecules are broken to form atoms, energy is absorbed and the system becomes more disorganized. Thus nitrogen gas consists of diatomic molecules for which the energy of dissociation is $\Delta H = 225$ kcal/mole of N_2. Equilibrium between nitrogen molecules and nitrogen atoms can be achieved either in a system at high temperature or in one with large volume. In either case it is necessary that $\Delta H = T \Delta S$. This equality may be achieved in a system by high temperature and a small entropy change or by low temperature and a large entropy change. Experimentally it is found that the higher the temperature for a sample of nitrogen, the smaller the volume for which atoms and molecules are in equilibrium.

For a system in its standard state, spontaneous change can occur provided that the free energy decreases. But the free energy change is equal to the difference between two separate quantities.

$$\Delta G° = \Delta H° - T \Delta S°$$

The enthalpy change is essentially determined by the bond energies characteristic of the components of the system in its initial and final states. Any system is likely to change in state spontaneously if a change means breaking weak bonds and forming strong bonds. Thus, fluorine gas reacts spontaneously with many other substances partly because the bond energy in a fluorine molecule is low (36.6 kcal/mole) and partly because fluorine atoms form strong bonds with most other atoms. The entropy change consists of change to a more (or less) disordered system.

15-17 SUMMARY

Experiments show that the ability of substances to react is not solely dependent upon the system's going to a state of low enthalpy. For many systems, the relative amounts of the components play a role in determining whether reaction will or will not occur. Control of reactions is therefore dependent upon control of the concentration. In many cases the final state reached by a system does respond to the addition or removal of a chemical component or of energy. The response of the system to these additions or removals is described by Le Chatelier's principle. A system in a state which does not change spontaneously with time but which responds reversibly to disturbances in a manner described by Le Chatelier's principle is said to be in an equilibrium state.

Whenever a chemical system changes in state, there is an energy change. At constant pressure and constant temperature the energy change is described as a change in enthalpy. Spontaneous changes are found, however, in some cases to be associated with increases in enthalpy and in other cases with decreases in enthalpy. Enthalpy change alone is not sufficient to indicate the direction of spontaneous change.

Whenever a chemical system changes in state, there is a change in the organization of the parts of the system. A change in organization can be measured by an energy change $T \Delta S$. The difference between the enthalpy change and the organization change, $\Delta H - T \Delta S$, is an indicator of the possibility of spontaneous change.

The difference, $\Delta H - T \Delta S$, is called the free energy change, ΔG.

$$\Delta G = \Delta H - T \Delta S$$

For any spontaneous change in state, ΔG is negative so that the free energy of the system always decreases.

Ex. 15-11 Write the expression for K_{eq} for the reactions

a. $HCN\ (aq) + H_2O\ (l) \rightleftarrows H_3O^+\ (aq) + CN^-\ (aq)$

b. $H_2S\ (aq) + 2H_2O\ (l) \rightleftarrows 2H_3O^+\ (aq) + S^{--}\ (aq)$

Ex. 15-12 *a.* Predict the effect of compression (at constant temperature) on the relative concentrations of the components of the following systems at equilibrium.

(1) $$CO \ (g) + 2H_2 \ (g) \rightleftarrows CH_3OH \ (g)$$

(2) $$H_2(g) + Cl_2 \ (g) \rightleftarrows 2HCl \ (g)$$

b. Predict how adding hydrogen gas will affect the quantity of product present (at constant temperature) in each of the systems at equilibrium.

Ex. 15-13 Consider an electrochemical cell consisting of a copper metal–Cu^{++} (1 *M*) half cell ($\varepsilon° = -0.337$ volt) coupled to a platinum metal–Sn^{++} (1 *M*) and Sn^{++++} (1 *M*) half cell ($\varepsilon° = -0.15$ volt).

a. Write the equation for the overall spontaneous reaction in the cell.

b. What is the potential difference for the cell?

c. What is the standard free energy change for the cell reaction?

Ex. 15-14 Explain how the equilibrium state of a solid phase–liquid phase system is analogous to the condition described in Section 15-16 for the equilibrium state of a liquid phase–gas phase system.

Ex. 15-15 *a.* If 1 liter of a solution formed by adding water to 0.01 mole of $CaSO_4$ (*s*) is 6.2×10^{-3} *M* in Ca^{++} (*aq*), what is the molar concentration of SO_4^{--} (*aq*) ions? How much $CaSO_4$ (*s*) remains undissolved?

b. What would happen to the Ca^{++} (*aq*) ion concentration if solid $CaSO_4$ is added to a saturated solution of $CaSO_4$?

Ex. 15-16 Calculate $T \Delta S°$ for each reaction listed in Table 15-5.

Ex. 15-17 Using the method of continuous variation, a student obtained the data listed in the table of data for the thallium chloride–water system at 25°C. The total volume of solution was 1 liter in each trial.

a. Make a continuous variation graph similar to Fig. 15-1 for the thallium chloride–water system.

b. What is the mole ratio of thallium ion to chloride ion in solid thallium chloride? What is the simplest formula for thallium chloride?

c. Make a graph, plotting the ratio of solid thallium chloride to initial quantity of thallium ion on the vertical axis, and the quantity of chloride ion on the horizontal axis.

d. Under what conditions is the ratio of thallium chloride (solid) to thallium ion at a maximum? Under what conditions is the maximum quantity of solid thallium chloride produced?

e. In trial 6 what was the amount, in millimoles, of thallium ion and chloride ion remaining in solution?

f. Write a net ionic equation representing the reaction.

g. Calculate the solubility product for thallium chloride from your answer in part *e.*

Trial	Initial Quantity of Thallium Ion, millimoles	Initial Quantity of Chloride Ion, millimoles	Quantity of Solid Thallium Chloride, millimoles	Ratio of Quantity of Solid Thallium Chloride to Initial Quantity of Thallium Ion
1	0	200	0	
2	20	180	20	1.0
3	40	160	36	0.90
4	60	140	53	0.88
5	80	120	69	0.86
6	100	100	85	0.85
7	120	80	68	0.57
8	140	60	51	0.36
9	160	40	35	0.22
10	180	20	19	0.11
11	200	0	0	

Ex. 15-18 Calculate the solubilities of the following substances in grams per liter from their solubility products.

Substance	Solubility Product
$BaSO_4$	1.1×10^{-10}
CuS	8.5×10^{-45}

Ex. 15-19 Estimate the standard free energy change for the reaction of each system represented in Table 15-2.

Ex. 15-20 For a boiling liquid at 1 atmosphere pressure $\Delta G° = 0$; thus, $\Delta H_v = T \Delta S$, where T is the boiling point of a liquid expressed in degrees Kelvin.

a. From the data in Table 8-7 and Section 15-16, calculate ΔS for HCl, HBr, and HI. Calculate the average ΔS.

b. Using the average ΔS obtained in part a, estimate the boiling point for H_2S ($\Delta H_v = 4.46$ kcal/mole), H_2Se ($\Delta H_v = 4.62$ kcal/mole), and H_2Te ($\Delta H_v = 5.55$ kcal/mole).

Ex. 15-21 a. Describe the relationship between the initial and the final states of the two systems described in Table 15-3.

b. By analogy with the systems described in Table 15-3, describe the final composition of a system whose initial composition is 0.1 mole of HF per liter of aqueous solution.

ACIDS AND BASES

DURING A CHEMICAL reaction, a chemical system changes in state from an initial state to a final state. Just two principles seem to be all that are needed. (1) In its final state the system should have as low an energy as possible. (2) The structural units of the system should have as little order as possible.

To apply these principles and test them, a variety of systems should be investigated. A sizable fraction of all known reactions can be classified as acid-base reactions. Are acid-base reactions governed by these two principles?

16-1 DEFINITION OF ACIDS AND BASES

In 1663 Robert Boyle concluded that there is a group of substances with a similar set of properties which are different from those of other substances. The substances in this group, which are called *acids,* have the following common properties.

1. They dissolve many substances.
2. They change the color of plant dyes (for example, litmus) from blue to red.
3. They precipitate sulfur from solutions of alkali metal polysulfides.
4. They lose all these properties when they react with alkali metal hydroxides.

This list of properties provides an operational definition of acids. In addition to the alkali metal hydroxides a number of other substances destroy or neutralize the characteristic properties of acids. Any substance which can neutralize an acid is called a **base.** The reaction of an acid with a base is called **neutralization.**

Bases can be defined operationally by a set of properties summarized as follows.

1. They precipitate many substances which are dissolved by acids.

2. They change the color of plant dyes (for example, litmus) from red to blue.

3. They lose all these properties when they react with acids.

Several experiments in *Investigating Chemical Systems* explore acid-base reactions. Do the many different substances which behave as acids have any common features of structure or energy that can be related to their properties?

A few reactions are listed in Expressions 16-1 to 16-6 for substances which have properties consistent with the operational definitions of acids and bases. The substance indicated by the first formula on the left in each equation is considered an acid, and the substance indicated by the second formula on the left is considered a base.

Acid   Base

$HCl\ (g)\ \ \ + xH_2O\ (l) \rightarrow H_3O^+\ (aq) + Cl^-\ (aq)$
$$\Delta H = -18.0 \text{ kcal} \quad (Exp.\ 16\text{-}1)$$

$HCl\ (aq)\ + NH_3\ (aq) \rightarrow NH_4^+\ (aq) + Cl^-\ (aq)$
$$\Delta H = -12.4 \text{ kcal} \quad (Exp.\ 16\text{-}2)$$

$2HCl\ (aq) + MgO\ (s) \rightarrow Mg^{++}\ (aq) + 2Cl^-\ (aq) + H_2O\ (l)$
$$\Delta H = -34.9 \text{ kcal} \quad (Exp.\ 16\text{-}3)$$

$HCl\ (1\ M) + NaF\ (1\ M) \rightarrow HF\ (0.5\ M) + NaCl\ (0.5\ M)$
$$\Delta H = +2.45 \text{ kcal} \quad (Exp.\ 16\text{-}4)$$

$BF_3\ (aq)\ \ \ + F^-\ (aq) \rightarrow BF_4^-\ (aq)\ \ \ \Delta H = +3 \text{ kcal} \quad (Exp.\ 16\text{-}5)$

$MgSO_4\ (s) + xH_2O\ (l) \rightarrow Mg\,(H_2O)_6^{++}\ (aq) + SO_4^{--}\ (aq)$
$$\Delta H = -21.8 \text{ kcal} \quad (Exp.\ 16\text{-}6)$$

Written in this fashion, these reactions seem dissimilar, but let us consider whether there are some features which are common to the molecules or ions of the substances identified as acids and other features common to those molecules or ions of the substances identified as bases. Why are HCl and BF_3 listed as acids, whereas H_2O and NH_3 are listed as bases? Is an explanation to be found in the kind of elements present in each substance? Is the structure or the type of bonding involved important? Is an explanation found in the way the atoms are arranged in space? Is the energy change in one acid-base reaction related to the energy change for any other? Is there a set of principles upon which the chemist can build a theory that will enable him to say whether or not a given substance should be classified as an acid or a base?

16-2 THE LEWIS THEORY OF ACIDS AND BASES

If Lewis structures are written for the reactants and products in Expressions 16-1 to 16-6, one striking similarity appears.

Acid   Base

$$H:\ddot{C}l: \quad + \quad H:\ddot{O}: \quad \rightarrow \quad \left[H:\overset{H}{\underset{}{O}}:H \right]^{+} \quad + \quad :\ddot{C}l:^{-}$$

(Eq. 16-7)

$$H:\ddot{C}l: \quad + \quad H:\overset{H}{\underset{H}{N}}: \quad \rightarrow \quad \left[H:\overset{H}{\underset{H}{N}}:H \right]^{+} \quad + \quad :\ddot{C}l:^{-}$$

(Eq. 16-8)

$$2H:\ddot{C}l: \quad + Mg^{++}:\ddot{O}:^{--} \rightarrow \quad Mg^{++} \quad + \quad 2:\ddot{C}l:^{-} \quad + \quad H:\overset{\ddot{O}:}{\underset{H}{}}$$

(Eq. 16-9)

$$H:\ddot{C}l: \quad + \quad Na^{+}:\ddot{F}:^{-} \quad \rightarrow \quad H:\ddot{F}: \quad + \quad :\ddot{C}l:^{-} \quad + \quad Na^{+}$$

(Eq. 16-10)

$$\overset{:\ddot{F}:}{\underset{:\ddot{F}:}{:F:B}} \quad + \quad :\ddot{F}:^{-} \quad \rightarrow \quad \left[\overset{:\ddot{F}:}{\underset{:\ddot{F}:}{:F:B:F:}} \right]^{-}$$

(Eq. 16-11)

$$Mg^{++}SO_4^{--} + \quad 6:\overset{O}{\underset{H}{O}}:H \quad \rightarrow \quad Mg\left(:\overset{\ddot{O}:H}{\underset{H}{}}\right)_{6}^{++} \quad + \quad SO_4^{--}$$

(Eq. 16-12)

In each equation one reactant (the base) furnishes a pair of electrons to form a new bond with part or all of the second reactant (the acid).

In 1923 G. N. Lewis defined a base as any substance which contains an ion or molecule which has one or more pairs of outer electrons that can form a covalent bond with another ion or molecule. An acid is any substance which contains an ion or molecule that can accept one of the pairs of outer electrons in a base to form a covalent bond. These are conceptual definitions of acids and bases.

The transfer of a proton to an ammonia molecule is an example of the formation of a covalent bond between an ion of an acid (proton) and a molecule of a base (ammonia).

$$
\text{H}^+ \; + \; \begin{matrix} \text{H} \\ \cdot\cdot \\ :\!\text{N}\!:\!\text{H} \\ \cdot\cdot \\ \text{H} \end{matrix} \;\rightarrow\; \left[\begin{matrix} \text{H} \\ \cdot\cdot \\ \text{H}\!:\!\text{N}\!:\!\text{H} \\ \cdot\cdot \\ \text{H} \end{matrix} \right]^+ \qquad (Eq.\ 16\text{-}13)
$$

In the same way a covalent bond is formed between a molecule of boron trifluoride and a fluoride ion (Equation 16-11).

SVANTE AUGUST ARRHENIUS   *1859–1927*

A Swedish physicist and chemist. Arrhenius learned to read when he was three years old. He studied at the universities of Upsala and Stockholm, and in 1884, at the age of twenty-five, he proposed in his doctoral dissertation the partial dissociation of acids, bases, and salts into charged ions when they are dissolved in water. Because of this revolutionary idea, the dissertation was passed at a grade just short of rejection, and only through the public support of his views by the eminent German physical chemist, Wilhelm Ostwald, did Arrhenius obtain a teaching position, an assistantship at the University of Upsala.

In 1891 Arrhenius became a lecturer at Stockholm University and in 1895 was promoted to professor of physics. For some years he was also the rector of the University of Stockholm and in 1905 became the director of the Nobel Institute for Physical Chemistry near Stockholm. He received the Nobel Prize in chemistry in 1903 for his dissociation theory, which was by that time generally accepted. At first, chemists had found it difficult to accept the idea that sodium chloride would dissociate into independent sodium and chlorine entities in water. The principal objection was that a solution of sodium chloride showed none of the properties of the elements sodium or chlorine. However, the theory was soon strongly supported by the research of other scientists on atomic structure and the properties of solutions.

Arrhenius had many interests in science. He pioneered in the application of physicochemical methods to the study of living organisms as chemical systems and lectured on immunochemistry in 1904 at the University of California. Among his publications were articles on cosmology, the causes of the ice ages, and the origin of life. Arrhenius has recorded what happened when he first announced his new ideas on ionic dissociation. "I came to my professor, Cleve, whom I admired very much, and I said, 'I have a new theory of electrical conductivity as a cause of chemical reactions.' He said, 'This is very interesting,' and then he said, 'Good-bye.'" Cleve had decided that among all the many current theories, the chance that Arrhenius's theory had significance was so small that it should be ignored.

Ex. 16-1 Identify the Lewis acid and the Lewis base in each of the following equations. Explain why each equation represents an acid–base reaction.

a.
$$\text{F:}\overset{..}{\underset{F}{B}} \; + \; :\overset{H}{\underset{H}{N}}\text{:H} \; \rightarrow \; \text{F:}\overset{F\ H}{\underset{F\ H}{B\text{:}N}}\text{:H}$$

b.
$$\text{Ag}^+ \; + \; 2\left(:\overset{H}{\underset{H}{N}}\text{:H}\right) \rightarrow \left[\overset{H \quad\ H}{\underset{H \quad\ H}{\text{H:N:Ag:N:H}}}\right]^+$$

Ex. 16-2 Which of these substances could be classified as Lewis acids? Lewis bases?

a. $\text{:}\overset{H}{\underset{..}{O}}\text{:H}$

b. $\text{:}\overset{:\overset{..}{Cl}\text{:}}{\underset{:\overset{..}{Cl}\text{:}}{Cl\text{:}P}}\text{:}$

c. $\left[\overset{\text{:}\overset{..}{O}\text{:}}{\underset{\text{:}\overset{..}{O}\text{:}}{\text{:O:S:O:}}}\right]^{--}$

d. $\text{:}\overset{..}{\underset{..}{Cl}}\text{:}Zn\text{:}\overset{..}{\underset{..}{Cl}}\text{:}$

e. H^+

f. $\left[\text{:}\overset{..}{\underset{..}{O}}\text{:H}\right]^-$

16-3 THE ARRHENIUS THEORY OF ACIDS AND BASES

A more restricted conceptual definition of acids and bases preceded the Lewis theory. Svante Arrhenius in 1884 suggested that substances which contain hydrogen and which yield hydrogen ions in aqueous solution are acids and that those which contain the OH group and yield hydroxide ions in aqueous solution are bases. Thus, he classified nitric acid, hydrochloric acid, and sulfuric acid as acids.

$$\text{HONO}_2 \; (l) \rightarrow \text{H}^+ \; (aq) + \text{ONO}_2{}^- \; (aq) \qquad (Eq.\ 16\text{-}14)$$

$$\text{HCl} \; (g) \rightarrow \text{H}^+ \; (aq) + \text{Cl}^- \; (aq) \qquad (Eq.\ 16\text{-}15)$$

$$(\text{HO})_2\text{SO}_2 \; (l) \rightarrow \text{H}^+ \; (aq) + \text{HOSO}_3{}^- \; (aq) \quad (Eq.\ 16\text{-}16)$$

And he classified sodium hydroxide and calcium hydroxide as bases.

$$\text{NaOH} \; (s) \rightarrow \text{Na}^+ \; (aq) + \text{OH}^- \; (aq) \qquad (Eq.\ 16\text{-}17)$$

$$\text{Ca(OH)}_2 \; (s) \rightarrow \text{Ca}^{++} \; (aq) + 2\text{OH}^- \; (aq) \qquad (Eq.\ 16\text{-}18)$$

Arrhenius described neutralization as the process in which hydrogen ion and hydroxide ion join to form a water molecule.

$$\text{H}^+ \; (aq) + \text{OH}^- \; (aq) \rightarrow \text{H}_2\text{O} \; (l) \qquad (Eq.\ 16\text{-}19)$$

According to the Arrhenius theory, Equation 16-19 represents the only acid-base reaction. With his theory Arrhenius was able to represent the reaction of numerous substances by one equation. Certainly this was a master stroke. As knowledge about the reactions of chemical substances has increased, however, the Arrhenius theory has become too restrictive. Nevertheless, chemists still use much of the terminology that Arrhenius established.

It is of considerable interest to gain more understanding of the nature of the hydrogen ion, H^+, since it not only is the central feature of an Arrhenius acid but also is an acid according to the Lewis theory. Some experimental evidence for the nature of hydrogen ions can be obtained using sulfur dioxide (SO_2) as a solvent. Water is insoluble in liquid sulfur dioxide. Hydrogen bromide is soluble in liquid sulfur dioxide, and the solution is nonconducting. If water is added to a solution of hydrogen bromide in liquid sulfur dioxide, the water dissolves; but no more than 1 mole of water will dissolve for each mole of HBr present. The solution of hydrogen bromide and water in sulfur dioxide is conducting, and if this solution is electrolyzed, bromine is produced at the positive electrode and hydrogen gas and water are produced at the negative electrode. These facts can be accounted for if we assume that hydrogen bromide in sulfur dioxide does not form ions but that the addition of water produces H_3O^+ and Br^- dissolved in SO_2. The hydrogen ion is considered to be a hydrated proton. For SO_2 solution,

$$HBr + H_2O \rightarrow H_3O^+ + Br^- \qquad (Eq.\ 16\text{-}20)$$

For electrolysis, at the positive electrode,

$$2Br^- \rightarrow Br_2 + 2e^- \qquad (Eq.\ 16\text{-}21)$$

and, at the negative electrode,

$$2H_3O^+ + 2e^- \rightarrow 2H_2O + H_2 \qquad (Eq.\ 16\text{-}22)$$

Recent research suggests that the hydrated proton in dilute aqueous solutions is not as simple as H_3O^+ but may have the formula $H_9O_4^+$ with four water molecules arranged tetrahedrally around the proton (Fig. 16-1b). We will represent the hydrated proton with the simpler formula H^+ (aq) except when the reaction of a proton with water is to be emphasized. Then the symbol H_3O^+ (aq) will be used to indicate the hydrated proton.

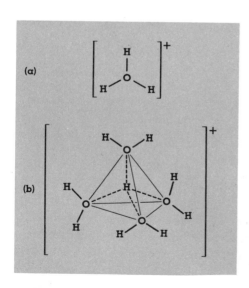

Fig. 16-1 *Structures of H_3O^+ and $H_9O_4^+$ ions.*

Ex. 16-3 Write the chemical equation for the reaction between four water molecules and a proton to form $H_9O_4{}^+$.

16-5 THE BRØNSTED-LOWRY THEORY OF ACIDS AND BASES

In the same year (1923) that the Lewis theory was published, another theory of acids and bases was proposed by J. N. Brønsted (Denmark) and independently by T. M. Lowry (England). They defined an acid as any substance consisting of molecules or ions that donate protons, and a base as any substance consisting of molecules or ions that accept protons. In the reaction of HBr with H_2O to form the hydrogen ion and a bromide ion in sulfur dioxide (Equation 16-20), HBr (proton donor) is an acid and H_2O (proton acceptor) a base.

Similarly in the reaction

$$(HO)_2SO_2 \ (l) + C_2H_5OH \ (l) \rightarrow C_2H_5OH_2{}^+ + HOSO_3{}^- \quad (Eq.\ 16\text{-}23)$$

$(HO)_2SO_2$ is an acid and C_2H_5OH (ethanol) a base. Some other reactions that have been observed in the absence of water are

$$HCl + CH_3COOH \rightarrow CH_3COOH_2{}^+ + Cl^- \quad (Eq.\ 16\text{-}24)$$

and $\quad (HO)_2SO_2 + HONO_2 \rightarrow H_2ONO_2{}^+ + HOSO_3{}^- \quad (Eq.\ 16\text{-}25)$

In each of the reactions in Equations 16-8, 16-23, 16-24, and 16-25, the acid imparts positive ion character to the base (for example, $C_2H_5OH_2{}^+$, $CH_3COOH_2{}^+$, $H_2ONO_2{}^+$, or $NH_4{}^+$ are formed from C_2H_5OH, CH_3-COOH, $HONO_2$, or NH_3, respectively). The means by which the acid does this is to transfer a proton to the base.

16-6 CONJUGATE ACIDS AND BASES

The Brønsted-Lowry theory implies by the definitions used that each acid-base system contains two acid-base pairs. Experimentally, acid-base reactions are reversible so that in a reaction an acid transfers a proton to become a base, to make one acid-base pair. A base gains a proton to become an acid, to make a second acid-base pair. Each pair made up of an acid and a base related by the transfer of a proton is called a *conjugate acid-base pair.*

In the following reactions the two conjugate pairs ($acid_1$-$base_1$ and $acid_2$-$base_2$) are identified by subscripts.

$$\text{Base}_1 + \text{Acid}_2 \rightleftarrows \text{Acid}_1 + \text{Base}_2$$

$$NH_3 + H_2O \rightleftarrows NH_4{}^+ + OH^- \quad (Eq.\ 16\text{-}26)$$

$$NH_3 + HCl \rightleftarrows NH_4{}^+ + Cl^- \quad (Eq.\ 16\text{-}27)$$

$$H_2O + HCl \rightleftarrows H_3O^+ + Cl^- \quad (Eq.\ 16\text{-}28)$$

Equation 16-26 suggests, by the Brønsted-Lowry theory, that the water acts as an acid since it transfers a proton to ammonia. Water is an acid in this reaction, and the negative ion remaining after proton transfer, OH^-, is the conjugate base. Ammonia ($base_1$) is the conjugate base of the new acid, NH_4^+, labeled $acid_1$. Equation 16-28 describes water as a base since it accepts a proton to form the conjugate acid H_3O^+.

Every acid-base reaction in the Brønsted-Lowry theory is a competition between two bases for possession of a proton. The extent of reaction can be described by the respective concentrations of the two bases in the system in its equilibrium state.

Charge cloud and hybridized orbital models show that the structure of a Brønsted-Lowry base must include at least one outer electron pair which is not shared between two nuclei to form a covalent bond. We have called this an unshared pair of electrons. Any substances in which this unshared pair of electrons can acquire a proton can act as a base. The ability of the unshared pair of electrons to acquire a proton will depend to a large extent on the charge and geometrical arrangement of the other nuclei present in the system.

JOHANNES NICOLAUS BRØNSTED   *1879–1947*

A Danish chemist. Brønsted first studied engineering and then chemistry at the Copenhagen Polytechnic Institute. He received his doctorate in 1908 and the same year was appointed professor of chemistry, teaching both at the University of Copenhagen and at the Polytechnic Institute. This position he held for the rest of his life. In 1947 he was elected to the Danish Parliament but died before he could take his seat.

In his early studies he recognized that the enthalpy of reaction was not an adequate measure of chemical reactivity. He made extensive studies of interactions between ions in solution, broadened the concept of acids and bases by emphasis on proton transfer, studied the acidic and basic catalysis of many reactions, and in his later years studied the energy properties of large molecules. Brønsted followed Wilhelm Ostwald's philosophy that an explanation of chemical behavior in terms of atomic or molecular models was not necessarily helpful for understanding chemical systems.

Ex. 16-4 Identify the Brønsted–Lowry conjugate acid-base pairs in each of the following reactions.

a. H_2CO_3 (aq) + H_2O → H_3O^+ (aq) + HCO_3^- (aq)

b. HCO_3^- (aq) + OH^- (aq) → H_2O + CO_3^{--} (aq)

c. HCO_3^- (aq) + HCO_3^- (aq) → H_2CO_3 (aq) + CO_3^{--} (aq)

Ex. 16-5 Identify each of the following reactions as an acid-base reaction in terms of the Lewis theory, the Brønsted–Lowry theory, or the Arrhenius theory. (Each of the reactions may exemplify more than one of these categories.) Give reasons for each selection.

a. $2CN^-$ (aq) + Ag^+ (aq) → $Ag(CN)_2^-$ (aq)

b. CH_3COOH (aq) + NH_3 (aq) → CH_3COO^- (aq) + NH_4^+ (aq)

c. CH_3COOH (aq) + $NaOH$ (s) → CH_3COO^- (aq) + Na^+ (aq) + H_2O (l)

16-7 COMPARISON OF ACID-BASE THEORIES

The Brønsted–Lowry generalization is narrower in scope than the electronic theory put forward by Lewis. The great usefulness of the Brønsted–Lowry concept is that it focuses attention not on what an acid is as an isolated substance but on what it does in a reaction. Acidic character is determined by the ability of a base to accept a proton from the acid with which the base reacts and vice versa.

The Arrhenius theory restricts acids to substances that produce hydrogen ions in solution and bases to substances that produce hydroxide ions in solution. The Brønsted–Lowry theory modified the narrower Arrhenius concept of acid not only to include both molecules and ions but also to widen the conceptual definition of a base to include all molecules and ions with reactive unshared electron pairs. The Lewis theory uses the Brønsted–Lowry concept of a base but draws attention to the idea that a base acts as an electron-pair donor rather than solely as a proton acceptor. The Lewis theory widens the definition of an acid to include both the proton and any substance which can form a covalent bond with an unshared electron pair in a base.

The Lewis theory includes not only the proton as an example of an acid but also other molecules and ions. An acid is any molecule or ion which can get close enough to an exposed pair of electrons so that the nuclei and electrons in both acid and base attract each other. For example, in the hydration of a magnesium ion (Equation 16-12), the product is probably $Mg(H_2O)_6^{++}$ with six water molecules arranged octahedrally around the magnesium ion as in Fig. 16-2.

The Brønsted–Lowry theory pictures acid-base reactions as involving the penetration of a charge cloud by a proton. A proton is unique among all molecules and ions with which a chemist deals. The unique feature is the lack of electrons around the proton as it is transferred.

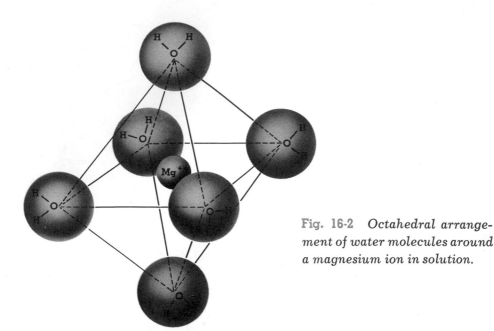

Fig. 16-2 *Octahedral arrangement of water molecules around a magnesium ion in solution.*

Every other ion which a chemist uses has two or more electrons associated with a positive nucleus. An ion formed by a nucleus and some surrounding electrons cannot penetrate into a charge cloud. Only in the case of the proton or hydrogen ion is penetration of an electron charge cloud unhindered by the presence of electrons accompanying the ion.

The applicability of each of the three theories (A, Arrhenius; B, Brønsted-Lowry; and L, Lewis) to the interpretation of reactions emerges in the classification of the following equations.

A, B, L
$$\text{H}^+ \ (aq) + \ :\!\overset{..}{\underset{..}{O}}\!:\!\text{H}^- \ (aq) \rightarrow \ :\!\overset{\overset{\text{H}}{..}}{\underset{..}{O}}\!:\!\text{H} \ (l) \qquad (Eq.\ 16\text{-}29)$$

B, L
$$\text{H}:\!\overset{..}{\underset{..}{O}}\!:\!\overset{:\overset{..}{O}:}{\underset{..}{N}}\!:\!:\!\overset{..}{O}: + \ :\!\overset{\text{H}}{\underset{\text{H}}{N}}\!:\!\text{H} \rightarrow \left[\overset{\text{H}}{\underset{\text{H}}{\text{H}:\!N\!:\!\text{H}}}\right]^+ + \left[:\!\overset{..}{\underset{..}{O}}\!:\!:\!\overset{\overset{:\overset{..}{O}:}{}}{\underset{\overset{..}{O}:}{N}}\right]^-$$

$$(Eq.\ 16\text{-}30)$$

B, L
$$2\text{H}:\!\overset{..}{\underset{..}{Cl}}\!: + \ :\!\overset{..}{\underset{..}{O}}\!:\!^{--} \rightarrow \ :\!\overset{\overset{\text{H}}{..}}{\underset{..}{O}}\!:\!\text{H} + 2:\!\overset{..}{\underset{..}{Cl}}\!:\!^- \qquad (Eq.\ 16\text{-}31)$$

L
$$\overset{:\overset{..}{F}:}{\underset{:\overset{..}{F}:}{:\overset{..}{F}:B}} + \ :\!\overset{..}{\underset{..}{F}}\!:\!^- \rightarrow \left[\overset{:\overset{..}{F}:}{\underset{:\overset{..}{F}:}{:\overset{..}{F}:B:\overset{..}{F}:}}\right]^- \qquad (Eq.\ 16\text{-}32)$$

L
$$\text{Mg}^{++} + 6:\!\overset{..}{\underset{\text{H}}{O}}\!:\!\text{H} \rightarrow \text{Mg}\!\left(:\!\overset{..}{\underset{\text{H}}{O}}\!:\!\text{H}\right)_6^{++} \qquad (Eq.\ 16\text{-}33)$$

Equation 16-29 represents an acid-base reaction by all three theories. Equations 16-30 and 16-31 cannot be said to represent acid-base reactions by the Arrhenius theory since hydroxide ions are not involved. But both reactions involve proton donors and acceptors so they are Brønsted-Lowry acid-base reactions as well as Lewis acid-base reactions. Equations 16-31 and 16-33 represent the reaction between oxide ion and hydrogen ion used in Experiment 14 where magnesium oxide is titrated with an acid.

In Equation 16-32, BF_3 is a Lewis acid since it reacts to form a new bond (boron–fluorine) with the base $:\ddot{F}:^-$, which has unshared pairs of electrons. All the reactions represented by Equations 16-29 to 16-33 are acid-base reactions by the Lewis theory.

A chemical theory is judged by its usefulness and is discarded when it is replaced by a theory of greater usefulness. All three of these acid-base theories are in current use because each can be applied with benefit to appropriate systems. The problem is similar to that of a man choosing a tool to cut a piece of wood. He might use a knife, a plane, or a saw. Any one of the three tools can cut wood, but each is best suited to a certain kind of cutting.

16-8 NEUTRALIZATION

In its most general sense, neutralization implies a canceling out of opposing factors. The observation that certain substances have the properties of acids (Section 16-1) but lose these properties when mixed with bases suggested to chemists many years ago that one substance neutralizes the other. After 1884, the ideas of Arrhenius had refined this concept of neutralization so that the formation of water was recognized as being common to all neutralizations.

$$HCl\ (aq) + NaOH\ (aq) \rightarrow NaCl\ (aq) + H_2O\ (l) \qquad (Eq.\ 16\text{-}34)$$

$$HONO_2\ (aq) + KOH\ (aq) \rightarrow KNO_3\ (aq) + H_2O\ (l) \qquad (Eq.\ 16\text{-}35)$$

$$(HO)_2SO_2\ (l) + Mg(OH)_2\ (s) \rightarrow$$
$$MgSO_4\ (aq) + 2H_2O\ (l) \qquad (Eq.\ 16\text{-}36)$$

Solutions of an acid and a base when mixed commonly give a reaction mixture that is a solution. Evaporating the solution to dryness gives a solid, nonvolatile crystalline product, for example, sodium chloride, potassium nitrate, or magnesium sulfate (Equations 16-34, 16-35, and 16-36). These products caught the fancy of early chemists who called them salts because so many of them looked like common salt, NaCl.

Before the development of the Lewis or Brønsted-Lowry theories, the acid-base reaction was described as the production of water and a salt. However, the "formation of a salt" in a neutralization reaction means little when the salt is not isolated from dilute aqueous solution. The ions of the salt exist in solution both before and after the reaction and cannot be said to have combined in any sense during the reaction until the water is evaporated to recover crystals of the salt.

Titration (Section 15-9) is used by chemists for determining end points in a great variety of reactions, including neutralization reactions. In addition to the disappearance of a solid, temperature change, color change, and electrode potential change are used to determine end points. Several of these methods of end-point determination are studied in *Investigating Chemical Systems*.

16-9 ENTHALPY CHANGES AND NEUTRALIZATION

Temperature data are used in Experiment 36 to compute enthalpy changes for a proton-transfer reaction involving hydrochloric acid and sodium hydroxide. The enthalpy data for this reaction, along with that for five other acid-base reactions, are assembled in Table 16-1. Each system shown in Table 16-1 was prepared by mixing equal volumes of solutions of acid and base each at 1 M concentration.

Enthalpy changes agreeing within 0.08 kcal/mole are found for the reactions of hydrochloric acid, nitric acid, or hydrobromic acid with sodium hydroxide. Other bases such as potassium hydroxide and cesium hydroxide may be substituted for sodium hydroxide without significant variation in the enthalpy changes. Enthalpy data of this kind lend support to the Arrhenius proposal that all acid-base reactions represent the same net reaction (Equation 16-19).

When the acid which reacts with sodium hydroxide is acetic acid rather than hydrochloric acid, the enthalpy change is 0.42 kcal/mole less. The replacement of sodium hydroxide by ammonia produces an even larger shift (1.08 kcal/mole) away from the enthalpy change for

TABLE 16-1 ENTHALPY CHANGE FOR NEUTRALIZATION AT 25°C[a]

Reaction	Enthalpy of Neutralization, ΔH kcal/mole of acid
$HBr\ (aq) + NaOH\ (aq) \rightarrow NaBr\ (aq) + H_2O\ (l)$	−13.76
$HNO_3\ (aq) + NaOH\ (aq) \rightarrow NaNO_3\ (aq) + H_2O\ (l)$	−13.76
$HCl\ (aq) + NaOH\ (aq) \rightarrow NaCl\ (aq) + H_2O\ (l)$	−13.84
$CH_3COOH\ (aq) + NaOH\ (aq) \rightarrow CH_3COONa\ (aq) + H_2O\ (l)$	−13.42
$HCl\ (aq) + NH_3\ (aq) \rightarrow NH_4Cl\ (aq)$	−12.76
$CH_3COOH\ (aq) + NH_3\ (aq) \rightarrow CH_3COONH_4\ (aq)$	−12.04

[a] Data are given for equal volumes of reactants each at 1 M concentration.

the reaction of hydrochloric acid and sodium hydroxide. Other acid-base reactions show even greater differences in the enthalpy changes.

In the Lewis acid-base theory, the reaction of magnesium ion or of copper ion with hydroxide ion is an acid-base reaction.

$$Mg^{++}\ (aq) + 2OH^-\ (aq) \rightarrow Mg\,(OH)_2\ (s)$$
$$\Delta H = -1.05\ kcal/mole\ of\ OH^- \qquad (Exp.\ 16\text{-}37)$$

$$Cu^{++}\ (aq) + 2OH^-\ (aq) \rightarrow Cu\,(OH)_2\ (s)$$
$$\Delta H = -7.2\ kcal/mole\ of\ OH^- \qquad (Exp.\ 16\text{-}38)$$

The differing enthalpy changes in acid-base reactions raise a question about the reason for the differences. Do different acids or bases react with different intensities, and is this what the different enthalpy changes reflect?

16-10 RELATIVE ACID STRENGTH

If a concentrated solution of hydrochloric acid is added to a dilute solution of sodium acetate so that the mole ratio of the two reactants is 1:1, an enthalpy change of several kilocalories per mole of acid occurs. However, an enthalpy change of less than 1 kcal/mole of acid occurs if concentrated acetic acid solution is added to sodium chloride solution so that the mole ratio of the two reactants is 1:1. In both these examples the corresponding properties of the two systems in their final states are identical. It is even possible to remove some acetic acid from both of these systems by distillation. But no hydrogen chloride can be removed from them by distillation. Acetic acid can be distilled from a solution of hydrogen ion, chloride ion, acetate ion, and sodium ion.

$$CH_3-C\substack{O\\\diagup\diagup\\\diagdown\\O^-}\ (aq) + HCl\ (aq) \rightarrow CH_3-C\substack{O\\\diagup\diagup\\\diagdown\\OH}\ (aq) + Cl^-\ (aq) \qquad (Eq.\ 16\text{-}39)$$

Vapors from boiling aqueous solutions have never been found to contain ions. Any solution which upon distillation yields some solute in the distillate is assumed to contain some of that solute in molecular or un-ionized form in the original solution. The fact that hydrogen chloride cannot be distilled from the same solution can be expressed by

$$CH_3-C\substack{O\\\diagup\diagup\\\diagdown\\OH}\ (aq) + Cl^-\ (aq) \rightarrow no\ reaction\ detected$$

Acetate ion exerts a greater attraction for a proton than chloride ion. Chloride ion and acetate ion are the conjugate bases of hydrochloric acid and acetic acid, respectively.

677

Hydrogen ion concentrations can be measured with the aid of a hydrogen electrode in solutions of hydrochloric acid and acetic acid. For solutions of the same molar concentration of acid the hydrogen ion concentration is ten to one hundred times greater in hydrochloric acid solutions than in acetic acid solutions. The production of hydrogen ions in each solution can be described as a reaction with water.

$$HCl\ (aq) + H_2O\ (l) \rightarrow H_3O^+\ (aq) + Cl^-\ (aq) \qquad (Eq.\ 16\text{-}40)$$

$$CH_3-C\overset{O}{\underset{OH}{\big\langle}}\ (aq) + H_2O\ (l) \rightarrow H_3O^+\ (aq) + CH_3-C\overset{O}{\underset{O^-}{\big\langle}}\ (aq)$$

$$(Eq.\ 16\text{-}41)$$

In each system, water acts as a base in competition for a proton either with chloride ion (Equation 16-40) or with acetate ion (Equation 16-41). It must be that water molecules can more readily remove a proton from a chloride ion than from an acetate ion. The addition of sodium chloride to water does not alter the hydrogen ion concentration, while the addition of sodium acetate to water gives a solution of slightly lower hydrogen ion concentration than is found for water alone. These experiments suggest that chloride ion is not a base in water but that acetate ion is slightly basic.

The conclusions just reached for hydrochloric acid, acetic acid, and water can be summarized as follows.

Acid	Donates proton
HCl	Either to CH_3COO^- or to H_2O
CH_3COOH	To H_2O but not to Cl^-
H_2O	Not to Cl^-, slightly to CH_3COO^-

The number of bases to which an acid will donate protons is an indication of the **strength of an acid.** The more bases to which an acid will donate protons, the stronger the acid. Similarly the more acids from which a base can remove protons, the stronger the base. Hydrochloric acid is stronger than acetic acid, which is stronger than water. Water is a weaker base than acetate ion, but it is stronger than chloride ion.

A great many acids are classified as to strength by comparing their abilities to transfer protons to water in solution. Measurement of hydrogen ion concentration gives a direct indication of the extent to which the acid has transferred protons to the water. Most systems containing acid and water exist in an equilibrium state.

16-11 IONIZATION CONSTANTS OF ACIDS

The concept of chemical equilibrium discussed in Chapter 15 provides a basis for developing a quantitative scale of acid strength. If, for example, we consider the ionization of an acid to be an equilibrium process,

$$\text{HBr } (aq) + \text{H}_2\text{O } (l) \rightleftharpoons \text{H}_3\text{O}^+ (aq) + \text{Br}^- (aq) \qquad \textit{(Eq. 16-42)}$$

$$\text{CH}_3{-}\overset{\displaystyle\text{O}}{\overset{\|}{\text{C}}}\diagdown_{\text{OH}} (aq) + \text{H}_2\text{O } (l) \rightleftharpoons \text{H}_3\text{O}^+ (aq) + \text{CH}_3{-}\overset{\displaystyle\text{O}}{\overset{\|}{\text{C}}}\diagdown_{\text{O}^-} (aq)$$

$$\textit{(Eq. 16-43)}$$

then we can write the following expressions for the equilibrium constants of hydrobromic acid and acetic acid.

$$\frac{[\text{H}_3\text{O}^+][\text{Br}^-]}{[\text{HBr}]} = K \quad \text{and} \quad \frac{[\text{H}_3\text{O}^+][\text{CH}_3\text{COO}^-]}{[\text{CH}_3\text{COOH}]} = K$$

In dilute solutions of hydrobromic acid, measurement of hydrogen ion concentration by the methods developed in Section 14-12 indicates that the number of moles of hydrogen ion formed equals the initial number of moles of hydrogen bromide within 0.1 percent or less. This has to mean that there are few if any molecules of hydrogen bromide present in a dilute aqueous solution of hydrogen bromide. The behavior of hydrogen chloride, hydrogen bromide, and hydrogen iodide in water solution is similar in that they show no evidence of un-ionized molecules. For this reason dilute solutions of these acids are described as being completely ionized.

With a concentration approaching zero for un-ionized hydrogen bromide, it is not possible to calculate a numerical value for an equilibrium constant since zero in the denominator of the equilibrium constant expression will give infinity instead of a number for K. For dilute solutions of acetic acid, experimentally measured hydrogen ion concentrations are shown in Table 16-2. These concentrations are only a small fraction of the initial quantity of acetic acid used to prepare the solutions. This implies that an acetic acid solution, unlike a solution of hydrobromic acid, contains a high percentage of un-ionized acid mole-

TABLE 16-2 CONCENTRATIONS IN AQUEOUS ACETIC ACID AT 25°C

Initial Concentration of Acetic Acid, mole/liter	Hydrogen Ion Concentration, mole/liter	Equilibrium Constant, K
0.0280×10^{-3}	0.0151×10^{-3}	1.77×10^{-5}
1.028×10^{-3}	0.1267×10^{-3}	1.79×10^{-5}
5.91×10^{-3}	0.317×10^{-3}	1.80×10^{-5}
50.0×10^{-3}	0.942×10^{-3}	1.81×10^{-5}

cules. The four numbers listed for K in Table 16-2 are nearly the same even though they represent solutions for which the acid concentration varies by a factor of 2,000. The experimentally determined concentrations give K values at 25°C which approach more and more closely the number 1.76×10^{-5} for acetic acid solutions as the concentration is lowered.

Hydrogen fluoride–water systems were discussed in Section 15-9. The reaction in solution is

$$\text{HF } (aq) + \text{H}_2\text{O } (l) \rightarrow \text{H}_3\text{O}^+ \ (aq) + \text{F}^- \ (aq) \quad (Eq.\ 16\text{-}44)$$

and this is another example of an acid-base reaction. For acetic acid the equilibrium constant is 1.76×10^{-5} at 25°C, while for hydrogen fluoride the equilibrium constant is 7.2×10^{-4} at 25°C.

Hydrobromic acid, hydrofluoric acid, and acetic acid can be listed in order of their equilibrium constants. The equilibrium constant describes a system in which a proton is transferred from the acid to water which acts as a base. The larger the equilibrium constant, the stronger the acid. Acids, such as hydrobromic acid, which ionize completely can be described by saying that the equilibrium constant is infinite. It is also customary to say that the smaller the equilibrium constant, the weaker the acid. Of the three acids just described, hydrobromic acid is the strongest and acetic acid is the weakest.

16-12 IONIZATION OF WATER

The potential of a hydrogen electrode in water and the small but measurable electric conductivity of pure water were discussed in Section 14-12. The experimental evidence is taken to imply that hydrogen ions are present in water. Hydrogen and hydroxide ions can be formed by proton transfer from one water molecule to another. Where only liquid water is present, an equilibrium constant can be written as

$$\text{H}_2\text{O } (l) + \text{H}_2\text{O } (l) \rightarrow \text{H}_3\text{O}^+ \ (aq) + \text{OH}^- (aq) \quad (Eq.\ 16\text{-}45)$$

$$K = [\text{H}_3\text{O}^+][\text{OH}^-] \quad (Eq.\ 16\text{-}46)$$

The experimentally determined hydrogen ion concentration in water at 25°C is

$$[\text{H}_3\text{O}^+] = 1.0 \times 10^{-7} \text{ mole of H}^+ \ (aq)/\text{liter}$$

With only water and its own ions present, each hydrogen ion must be matched by a hydroxide ion, as indicated by Equation 16-45, so

$$[\text{OH}^-] = 1.0 \times 10^{-7} \text{ mole of OH}^- \ (aq)/\text{liter}$$

From measured concentrations, the equilibrium constant is

$$K = 1.0 \times 10^{-7} \times 1.0 \times 10^{-7} = 1.0 \times 10^{-14}$$

Since the equilibrium constant for water is represented by the product of the concentration of two ions, it is often called the **ion product constant** and is given the symbol K_w. One use of this constant is to calculate hydroxide ion concentrations in solutions when the hydrogen ion concentration can be measured.

$$[OH^-] = \frac{K_w}{[H_3O^+]} \qquad (Eq.\ 16\text{-}47)$$

With hydroxide ion concentrations calculated from measured hydrogen ion concentration it is possible to evaluate equilibrium constants for bases in water solution.

Ex. 16-6 List the conjugate acid-base pairs for the reaction represented by Equation 16-45.

Ex. 16-7 *a.* If $[H_3O^+] = 1.0 \times 10^{-8}$, what is $[OH^-]$?

b. If $[OH^-] = 1.0 \times 10^{-2}$, what is $[H_3O^+]$?

16-13 IONIZATION OF AMMONIA IN WATER

Ammonia acts as a base when it is dissolved in water, while toward ammonia the water acts as an acid. Concentration measurements imply that ions are in equilibrium with un-ionized ammonia and water.

$$H_2O\ (l) + NH_3\ (aq) \rightleftarrows NH_4^+\ (aq) + OH^-\ (aq) \qquad (Eq.\ 16\text{-}48)$$

The system in its equilibrium state is described by

$$K = \frac{[NH_4^+][OH^-]}{[NH_3]}$$

The total concentration of ammonia in solution can be measured by titration of the solution with an acid as in Experiment 17. Hydroxide ion concentration can be calculated from Equation 16-47, using experimentally determined hydrogen ion concentrations. Since solutions are always electrically neutral, in an aqueous solution of ammonia

$$[NH_4^+] = [OH^-]$$

TABLE 16-3 CONCENTRATIONS OF AMMONIA AND IONS IN AQUEOUS AMMONIA AT 25°C

Initial Concentration of Ammonia, mole/liter	Equilibrium Concentration of Ammonia, mole/liter	Equilibrium Concentration of Hydroxide Ion, mole/liter	Equilibrium Concentration of Ammonium Ion, mole/liter	Equilibrium Constant, K
0.1000	0.099	0.00131	0.00131	1.73×10^{-5}
0.0100	0.0096	0.00041	0.00041	1.75×10^{-5}

The hydroxide ion concentration will be about 10^8 times the hydrogen ion concentration. The latter can be neglected so far as any contribution to the total concentration of positive ions. A summary of concentration data is given in Table 16-3 for two different solutions of aqueous ammonia. At still lower concentrations of ammonia the equilibrium constant approaches 1.77×10^{-5} at 25°C.

16-14 ENERGY CHANGES IN PROTON-TRANSFER REACTIONS

Hydrogen fluoride, water, and ammonia have molecules that are isoelectronic (see Section 7-17). Yet ammonia can remove a proton completely from hydrogen fluoride, while the equilibrium for hydrogen fluoride in water indicates that water has much less ability to remove a proton.

This difference between the abilities of water and ammonia to remove a proton from hydrogen fluoride is puzzling. The electron charge cloud model leads to the conclusion (Section 7-22) that hydrogen fluoride should transfer its proton to any isoelectronic structure with a lower nuclear charge and one or more available sites for protons. Both water and ammonia fulfill this requirement. The fact that water is less able to remove a proton from hydrogen fluoride than is ammonia, however, does fit in with the order of nuclear charge. Ammonia, with a central nuclear charge of $\oplus 7$, exerts a stronger attraction for the proton in hydrogen fluoride than water, with a central nuclear charge of $\oplus 8$. The electron charge cloud model by itself implies an all-or-none transfer, however, and not the incomplete transfer that is observed. The Brønsted-Lowry theory also implies an all-or-none transfer of a proton.

Section 15-7 presented a discussion of the relation between a standard free energy change and an equilibrium constant for a chemical system. At 25°C this relation for the standard free energy change in kilocalories per mole is

$$\Delta G° = -1.36 \log K$$

From the equilibrium constants in Tables 15-4 and 16-3 and the constant for water (Equation 16-46), it is possible to compute standard free energy changes for three reactions.

$$HF + H_2O \rightarrow H_3O^+ + F^- \quad \Delta G° = +4.3 \text{ kcal} \quad (Exp.\ 16\text{-}49)$$

$$NH_3 + H_2O \rightarrow NH_4^+ + OH^- \quad \Delta G° = +6.5 \text{ kcal} \quad (Exp.\ 16\text{-}50)$$

$$H_2O + H_2O \rightarrow H_3O^+ + OH^- \quad \Delta G° = +19.1 \text{ kcal} \quad (Exp.\ 16\text{-}51)$$

These data mean that for ions to form in each system, when each component is at unit concentration, work has to be done on the system. So far as work is concerned, the system moves from low to high energy in going from molecules to ions in all three reactions since $\Delta G°$ is positive. Yet the charge cloud model implies that each system should go from high to low electric energy. How are the energy relationships of each system to be interpreted?

It is possible to determine the thermal energy produced or absorbed for acid-base reactions by methods developed in Section 9-3.

$$\text{NaF } (aq) + \text{HCl } (aq) \rightarrow \text{HF } (aq) + \text{NaCl } (aq) \qquad (Eq.\ 16\text{-}52)$$

In Equation 16-52 all but the HF are completely ionized substances in water solution, so the equation can be written

$$\text{Na}^+ + \text{F}^- + \text{H}_3\text{O}^+ + \text{Cl}^- \rightarrow \text{HF } (aq) + \text{Na}^+ + \text{Cl}^- + \text{H}_2\text{O}$$

Since Na^+ and Cl^- appear unaltered on both sides of the equation, the net reaction is given by Equation 16-53.

$$\text{F}^- \ (aq) + \text{H}_3\text{O}^+ \ (aq) \rightarrow \text{HF } (aq) + \text{H}_2\text{O } (l) \qquad (Eq.\ 16\text{-}53)$$

When sodium fluoride and hydrochloric acid, both at 1 M concentrations, are mixed, the measured thermal energy gives $\Delta H = +3.0$ kcal for the reaction represented by Equation 16-53. This measured enthalpy change should be approximately the same as the standard enthalpy change $\Delta H°$. So for the reaction described by Expression 16-54, $\Delta H° = -3.0$ kcal/mole of HF ionized in water.

$$\text{H}_2\text{O } (l) + \text{HF } (aq) \rightarrow \text{F}^- \ (aq) + \text{H}_3\text{O}^+ \ (aq)$$
$$\Delta H = -3.0 \text{ kcal} \qquad (Exp.\ 16\text{-}45)$$

A similar study of the ammonia–water system gives $\Delta H° = +1.2$ kcal/mole of NH_3 reacting with water.

$$\text{H}_2\text{O } (l) + \text{NH}_3 \ (aq) \rightarrow \text{NH}_4^+ \ (aq) + \text{OH}^- \ (aq)$$
$$\Delta H° = +1.2 \text{ kcal} \qquad (Exp.\ 16\text{-}55)$$

For the self-ionization of water, $\Delta H° = +13.5$ kcal/mole of H_3O^+ formed.

$$2\text{H}_2\text{O} \rightarrow \text{H}_3\text{O}^+ \ (aq) + \text{OH}^- \ (aq) \quad \Delta H° = +13.5 \text{ kcal} \qquad (Exp.\ 16\text{-}56)$$

TABLE 16-4 STANDARD ENTHALPY CHANGES AND STANDARD FREE ENERGY CHANGES FOR THE IONIZATION OF SOME COMPOUNDS AT 25°C

Reaction	$\Delta H°$, kcal/mole	$\Delta G°$, kcal/mole
$\text{HF } (aq) + \text{H}_2\text{O } (l) \rightarrow \text{H}_3\text{O}^+ \ (aq) + \text{F}^- \ (aq)$	-3.0	$+4.3$
$\text{NH}_3 \ (aq) + \text{H}_2\text{O } (l) \rightarrow \text{NH}_4^+ \ (aq) + \text{OH}^- \ (aq)$	$+1.2$	$+6.5$
$\text{H}_2\text{O } (l) + \text{H}_2\text{O } (l) \rightarrow \text{H}_3\text{O}^+ \ (aq) + \text{OH}^- \ (aq)$	$+13.5$	$+19.1$

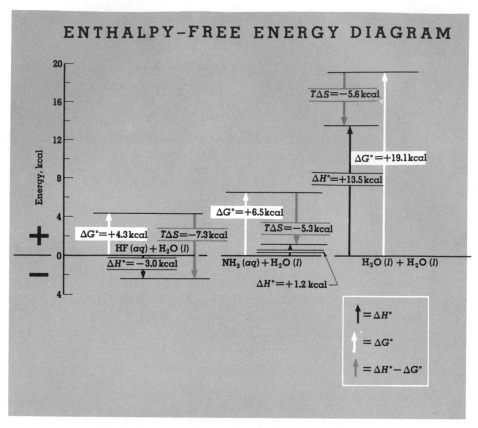

Fig. 16-3   *Standard enthalpy changes and standard free*
energy changes for the ionization of HF, NH₃, and H₂O at 25°C.

The energy relations summarized in Table 16-4 can be represented by the free energy diagram in Fig. 16-3.

Comparison of the energy changes in the free energy diagram of Fig. 16-3 indicates that the reaction of hydrogen fluoride with water does lead to a lowering of the enthalpy of the system. On this basis hydrogen fluoride should be a strong acid. It is not a strong acid, however, because ionization also increases the organization (decreases the entropy) of the system. The organization change is measured by

$$T \, \Delta S^\circ \; = \; \Delta H^\circ \; - \; \Delta G^\circ \; = \; -7.3 \text{ kcal/mole of HF}$$

So even though a system composed of hydrogen ions and fluoride ions is lower in enthalpy than a system of hydrogen fluoride molecules dissolved in water, the ionic form is a more highly organized system and therefore less probable.

Likewise the reaction of ammonia with water leads to an increase in enthalpy as well as to an increase in organization, so in the system in its equilibrium state only a small portion of the ammonia is present in the form of ions. The same conclusion is true for water ionizing by itself. The interpretation of acid-base reactions is thus more complete if changes in structure are considered along with changes in energy.

Ex. 16-8 Explain how the Brønsted-Lowry theory broadens the Arrhenius theory.

16-15 HYDROGEN HALIDES AS ACIDS

In Experiment 17 reactions of hydrochloric acid with ammonia, water, and hydroxide ion were investigated.

$$
\begin{array}{cccc}
\text{Acid}_2 & \text{Base}_1 & \text{Acid}_1 & \text{Base}_2 \\
\text{HCl} + \text{NH}_3 & \rightarrow & \text{NH}_4^+ + \text{Cl}^- & (Eq.\ 16\text{-}57) \\
\text{HCl} + \text{H}_2\text{O} & \rightarrow & \text{H}_3\text{O}^+ + \text{Cl}^- & (Eq.\ 16\text{-}58) \\
\text{HCl} + \text{OH}^- & \rightarrow & \text{H}_2\text{O} + \text{Cl}^- & (Eq.\ 16\text{-}59)
\end{array}
$$

In these three examples the reactions are essentially complete. That is, hydrogen chloride is a much stronger acid than the ammonium ion, hydrogen ion, or water. Or we can say that ammonia, water, and hydroxide ion are bases of considerably more strength (as proton acceptors) than the chloride ion.

The same conclusion is reached for the other halogen acids, HBr and HI. How can we estimate the relative strengths of the halogen acids? In any particular case we would like to have at least some qualitative idea as to the position of the equilibrium,

$$ \text{H}:\ddot{\text{X}}: \rightleftarrows \text{H}^+ + :\ddot{\text{X}}:^- $$

when $:\ddot{\text{X}}:^-$ might be any of the halogen ions, F^-, Cl^-, Br^-, or I^-.

But a proton cannot remain uncombined. Therefore, any experiment designed to study the relative strengths of the halogen acids must include the use of a proton acceptor (that is, a base) in the reaction mixture, and we must study the following equilibrium in which B: represents a base.

$$ \text{H}:\ddot{\text{X}}: + \text{B}: \rightleftarrows \text{H}:\text{B}^+ + :\ddot{\text{X}}:^- \qquad (Eq.\ 16\text{-}60) $$

If the base chosen is a negatively charged ion, the reaction will be

$$ \text{H}:\ddot{\text{X}}: + \text{B}:^- \rightleftarrows \text{H}:\text{B} + :\ddot{\text{X}}:^- \qquad (Eq.\ 16\text{-}61) $$

In practice there are many moderately weak acids for which water serves as a suitable base. For hydrogen chloride, hydrogen bromide, and hydrogen iodide, however, water is most unsuitable as a base with which to make quantitative studies. In each of these cases the acid is so strong that ionization (proton transfer) goes essentially to completion in dilute solutions. In other words, water is too strong a base and too attractive for a proton. The test does not discriminate among the differences we wish to measure.

Suppose that instead of water a different compound, formic acid (HCOOH), is used as the proton acceptor. When formic acid is dissolved in water, the reaction is given by the chemical equation in Expression 16-62.

$$\underset{\substack{\text{Formic}\\\text{acid}}}{\underset{\text{Acid}_1}{HCOOH}} + \underset{\text{Base}_2}{H_2O} \rightarrow \underset{\text{Acid}_2}{H_3O^+} + \underset{\substack{\text{Formate}\\\text{ion}}}{\underset{\text{Base}_1}{HCOO^-}} \qquad K = 1.77 \times 10^{-4}$$

(Exp. 16-62)

The equilibrium constant K suggests that formic acid is a weak acid in water solution but stronger than acetic acid. As a base, however, formic acid is not sufficiently strong to remove a proton from water. This is another way of saying that formic acid is a weaker base than water. Hence, it should be less able than water to accept a proton from each of the hydrogen halides. It does contain unshared electron pairs on the oxygen atoms, however, so that a molecule of formic acid can presumably accept a proton from strong acids. The reaction in which formic acid is a base would be

By measuring the extent to which the reaction proceeds toward completion in each case (that is, by measuring the composition of the system in its equilibrium state), one gets an indication of the relative acid strengths of the hydrogen halides. Such experiments show that hydrogen iodide is the strongest acid in this series, followed by hydrogen bromide, hydrogen chloride, and then hydrogen fluoride as the weakest acid.

16-16 FORMIC ACID IONIZATION

In Section 7-22 proton transfer from an acid to a base was discussed in terms of the charges present in molecules. Repulsion between a proton and other nearby nuclei provides the motivating force for the transfer of a proton from one molecule or ion to another molecule or ion. Does this model provide any basis for an interpretation of the behavior of formic acid?

In Section 16-15 formic acid was considered as an acid and as a base. In Fig. 16-4 a charge cloud model for a molecule of formic acid is shown.

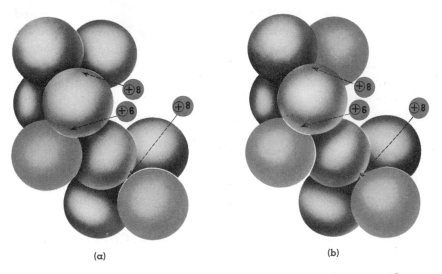

Fig. 16-4 (a) *Charge cloud model for a molecule of formic acid.*
(b) *Model for a positive ion formed by transfer of a proton to a*
formic acid molecule. Colored spheres represent two-electron charge
clouds that contain protons.

Although there are two protons in the formic acid structure, only one can be transferred to a base. One proton is close to an oxygen nucleus ($\oplus 8$), while the other is close to a carbon nucleus ($\oplus 6$). Repulsion between an oxygen nucleus and a proton is greater than between a carbon nucleus and a proton. It is the proton close to the oxygen nucleus that is transferred to water, ammonia, hydroxide ion, or other bases. Transfer of the second proton could be feasible only to a much stronger base than either water or ammonia and has never been accomplished in the laboratory.

Formic acid should act as a base since there are six outer electron clouds without nuclei inside any of them. Confronted with a sufficiently good source of protons, a formic acid molecule should be able to accept at least one. Upon accepting one proton, the resulting structure is necessarily a positive ion. This net positive charge makes the accept-ance of a second proton much less likely even though additional un-occupied charge clouds are available.

Since both formic acid and water contain oxygen as the center of highest nuclear charge, the transfer of protons between formic acid and water is not likely to be attended by much energy lowering. In formic acid a proton is repelled by two oxygen nuclei per molecule, while in water there is just one oxygen nucleus, and this difference should favor the transfer of a proton from acid to water.

Acid strength can be expressed quantitatively by an equilibrium constant. The equilibrium constant describes a system of the acid and some base, such as water, in an equilibrium state.

A comparison of various acids should give further information as to how the structure and strength of an acid are related. Presumably a major structural feature of an acid will be the magnitude and distribution of charge.

Water can be considered to be a rather weak acid with $K_w = 1 \times 10^{-14}$ at 25°C. If one hydrogen atom in water is replaced by a different atom, the acidity of the new molecule differs from water. Thus, with chlorine, a substance ClOH can be formed. This substance ClOH has been named hypochlorous acid, or, by the Stock nomenclature, hydrogen chlorate (I). In water solution the ionization of ClOH is described by

$$ClOH \ (aq) + H_2O \ (l) \rightarrow ClO^- \ (aq) + H_3O^+ \ (aq)$$
$$K = 9.6 \times 10^{-7} \quad (Exp. \ 16\text{-}64)$$

On the other hand, with potassium, potassium hydroxide (KOH) can be formed. In water solution, its ionization is described by

$$KOH \ (s) \rightarrow K^+ \ (aq) + OH^- \ (aq) \quad (Exp. \ 16\text{-}65)$$

Potassium hydroxide is a strong base with no detectable quantity of molecules of KOH in solution or in the crystalline solid.

A general class of compounds can be represented by the formula MOH. Hypochlorous acid and potassium hydroxide indicate that MOH can ionize in two ways.

$$MOH \rightarrow MO^- + H^+ \quad (Eq. \ 16\text{-}66)$$

$$MOH \rightarrow M^+ + OH^- \quad (Eq. \ 16\text{-}67)$$

If M is an atom with a kernel of small radius and large charge, as is true of chlorine, MOH tends to give up a proton and act as an acid. Conversely, if M is an atom with a kernel of large radius and small charge, MOH tends to lose a hydroxide ion and act as a base. A related comparison of ClOH and KOH is given by noting that the electronegativity of chlorine is 3.0 and that the electronegativity of potassium is 0.8. If in MOH the atom M represents an element of high electronegativity, MOH is acidic; if M has low electronegativity, MOH is basic.

Hypochlorous acid (ClOH) is one of three acids with similar formulas. The others are hypobromous acid (BrOH) and hypoiodous acid (IOH). None of these compounds have ever been isolated, but in water solution they behave as weak acids. The equilibrium constants are listed in Table 16-5. Increase in size of the kernel of the halogen atom

TABLE 16-5 FIRST IONIZATION CONSTANTS FOR SEVERAL ACIDS
IN WATER SOLUTION AT 25°C

(a)	Hypochlorous acid, HOCl	9.6×10^{-7}
	Hypobromous acid, HOBr	2×10^{-9}
	Hypoiodous acid, HOI	1×10^{-11}
(b)	Hypochlorous acid, HOCl	9.6×10^{-7}
	Chlorous acid, HOClO	1×10^{-2}
	Chloric acid, HOClO$_2$	About 10^3
	Perchloric acid, HOClO$_3$	About 10^8
(c)	Sulfurous acid, (HO)$_2$SO	1.3×10^{-2}
	Sulfuric acid, (HO)$_2$SO$_2$	About 10^3
(d)	Water, H$_2$O	1×10^{-14}
	Hydrogen sulfide, H$_2$S	1.1×10^{-7}
	Hydrogen selenide, H$_2$Se	1.9×10^{-4}
	Hydrogen telluride, H$_2$Te	2.3×10^{-3}
(e)	Phosphoric acid, (HO)$_3$PO	7.5×10^{-3}
	Sulfuric acid, (HO)$_2$SO$_2$	About 10^3
	Perchloric acid, HOClO$_3$	About 10^8

SOURCE: Linus Pauling, *Nature of the Chemical Bond and the Structure of Molecules
and Crystals*, 3d ed., Cornell University Press, Ithaca, N.Y., 1960, p. 325.

without change in charge from chlorine to bromine to iodine results
in a progressively weaker acid.

A series of acids are related to hypochlorous acid. These are listed
in part (b) of Table 16-5. The members of the series differ in the
number of the oxygen atoms attached to the central chlorine atom.
As the number of oxygen atoms increases, the strength of the acids
increases markedly. Perchloric acid is completely ionized in solution
and one of the strongest acids available. It must be that the presence
of several oxygen atoms around the central chlorine atom tends to shift
electrons away from the chlorine atom. A shift of electrons away from
the chlorine atom should tend to make the chlorine atom more positive
and hence more repulsive for the proton of the acid. Since each of the
oxygen-containing acids of chlorine is unstable and since only perchloric acid has ever been isolated, not much is known experimentally
about the geometry of the molecules of these acids. The perchlorate
ion, ClO$_4^-$, is known to be a tetrahedral arrangement of four oxygen
nuclei around a central chlorine nucleus, as would be expected from
consideration of atomic orbital models as described in Section 10-22.

Isoelectronic with perchloric acid are two other acids often used by chemists. These are sulfuric acid and phosphoric acid. Their acid strengths are indicated in part (e) of Table 16-5. Decrease in charge of the central kernel from $\oplus 7$ for chlorine to $\oplus 5$ for phosphorus results in a decrease in acid strength.

16-18 POLAR COVALENT BONDS

Acids and bases have been discussed in terms of atoms held together by ionic and covalent bonds. Initially these two bond types were rather sharply differentiated. An ionic bond was pictured as the result of the interaction of oppositely charged ions. Each ion was treated as a hard sphere with a charge at the center. Attracted toward each other, the ions were considered to approach until their outer edges were in contact.

Atoms joined by covalent bonds overlap each other so that one or more electrons are shared mutually by the two atoms. For identical atoms, the electrons are shared equally and the whole structure is electrically symmetrical.

The properties of acids and bases reflect a general feature of molecules. For most molecules, the bonds between atoms are neither simply ionic nor simply covalent but a blend of the two. The joined atoms overlap partially as in a covalent bond, but electrons are shared unequally as in an ionic bond. Bonds with unequally shared electrons were defined in Section 12-11 as polar covalent bonds. Substances which contain such bonds have properties intermediate between those of covalent and ionic substances.

Hydrogen chloride is an example of a substance with a polar covalent bond. In the gas phase at room temperature hydrogen chloride molecules interact with each other only slightly (Section 8-17). With water, hydrogen chloride interacts extensively to produce ionic solutions.

A polar covalent bond is formed whenever two atoms join which differ in electronegativity. Since most pairs of atoms do differ in electronegativity, most bonds are more or less polar. Acids and bases are a group of substances which can be considered to be polar covalent substances. The strongest bases, such as the alkali metal hydroxides, form ionic solids rather than polar covalent molecules.

16-19 SUMMARY

When chemical reactions are classified, a frequently encountered type of chemical change is called an acid-base reaction. Operationally, acids and bases are recognized by their abilities to neutralize each other, by their effect on dyes or indicators, by the ability of a stronger acid to replace a weaker acid in a compound, and by precipitation of sulfur from polysulfide solutions by acids.

In considering acids and bases, it is not possible to divide substances sharply into covalently and ionically bonded substances. Unequal attraction for electrons by two bonded atoms leads to unequal sharing of electrons. A covalent bond formed by a pair of electrons between two nuclei is said to be polar when the electrons are closer to one nucleus than to the other. Acids and bases are found to consist of structural units that are polar and even in some cases ionic.

Three conceptual definitions of acids have been discussed. Lewis proposed the broadest concept in which an acid-base reaction is characterized by the formation of a covalent bond. Any molecule or ion which has an empty orbital can act as an acid (electron-pair acceptor), whereas any molecule or ion with an exposed pair of electrons can act as a base (electron-pair donor).

An early and still widely used concept proposed by Arrhenius limited acids and bases to compounds. Acids, according to Arrhenius, contain hydrogen and in water solution produce hydrogen ions, whereas bases contain hydroxyl groups and in water solution produce hydroxide ions (OH^-).

Brønsted and Lowry each proposed a theory of acid-base reactions based on proton transfer. Any substance is an acid if it consists of molecules or ions which can donate a proton, whereas any substance is a base which consists of molecules or ions which can accept a proton. In this view different bases are considered to compete with each other for a proton.

The competition among bases for protons is often an uneven one. Where the balance is struck depends upon the relative strengths of the acids and the bases involved. A quantitative measure of acid and base strength is provided by a calculation of the equilibrium constant for an acid-base system.

Since the large attraction for a positive proton implies a small attraction for negative electrons, electronegativity can often be used as a guide to relative acid or base strengths. An atom of high electronegativity joined to a hydrogen atom or to a hydroxyl group will be likely to produce an acid. Conversely, an atom of low electronegativity attached to a hydroxyl group is much more likely to react to produce a base.

Structural changes as interpreted by electronic models describe potential energy changes. These changes are related experimentally to enthalpy changes. In some systems, and particularly in water solution, the extent of reaction is governed more by entropy changes than by enthalpy changes. This is true in acid-base systems as in other cases.

Ex. 16-9 Calculate $T \Delta S°$ for the reactions listed in Table 16-4.

Ex. 16-10 How can BrOH, NaOH, and CH_3OH be identified as acids or bases by use of the Arrhenius theory?

Ex. 16-11 Compare Lewis acid-base reactions with Brønsted-Lowry acid-base reactions.

Ex. 16-12 a. In the light of laboratory experience and Chapter 16, which base will be the winner of the competition for a proton in the reactions described by Equations 16-26 to 16-28?

b. List the bases Cl^- (aq), OH^- (aq), H_2O, and NH_3 (aq) in order of increasing base strength.

Ex. 16-13 For each of the compounds listed, designate by using the symbols $\oplus$ and $\ominus$ the polarity of the bonds between atoms. For example, the bond in HCl would be designated $H\oplus-\ominus Cl$, on the basis of electronegativities of the elements hydrogen and chlorine.

HBr	H_2O	ClF
MgO	CCl_4	PH_3
ClOH	$Mg(OH)_2$	SO_2

Ex. 16-14 Examine the equations for the Brønsted-Lowry acid-base reactions in Section 16-6, and answer the following questions.

a. How does the strength of the reactant acid and base compare with the strength of the product acid and base? Illustrate your answer with a specific example.

b. How is it possible for a substance to act as an acid in one reaction and a base in another reaction? Illustrate your answer with a specific example.

Ex. 16-15 Each set of acids listed in Table 16-5 illustrates the effect of changing some variable related to acid strength. For each set, identify the variable and describe the effect of each variable on relative acid strength.

Ex. 16-16 List the acids within each of the following sets in order of increasing acid strength, and relate the order to some feature of structure.

a. HI, HCl, HF, HBr

b. $(HO)_2HPO$, $(HO)_2SO$, $HOClO_2$

c. AsH_3, PH_3, NH_3

d. NaOH, $Al(OH)_3$, $SiO(OH)_2$, $Mg(OH)_2$

e. $(HO)_3PO$, $(HO)_3AsO$, $HONO_2$

Ex. 16-17 Table 16-4 shows $\Delta H^\circ = 13.5$ kcal/mole of H_3O^+ for the reaction

$$H_2O \ (l) + H_2O \ (l) \rightarrow H_3O^+ \ (aq) + OH^- \ (aq)$$

Describe how NaOH, HCl, and NaCl can be used to determine ΔH° for this reaction.

Ex. 16-18 a. The equilibrium constant K for the reaction

$$HCN \ (aq) + H_2O \ (l) \rightarrow H_3O^+ \ (aq) + CN^- \ (aq)$$

is 7.2×10^{-10} at 25°C. Estimate the H_3O^+ concentration in a 1.0 M HCN solution.

b. Estimate the equilibrium constant K for iodic acid, HIO_3, if $[H_3O^+]$ of a 0.10 M solution is 0.0335 mole/liter.

c. On the basis of your answers to parts a and b of this exercise and information in Sections 16-10 and 16-11, list the following acids in order of increasing strength: HBr, CH_3COOH, HF, HCN, and HIO_3.

Ex. 16-19 a. From the spontaneous reactions in water solution represented by the equations below, list the acids H_3O^+, NH_4^+, H_2O, HSO_4^-, HCO_3^-, NH_3, H_2CO_3, and H_2SO_4 in order of decreasing acid strength.

Acid₁		Base₂		Acid₂		Base₁
H_2SO_4	+	H_2O	→	H_3O^+	+	HSO_4^-
H_3O^+	+	SO_4^{--}	→	HSO_4^-	+	H_2O
HSO_4^-	+	HCO_3^-	→	H_2CO_3	+	SO_4^{--}
H_2CO_3	+	NH_3	→	NH_4^+	+	HCO_3^-
NH_4^+	+	CO_3^{--}	→	HCO_3^-	+	NH_3
HCO_3^-	+	OH^-	→	H_2O	+	CO_3^{--}
H_2O	+	NH_2^-	→	NH_3	+	OH^-

b. List the bases SO_4^{--}, HCO_3^-, NH_2^-, NH_3, OH^-, H_2O, CO_3^{--}, and HSO_4^- in order of increasing base strength.

17 TIME AND CHEMICAL CHANGE

THE EQUILIBRIUM STATE of a system represents the final state of a system in which no spontaneous change in state is possible. Many systems change in state so quickly that it is not possible to determine the concentrations of components of the system between initial and final states. Reactions in other systems are so slow that chemical change is almost imperceptible, even though the composition of the system in its equilibrium state is very different from that in the initial state. Still other systems lie between these two extremes and change from initial to final state in a matter of microseconds (dynamite explosion and bunsen burner reaction), minutes (boiling of a fresh egg to form a hard-boiled egg), hours (digestion of food), days (souring of milk), and years (rusting of iron).

The initial and final states for a chemical system seem, then, not to provide the basis for a complete description of a chemical change in a system. The discussion so far gives us no answers to questions concerned with the time interval required for a chemical change in a system. The time interval required for a chemical change is called the *reaction time.*

For any of the systems that we have discussed previously, the question may be asked, "How long a time does the change require?" Once the time for change has been established, a second question might be asked, "Why do the times for different changes turn out as they do?"

17-1 IONIC SYSTEMS

The system produced by mixing of solutions of calcium chloride and sodium sulfate is an example of an ionic system (Section 13-6). Calcium sulfate precipitates from the reaction mixture.

$$Ca^{++} (aq) + SO_4^{--} (aq) \rightarrow CaSO_4 (s)$$

When solutions about 1 M in concentration are mixed in a beaker, the reaction takes place as quickly as mixing takes place. Of course, when the solutions are mixed in this way, it is possible only to conclude that the reaction is complete in a time interval that is less than several seconds. Observation of solutions mixed in beakers does not permit one to decide if a reaction might require a time interval of the order of a fraction of a second.

For reactions in solutions, experimental arrangements can be set up by which it is possible to observe directly reactions which are complete in an interval of less than one second. One way to do this is to observe the solutions as they mix. If the solutions flow through separate tubes into a junction and in a common tube away from the junction, the point downstream from the junction can be located where reaction is first seen to occur. An apparatus for this purpose is shown in Fig. 17-1.

With proper design of the junction, mixing can be completed between the time the solutions enter and leave the junction (between lines C and D, respectively). The farther downstream from the junction the reaction is observed to take place, the longer the time required for reaction. If the rate at which the solutions enter the junction is known, it is possible to calculate the time required for any portion of the solution to travel to a given distance downstream, for example, from D to E.

Apparatus carefully designed for mixing makes possible the observation of reaction times of a fraction of a second. Practical problems put a lower limit of about 0.001 second (one millisecond) on the reaction time which can be measured in this way.

When calcium chloride and sodium sulfate are mixed in a flow system similar to that shown in Fig. 17-1, the reaction begins in the

Fig. 17-1 *Flow system for measuring reaction time.*

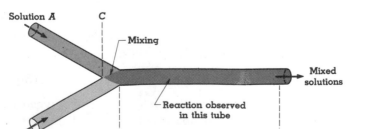

mixing chamber itself, between C and D. Experiments of this kind put the reaction time, then, at less than a millisecond. All other attempts at a time measurement for the reaction in this system yield the same conclusion. Reaction occurs as fast as the solutions are mixed. For the present we will consider that reactions which are complete in less than a millisecond are **instantaneous.** Many other ionic systems react instantaneously.

In Chapter 16 reactions between certain ions were studied which did not result simply in the precipitation of ionic solids. These reactions were proton-transfer reactions. The acid-base titration procedures developed in the laboratory included the assumption that the reaction between an acid and a base is so rapid that no account need be taken of reaction time. No warning was given to wait for any period of time after addition of a solution of an acid to a sample of a base, in order to be certain that the reaction was complete. If acid and base solutions are passed into the two entry tubes of a flow system similar to that shown in Fig. 17-1, temperature measurements, indicator studies, and pH determinations all indicate that the reaction is instantaneous within experimental error. This conclusion is reached not only for the reaction of hydrogen ion and hydroxide ion,

$$H^+ \ (aq) + OH^- \ (aq) \rightarrow H_2O \ (l) \qquad (Eq. \ 17\text{-}1)$$

but also for the other proton-transfer reactions previously studied, such as those represented in Equations 17-2, 17-3, and 17-4.

$$H_3O^+ \ (aq) + NH_3 \ (aq) \rightarrow NH_4^+ \ (aq) + H_2O \ (l) \quad (Eq. \ 17\text{-}2)$$

$$CH_3COOH \ (aq) + OH^- \ (aq) \rightarrow$$
$$CH_3COO^- \ (aq) + H_2O \ (l) \qquad (Eq. \ 17\text{-}3)$$

$$NH_3 \ (g) + HCl \ (g) \rightarrow NH_4^+Cl^- \ (s) \qquad (Eq. \ 17\text{-}4)$$

The examples considered in Equations 17-1 to 17-4 give reaction times so short as to be indistinguishable from zero time. One type of reaction involved the combining of ions to form an ionic solid, while the other type involved the transfer of a proton from one molecule or ion to another.

17-2 COVALENT BOND BREAKING AND BOND MAKING

In previous chapters a number of reactions have been discussed where charge cloud and atomic orbital theories indicated that the molecules involved are covalent, as in the synthesis of water.

$$H_2 \ (g) + \tfrac{1}{2}O_2 \ (g) \rightarrow H_2O \ (l) \qquad (Eq. \ 17\text{-}5)$$

If the system is prepared by bringing hydrogen and oxygen gas together at room temperature, no observable chemical change occurs.

Such a system can be left at room temperature for years without evidence of change. Inadequate mixing is hardly the reason for the lack of reaction, since gases mix spontaneously and completely.

The reaction between hydrogen and oxygen does proceed when the temperature is raised. At about 500°C, a chemical change occurs in the system; the product is steam. Under most conditions the change is so rapid and so exothermic as to be called an explosion. Although they are not impossible to study, explosions do not lend themselves to easy measurement of reaction time. The water synthesis seems to proceed either extremely rapidly or not at all. It is difficult to synthesize water from hydrogen and oxygen under any conditions where the change proceeds slowly enough to give easily measured reaction times.

Some systems that change in a reasonable time are known. One example is the reaction of methyl bromide, CH_3Br, with chloride ion. The reaction can be studied in solution. Since methyl bromide is not soluble in water, the reaction is carried out in acetone, a solvent which dissolves both methyl bromide and lithium chloride. About a minute after mixing the components, a measurable change can be observed. The net reaction is the displacement of bromide by chloride in methyl bromide to form methyl chloride, CH_3Cl.

$$Cl^- + CH_3Br \rightarrow CH_3Cl + Br^- \qquad (Eq.\ 17\text{-}6)$$

To carry out a reaction time measurement, the mixture is kept at a constant temperature for some convenient length of time. After a known time interval, the reaction mixture is poured into water, which stops the reaction because the two ions (Br^- and Cl^-) are soluble in water whereas methyl bromide and methyl chloride are not soluble. The extent of reaction is determined by finding the amount of bromide ion liberated or chloride ion consumed. Silver nitrate will precipitate both ions, forming a mixture of silver chloride and silver bromide. The methyl bromide and methyl chloride will not react measurably with silver nitrate. To determine how much of the precipitate is silver bromide, at least two procedures are possible. As mentioned in Section 13-8, silver chloride is quite soluble in aqueous ammonia. However, silver bromide is only slightly soluble in aqueous ammonia. Silver chloride can therefore be dissolved and the silver bromide filtered, dried, and weighed. We may also proceed as follows. For every Cl^- ion that reacts, one Br^- ion forms. Suppose we begin with 0.1 mole of Cl^-. Precipitation with silver nitrate at the start of the reaction gives 0.1 mole of AgCl or $0.1 (107.9 + 35.5) = 14.3$ g of AgCl. At the end of the reaction the precipitate would consist of 0.1 mole of AgBr or $0.1 (107.9 + 79.9) = 18.8$ g of AgBr. During the reaction, mixtures of silver chloride and silver bromide will be precipitated, weighing be-

TABLE 17-1 DATA FOR THE REACTION OF LITHIUM CHLORIDE AND METHYL BROMIDE IN ACETONE SOLUTION AT 34.04°C

Time Interval, seconds	Concentration of Br^-, millimoles/liter	Concentration of LiCl, millimoles/liter	Concentration of CH_3Br, millimoles/liter
0	0.0	50.3	134.3
65	4.4	45.9	129.9
90	6.1	44.2	128.2
100	6.9	43.4	127.4
135	8.6	41.7	125.7
195	12.8	37.5	121.5
255	16.5	33.8	117.9
315	18.7	31.6	115.6
375	21.0	29.3	113.3
420	22.7	27.6	111.6
660	29.8	20.5	104.5

SOURCE: Hughes, Ingold, and Mackie, *Journal of the Chemical Society* (London), 1955: 3175.

tween 14.3 and 18.8 g. From the mass of precipitate the ratios of AgCl/AgBr and hence the quantity of bromide ion present can be calculated.

Data for the reaction of lithium chloride and methyl bromide at 34.04°C are given in Table 17-1. The concentrations of bromide ion, of lithium chloride, and of methyl bromide are given in Table 17-1 at different times after mixing. Table 17-1 shows that the system in its initial state contained lithium chloride at a concentration of 50.3 millimoles/liter and methyl bromide at a concentration of 134.3 millimoles/liter. Since, according to Equation 17-6, each bromide ion liberated corresponds to the reaction of one chloride ion and one methyl bromide molecule, the bromide ion concentrations that are experimentally determined can be used to calculate the lithium chloride and methyl bromide concentrations. After 315 seconds, for instance, the concentration of Br^- was 18.7 millimoles/liter of solution. Therefore, the concentration of Cl^- has been reduced by 18.7 millimoles/liter. The concentration of lithium chloride remaining must be $50.3 - 18.7 = 31.6$ millimoles of LiCl/liter in agreement with the concentration given in Table 17-1. The data in Table 17-1 are plotted in Fig. 17-2.

17-3 REACTION RATE

The most obvious interpretation of the data of Table 17-1 is that time is required for a given amount of substance to react. In a word, the reaction has a rate. **Reaction rate** can be defined as the amount of

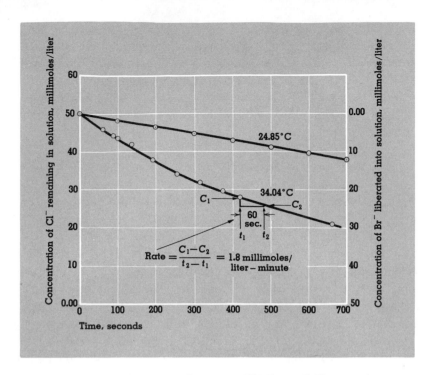

Fig. 17-2 *Rate of reaction between CH_3Br and Cl^- in acetone at $24.85°C$ and $34.04°C$.*

change in concentration divided by the corresponding time interval, or the concentration change per unit time. Just as we might determine the speed or rate of motion of an automobile by measuring the distance traveled in a given time, so for a chemical system we can determine the rate of reaction by measuring the concentration change in a given

TABLE 17-2 CONCENTRATION CHANGE PER MINUTE

Time Interval Number	Rate of Concentration Change $(\Delta C/\Delta t)$, millimoles/minute-liter
1	5.1
2	4.1
3	3.6
4	3.2
5	2.8
6	2.5
7	2.2
8	1.8
9	1.7
10	1.5
11	1.3

time. From the graph in Fig. 17-2, we can evaluate the change in lithium chloride concentration in a one-minute interval at different times. In Table 17-2 are listed concentration changes per minute estimated from the plot. The first time interval is the minute which begins at zero time. Each successive minute is a new time interval. The right-hand column is therefore

$$\frac{\Delta C}{\Delta t} = \frac{C_1 - C_2}{t_2 - t_1} \qquad\qquad (Eq.\ 17\text{-}7)$$

where ΔC is the concentration change and Δt is the time interval (one minute). For the eighth time interval (from 420 to 480 seconds) the concentration change ΔC is 1.8 millimoles/liter (see Fig. 17-2).

As the conversion of methyl bromide to methyl chloride proceeds, the rate of the reaction decreases steadily. Practically all chemical reactions show this same type of behavior. The longer any reaction runs, the more slowly it proceeds. Indeed, the data for most reactions suggest that each reaction seems simply to go more and more slowly but never to reach an end. For practical purposes, we will say the reaction has stopped when the rate of change has become too small to determine. This conclusion may well represent the limitations of the measurement technique rather than the demonstration that the reaction has reached a zero rate.

17-4 FACTORS INFLUENCING REACTION RATES

As can be seen from the decrease in the rate of concentration change in Table 17-2, the rate of reaction between LiCl and CH_3Br in acetone decreases as the reaction proceeds. This reduction in rate could be due to the decrease in concentration of reactants or to the increase in concentration of products. However, doubling the initial concentration of either of the reactants doubles the rate of the reaction, while doubling the concentration of products does not lead to a measurable change in rate. If only the products LiBr and CH_3Cl are mixed, no LiCl or CH_3Br can be detected by the method described in Section 17-2. We can conclude, therefore, that the rate of the reaction of LiCl and CH_3Br is dependent on the concentrations of the reactants. The study of other reactions leads to the conclusion that, in most cases, reaction rate is dependent on the concentrations of the reactants. Occasionally, the rate is dependent on the concentration of only one of the reactants.

Common experience supplies further examples of the effect of concentration on reaction rate. Fanning a slow-burning wood fire increases the concentration of oxygen next to the wood. Steel wool oxidizes slowly in air (21 percent oxygen) but more rapidly in oxygen.

As seen from Fig. 17-2, a second factor influencing reaction rate in the LiCl-CH_3Br system is the temperature. At 24.85°C the lithium chloride concentration decreases more slowly than at 34.04°C. At 24.85°C more than 500 seconds are needed for the lithium chloride concentration to fall to 40 millimoles/liter. At 34.04°C the corresponding time is about 150 seconds. Heating the copper–sulfur system as described in Chapter 2 increases the rate of the reaction, and an increase in the temperature of the hydrogen–oxygen system leads to an explosive reaction (Section 17-2). Sometimes a reaction rate is controlled only by the intensity of light shining on the reactants.

The rate of a reaction can often be influenced by introducing into the reacting system a substance which does not decrease in concentration during the reaction. For example, methyl bromide reacts with water to produce methanol, hydrogen ion, and bromide ion.

$$2H_2O + CH_3Br \rightarrow CH_3OH + H_3O^+ + Br^- \quad (Eq.\ 17\text{-}8)$$

The reaction (Equation 17-8) can be made to go much faster by the addition of a small amount of sodium iodide. The concentration of iodide ion is found to be the same at the end as at the beginning of the reaction. The increase in rate can be explained if we postulate a reaction between iodide ion and methyl bromide analogous to the chloride ion reaction of Equation 17-6.

$$I^- + CH_3Br \rightarrow CH_3I + Br^- \quad (Eq.\ 17\text{-}9)$$

The reaction of methyl iodide with water then would give the product (methanol) and would liberate the iodide ion again.

$$H_2O + CH_3I \rightarrow CH_3OH + H_3O^+ + I^- \quad (Eq.\ 17\text{-}10)$$

However, for this assumed two-step process to be an adequate explanation of the effect of added iodide ion, each step must be a faster reaction than the direct reaction of methyl bromide and water (Equation 17-8). This has in fact been found experimentally to be the case. The proposed two steps of Equations 17-9 and 17-10 are spoken of as a possible mechanism for the methyl bromide–water–sodium iodide reaction. A **reaction mechanism** is a series of reactions which together comprise the steps in the overall change observed. The term reaction mechanism is also used to mean the detailed way in which electrons and nuclei in the reactants rearrange to form the products. A substance such as iodide ion which alters the rate of a reaction, but whose concentration is the same at the beginning and at the end of the reaction, is known as a **catalyst**. A second example of a catalyst is nickel metal, which increases the rate of reaction of hydrogen with vegetable oils in the production of hydrogenated fats used for oleomargarine, soap, and many other products.

Given the information that rates of reactions are affected by the nature of the reactants, by concentration changes of reactants, by temperature, by catalysts, and sometimes by light, what model of a reaction in a system can be constructed which will account for the above observations? The model for reaction rates must be different in one important respect from the models we have used so far. It must include in some way a reason why changes occur over a definite period of time.

The charge cloud model and the orbital model provide descriptions of the arrangement in space of the parts of a molecule or ion. These models can be used to predict, in many cases, which arrangement among several possible arrangements of structural units is likely to be the most stable. But the models cannot be used to predict how long it might take for a less stable arrangement to rearrange itself to a more stable one. Similarly, the kinetic-molecular model supplies a picture of molecular motion and even allows us to obtain measures of relative velocities of molecules (Experiment 18). But the kinetic-molecular theory has so far not given an indication as to how molecular motions influence the rates of chemical reactions. How can some property be built into the models that will be useful in interpreting the fact that the chemical reactions take time? Can the model also be modified to interpret the variations in reaction time in systems of different compositions or in different states?

17-5 A MODEL FOR REACTION RATES

A model for reaction rates which chemists have found useful combines the kinetic-molecular model with the charge cloud or orbital model and uses also the energy model developed in Chapter 9. The reaction rate model can be developed in stages in connection with each of the factors that we have found to affect the rate.

(1) Collisions. Mention was made earlier of the fact that, in the chloride ion–methyl bromide reactions, the rate is doubled if either the methyl bromide concentration or the chloride ion concentration is doubled. In discussing proton-transfer reactions in Section 7-22, it was assumed that the molecules or ions of the two reactants were in contact when the proton was transferred. Collision between methyl bromide and chloride ion can be assumed to be necessary for reaction to occur. Then, doubling the concentration of methyl bromide will double the number of collisions per unit time with chloride ion because the chloride ion will thus have twice the chance of meeting a methyl bromide molecule during its movements in the solution. It is reasonable to assume that the number of collisions occurring in unit time is an important factor in determining the rate of reaction.

In gas reactions one simple way of increasing the number of molecular collisions is by increasing the pressure. An increase in pressure on a gas increases the density of the substance and hence the concentration of molecules or the number of moles per unit volume of gas. It is possible therefore to increase the concentration of a reactant in the gas phase without adding more of the reactant.

Hydrogen and iodine react to form hydrogen iodide.

$$H_2 \ (g) + I_2 \ (g) \rightarrow 2HI \ (g)$$

An increase in the concentration either of hydrogen or of iodine is found to increase the rate of the reaction. Compression of the system raises the concentrations of both hydrogen and iodine and leads to an increase in the rate of the reaction as well. Addition of reactant and compression of the system serve equally well as ways of increasing the concentration of reactants and hence increasing the number of collisions per second.

(2) Orientation. In the reaction of chloride ion and methyl bromide, it is necessary for the ion and the molecule to collide if reaction is to occur. Collision must occur so as to permit the chloride ion to attach itself to the molecule and the bromide ion to escape. If the chloride ion collides with the bromide part of the methyl bromide molecule, however, it would seem unlikely that reaction could occur. In other words, the ion and the molecule must be properly oriented for reaction. It is believed that the chloride ion reacts by colliding with the methyl bromide molecule on the side opposite to the bromide. In this orientation the chloride can become attached on one side while the bromide escapes from the opposite side. In addition to collision, the model therefore requires proper orientation of the colliding molecules or ions in order for reaction to occur.

(3) Energy. If in two different systems the concentrations of reactants and the orientation possibilities are the same, one might expect the two reactions to occur at the same rate. This however is not always the case. While hydrogen and fluorine molecules react explosively at room temperature, hydrogen and oxygen under the same conditions do not react measurably. Why do fluorine and oxygen react differently with hydrogen? This enormous difference in rate cannot possibly be accounted for by a difference in the number of favorable orientations of reacting molecules because fluorine and oxygen both consist of diatomic molecules and their sizes are very similar. To account for such differences, a useful model might be developed by considering the experimental data in terms of energy changes. Enthalpy changes or equilibrium considerations are of little immediate help. Although free energy changes can be used to predict the equilibrium position for a chemical system, free energy change yields no information at all concerning the rate at which the equilibrium state will be reached. The standard free energy change for the formation of water at 25°C is

−56.7 kcal/mole, whereas it is −64.7 kcal/mole for the formation of hydrogen fluoride.

$$H_2 \ (g) + \tfrac{1}{2}O_2 \ (g) \rightarrow H_2O \ (l) \quad \Delta G° = -56.7 \ \text{kcal/mole} \quad (Exp. \ 17\text{-}11)$$

$$\tfrac{1}{2}H_2 \ (g) + \tfrac{1}{2}F_2 \ (g) \rightarrow HF \ (g) \quad \Delta G° = -64.7 \ \text{kcal/mole} \quad (Exp. \ 17\text{-}12)$$

Yet the second reaction proceeds many thousands of times faster than the first at 25°C. If neither enthalpy change nor free energy change is correlated with reaction rate, what information can be correlated with reaction rate?

That an energy must play a part in controlling reaction rate is suggested by the effect of temperature on the reaction of CH_3Br with LiCl. Examination of Fig. 17-2 shows that a 10°C rise in temperature reduces by a factor of 3 the time needed for the chloride ion concentration to fall from 0.05 mole/liter to 0.04 mole/liter (Section 17-4).

Now a rise in temperature increases both the average velocity and the average kinetic energy of molecules. An increase in the average velocity of molecules will increase the number of collisions. Faster-moving molecules collide with each other more often. Changes in velocity are related to changes in the absolute temperature (Section 8-11). The square of the average velocity is proportional to the absolute temperature. An increase of 10°C at 298°K (25°C) produces at most an increase of $\sqrt{308}/\sqrt{298}$ in the number of collisions, a factor quite insufficient to account for the change by a factor of 3 in the reaction time for the chloride ion–methyl bromide reaction. Does the effect of temperature on the kinetic energy of molecules lead us further?

An increase in temperature leads to an increase in the number of collisions, but at the same time, it leads to more energetic collisions. Each colliding molecule possesses, on the average, more energy than it possessed at a lower temperature. Chemical reactions involve the breaking of bonds. It is reasonable, therefore, to assume that collisions even for properly oriented molecules will not lead to reaction unless sufficient energy is present during collision to break the bonds involved in the reaction. The difference between the least kinetic energy needed for reaction to occur and the average kinetic energy of all collisions in the same system of molecules is known as the *activation energy.*

A 10°C rise in temperature increases the average kinetic energy of a system of molecules by a relatively small amount. However, a 10°C rise in temperature increases by as much as a factor of 2 the number of high-energy molecules. For this reason a study of the rate of a reaction at different temperatures can be used to provide an estimate of the magnitude of an activation energy for the reaction. For fast reactions the activation energy is low, whereas for slow reactions the activation

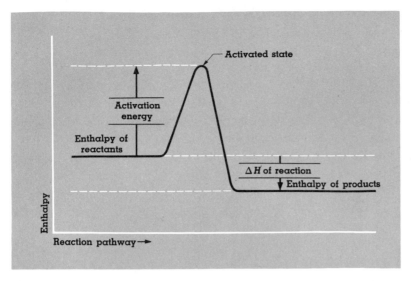

Fig. 17-3 *Energy diagram of an exothermic spontaneous reaction showing activation energy.*

energy is high. Proton-transfer reactions and many reactions among ions proceed so rapidly as to suggest no activation energy at all. Reactions which take from a few minutes to a few hours to complete have rates most easily measured in the laboratory. Rates of this magnitude are associated with activation energies of about 20 kcal/mole of reactant.

Activation energies are often shown in energy diagrams as humps or barriers separating reactants and products. Figure 17-3 is an energy diagram for an exothermic spontaneous reaction, and Fig. 17-4 is a

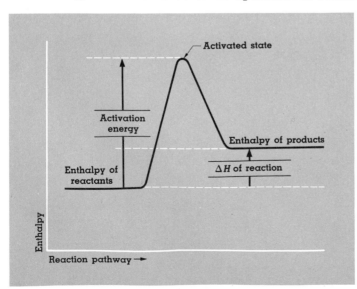

Fig. 17-4 *Energy diagram of an endothermic spontaneous reaction showing activation energy.*

diagram for an endothermic spontaneous reaction. The diagrams show an energy hump as an obstacle or barrier which the reactants must overcome. In Fig. 17-3 the products are represented as having less average energy than the reactants. Those molecules which collide with an energy equal to the average energy plus the activation energy (represented by the hump) are the only molecules which react.

Molecules which collide with kinetic energy equal to the average kinetic energy plus the activation energy are said to be in an **activated state** at the instant of collision. Only from the activated state can further change lead to reaction products.

The top of the energy barrier corresponds to the activated state of a system of reacting molecules. The activated state is a state of the system in which the composition is partway between reactants and products. For the chloride ion–methyl bromide system, the activated state can be depicted as in Equation 17-13.

$$Cl^- + H-\underset{\underset{\textstyle H}{|}}{\overset{\overset{\textstyle H}{\diagdown}}{C}}-Br \rightarrow \left[Cl^- \cdots \cdots \underset{\underset{\textstyle H \quad H}{\diagup \diagdown}}{\overset{\overset{\textstyle H}{|}}{C}} \cdots \cdots Br \right] \rightarrow Cl-\underset{\underset{\textstyle H}{\diagdown}}{\overset{\overset{\textstyle H}{\diagup}}{C}}-H + Br^-$$

Initial state   Activated state   Final state

(Eq. 17-13)

At any temperature above absolute zero, molecules and ions possess some kinetic energy. The average velocity and average kinetic energy are determined for the molecules or ions of any substance by the absolute temperature. But the velocity of a single molecule in a system at a fixed temperature will be continually changed by collisions—a head-on collision slowing it down, one from behind speeding it up. At any instant, there will then be a distribution of molecular velocities, from a minimum of zero to high velocities. A large number of molecules will have velocities near the average velocity, but a few will have much higher velocities and a few will have lower than average velocities.

The probable distribution of molecular velocities in a collection of molecules is illustrated in Fig. 17-5 at two different temperatures. The heavy vertical line in Fig. 17-5 represents for a particular system the minimum velocity needed by reacting molecules for reaction to occur on collision. This velocity therefore corresponds to an activation energy for that system.

The form of the distribution of molecular velocities is such that at any temperature there will be some molecules with energy in excess of the activation energy, and hence there will be the possibility of chemical reaction. As the temperature is raised, the number of high-energy molecules is increased, and a larger fraction of the molecules

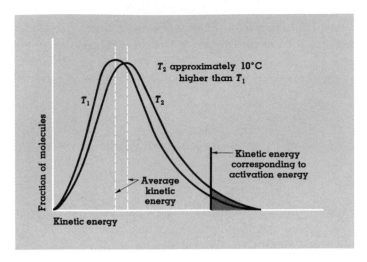

Fig. 17-5 *Distributions of kinetic energies of mole-cules in a system at two different temperatures, T_1 and T_2. Shaded areas under curves at right show the relative fractions of molecules having kinetic energies greater than the activation energy for a reaction.*

possess more than the activation energy. A measure of the effect of increased temperature on the number of molecules having more than the necessary velocity for reaction may be obtained by comparing the shaded areas under the curves for T_2 and T_1 in Fig. 17-5. A small in-crease in average kinetic energy is accompanied by marked increase in the number of molecules with the required activation energy and hence an increase in the number of collisions between molecules that can react. This makes possible a marked increase in the rate of the reaction. A useful generalization is that, in water solutions, a 10° in-crease in temperature will double the rate of reaction. For many reac-tions in the gas phase, the increase with temperature is greater than this, but it can be smaller.

17-6 REACTION PATHWAY

Although the numerical value of the free energy change determines whether or not a given reaction can take place spontaneously at con-stant temperature and pressure, it is the size of the activation energy and the chances of properly oriented collisions which determine whether or not the reaction will proceed at a reasonable rate. Of two reactions leading to the same product and equally probable in terms of the change in free energy, the one with the lower activation energy is more likely to proceed at a measurable rate.

It is not always possible to alter a chemical system so as to achieve a change in the rate of reaction and still obtain the desired product.

For many systems it is possible to change the reaction rate by introducing an additional substance into the reaction mixture. When this is done, there are two possible situations. (1) The added substance C enters into the reaction and contributes to one or more of the products.

$$A + B + C \rightarrow G + H$$

(2) The added substance enters into the reaction but is not consumed as the reaction proceeds. Such a substance was called a catalyst in Section 17-4.

$$A + B \overset{C}{\rightarrow} D + E$$

The first case is an obvious change in reaction path since the amount of C used is determined by the total mass of material reacting. The second case implies that a small amount of substance C can be used over and over and thus participates in the reaction of a large amount of the reactants A and B.

It is generally assumed that a catalyst is effective by changing the activation energy of the reaction. Figure 17-6 illustrates the lowering of the activation energy by the introduction of a catalyst. There are many mechanisms by which catalysts can change activation energies and hence reaction rates. Some catalysts, such as nickel (Section 17-4), provide a surface on which one or more of the reactants can be ad-

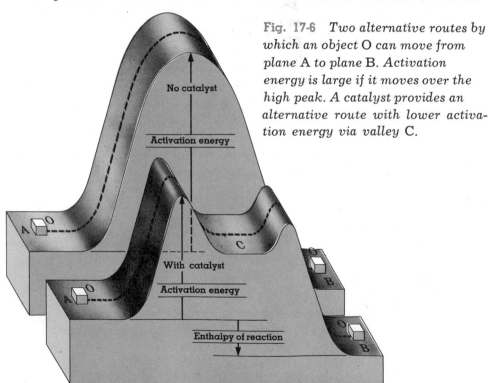

Fig. 17-6 *Two alternative routes by which an object* O *can move from plane* A *to plane* B. *Activation energy is large if it moves over the high peak. A catalyst provides an alternative route with lower activation energy via valley* C.

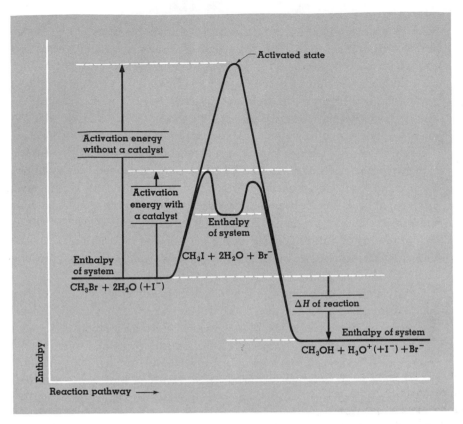

Fig. 17-7 *Activation energy is decreased when* I^- *is used as a catalyst for the reaction* $CH_3Br + 2H_2O \rightarrow CH_3OH + H_3O^+ + Br^-$. *The enthalpy change for the reaction is not altered by the catalyst.*

sorbed. In the adsorbed form, one of the bonds in one of the reactants may be stretched and weakened so much that a less energetic collision is sufficient to cause reaction. Adsorption on the surface of a catalyst may also provide the correct geometry so that orientation of a colliding molecule may be easier. In other words, a surface catalyst may provide a suitable arrangement for reacting molecules, whereas such a favorable arrangement is improbable in space.

Other catalysts may combine with a reactant to yield a distinct compound which on further reaction regenerates the catalyst. This was suggested to be the case in the catalysis by iodide ion of the methyl bromide–water reaction (Section 17-4). Here there must be two energy barriers, each of them with an activated state which is lower than that of the uncatalyzed path. An energy diagram for this reaction is shown in Fig. 17-7.

Figures 17-6 and 17-7 show that the enthalpy change is the same for both the catalyzed and uncatalyzed reaction of a system. The enthalpy change is determined only by the initial and final states of the system and not by the reaction pathway. This is true also for the free energy change for the reaction and for the equilibrium constant. Catalysts have no influence on either of these quantities. They only modify the rate at which the equilibrium (or final) state is reached. The water synthesis has high activation energy. This is why the reaction is slow. The free energy change for the water synthesis is large and negative. Therefore, if the high energy barrier can be bypassed, the reaction will go rapidly to completion, leaving no noticeable traces of hydrogen and oxygen if their molar ratio was initially 2:1. One might say that a catalyst is only capable of locating a pass through the mountain range between the reactants and products and not of altering the elevation of the mountains or of the plains on either side of the mountains. Thus, the introduction of a catalyst can never cause a reaction to go spontaneously if the change in free energy is positive.

Catalysis is an important and exciting field for research and discovery. Although a great many catalysts are known and used, in very few cases is the mechanism of operation fully understood. Many catalysts influence the path and rate of chemical reactions even though they may be present in remarkably small amounts. This is particularly true of enzymes, organic materials that catalyze biological reactions. One enzyme, urease, when present in concentrations of only 10^{-9} mole/liter, catalyzes the reaction of water with urea, $(NH_2)_2CO$, to form ammonia and carbon dioxide. The size, structure, and mode of action of many enzymes present extremely important and challenging problems in understanding the chemistry of living systems. It is believed that enzymes are the key to the chemistry of the human body. A complete understanding of the chemistry of enzymes would undoubtedly be a major step forward in the elimination of disease.

17-7 EXAMPLES OF REACTION PATHWAYS

For a reaction to take place, there must exist some sequence of steps (called the reaction pathway or mechanism) by which the structural units in the components of a system can become rearranged. It is assumed that along this pathway structural units of the reactants must come in contact with each other to form structural units of the products. Not only must the reacting atoms come in contact, but they must also separate themselves from the other atoms to which they are joined in the reactants. Without a pathway, it is clear that no reaction can occur.

The study of reaction mechanisms is an important part of chemistry. One type of reaction mechanism is exemplified by the reaction of Cl_2 and CH_4. Chlorine and methane do not react measurably in the dark at room temperature, but reaction can be initiated by increasing the temperature or by the action of ultraviolet light. Once the reaction is

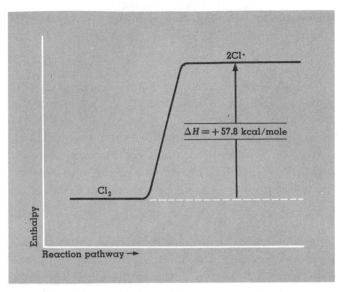

Fig. 17-8 *The enthalpy of dissociation of Cl_2 into two $Cl\cdot$ atoms is the bond energy, $+57.8$ kcal/mole.*

started, it proceeds rapidly without further application of heat or light. A reaction pathway which accounts for the observed facts is

$$Cl_2 \overset{h\nu}{\rightarrow} 2Cl\cdot \qquad\qquad (Eq.\ 17\text{-}14)$$

where $h\nu$ represents a photon of light absorbed by chlorine to produce separated chlorine atoms. The symbol $Cl\cdot$ indicates that the chlorine atom has one unpaired electron. A chlorine atom then reacts with additional methane to produce the products HCl and H_3CCl as well as another chlorine atom.

$$Cl\cdot + CH_4 \rightarrow HCl + H_3C\cdot \qquad (Eq.\ 17\text{-}15)$$

$$H_3C\cdot + Cl_2 \rightarrow H_3CCl + Cl\cdot \qquad (Eq.\ 17\text{-}16)$$

A series of reactions in which a reagent is produced again in the last step of the series is called a **chain reaction.** The chain reaction between chlorine and methane is said to be propagated by a free-radical mechanism. A **free radical** is a fragment of a molecule bearing an unpaired electron (shown in Equations 17-14, 17-15, and 17-16 as a dot). A single atom of chlorine bearing an unpaired electron is more accurately described as a free chlorine atom. The chain-initiating step is the production of two free chlorine atoms by the dissociation (Equation 17-14) of a chlorine molecule (Fig. 17-8). The 57.8 kcal/mole required for this reaction can be supplied by thermal energy or by the absorption of one photon of light (per chlorine molecule) with a frequency high enough to supply the requisite energy to break the Cl—Cl bond. The enthalpy changes involved in the three reaction steps are as follows.

$$Cl_2 \rightarrow 2Cl \cdot \quad \Delta H = +57.8 \text{ kcal} \qquad (Exp.\ 17\text{-}17)$$

$$Cl \cdot + CH_4 \rightarrow HCl + H_3C \cdot \quad \Delta H = -2 \text{ kcal} \qquad (Exp.\ 17\text{-}18)$$

$$H_3C \cdot + Cl_2 \rightarrow CH_3Cl + Cl \cdot \quad \Delta H = -22 \text{ kcal} \qquad (Exp.\ 17\text{-}19)$$

The overall reaction which converts methane to methyl chloride is exothermic to the extent of 23.8 kcal/mole of CH_3Cl on the basis of Expressions 17-18 and 17-19. The overall reaction and the experimentally determined enthalpy change are shown in Expression 17-20.

$$Cl_2 + CH_4 \rightarrow CH_3Cl + HCl \quad \Delta H = -23.8 \text{ kcal} \qquad (Exp.\ 17\text{-}20)$$

Once a single molecule of chlorine has been dissociated in the reaction, no further step of this kind is required to maintain the reaction unless the chlorine atoms produced in the third step of the chain are lost. Loss can occur through some reaction not part of the reaction chain, for example, the combination of two chlorine atoms to form a molecule. For this reason, the 57.8 kcal absorbed when 1 mole of chlorine molecules dissociates is not a measure of the activation energy of the chlorine–methane reaction once reaction is underway. The dissociation of a chlorine molecule need happen but once to provide for the production of many molecules of product. By contrast, every molecule of CH_3Cl that is produced requires that $Cl \cdot$ and CH_4 react. The reaction of $Cl \cdot$ with CH_4 has been found to have an activation energy of only 4 kcal/mole as illustrated in Fig. 17-9. This reaction (Expression 17-18) is

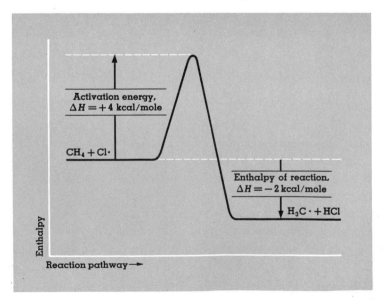

Fig. 17-9 *Enthalpy diagram for the reaction Cl· + CH₄ → H₃C· + HCl.*

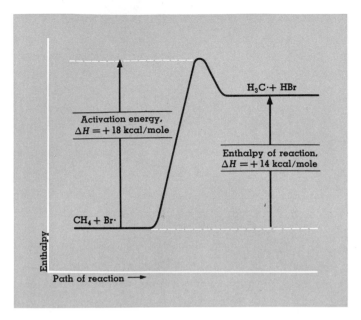

Fig. 17-10 *Enthalpy diagram for the reaction $Br \cdot + CH_4 \rightarrow H_3C \cdot + HBr$.*

Within the figure:

H₃C·+ HBr

Activation energy,
$\Delta H = +18$ kcal/mole

Enthalpy of reaction,
$\Delta H = +14$ kcal/mole

CH₄ + Br·

Enthalpy

Path of reaction ⟶

simply the breaking of a C—H bond followed by the formation of the HCl molecule. Thus, its reaction energy may be calculated by adding the appropriate bond energies from Table 9-5 as indicated in Expressions 17-21 and 17-22.

$$CH_4 \rightarrow H_3C \cdot + H \cdot \quad \Delta H = 101 \text{ kcal} \qquad (Exp.\ 17\text{-}21)$$

$$H \cdot + Cl \cdot \rightarrow HCl \quad \Delta H = -103 \text{ kcal} \qquad (Exp.\ 17\text{-}22)$$

Combination of two expressions gives the reaction (Expression 17-18) with $\Delta H = -2$ kcal/mole.

The analogous reaction of gaseous bromine with methane has different energy requirements.

$$Br_2 \rightarrow 2Br \cdot \quad \Delta H = +46 \text{ kcal} \qquad (Exp.\ 17\text{-}23)$$

$$Br \cdot + CH_4 \rightarrow H_3C \cdot + HBr \quad \Delta H = +14 \text{ kcal} \quad (Exp.\ 17\text{-}24)$$

$$H_3C \cdot + Br_2 \rightarrow H_3CBr + Br \cdot \quad \Delta H = -21 \text{ kcal} \quad (Exp.\ 17\text{-}25)$$

The overall reaction shown in Expression 17-26 is considerably less exothermic than is the chlorination reaction.

$$Br_2 + CH_4 \rightarrow H_3CBr + HBr \quad \Delta H = -7 \text{ kcal} \quad (Exp.\ 17\text{-}26)$$

In Fig. 17-10, the endothermic reaction of a bromine atom with a methane molecule is represented (Expression 17-24). The high activation energy for this reaction (18 kcal) explains why the bromination of methane is slow.

REACTIONS BY COLLISION BETWEEN MOLECULES

It must not be supposed from the previous discussion that all reactions of covalent molecules with each other are processes in which free atoms or free radicals are present. For example, hydrogen and iodine react by a process which does not involve the independent existence of hydrogen or iodine atoms. A hydrogen molecule collides with an iodine molecule. The energy of this collision causes the bond in the iodine molecule to be stretched, and the electrons rearrange themselves so that both the I—I bond and the H—H bond break and two H—I bonds are formed. The breaking of the two bonds and the forming of two new bonds occur while the four atoms (2 hydrogen atoms and 2 iodine atoms) are in contact, and no chain reaction occurs (Fig. 17-11).

This type of reaction, in which atoms change partners without ever really being separated into free atoms or radicals nor into recognizable ionic species, is especially common in those reactions which take place in the liquid phase. In liquids the presence of close neighbors often stabilizes the complex of molecules in collision and makes it easier for the electron pairs to change from a bond between one pair of atoms to a bond between another pair.

Fig. 17-11 *A hydrogen molecule colliding with sufficient kinetic energy and in the proper orientation with an iodine molecule combines to form a a complex, H_2I_2. The energy of the collision causes the I—I bond to stretch and break with the formation of two molecules of HI.*

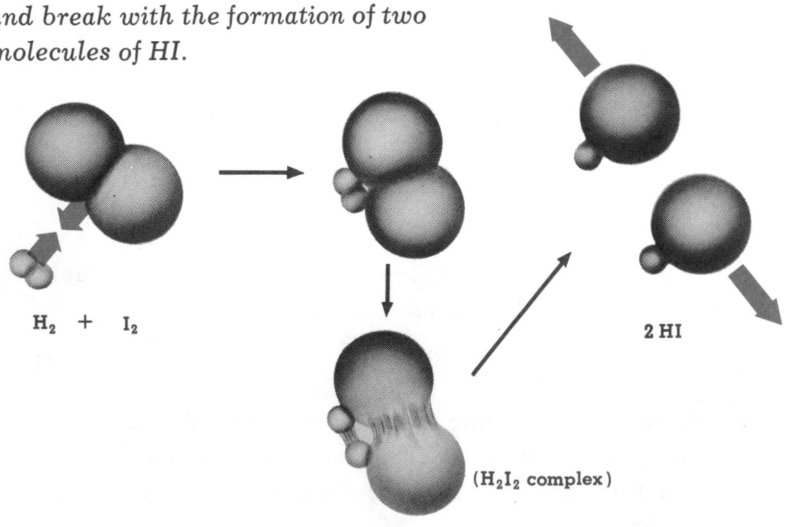

H₂ + I₂

(H₂I₂ complex)

2 HI

17-9 DYNAMIC EQUILIBRIUM

Chemical systems in an equilibrium state are unable to change spontaneously. When disturbed, a chemical system in an equilibrium state will change in state in response to the disturbance in a manner described by Le Chatelier's principle. A chemical equilibrium can therefore be described as stable but sensitive. How is it possible for both stability and sensitivity to be characteristic of a single system?

Observations on the rates of reactions are made with systems not in equilibrium states. As the reaction proceeds, the system approaches an equilibrium state. Nothing, however, is included in the idea of a reaction mechanism to indicate that the reaction between components ceases once an equilibrium state is achieved.

It is assumed that reaction between components continues in a system at equilibrium. Stability is characteristic of equilibrium states because there are at least two reactions taking place. These two reactions consist of reactants combining to form products and products combining to form reactants.

In the reaction of hydrogen with iodine to form hydrogen iodide, initially only hydrogen and iodine might be present in the system.

$$H_2 \ (g) + I_2 \ (g) \rightarrow 2HI \ (g)$$

Alternatively the system might be composed only of hydrogen iodide which reacts to form hydrogen and iodine.

$$2HI \ (g) \rightarrow H_2 \ (g) + I_2 \ (g)$$

At equilibrium all three components are present and both reactions are taking place.

If the reaction which produces hydrogen iodide proceeds at a rate exactly equal to the rate of the reaction by which hydrogen iodide decomposes, the amount of hydrogen iodide in the system will be constant. Under these conditions the system has a fixed composition and is stable.

Any condition which alters the rate of one reaction more than the rate of the other will cause a change in the state of the system. Thus, addition of more hydrogen will speed up the production of hydrogen iodide. As the concentration of hydrogen iodide increases, its own decomposition will proceed more rapidly, and so a new equilibrium state will be achieved. A chemical equilibrium is therefore sensitive as well as stable.

The assumption that there are reactions occurring in a system at equilibrium is the basis for referring to a chemical system as being in a state of dynamic equilibrium. If a small amount of a radioactive isotope of iodine is introduced into a hydrogen–iodine–hydrogen iodide system, it has no effect upon the chemical properties of the system including the equilibrium state. It is possible, however, to measure the amount of radioactive or isotopic iodine in each of the components of the system. After a time, even though the system has been at equilibrium throughout, some of the radioactive iodine is found in the hydrogen iodide. Conversely, if hydrogen iodide containing radioactive iodine is introduced into an equilibrium system, some of the radioactive iodine can be found later in the molecular iodine. This demonstrates experimentally the dynamic character of the system in an equilibrium state.

17-10 SUMMARY

In many chemical systems a measurable time is required for the change from initial to final state. The amount of change in concentration per unit time is called the reaction rate. For reactions among ions and for many proton-transfer reactions, the times required are less than a microsecond and indeed so short as to be difficult to measure. Such reactions are commonly referred to as being instantaneous.

In reactions where bonds are broken and bonds are formed, reaction rates may be of measurable magnitude—for example, the reaction of chloride ion with methyl bromide to form methyl chloride and bromide ion. In such cases, the measured reaction rate decreases as the reaction proceeds. The rate is found to depend upon the concentrations of the reacting substances. This dependence upon concentration is taken to imply that collisions between molecules or ions must occur before they will react. The higher the concentrations, the greater the collision rate.

Reaction rates also depend upon temperature. In general the higher the temperature, the faster the reaction. Higher temperature implies greater energy of collision for molecules or ions. The nature of dependence of reaction rate upon temperature is the basis for assuming that a reaction involves an activation energy. This energy has to be supplied initially to break some bond or to rearrange the atoms in a molecule before reaction can proceed to give the products. The higher the activation energy, the slower the reaction. Instantaneous reactions have no activation energy. Reactions for which rate depends upon temperature indicate that only a fraction of all collisions lead to reaction.

Reaction rates are dependent not only upon temperature and reactant concentration but also upon other components of the system. Other components that affect the rate of reaction but not the composition of the products are called catalysts. Catalysts increase reaction rates and are therefore considered to provide lower activation energies.

A study of reaction rates and their dependence upon concentration and temperature gives further understanding of chemical systems. This understanding provided by the study of reaction rates is usually expressed as a mechanism for the reaction being investigated. A reaction mechanism is a detailed description of the steps by which reactants are converted to products.

Ex. 17-1 How does the kinetic-molecular theory explain why small changes in temperature are often associated with large changes in the reaction rates in systems composed of gases?

Ex. 17-2 Sugar burns in air at a temperature greater than 500°C and produces H_2O and CO_2. Explain how it is possible for living organisms to metabolize (burn) sugar at a temperature of 37°C to produce H_2O and CO_2. Which case has the greater change in enthalpy for the reaction $C_{12}H_{22}O_{11} + 6O_2 \rightarrow 11H_2O + 6CO_2$, when the sugar burns in air at 500°C or when it metabolizes in the body at 37°C? Assume that the initial and final states are identical in each case.

Ex. 17-3 Some bromine molecules (Br_2) are dissociated into free radicals ($Br \cdot$) when ultraviolet light is absorbed by bromine gas. Propose a pathway to explain how bromine and hydrogen react in the presence of ultraviolet light to produce HBr.

Ex. 17-4 a. What are the characteristics of a system which indicate that it is in an equilibrium state?

b. Which of the following systems are in an equilibrium state?

(1) $H_2 + O_2$ at 25°C

(2) H_2O (liquid) and H_2O (gas) in a closed container at 100°C and 1 atmosphere pressure

(3) An iron gate exposed to the weather

(4) An iceberg floating in seawater at 0°C

(5) A 3 percent aqueous solution of acetic acid (vinegar) at 25°C in a closed container

Ex. 17-5 The mass of salt dissolved per unit time is proportional to the surface area of the salt exposed to the solvent liquid. By what factor will the rate of solution be increased if a cubical crystal 1 cm on a side is ground into a powder made up of crystal fragments whose particles are cubes with each edge having a length of 10^{-3} cm?

Ex. 17-6 Explain why equilibrium constants are not directly useful for predicting reaction rates.

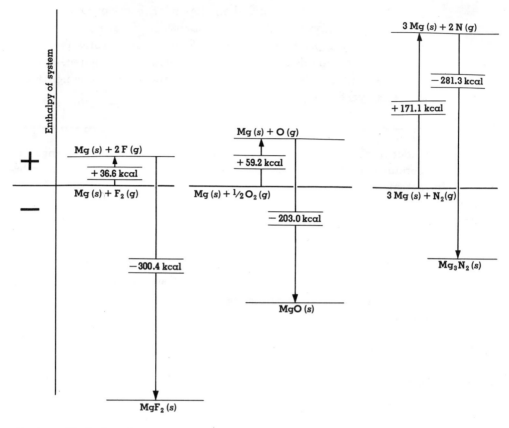

Ex. 17-7 Enthalpy diagrams for the reaction at 25°C of magnesium and fluorine, of magnesium and oxygen, and of magnesium and nitrogen are shown above.

a. Write the overall equation for each reaction.

b. Which reaction will most probably occur at room temperature? Why?

c. In which case will heat most probably be required initially for the reaction to proceed at an observable rate? Why?

d. Explain how both the activation energy and the overall enthalpy change accompanying the reaction are important to the understanding of a chemical reaction.

Ex. 17-8 a. Why is it improbable that a catalyst which alters the change in enthalpy ΔH for a reaction will be discovered?

b. Catalysts decrease the activation energy necessary to carry out a reaction. Does this affect the overall change in free energy ΔG for the reaction? Why or why not?

Ex. 17-9 The reaction Ca^{++} (aq) + $2OH^-$ (aq) → $Ca(OH)_2$ (s) is extremely fast, while the reaction $Ca(OH)_2$ (s) + $2H^+$ (aq) → Ca^{++} (aq) + $2H_2O$ (l) is fairly slow. How can the difference in rates be explained?

Ex. 17-10 The table lists data for the concentration of Br^- as a function of time at 79.63°C for the reaction between lithium chloride, LiCl, and isopropyl bromide, $(CH_3)_2CHBr$, in acetone containing some lithium bromide.

Time, minutes	Concentration of Br^-, millimoles/liter	Time, minutes	Concentration of Br^-, millimoles/liter
0	1.03	360	4.00
125	1.92	410	4.35
180	2.40	480	4.59
225	2.81	515	4.93
250	3.09	600	5.32
290	3.40	1,050	6.65

a. Make a graph plotting $[Br^-]$ against time (use 100-minute time intervals). Compare the shape of the curve obtained with the shape of the curve in Fig. 17-2.

b. Compare the reaction rate within the time interval of 100 to 200 minutes with the reaction rate within the time interval of 500 to 600 minutes. Compare the reaction rate in the LiCl–isopropyl bromide system with the reaction rate of the LiCl–methyl bromide system (Table 17-2).

c. Predict what effect increasing the temperature of the reaction would have on the reaction rate.

d. The Couper structure of methyl bromide, CH_3Br, is

$$H-\overset{\displaystyle H}{\underset{\displaystyle H}{C}}-Br$$

and the Couper structure of isopropyl bromide, $CH_3CHBrCH_3$, is

$$H-\overset{\displaystyle H}{\underset{\displaystyle H}{C}}-\overset{\displaystyle H}{\underset{\displaystyle Br}{C}}-\overset{\displaystyle H}{\underset{\displaystyle H}{C}}-H$$

In terms of the model for reaction rates (Section 17-5), list several reasons which might explain the fact that the LiCl-CH_3Br reaction is much faster than the LiCl-$CH_3CHBrCH_3$ reaction.

WATER

18

FROM YOUR EARLIEST studies of science you have learned repeatedly of the great abundance of water on earth and in the earth's atmosphere. There are 3.4×10^8 cubic miles (1.5×10^{18} tons) of water in the oceans, every living tissue contains water, and many seemingly dry materials contain water. Water serves both as solvent and as raw material in countless chemical operations carried on by chemical industry as well as by all living organisms.

18-1 ABUNDANCE OF WATER

To get an impression of the amount of water in relation to the amounts of other substances, consider Table 18-1 which shows the abundance of a number of elements. Oxygen is, by a wide margin, the most abundant element in the earth's crust, no matter whether one considers it on the basis of mass in grams or on the basis of number of atoms. At the same time the amount of oxygen in the atmosphere is less than 1 percent of the total quantity of oxygen present in the earth's crust. Water itself represents less than 1 percent of all the oxygen atoms present. The amount of water present in the earth's crust is limited by the number of hydrogen atoms available to combine with oxygen. This leads us to wonder what kinds of oxygen compounds are most abundant.

TABLE 18-1 TWELVE MOST ABUNDANT ELEMENTS IN THE EARTH'S CRUST

Rank	Element	Atomic Number	Atoms of the Element, per 1,000 atoms in the Earth's Crust	Grams of the Element, per 1,000 g of the Earth's Crust
1	Oxygen	8	605	466
2	Silicon	14	205	277
3	Aluminum	13	63	81
4	Hydrogen	1	27	1.3
5	Sodium	11	26	29
6	Calcium	20	18	36
7	Iron	26	19	50
8	Magnesium	12	18	21
9	Potassium	19	14	26
10	Titanium	22	2.7	6.3
11	Phosphorus	15	0.9	1.3
12	Carbon	6	0.6	0.3

We must conclude that most of the oxygen is present in combined form. Indeed, of the elements listed in Table 18-1, silicon forms the bulk of the oxygen compounds. This is reasonable since most rocks, sands, and clays are primarily silicon–oxygen compounds with a silicon/oxygen atom ratio of about 1:2.

Since silicon–oxygen compounds are crystalline solids over a wide range of temperature, it is easy to see why such compounds are so conspicuous on the earth. Water, on the other hand, boils at a relatively low temperature. In addition, the molecular mass of water is only 18. No other substance with a molecular mass so low as this is found in appreciable amounts in the atmosphere or exposed on the earth's surface. Is this reasonable in terms of our ideas about the structure and behavior of molecules?

From our discussion of a kinetic model of matter in Chapter 8, we concluded that all molecules are in motion. Since the average kinetic energy is the same for all molecules at a given temperature, the lighter molecules will move faster than the heavier molecules. Table 18-2 lists substances found in the atmosphere in order of increasing molecular mass. For a molecule to escape from the earth's atmosphere, a velocity of about 25,000 mph directed away from the earth is needed. This means that the lighter molecules with the highest velocities will have the best chance of escape.

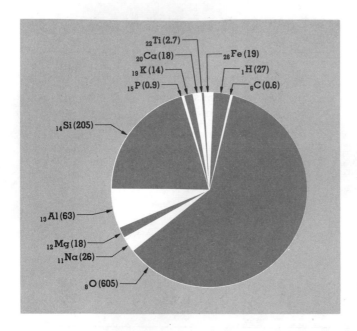

Fig. 18-1 *The twelve most abundant elements in the earth's crust. The number in parentheses is the number of atoms of the element per 1,000 atoms in earth's crust.*

Fig. 18-2 *Relationship between molecular masses of components of the atmosphere and their abundance in the atmosphere. Water is about one thousand times more abundant than other substances with molecular masses of the same order of magnitude.*

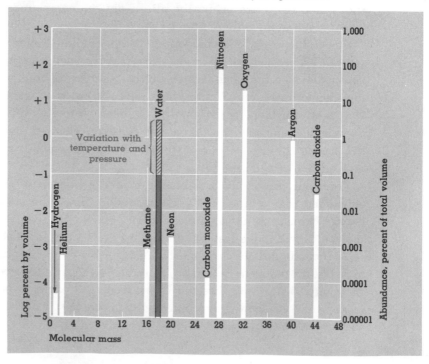

TABLE 18-2   COMPONENTS OF THE EARTH'S ATMOSPHERE

Component	Molecular Mass, amu	Percentage by Volume
H_2	2	0.5×10^{-4}
He	4	5.2×10^{-4}
CH_4	16	7.4×10^{-4}
H_2O	18	0.1–2.8
Ne	20	$18. \times 10^{-4}$
CO	28	$1. \times 10^{-4}$
N_2	28	78.
O_2	32	21.
Ar	40	0.93
CO_2	44	0.03

SOURCE: N. A. Lange, *Handbook of Chemistry*, 10th ed., McGraw-Hill Book Company, Inc., New York, 1961.

Those substances in the atmosphere whose molecular masses are 20 amu or less are present in only small amounts compared with oxygen and nitrogen. The one exception to this is water, which, though present in the atmosphere in widely variable amounts, is about one thousand times more abundant than other materials of similar molecular mass. Can our model for a water molecule show that the abundance of water, though inconsistent with molecular mass data, is consistent with other properties of water?

18-2   SOLID, LIQUID, AND VAPOR

To give any reason for the abundance of water, it is necessary to consider some other properties of the solid and liquid forms of water. Of all the water in the world, about 3 percent is in the form of ice. Most of the ice on earth is found in the great sheets that cover the Antarctic Continent and Greenland.

Ice floats on water. What practical problems or benefits does this fact bring in northern climates to fishermen, skaters, fish, plumbers, and others? In contrast, most solids are more dense than the liquid formed as each solid melts. The kinetic-molecular theory suggests that as a solid is raised in temperature, the structural units should vibrate more vigorously. More vigorous vibration results in expansion of the solid. On melting, the molecules should require still more space for motion. As one result of a rise in temperature, we expect a substance to show an increase in volume and hence a decrease in density.

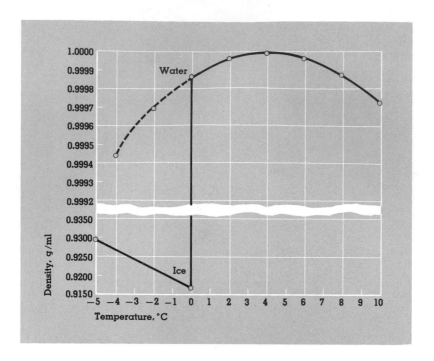

Fig. 18-3 *Density of water and ice at different temperatures. (Note difference in the scales in the upper and lower sections of the graph.)*

Density data for water around 0°C are plotted in Fig. 18-3. Included are data for liquid water below its usual freezing point; it is possible to cool water below 0°C if it is completely free of dirt. So long as water remains liquid, its density decreases with rise in temperature above 4°C. Liquid water, however, shows a density higher, not lower, than that of the solid. In addition, the greatest density of water is at 4°C. In other words, below 4°C a sample of liquid water increases in volume as its temperature falls, a most curious behavior and quite different from that of most other substances.

18-3 HEAT CAPACITY OF WATER

It is not at all unusual to find that the site selected for a manufacturing plant is based upon the availability of water for use as a coolant because water is particularly efficient as an absorber of heat. Since the heat capacity (Section 3-22) of a substance is defined as the amount of heat required to raise the temperature of one gram of the substance by one degree Celsius, we would expect an efficient coolant to be one which has a high heat capacity, that is, one which will absorb large quantities of heat with only a small rise in temperature. The heat capacities of some substances are listed in Table 18-3.

Under some circumstances, liquids other than water are used as coolants. For example, in liquid-cooled internal-combustion engines which operate at high temperatures, water would quickly evaporate, even with its relatively high boiling point. Ethylene glycol, with a boiling point of about 200°C, is used as a coolant for many liquid-cooled aircraft piston engines. The molecules of ethylene glycol, like those of glycerol and water, contain covalently bonded OH groups. On the other hand, in cold climates, water is not practical as a coolant in automobile engines because of the danger of freezing. Here water solutions of glycols or alcohols, which have low melting points, find great use.

18-4 HEATS OF FUSION AND VAPORIZATION

Water is also set apart from other covalent substances by its large heats of fusion and vaporization. The heat of fusion is defined as the amount of heat absorbed when a known quantity of a substance, usually either one gram or one mole, is converted from the solid phase to the liquid phase at its melting point. Heat of vaporization is defined (Section 8-21) as the amount of heat required to vaporize one gram

TABLE 18-3 HEAT CAPACITIES OF SOME REPRESENTATIVE SUBSTANCES

Substance	Formula	Temperature, °C	Phase	Heat Capacity[a]	
				cal/mole	cal/g
Metallic:					
Copper	Cu	25	s	5.85	0.092
Iron	Fe	25	s	6.03	0.108
Aluminum	Al	25	s	5.82	0.216
Ionic:					
Barium sulfate	$BaSO_4$	25	s	24.3	0.111
Sodium chloride	NaCl	25	s	11.9	0.204
Covalent:					
Chlorine	Cl_2	25	g	8.1	0.114
Benzene	C_6H_6	20	l	31.7	0.406
Methane	CH_4	15	g	8.5	0.528
Polar covalent:					
Ammonia	NH_3	25	g	8.8	0.501
Ethanol	C_2H_5OH	25	l	26.8	0.577
Water	H_2O	15	l	18.0	1.00

[a] Heat capacities were measured at 1 atmosphere pressure.

TABLE 18-4 HEATS OF FUSION AND VAPORIZATION OF SOME REPRESENTATIVE SUBSTANCES

Substance	Formula	Heat of Fusion		Heat of Vaporization	
		kcal/mole	cal/g	kcal/mole	cal/g
Metallic:					
Copper	Cu	3.11	48.9	72.8	1145.
Aluminum	Al	2.6	96.2	67.9	2570.
Ionic:					
Sodium chloride	NaCl	6.8	116.	40.8	698.
Calcium fluoride	CaF_2	7.1	91.	83.	1060.
Covalent:					
Chlorine	Cl_2	1.53	21.6	4.88	68.6
Benzene	C_6H_6	2.35	30.1	7.35	94.1
Methane	CH_4	0.225	14.0	1.90	122.
Polar covalent:					
Ethanol	C_2H_5OH	1.20	26.1	9.21	200.
Ammonia	NH_3	1.35	79.3	5.58	327.
Glycerol	$C_3H_5(OH)_3$	4.37	47.5	(decomposes)	
Water	H_2O	1.44	79.7	9.72	539.6

or one mole of liquid at the boiling point of the substance. Some representative data are listed in Table 18-4.

The large heats of vaporization of metals and ionic substances are expected, as are the small heats of vaporization for covalent substances which have weak van der Waals attraction. Water and ammonia are conspicuous by having large heats of vaporization but small molecular masses. Thus the conversion of water to steam requires considerable energy—energy which can be partially recovered as work when the steam condenses to water.

18-5 WATER AS A SOLVENT

Another striking property of water is its ability to dissolve many compounds. The oceans of the earth serve, in consequence, as an almost inexhaustible source of such important elements as magnesium and bromine (dissolved as salts), as well as of substantial quantities of many other materials (Table 18-5), including silver and gold, although the concentration is small. Magnesium and bromine are extracted from seawater on a commercial basis in considerable quantity. Sodium chloride and iodine are also extracted on a limited scale.

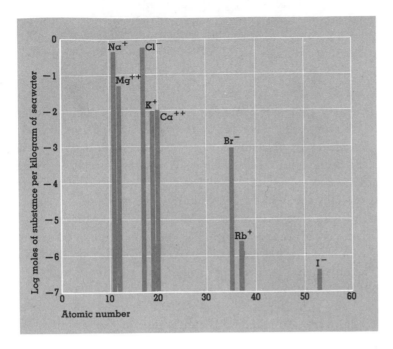

Fig. 18-4 *Graph showing the number of moles of various ions per kilogram of seawater.*

A tremendous number of substances, the majority of which are ionic salts and polar covalent compounds, are soluble in water. On the other hand, materials such as mothballs, oil, gasoline, resin, and plastics (covalent), or lead, silver, and mercury (metals), or barium sulfate and silver chloride (salts) are insoluble. But even the so-called insolu-

TABLE 18-5   APPROXIMATE AMOUNTS OF SUBSTANCES DISSOLVED (as salts) IN 1 kg OF SEAWATER

Element	g	mole
Chlorine	19.	0.53
Sodium	11.	0.48
Magnesium	1.3	0.05
Sulfur	0.88	0.03
Calcium	0.40	1.0×10^{-2}
Potassium	0.38	1.0×10^{-2}
Bromine	6.5×10^{-2}	8.1×10^{-4}
Rubidium	2×10^{-4}	2×10^{-6}
Iodine	5×10^{-5}	4×10^{-7}
Silver	3×10^{-7}	3×10^{-9}
Gold	6×10^{-9}	3×10^{-11}

ble salts (for example, $BaSO_4$, $AgCl$, and AgI) dissolve in water to a slight extent. In addition to the role it plays in chemical reactions, water is outstanding as a solvent.

18-6 NEUTRAL CHARACTER OF WATER

Another property that sets water apart from other polar covalent compounds of hydrogen is the essentially neutral character of water. Water may act either as an acid or as a base in reactions with other substances. The acidic and basic properties of water are relative. Water is in the middle range of acidity and basicity in a list of compounds found on earth. This accident makes us call water neutral.

In contrast to water, any ammonia in the earth's atmosphere would quickly be removed by reaction with the common acids produced by natural and industrial processes (carbon dioxide, sulfur dioxide, and so on), while any hydrogen fluoride would be rapidly removed by reaction with the more basic materials common in the earth's crust (calcium carbonate). Water has dissolved the products of acid-base reactions. These products, called salts, are found in the oceans.

18-7 STRUCTURE OF WATER MOLECULES

In Section 7-17 the structure of water molecules was compared with that of a set of isoelectronic substances. Some properties of the substances in this set are shown in Table 18-6. The hydrogen compounds of the elements in group VI of the periodic table, with the general formula H_2Y, are also given in Table 18-6. In both sets, water has the highest boiling point and melting point and the largest heat of vaporization and heat of fusion. Can our ideas about structure and energy provide a comprehensive interpretation of the properties of water?

Charge cloud models of a water molecule and of other isoelectronic hydride molecules give a tetrahedral arrangement of electron clouds. The three nuclei in water form a V-shaped molecule with the oxygen nucleus at the vertex of the V, although the angle is obtuse rather than the acute angle of a true V.

Because of repulsive forces between the protons and the positive oxygen nucleus, each proton is pushed outward away from the center of the cloud while the negative charge on the electrons is approximately symmetrical about the oxygen nucleus. The center of positive charge is therefore between the oxygen nucleus and the protons while the center of negative charge is much closer to the oxygen nucleus. With different centers for negative charge and positive charge, a water molecule is a permanent dipole.

Hydrogen fluoride, ammonia, and water are each electrically unsymmetrical molecules and therefore tend to attract other molecules.

This attraction (Section 8-21) leads to a large energy absorption during vaporization, as well as to high boiling and melting points. In contrast, neon and methane have low boiling and melting points. In both neon and methane the distribution of electric charge is symmetrical except for temporary dipoles produced by vibration. With only weak van der Waals attraction between molecules, neon and methane have much lower boiling and melting points than do hydrogen fluoride, water, and ammonia where the van der Waals attraction includes both temporary and permanent dipoles.

A quantitative description of a dipole is based on the magnitude of the separated charge and the distance by which the charges are separated, as shown in Fig. 18-5. The product of the charge q and the distance r between positive and negative charge centers is called the **dipole moment** μ, so that

$$\mu = qr \qquad \text{(Eq. 18-1)}$$

The dipole moment may be large if the distance between the charge centers is large or if the magnitude of the charge is large. Ordinarily, in neutral molecules the charge can be thought of as some multiple (usually 1) of the charge on an electron or proton, 4.80×10^{-10} electrostatic unit (esu). The distance between charge centers will vary among different molecules, but it will be in the range of internuclear distances (10^{-8} to 10^{-7} cm). A typical dipole moment will therefore have a numerical value near 4.8×10^{-10} esu $\times 1 \times 10^{-8}$ cm, or 4.8×10^{-18} esu-cm. The unit of 10^{-18} esu-cm is often referred to as a Debye unit

TABLE 18-6 PROPERTIES OF SUBSTANCES WITH STRUCTURES SIMILAR TO THAT OF WATER

Substance	Boiling Point, °C	Heat of Vaporization, kcal/mole	Melting Point, °C	Heat of Fusion, kcal/mole	Dielectric Constant	Dipole Moment, Debye units
Methane	−161.4	1.96	−183	0.23		0.00
Ammonia	−33.4	6.66	−77.7	1.35	22.4	1.46
Water	+100.0	9.72	0.0	1.44	80.4	1.80
Hydrogen fluoride	+19.9	1.8	−83.1	1.09		1.98
Neon	−245.9	0.43	−248.7	0.08		0.00
Water	+100.0	9.72	0.0	1.44	80.4	1.80
Hydrogen sulfide	−60.3	4.46	−85.5	0.57		1.10
Hydrogen selenide	−41.3	4.62	−65.7	0.60		
Hydrogen telluride	−2.2	5.55	−51	1.0		

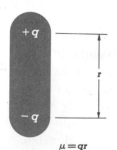

Fig. 18-5 *Diagram showing the relationship of the dipole moment μ to charge magnitude and distance of charge separation.*

+q

−q

$\mu = qr$

after Peter Debye of Cornell University, who developed much of the theory of dipole moments of molecules.

Dielectric constant measurements (Section 5-14) reflect dipole moments of the molecules in a system. Through the work of Debye and others, dipole moments of molecules can be calculated from dielectric constant data. Dipole moments of water and related isoelectronic molecules are listed in Table 18-6.

The dipole moment data in the right-hand column of Table 18-6 suggest that the dipole moment for hydrogen fluoride is larger than that of either water or ammonia. Since electrical asymmetry is measured by the dipole moment, why does hydrogen fluoride not have a higher boiling point and a higher melting point than water?

18-8 ICE

Data from x-ray studies of ice crystals indicate that each water molecule is surrounded by only four nearest neighbors. Methane, on the other hand, forms crystals with each molecule having twelve nearest neighbors in a face-centered cubic lattice. This evidence indicates that water molecules fit together rather loosely in ice.

If a charge cloud with a proton in it forms a positive site in a molecule while a charge cloud without a proton produces a negative site, then a water molecule has two negative sites and two positive sites. These four sites are arranged about the central oxygen kernel at the corners of a tetrahedron. Attraction between positive sites and negative sites in adjacent molecules should result in each molecule's being surrounded by four other molecules.

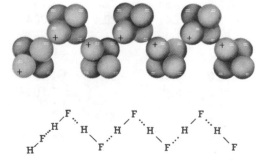

Fig. 18-6 *Diagram of the charge cloud model of a chain of HF molecules joined by hydrogen bonds.*

In ice each water molecule is joined to other molecules so that a proton lies between two oxygen nuclei. When two molecules are held together so that a proton lies between two other nuclei, the arrangement is called a hydrogen bridge, or **hydrogen bond.** Hydrogen bonds are formed in water, in ammonia, and in hydrogen fluoride. In hydrogen fluoride the joining of molecules can be considered to begin by the attraction of the single positive site in a molecule to one of the three negative sites in a second molecule. Then the group of two molecules joins a third molecule, and so on. The joining together of molecules will produce a chain or ring (Fig. 18-6). The outside of the chain or ring will consist almost entirely of negative sites so that two chains or rings will not join.

An ammonia molecule has one negative site and three positive sites so that ammonia molecules form chains and rings readily. The outside of the chains is positively charged in the case of ammonia molecules. As with hydrogen fluoride, chains and rings cannot join in ammonia.

Water molecules have two positive sites and two negative sites. Several chains may therefore hook together side by side to form a hydrogen bridge network extending in three dimensions. Water molecules, with equal numbers of positive and negative sites, give quite a different arrangement from what is possible for either hydrogen fluoride or ammonia molecules with only one positive or one negative site.

Ammonia molecules, water molecules, and hydrogen fluoride molecules are each polar and tend to attract other polar molecules. Hydrogen fluoride, with the largest dipole moment, has the greatest attraction. The molecule of each of the polar substances contains one or more hydrogen nuclei. In hydrogen fluoride attraction leads to the joining of one hydrogen fluoride molecule to not more than two other polar molecules by hydrogen bonds. Geometrical considerations, however, indicate that one water molecule can form hydrogen bonds with as many as four other polar molecules.

Water has a higher freezing point (0°C) than hydrogen fluoride (−83.1°C), but not because of greater attractive forces between water molecules. Water molecules fit together more compactly in ice than hydrogen fluoride molecules in the solid phase. This accounts for water's unusually high melting point and boiling point and large heat of vaporization. The low volatility of water compared with other substances of comparable molecular mass is at least part of the basis for understanding the abundance of water on the earth.

18-9 STRUCTURE AND PHASE CHANGES FOR WATER

The structure of ice provides a way of accounting for the density changes observed when ice melts. As shown in Fig. 18-7, the arrange-

Fig. 18-7 *Arrangement of water molecules in the crystal lattice characteristic of ice.*

ment of water molecules in ice leaves large holes among the molecules. Each molecule is surrounded by four other molecules to give a co-ordination number of 4 for each molecule in ice. When ice melts, the structure begins to break up and some molecules fall into the holes. Recent x-ray studies are interpreted to mean that water molecules have a coordination number close to 6 in liquid water. For water the volume of liquid is found to be less than the volume of the same quantity of solid. Not all the hydrogen bonds are broken during the change in phase of water at 0°C so that further collapse of the structure continues even as the rise in temperature leads to greater motion of the molecules and to a tendency for the liquid to expand.

Between 0 and 4°C the effect of the collapse of the water structure is more pronounced than the effect of thermal expansion on the volume of a sample of water. Above 4°C thermal expansion is more significant than collapse of structure. At 4°C the density of liquid water is greater than at any other temperature.

It is possible to estimate the energy required to break a hydrogen bond between two water molecules. To do this we can presume that in ice at 0°C each molecule has a complete set of hydrogen bonds which binds it to four other molecules. Water vapor, on the other hand, behaves as if the molecular units are separated water molecules of mass 18 amu. So the process by which ice is converted to vapor is a process in which all the hydrogen bonds are broken.

Methane, in contrast to water, can form no hydrogen bonds in the solid phase. For solid methane, the sublimation process requires 2 kcal/mole at −182.5°C.

$$CH_4 \ (s) \ \rightarrow \ CH_4 \ (g) \quad \Delta H = 2 \ \text{kcal/mole} \quad (Exp. \ 18\text{-}2)$$

For ice, the enthalpy of sublimation is 12.2 kcal/mole at 0°C.

$$H_2O \ (s) \ \rightarrow \ H_2O \ (g) \quad \Delta H = 12.2 \ \text{kcal/mole} \quad (Exp. \ 18\text{-}3)$$

The enthalpy change for the sublimation of methane represents an energy to separate molecules against van der Waals attraction, and this is a requirement for any system of molecules, including water. On this basis the breaking of the hydrogen bonds in water absorbs $12 - 2 \approx 10$ kcal/mole (Fig. 18-8). Since each water molecule can be connected to other water molecules by four hydrogen bonds but each bond connects two water molecules, there are two hydrogen bonds per water molecule. One mole of ice, therefore, can be considered to contain 2 moles of bonds which on complete rupture absorb 10 kcal of energy. The hydrogen bond can be considered to represent an energy of about 5 kcal/mole of bonds. This can be contrasted with the bond energies of the order of 50 to 100 kcal/mole for ionic, covalent, or metallic bonds (Section 9-8 and Table 11-2). Ordinary covalent bonds are ten to twenty times as strong as hydrogen bonds.

Although hydrogen bonds are weak compared to other chemical bonds, they are still strong enough to influence the behavior of many substances. When ice melts, about 1.4 kcal of thermal energy is absorbed per mole of water. This is about 15 percent of the total energy absorbed by the breaking of all hydrogen bonds. We can conclude that the melting of ice breaks about 15 percent of the hydrogen bonds and leaves the remainder intact.

The properties of water are intimately related to the hydrogen bonds. Because every molecule of water can form four hydrogen bonds and because each molecule contributes two protons and two electron pairs

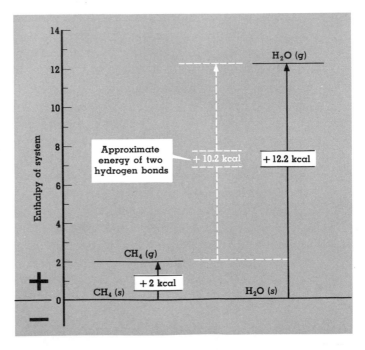

Fig. 18-8 *The energy of the hydrogen bond, about 5 kcal/mole, is approximated by comparing the sublimation energies of solid methane and ice.*

to hydrogen-bond formation, water forms an unusually stable structure as either a liquid or a solid. The questions we have raised about abundance, melting, vaporizing, and density seem to go back in one way or another to the hydrogen-bonded structure for answers. Of course behind the hydrogen-bonded structure lurk the ideas of electrostatic forces and the Pauli exclusion principle.

18-10 HYDRATION

Many ionic substances crystallize from water solution with water molecules and ions built into a crystal lattice. These crystalline substances are called hydrates. Thus lithium chloride separates from water as $LiCl \cdot 2H_2O$. At temperatures near 0°C sodium chloride will also separate as $NaCl \cdot 2H_2O$, but the water evaporates at room temperature, leaving NaCl. Potassium chloride does not form an identifiable hydrate. Some more common hydrates of ionic substances are

$$MgCl_2 \cdot 6H_2O \qquad CuSO_4 \cdot 5H_2O$$
$$CaCl_2 \cdot 6H_2O \qquad CaSO_4 \cdot 2H_2O$$
$$AlCl_3 \cdot 6H_2O \qquad BaCl_2 \cdot 2H_2O$$

The tenacity with which these water molecules are held by the central metal ion in the hydrate varies considerably from element to element. The effect of heat on a hydrate is the subject of investigation in Experiment 38.

These hydrates illustrate a rather general rule. A small positive ion of high charge commonly forms salts in which a large number of molecules of water of hydration are present. Salts containing large positive ions of low charge do not form hydrates of sufficient stability to permit their isolation in solid form. Of the alkali metals, then, lithium and sodium ions form hydrates in most salts, whereas potassium, rubidium, and cesium form only a few hydrates. An ammonium ion is about the same size (1.48 A) as a rubidium ion; ammonium salts also are generally not hydrated. Potassium salts are often used instead of sodium salts in the laboratory, even though sodium salts are cheaper. Potassium salts are more easily prepared and more easily kept in anhydrous form than sodium salts.

Since negative ions are commonly larger than positive ions with the same nuclear charge, hydrates are usually associated with the cation rather than with the anion. In the case of copper (II) sulfate five hydrate ($CuSO_4 \cdot 5H_2O$), there is experimental evidence to suggest that one of the five water molecules is associated more with the sulfate ion whereas the other four are associated with the copper ion.

Solubility in water appears to be largely a result of reaction between the water and the substance which dissolves. In the case of substances like carbon tetrachloride, which are insoluble in water, there is no reaction between water molecules and the symmetrical molecules of the insoluble substances.

18-11 HYDROLYSIS REACTIONS

The structure for the hydrate of copper (II) sulfate suggests that, during hydrolysis of anhydrous copper sulfate, a new bond is formed from copper to oxygen but that no bond initially present in a water molecule is broken. When water combines with another substance without any bonds in the water being broken, the change is called a **hydration reaction.** If a hydrogen–oxygen bond is broken in a chemical reaction with water, the change is called a **hydrolysis reaction.** Hydrates often undergo hydrolysis reactions.

Solutions of such salts as $Al_2(SO_4)_3$ and, to a lesser degree, $MgCl_2$ are acidic, whereas solutions of NaCl are neutral. The reactions of salts like aluminum sulfate and magnesium chloride with water to give acidic solutions are examples of hydrolysis.

Considering the chlorides of elements of the third period, we find that the acidity of aqueous solutions of these chlorides increases in the order Na^+ (neutral), Mg^{++}, and Al^{+++}. In solution, each of these positive ions is surrounded by six (coordination number = 6) water molecules. We may write the formulas of the dissolved ions as $Na(H_2O)_6^+$, $Mg(H_2O)_6^{++}$, and $Al(H_2O)_6^{+++}$. The relative sizes of these ions are given in Fig. 12-15 and are compared with the size of a water molecule in Fig. 18-9.

The distance between the nucleus of the aluminum ion and either of the hydrogen atoms on the water molecule is shorter than for the other two ions. This short distance, together with the greater charge density for the aluminum ion, leads to a tendency for proton transfer when even a base as weak as water is available in the surrounding solution to help remove the proton.

We may argue that the proximity of the high ionic charge (3+) on the aluminum repels the proton, thus lengthening and weakening the O—H bond. This repulsion will be greater the shorter the distance

Fig. 18-9 *Relative sizes of H_2O molecules and Na^+, Mg^{++}, and Al^{+++} ions.*

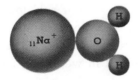

between the proton and the central ion. It will also be greater the higher the charge on the ion. Alternatively, we may argue that the weakening of the O—H bond occurs because the electron charge clouds of the water molecule are attracted by the metal ion. The greater the charge on the metal ion, the more the electron cloud will be attracted to the ion and pulled away from the proton.

The hydrolysis reactions of the hydrated ions are represented as

$$[Al(H_2O)_6]^{+++} + H_2O \rightarrow [Al(H_2O)_5OH]^{++} + H_3O^+ \quad (Eq.\ 18\text{-}4)$$
$$\text{Acid}_1 \qquad\qquad \text{Base}_2 \qquad\qquad \text{Base}_1 \qquad\qquad \text{Acid}_2$$

$$[Mg(H_2O)_6]^{++} + H_2O \rightarrow [Mg(H_2O)_5OH]^+ + H_3O^+ \quad (Eq.\ 18\text{-}5)$$
$$\text{Acid}_1 \qquad\qquad \text{Base}_2 \qquad\qquad \text{Base}_1 \qquad\qquad \text{Acid}_2$$

$$[Na(H_2O)_6]^+ \quad + H_2O \rightarrow \text{no reaction}$$

The hydrated aluminum ion reacts to a larger extent with water than does the hydrated magnesium ion. The hydrated sodium ion does not react with water at all. Using the Brønsted-Lowry concept, we can say that acid$_1$ in Equation 18-4 is a stronger acid than acid$_1$ in Equation 18-5. The hydrated sodium ion is not an acid when water is the base. The reactions lead to equilibrium states in each system with relatively little hydrogen ion formed. In other words, $[Al(H_2O)_6]^{+++}$ and $[Mg(H_2O)_6]^{++}$ are weak acids so far as their ability to react with water is concerned.

When a base stronger than water, such as ammonia or hydroxide ion, is added to a solution containing hydrated magnesium ion, reaction does take place. In the case of ammonia and hydrated magnesium ion the reaction can be described by

$$[Mg(H_2O)_6]^{++}\ (aq) + 2NH_3\ (aq) \rightarrow$$
$$4H_2O + Mg(OH)_2\ (s) + 2NH_4^+\ (aq) \quad (Eq.\ 18\text{-}6)$$

In effect, the ammonia removes protons from water in the hydrated magnesium ion to leave a neutral structure, $Mg(OH)_2$, which is insoluble. The presence of the positively charged magnesium ion has weakened the attraction of protons for the water molecules. The water surrounding the magnesium ion can be regarded as being more acidic than liquid water because of the effect of the positively charged magnesium ion. The Lewis theory of acids describes magnesium ion as an acid, and so its formation of a hydrate is an acid-base reaction. This same effect is produced in varying degrees by other positive ions of small size and high charge.

Another way of producing the transfer of a proton out of a water molecule is by the use of some suitable negative ion. Water solutions can be examined to see whether an excess of hydroxide ions has been formed as a result of proton transfer. Many negative ions do act as bases in water solution. Their sodium salts dissolved in water can be used to demonstrate the effect. Some examples, in order of increasing base strength, are

Sulfate ion:
$$\underset{\text{Base}_1}{SO_4^{--} \ (aq)} + \underset{\text{Acid}_2}{H_2O \ (l)} \rightleftarrows$$
$$\underset{\text{Acid}_1}{HSO_4^- \ (aq)} + \underset{\text{Base}_2}{OH^- \ (aq)} \quad K = 8.3 \times 10^{-13}$$

Acetate ion:
$$\underset{\text{Base}_1}{CH_3COO^- \ (aq)} + \underset{\text{Acid}_2}{H_2O \ (l)} \rightleftarrows$$
$$\underset{\text{Acid}_1}{CH_3COOH \ (aq)} + \underset{\text{Base}_2}{OH^- \ (aq)} \quad K = 5.7 \times 10^{-10}$$

Carbonate ion:
$$\underset{\text{Base}_1}{CO_3^{--} \ (aq)} + \underset{\text{Acid}_2}{H_2O \ (l)} \rightleftarrows$$
$$\underset{\text{Acid}_1}{HCO_3^- \ (aq)} + \underset{\text{Base}_2}{OH^- \ (aq)} \quad K = 1.8 \times 10^{-4}$$

Phosphate ion:
$$\underset{\text{Base}_1}{PO_4^{---} \ (aq)} + \underset{\text{Acid}_2}{H_2O \ (l)} \rightleftarrows$$
$$\underset{\text{Acid}_1}{HPO_4^{--} \ (aq)} + \underset{\text{Base}_2}{OH^- \ (aq)} \quad K = 2.1 \times 10^{-2}$$

When the isoelectronic ions PO_4^{---}, SO_4^{--}, and ClO_4^- are compared as to base strength, it is found that a smaller net ionic charge is associated with a lesser ability to remove protons from water molecules. In fact, perchlorate ion, ClO_4^-, reacts with water hardly at all. Comparison of carbonate with nitrate ion shows a similar relationship.

18-12 REACTIONS OF WATER WITH ELEMENTS

One of the spectacular reactions of chemistry is that of a metal such as sodium or potassium with water. These metals displace hydrogen from water vigorously. Sodium reacts rapidly with cold water so that the sodium melts and forms a molten ball that dances over the water as the hydrogen gas is evolved. Potassium reacts more vigorously, evolving enough heat generally to set the hydrogen on fire. How would you expect the other elements in group I to behave? Magnesium in group II reacts less vigorously than sodium with cold water, but violently with hot water.

$$Na \ (s) + H_2O \ (l) \rightarrow NaOH \ (aq) + \tfrac{1}{2}H_2 \ (g) \qquad (Eq. \ 18\text{-}7)$$

$$Mg \ (s) + 2H_2O \ (l) \rightarrow Mg(OH)_2 \ (s) + H_2 \ (g) \qquad (Eq. \ 18\text{-}8)$$

What would you predict for the behavior of other elements in group II?

The water gas reaction (Section 9-2) provides a test of our ideas about structure and energy. Why does the reaction proceed and what is the role of the high temperature? Enthalpy measurements show that the reaction is endothermic, and in the industrial production of water gas, heat is transferred into the system.

$$C \ (s) + H_2O \ (g) \rightarrow CO \ (g) + H_2 \ (g)$$

Electronic structures have been discussed in Chapters 7 and 10 for each of the substances present in the carbon–water reaction. Carbon monoxide consists of an unusually stable molecule with six electrons involved in the bond between carbon and oxygen. Carbon is a solid with a network of covalent bonds so that graphite is a highly organized material as well as a substance of low energy.

Energy changes that accompany the water gas reaction are plotted in Fig. 18-10 for various temperatures. At all temperatures ΔH is positive so that graphite and water form a system of lower enthalpy than do carbon monoxide and hydrogen. At any temperature much below 1000°K, the standard free energy change is positive so that appreciable quantities of water gas will not be present.

As the temperature of the system is increased, the term $T \Delta S$ increases. It must be that at high temperature the gaseous CO and H_2 are much more disordered than is solid carbon and steam. Above 1000°K therefore, the reaction proceeds in favor of water gas rather

Fig. 18-10   *Energy changes for the water gas reaction,* C *(s)* $+ H_2O$ *(g)* $\rightarrow CO$ *(g)* $+ H_2$ *(g)*.

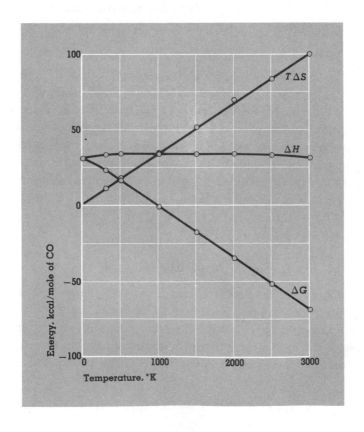

than solid carbon. Once the gaseous products are formed, swept out of the reaction chamber, and cooled below $1000°K$, the reaction between carbon monoxide and hydrogen proceeds too slowly for any significant amounts of carbon and water to be produced from the mixture of CO and H_2O.

18-13 DERIVATIVES OF WATER

When water reacts with another substance to give a product containing one or both of the elements of the water, the product can be called a **derivative of water.** This is a thoroughly arbitrary decision as to what is a derivative of what, but the idea is often useful nonetheless. Of the possible derivatives, those in which only one hydrogen atom is replaced would be expected to be most similar to water.

In Chapter 16, compounds with the general formula MOH were discussed. These can be regarded as derivatives of water. When M is an element of high electronegativity, the derivative is more acidic than water. On the other hand when M is an element of low electronegativity, the derivative is more basic than water.

Methanol (CH_3OH) can also be thought of as a derivative of water. Like water it is essentially neutral. The replacement of hydrogen by a methyl group (CH_3) does not appreciably alter the ability of the oxygen atom to attract or release protons. A Lewis formula for methanol,

$$\begin{array}{c} H \\ \ddot{}\ \ \ddot{} \\ H\!:\!\ddot{C}\!:\!\ddot{O}\!:\!H \\ \ddot{}\ \ \ddot{} \\ H \end{array}$$

indicates that the carbon and the hydroxyl group are joined by a single electron pair. Compounds in which this is the situation are called **alcohols.**

18-14 PROPERTIES OF ALCOHOLS

Further modifications in the properties of the OH group in the water molecule can be made by substituting other carbon-containing groups for one or more of the three hydrogen atoms in the CH_3 group of methanol. The physical properties of some alcohols are listed in Table 18-7.

If the collection of carbon and hydrogen atoms attached to the OH group is represented by the symbol R, a single general formula representing all alcohols may be written as ROH. An inspection of Table 18-7 indicates that the smaller the group represented by R, the more

TABLE 18-7 PROPERTIES OF ALCOHOLS

Formula	Name	Melting Point, °C	Boiling Point, °C	Density, g/ml	Solubility in H$_2$O[a]
CH$_3$OH	Methanol	−98	66	0.792	Miscible
C$_2$H$_5$OH	Ethanol	−115	78	0.789	Miscible
C$_3$H$_7$OH	1-Propanol	−127	98	0.804	Miscible
C$_4$H$_9$OH	1-Butanol	−90	118	0.810	9
C$_5$H$_{11}$OH	1-Pentanol	−79	138	0.818	2.7
C$_6$H$_{13}$OH	1-Hexanol	−52	158	0.822	0.6
C$_7$H$_{15}$OH	1-Heptanol	−35	176	0.824	0.2
C$_8$H$_{17}$OH	1-Octanol	−17	195	0.829	0.05
C$_{12}$H$_{25}$OH	1-Dodecanol	24	256	0.831	Insoluble
C$_{18}$H$_{37}$OH	1-Octadecanol	58			Insoluble

[a] Solubility in grams per 100 g of H$_2$O.

soluble is the alcohol in water. The boiling points of alcohols containing three carbon atoms or fewer are lower than that of water, suggesting that hydrogen bonding is less significant in alcohols than it is in water. Molecules of alcohols, however, do interact to some extent through the formation of hydrogen bonds. Some evidence for this is available in comparison of the boiling points of alcohols with those of compounds of comparable molecular mass in which hydrogen bonding cannot occur (Table 18-8). For example, ethanol and dimethyl ether (CH$_3$OCH$_3$) have identical compositions but boiling points that differ by about 100°C. Molecules of dimethyl ether do not contain an OH group and cannot, therefore, enter into hydrogen-bond formation.

In chemical reactions, alcohols exhibit the same properties as water where the reaction depends on breaking the O—H bond, but deviate in properties where the presence of an R group is significant.

Alcohols behave in exactly the same way as water when treated with an alkali metal such as sodium. Methanol reacts almost as rapidly as water; but as the number of carbon atoms per molecule of the alcohol increases, the rate of the reaction decreases. The ions found in the reactions with an alcohol remain dissolved in the alcohol, as is indicated by the symbol (solv) in Equation 18-10.

$$\text{Na (s)} + \text{HOH (l)} \rightarrow \text{Na}^+ \text{ (aq)} + \text{OH}^- \text{ (aq)} + \tfrac{1}{2}\text{H}_2 \text{ (g)} \quad \text{(Eq. 18-9)}$$

$$\text{Na (s)} + \text{HOR (l)} \rightarrow \text{Na}^+ \text{ (solv)} + \text{OR}^- \text{ (solv)} + \tfrac{1}{2}\text{H}_2 \text{ (g)}$$
$$\text{(Eq. 18-10)}$$

One must actually apply heat to get a complete reaction in a reasonable time even with 1-pentanol.

Calcium chloride can be used to remove water from the air and from liquids in which it is insoluble, but it cannot be used as a drying agent for alcohols because it reacts with the alcohols.

$$CaCl_2 \ (s) + 6H_2O \ (l) \rightarrow CaCl_2 \cdot 6H_2O \ (s) \qquad (Eq. \ 18\text{-}11)$$

$$CaCl_2 \ (s) + 4CH_3OH \ (l) \rightarrow CaCl_2 \cdot 4CH_3OH \ (s) \qquad (Eq. \ 18\text{-}12)$$

As the product with water is called a hydrate, so the product with an alcohol is called an alcoholate. Some other salts form alcoholates, for example, $CuSO_4 \cdot 3CH_3OH$ and $MgCl_2 \cdot 6CH_3OH$. The size of the alcohol molecule determines to some extent the number of alcohol molecules present in the alcoholate.

The reaction of water with such acids as hydrochloric and sulfuric has been discussed previously (Section 16-6). The reaction of Equation 18-13 can serve as a guide to the initial reaction of alcohols with hydrochloric acid, but further changes occur in this case.

$$HCl \ (g) + HOH \ (l) \rightleftarrows H_3O^+ \ (aq) + Cl^- \ (aq) \qquad (Eq. \ 18\text{-}13)$$

The dielectric constant of water is considerably higher than that of alcohol, and the equilibrium state for Equation 18-13 lies considerably farther to the right than that for Equation 18-14.

$$HCl \ (g) + ROH \ (l) \rightleftarrows ROH_2^+ \ (solv) + Cl^- \ (solv) \qquad (Eq. \ 18\text{-}14)$$

TABLE 18-8 BOILING POINTS IN RELATION TO HYDROGEN-BOND FORMATION

Compound	Formula	Formula Mass	Boiling Point, °C
Liquids that form hydrogen bonds:			
Water	H_2O	18	100
Methanol	CH_3OH	32	66
Ethanol	C_2H_5OH	46	78
Formic acid	$HCOOH$	46	100
Acetic acid	CH_3COOH	60	118
Liquids that do not form hydrogen bonds:			
Methane	CH_4	16	-161
Ethane	C_2H_6	30	-89
Dimethyl ether	CH_3OCH_3	46	-24
Methyl chloride	CH_3Cl	50.5	-24
n-Butane	C_4H_{10}	58	0

However, the reaction described by Equation 18-14 is complicated by the possibility of further reaction (Equation 18-15) to form products that are not possible in the reaction with H_2O.

$$ROH_2^+ \ (solv) + Cl^- \ (solv) \rightleftarrows RCl \ (solv) + H_2O \ (solv) \quad (Eq. \ 18\text{-}15)$$

An analogous reaction with sulfuric acid can be written for water (Equation 18-13) and an alcohol (Equation 18-14), except that the anion will be different (Equation 18-16) and, of course, the products have a different character with an alcohol as the starting compound (Equation 18-17).·

$$HOSO_2OH + HOH \rightleftarrows H_3O^+ + {}^-OSO_2OH \quad (Eq. \ 18\text{-}16)$$

$$HOSO_2OH + ROH \rightleftarrows ROH_2^+ + {}^-OSO_2OH \quad (Eq. \ 18\text{-}17)$$

$$ROH_2^+ + {}^-OSO_2OH \rightleftarrows ROSO_2OH + H_2O \quad (Eq. \ 18\text{-}18)$$

The carbon-containing product, $ROSO_2OH$, still has a hydrogen–oxygen bond, and one might expect this product to be acidic in character. That is, indeed, the case and its usefulness lies in the possibility of taking advantage of this property. The charged end of the negative ion makes the compound soluble in water. The nonpolar chain can attach itself to nonpolar substances in grease or oil. In general, this duality of function is necessary for dispersing dirt in water. Obviously other chains could be used in the same way. When R is a long chain, containing, for example, 12 carbon atoms, the neutralization of the acid with sodium hydroxide gives a salt that can be used as a detergent, for example, sodium lauryl sulfate.

$$CH_3 (CH_2)_{10}CH_2OH + HOSO_2OH \rightarrow$$
$$CH_3 (CH_2)_{10}CH_2OSO_2OH + H_2O \quad (Eq. \ 18\text{-}19)$$

$$CH_3 (CH_2)_{10}CH_2OSO_2OH + Na^+OH^- \rightarrow$$
Lauryl hydrogen sulfate

$$CH_3 (CH_2)_{10}CH_2OSO_3{}^-Na^+ + H_2O \quad (Eq. \ 18\text{-}20)$$
Sodium lauryl sulfate

18-15 SUMMARY

Water has a set of properties which seem peculiar in many ways. Of substances with low molecular mass, water appears to have an unusually high boiling point. Compared to substances isoelectronic with water, water is many times more abundant on the earth. Water is also unusual in the fact that it is more dense than ice.

These and other characteristics of water can be related to the properties of other substances through a structural interpretation. Each water molecule can form four hydrogen bonds. Two of these bonds are formed by positive sites, and two by negative sites. This relation of positive and negative sites is peculiar to water molecules and leads to a three-dimensional network in water and ice.

The polar character of water makes it an excellent solvent for many other polar and ionic substances. Water dissolves other substances by interaction with the other substance. Both structural and energetic considerations are necessary to any complete interpretation of the nature of water as a solvent.

Water becomes incorporated into the crystal lattice of salts to form hydrates. It also enters into interactions which lead to the breaking of one or more hydrogen–oxygen bonds in a reaction called hydrolysis.

At least three different kinds of compounds can be formed by replacing one of the hydrogen atoms in water with a different atom. Where the replacement atom is of low electronegativity, the derivative is basic (NaOH). Where the replacement atom is of high electronegativity, the derivative is acidic (HOCl). When carbon is the replacement atom, the derivative is neutral (CH_3OH).

A compound made up of molecules in which carbon is joined by a single bond to an OH group is represented by ROH and is called an alcohol. Alcohols have some properties which are identical with those of water but which differ more radically from those of water as the number of carbon atoms in the R group increases.

Ex. 18-1 At 1 atmosphere pressure, the density of ice is 0.917 g/ml and the density of water is 0.998 g/ml. What will happen to the ice if it is compressed?

Ex. 18-2 a. Freon-12, CF_2Cl_2, is a nontoxic compound used as a refrigerant in household refrigerators. The heat of vaporization of Freon-12 is 40 cal/g at its boiling point, −28°C. Compare Freon-12 and ammonia as refrigerants.

b. Water has a large heat of vaporization and also a relatively high boiling point. Suggest a situation in which water could be used as a refrigerant.

Ex. 18-3 a. What is the maximum quantity of gold that could be extracted from 1 cubic mile of seawater? (1 mile = 1,630 meters; 1 cubic meter of seawater has a mass of about 1,000 kg.)

b. Suppose that the molecules in 1 mole of water could be tagged and poured into the ocean at Atlantic City. Allowing a few thousand years or so for equilibrium to be established, how many of these molecules would you expect to find at San Francisco in 1 mole of water collected at the later time?

Ex. 18-4 Since water gas is made from coal, why is water gas considered to be a more energetic fuel than coal? Pound for pound, which fuel would release more energy when burned in air? How many pounds of water at 100°C could be converted to steam by this energy?

Ex. 18-5 Sketch electron charge cloud structures for HF, H_2O, and NH_3. Indicate negative and positive sites on the structures.

Ex. 18-6 The densities of five isoelectronic substances in the liquid phase at their boiling points are

CH_4	0.422 g/ml
NH_3	0.677 g/ml
H_2O	0.958 g/ml
HF	0.987 g/ml
Ne	1.204 g/ml

Calculate the volume occupied by 1 mole of each liquid. What is a reasonable interpretation of the relation between the volume occupied by 1 mole of each substance and the magnitude of the positive charge on the central nucleus in a molecule of each substance?

Ex. 18-7 Explain why the only alkali metal ions normally hydrated in ionic solids are Li^+ and Na^+ ions, whereas all the alkaline-earth metal ions are normally hydrated at room temperature.

Ex. 18-8 Which of these reactions are hydration reactions? Which are hydrolysis reactions?

a. $PI_3 + 3H_2O \rightleftarrows HPO(OH)_2 + 3HI$

b. $CuSO_4 + 5H_2O \rightleftarrows CuSO_4 \cdot 5H_2O$

c. $Cd^{++} + 4H_2O \rightleftarrows Cd(H_2O)_4{}^{++}$

d. $NH_4{}^+ + H_2O \rightleftarrows NH_3 + H_3O^+$

e. $CH_3COO^- + H_2O \rightleftarrows CH_3COOH + OH^-$

Ex. 18-9 How many moles of water will be liberated when 24.4 g of barium chloride dihydrate is heated?

PART FIVE: ORDER, DISORDER, AND CHANGE

Chapters 14 to 18

IN EARLIER CHAPTERS substances have been thought of as having three-dimensional structures. Initially the structural units were considered to be atoms. Subsequently, electrons and nuclei have been developed as structural units. In this latter view each substance is a collection of units held together by electric attraction. Chemical change represents the rearrangement of electrons and nuclei from one structure to yield a new structure. On this basis chemical change in a system should be possible if it results in a new structure of lower energy than the original structure. In agreement with this view many reactions are found to be spontaneous and exothermic.

During many chemical reactions, only a fraction of the original components reacts to form products. Experimentally it is found that most reactions cease even though reactants are still present. Yet if the products of a reaction possess lower energy than the reactants, why does the reaction not proceed until all traces of reactants have disappeared?

Reactions which do not proceed to completion are generally found to be reversible. The behavior of reversible reactions can be described by Le Chatelier's principle. Chemical systems which undergo reactions described as (1) incomplete, (2) reversible, and (3) corresponding to

Le Chatelier's principle are said to be systems in an equilibrium state.

A chemical system in an equilibrium state is never observed to undergo further spontaneous changes in state. In a system in an equilibrium state, spontaneous changes which correspond to an exothermic reaction are seemingly not possible.

The equilibrium state of a chemical system is characterized by a constant relationship among the concentrations of those components that are in solution. Thus, in the equilibrium state there is an absence of change, not for lack of reactants but because the concentration of the reactants is relatively low while the concentration of the products is relatively high. The quantitative relation of product and reactant concentrations at equilibrium is described by an equilibrium constant. Concentration of components, not total quantity of components, controls the possibility for spontaneous chemical change.

Electrochemical cells can be used to demonstrate that energy is absorbed whenever dissolved material is transferred from low concentration to high concentration at a constant temperature. The energy transferred cannot be heat but must be electric energy or some other form of work. As the material is transferred from low to high concentration and as the work is transferred into the system, heat is transferred out of the system. In the simplest case the energy transferred in as work exactly equals the energy transferred out as heat. In such a case, the transfer of material from low to high concentration is accompanied by a conversion of work into heat, but there is no change in the energy of the system.

A system which undergoes a change in state accompanied by the conversion of work into heat at constant temperature decreases in entropy. If the energy of the system does not change, then the work transferred in equals the heat transferred out. Under these circumstances the least quantity of work which has to be transferred in is said to produce an increase in free energy ΔG, and the heat transferred out produces a change in state represented by $T \Delta S$ where ΔS is called the entropy change. When the quantities of work and heat are equal, $\Delta G = -T \Delta S$ if the energy of the system does not change.

Quite commonly reactions proceed under conditions such that the final pressure and temperature are the same as the initial pressure and temperature. In Chapter 9 it was pointed out that these conditions lead to a change in enthalpy (ΔH) for the system. For the general case of a reaction then,

$$\Delta H = \Delta G + T \Delta S$$

or
$$\Delta G = \Delta H - T \Delta S$$

An enthalpy change can be calculated from calorimetric data, and a free energy change can be calculated either from the potential of a cell or from an equilibrium constant. The magnitude of $T \Delta S$ cannot be determined as directly as the enthalpy change or free energy change. Ordinarily $T \Delta S$ is evaluated as the difference, $\Delta H - \Delta G$.

Experimental data for heat transferred out of a chemical system can be interpreted as an enthalpy change in the system. The structures of substances can be interpreted in terms of bond energies which can in turn be evaluated in terms of enthalpy changes. Changes in order and disorder accompanying a reaction can be related to $T \Delta S$. There is no direct relationship between the nature of a system and the free energy change. Thus, the free energy change can be calculated from experimental data but not directly related to a mental model for a chemical system. The equation $\Delta G = \Delta H - T \Delta S$ provides a means of linking observation and theory for chemical reactions.

The chemical substance water provides an interesting example of the use of ideas to link diverse observations. Phase changes for water seem to present a different picture from that characteristic of many other substances. Thus, the molar volume of water is smaller than the molar volume of ice, while the molar heat of vaporization of water is unusually large. If water is assumed to have a structure in which individual molecules are linked by hydrogen bonds, then the characteristics of the observed phase changes are consistent with the characteristics of other substances. Indeed, phase changes provide an example of the interrelation of structure and disorder as a guide to the interpretation of systems.

Every reaction requires some time for its completion. In many reactions, however, the time required is comparable to the time required to mix the reagents. Reactions which involve only the approach and joining of ions without rearrangement of the electrons and nuclei generally proceed rapidly. Other reactions are observed which take comparatively longer times. Most of these slow reactions, which have speeds that decrease as the concentration of reagents decreases, involve the rearrangement of electrons and nuclei.

Temperature changes also alter the speed of a reaction so that the higher the temperature, the faster the reaction. Observations of the relation between temperature and speed are interpreted by assuming that molecules must collide for reaction to occur. When molecules collide, they must be oriented properly and must possess sufficient kinetic energy to provide for the rearrangement upon which further reaction depends. Slow reactions are interpreted, therefore, as evidence that the reactants need a considerable activation energy.

Colliding molecules of reactants can react to produce molecules of products provided that the structure produced by collision (activated complex) possesses sufficient energy. It seems as though the reactants have to surmount an energy barrier. The ability of the reactants to surmount the barrier is related to temperature. The height of the barrier can be altered by the presence of other substances called catalysts.

Structure and order determine the composition of a system in its final state. Concentration and temperature determine the speed with which the reaction will proceed. Catalysts can be used to increase the speed of a reaction, but they cannot change the equilibrium state.

Composition, concentration, and temperature are the means for controlling chemical reactions. Study of their effects on chemical systems provides the data for interpreting the nature of reactions. Our study indicates that each chemical system represents a set of structural units arranged in a way that combines aspects of order and of disorder. All the chemical changes observed appear to reflect the possibilities for altering the relationship between the order and the disorder of a system.

APPENDIX: STOCK NOMENCLATURE OF COMPOUNDS

ALTHOUGH MANY chemical compounds have trivial names, some of which have been used for hundreds of years, most substances are named by chemists in one of two ways—by the classical system or by the Stock system. In the classical system, which is still in use, names of compounds are devised by adding various prefixes and suffixes to the names of certain elements in the compounds. For example, in the classical system, the compound with the formula FeO is called ferrous oxide. Here the suffix –ous is added to the root of the Latin word *ferrum* meaning iron. Another oxide of iron, Fe_2O_3, is called ferric oxide in the classical system.

To provide names which would better indicate the formulas of compounds, the Stock system was recommended in 1940[*,†] by the International Union of Pure and Applied Chemistry. In this system, which is now used by many chemists, Roman numerals replace some of the prefixes and suffixes. Thus, in the Stock system, FeO is called iron (II) oxide and Fe_2O_3 is called iron (III) oxide. The Roman numerals in these names indicate the oxidation state of the iron in an unambiguous way.

---

[*] W. P. Jorissen, H. Bassett, A. Damiens, F. Fichter, and H. Rémy, *Journal of the American Chemical Society*, **63**:899, 1941.

[†] H. Bassett and A. Silverman, *ibid.*, **82**:5523, 1960.

TABLE 1   FORMULAS AND NAMES OF SOME COMPOUNDS OF METALS WITH NONMETALS

Formula	Classical Name	Stock Name
$CuCl_2$	Cupric chloride	Copper(II) chloride
CuO	Cupric oxide	Copper(II) oxide
Cu_2O_3	Copper trioxide	Copper(III) oxide
Fe_3O_4	Triiron tetroxide (magnetic oxide of iron)	Iron(II, III) oxide
Pb_3O_4	Lead tetroxide	Lead(II, II, IV) oxide
$MnCl_2$	Manganous chloride	Manganese(II) chloride
$MnCl_3$	Manganic chloride	Manganese(III) chloride
$MnCl_4$	Manganese tetrachloride	Manganese(IV) chloride
Mn_2O_5	Manganese pentoxide	Manganese(V) oxide
Mn_2O_7	Manganese heptoxide	Manganese(VII) oxide

Some examples of compounds named by the classical system and by the newer Stock system are listed in Table 1.

In 1940 the Stock nomenclature was recommended for two-element compounds of metals with nonmetals. It has recently been suggested* that the Stock system be extended and used to name the compounds of nonmetals with other nonmetals. The compounds listed in Table 2 are named by the classical system and by the Stock system.

A method for naming complex ions was suggested by A. Werner, and its modification to include Roman numerals to indicate the oxida-

* Robert C. Brasted, *Journal of Chemical Education,* 35:136, 1958. Reprinted in *Supplementary Readings for Chemical Bond Approach,* by R. K. Fitzgerel and William F. Kieffer, Division of Chemical Education of the American Chemical Society, Easton, Pa., 1960.

TABLE 2   FORMULAS AND NAMES OF SOME COMPOUNDS OF NONMETALS WITH NONMETALS

Formula	Classical Name	Stock Name
N_2O	Nitrous oxide	Nitrogen(I) oxide
NO	Nitric oxide	Nitrogen(II) oxide
NO_2	Nitrogen dioxide	Nitrogen(IV) oxide
N_2O_4	Nitrogen tetroxide	Dimer of nitrogen(IV) oxide
N_2O_5	Nitrogen pentoxide	Nitrogen(V) oxide
Cl_2O	Chlorine monoxide	Chlorine(I) oxide
ClO_2	Chlorine dioxide	Chlorine(IV) oxide

TABLE 3   FORMULAS AND NAMES OF SOME COMPLEX ANIONS

Formula	Classical Name	Stock Name
$Fe(CN)_6^{---}$	Ferricyanide ion	Hexacyanoferrate(III) ion
$Fe(CN)_6^{----}$	Ferrocyanide ion	Hexacyanoferrate(II) ion
$PtCl_4^{--}$	Chloroplatinite ion	Tetrachloroplatinate(II) ion
$Au(CN)_2^{-}$	Cyanoaurite ion	Dicyanoaurate(I) ion
$Zn(OH)_4^{--}$	Zincate ion	Tetrahydroxozincate(II) ion

tion state of the metal is also a part of the Stock system. To construct the name of a complex anion which contains a metal atom as the central atom, the first step is to indicate the number of atoms or groups of atoms coordinated with the metal by using a prefix (for example, mono, di, tri, tetra). Next, the coordinating groups are given names ending in –o (for example, NO_2^{-}, nitro; Cl^{-}, chloro; CN^{-}, cyano; H_2O, aquo). An exception is NH_3 which is called ammine in complex ions. Finally, the metal is named and, in an anion, is given the suffix –ate, and the oxidation number is indicated by a Roman numeral. For example, the ion $Fe(CN)_6^{----}$ is called hexacyanoferrate(II) ion. Some examples of complex anions with their classical names and their Stock names are given in Table 3.

TABLE 4   FORMULAS AND NAMES OF SOME COMPLEX CATIONS

Formula	Classical Name	Stock Name
$Cu(H_2O)_4^{++}$	Tetrahydrocupric ion	Tetraaquocopper(II) ion
$Ag(NH_3)_2^{+}$	Silver ammonia complex ion	Diamminesilver(I) ion

TABLE 5   SUGGESTED NAMES FOR SOME OXYANIONS

Formula	Classical Name	Suggested Stock Name
NO_2^{-}	Nitrite ion	Nitrate(III) ion
NO_3^{-}	Nitrate ion	Nitrate(V) ion
SO_2^{--}	Sulfoxylate ion	Sulfate(II) ion
SO_3^{--}	Sulfite ion	Sulfate(IV) ion
SO_4^{--}	Sulfate ion	Sulfate(VI) ion

Complex cations are named first by using the prefix to indicate the number of complexing groups, second by naming the complexing group or groups, and then by adding the name of the metal without a suffix. Examples are given in Table 4.

It has been suggested* that the Stock system of nomenclature be extended to include oxyanions. In the Stock system, the names of all oxyanions would end in –ate, and the oxidation state of the central atom would be indicated by a Roman numeral. Some oxyanions and their suggested names are given in Table 5.

---

* Robert C. Brasted, *Journal of Chemical Education,* **35**: 136, 1958. Reprinted in *Supplementary Readings for Chemical Bond Approach,* by R. K. Fitzgerel and William F. Kieffer, Division of Chemical Education of the American Chemical Society, Easton, Pa., 1960.

ACKNOWLEDGMENTS

THE CHEMICAL BOND APPROACH PROJECT has been fortunate in having the services of a great many persons. Without the aid of these persons, it would not have been possible to develop the course. Of all those who aided the project, the most important group is made up of the teachers who used the preliminary editions with students and evaluated text, laboratory guide, tests, and demonstrations for the project staff. The official group of teachers in the evaluation and their schools are

HARRY E. ADAMS, *Bergenfield High School, Bergenfield, New Jersey*
BARRY B. BARNHART, *Palmyra Area High School, Palmyra, Pennsylvania*
FRANCIS G. BARTLE, *Moses Lake High School, Moses Lake, Washington*
CHARLES BECK, *Mt. Lebanon Senior High School, Pittsburgh, Pennsylvania*
WILLIAM H. BENJAMIN, *Kearsley High School, Flint, Michigan*
ARNOLD E. BEREIT, *Central High School, Phoenix, Arizona*
PAUL P. BETHUNE, *The University School, Tallahassee, Florida*
CLARENCE A. BEYER, *Grant High School, Portland, Oregon*
PAUL BILLETT, *Lebanon Senior High School, Lebanon, Pennsylvania*
GEORGE BIRRELL, *South Salem Senior High School, Salem, Oregon*
LOUIS W. BIXBY, *Weedsport Central School, Weedsport, New York*
J. DOUGLAS BOOKHOUT, *Claremont Senior High School, Claremont, California*
KENNETH E. BORST, *Leonia High School, Leonia, New Jersey*
WILLIAM C. BUNGERT, *Dixie Hollins High School, North St. Petersburg, Florida*
JOHN C. CAMP, *Western Reserve Academy, Hudson, Ohio*

WILLIARD S. CAMPBELL, *Central High School of Hopewell Township, Pennington, N.J.*
DURWOOD CANHAM, *South Mountain High School, Phoenix, Arizona*
JOSEPH B. CARANCI, *Cranston High—West, Cranston, Rhode Island*
GEORGE K. CARLSON, *Thurston High School, Springfield, Oregon*
PAUL CHAPIN, *Findlay Senior High School, Findlay, Ohio*
KENNETH COOK, *Grosse Pointe High School, Grosse Pointe Farms, Michigan*
ROBERT COOK, *Maine Township High School, Park Ridge, Illinois*
MISS HELEN W. CRAWLEY, *Natick High School, Natick, Massachusetts*
DONALD DAILEY, *Nicolet High School, Milwaukee, Wisconsin*
ROLLY A. DAVIS, JR., *Marple-Newtown Senior High School, Newtown Square, Pa.*
JAMES V. DEROSE, *Marple-Newtown Senior High School, Newtown Square, Pa.*
ROBERT DIXON, *Beaverton High School, Beaverton, Oregon*
ALBERT DOLAN, JR., *South High School, Willoughby, Ohio*
JOHN DOMIJAN, *Amity Regional High School, Woodbridge, Connecticut*
HARRY DORFMAN, *Fort Lee High School, Fort Lee, New Jersey*
MRS. JOAN DUNN, *Tilden Technical High School, Chicago, Illinois*
WILLIAM J. ELLIOTT, *Highlands High School, Fort Thomas, Kentucky*
CHARLES ELMER, *Harvey High School, Painesville, Ohio*
HAROLD EMMITT, *Conestoga Valley High School, Lancaster, Pennsylvania*
ROBERT K. FITZGEREL, *R. B. Worthy High School, Saltville, Virginia*
JOSEPH F. FOOS, *Flint Central High School, Flint, Michigan*
ALLEN FURBER, *Boston Technical High School, Roxbury, Massachusetts*
EMIL GEORGE, *Hoover High School, North Canton, Ohio*
BERNARD GOLLIS, *Bedford High School, Bedford, Massachusetts*
ORRIN GOULD, *University High School, Urbana, Illinois*
MRS. IRMA GREISEL, *Gresham Union High School, Gresham, Oregon*
O. W. HARGROVE, *Baton Rouge High School, Baton Rouge, Louisiana*
F. STUART HARMON, JR., *The Lawrenceville School, Lawrenceville, New Jersey*
ROBERT W. HART, *Libertyville-Fremont High School, Libertyville, Illinois*
MISS KATHRYN HARTMAN, *Libertyville-Fremont High School, Libertyville, Illinois*
ROBERT HENRICH, *Columbia High School, Richland, Washington*
HARRY J. HERDER, *Milwaukee Country Day School, Milwaukee, Wisconsin*
DONALD HOLMQUIST, *Park County High School, Livingston, Montana*
RICHARD W. HOLSTEIN, *Wayland Academy, Beaver Dam, Wisconsin*
E. C. HOSTETLER, *Colton Union High School, Colton, California*
WALLACE I. HUGDAHL, *Cedarburg High School, Cedarburg, Wisconsin*
WALTER E. HUNTER, *Rich Township High School, Park Forest, Illinois*
MORRIS M. HUTCHISON, *Everett High School, Everett, Washington*
MRS. ELIZABETH HYDE, *Norwich Free Academy, Norwich, Connecticut*
STANLEY E. INNES, *Walpole High School, Walpole, Massachusetts*
WILLIAM M. JACKSON, *Roger Ludlowe High School, Fairfield, Connecticut*
JAMES F. JAKLICH, *Baldwin High School, Pittsburgh, Pennsylvania*
CLINTON S. JOHNSON, *Cranston High—East, Cranston, Rhode Island*
ALFRED J. KINNEY, *Parma Senior High School, Parma, Ohio*
FRANCIS A. KITTEL, *Waupun High School, Waupun, Wisconsin*
MRS. BARBARA KMETZ, *Bassick High School, Bridgeport, Connecticut*
CONRAD KNOX, *Alva High School, Alva, Oklahoma*
ELTON H. KNUTSON, *Hawken Independent School, Cleveland, Ohio*
MISS KAREN B. KRITZ, *Wauwatosa High School, Wauwatosa, Wisconsin*
HENRY KUMADA, *Los Angeles High School, Los Angeles, California*
MISS JUNE A. KURZ, *Evergreen Park High School, Evergreen Park, Illinois*
FRANCIS M. LAMOUREUX, *Technical High School, Springfield, Massachusetts*

In 1961 the high school teachers were organized into regional groups. Consultants for these groups were

BENJAMIN DAILEY, *Columbia University, New York, New York*
ROBERT D. EDDY, *Tufts University, Medford, Massachusetts*
JACK EICHINGER, *Florida State University, Tallahassee, Florida*
LELAND HARRIS, *Knox College, Galesburg, Illinois*
MALCOLM KENNEY, *Case Institute of Technology, Cleveland, Ohio*
R. J. KRANTZ, *University of Redlands, Redlands, California*
W. T. LIPPINCOTT, *Ohio State University, Columbus, Ohio*
ARTHUR H. LIVERMORE, *Reed College, Portland, Oregon*
H. A. NEIDIG, *Lebanon Valley College, Annville, Pennsylvania*
ROBERT M. SHERMAN, *Roger Williams Junior College, Providence, Rhode Island*
BROTHER B. WILLIAM SPINNER, *LaSalle Academy, Providence, Rhode Island*
ROBERT D. SPRENGER, *University of Puget Sound, Tacoma, Washington*

The headquarters for the CBA Project is at Earlham College. The development of laboratory experiments was carried on at Lebanon Valley College. The development of examinations, the supervision of evaluation schools, and the development of lecture demonstrations were the concern of groups at Reed College, University of Illinois, and Tufts University, respectively. Staff personnel are listed below, together with the institution where they served as project staff members.

Earlham College, Richmond, Indiana

LAURENCE E. STRONG	MARCO H. SCHEER	JOSEPH HAINES
O. THEODOR BENFEY	MRS. LUCILLE B. RICE	MISS HELEN STRONG
M. DANIEL SMITH	MRS. EDLINE SHELTON	MRS. LILY BUTLER
EARLE S. SCOTT	MRS. HETTY REMPT	MRS. JACQUELINE SAWYER
WALTER E. HUNTER		

Lebanon Valley College, Annville, Pennsylvania

H. A. NEIDIG	MRS. BERNICE K. LILES	MRS. FLORENCE C. KIEFFER
THOMAS G. TEATES	MRS. GLORIA A. BOYER	RICHARD T. YINGLING
HANS SCHNEIDER	MRS. MARY E. ZAREK	JOSEPH B. DIETZ
JAMES V. DEROSE		

Reed College, Portland, Oregon

ARTHUR H. LIVERMORE	MRS. DOROTHY SETTERBERG

University of Illinois, Urbana, Illinois

PAUL WESTMEYER	MRS. RONETTE SNYDER	MISS JO ELLEN PUTT
ORRIN GOULD	MRS. DIANE LEAF	

Tufts University, Medford, Massachusetts

ROBERT D. EDDY	MISS HELEN W. CRAWLEY	MRS. KATHERINE MCDONOUGH

LAURENCE E. STRONG
DIRECTOR

crystal structure of, 474
electron-in-a-box diagram for, 415
electronic configuration for, 418
energy levels in, 418
heat of vaporization for, 502
melting point of, 502
orbitals in, 413
Calcium chloride, boiling point of, 507
enthalpy of formation for, 507
enthalpy of solution for, 574
flame color for, 389
heat of fusion for, 507
heat of vaporization for, 507
melting point of, 507
Calcium chloride–sodium sulfate system, 562
Calcium fluoride, cleavage plane in, 509
crystal of, 509
heat of fusion for, 726
heat of vaporization for, 726
Calcium hydroxide, solubility of, 636, 637
Calcium oxide, 101
flame color for, 389
Calcium sulfate, boiling point of, 503
equilibrium of, in solution, 624–630
heat of vaporization for, 503
melting point of, 503
precipitation of, 563, 626
saturated solution of, 631
Calorie, 144
Calorimeter, 104, 177, 347, 348
bomb, 350
Calorimetry, *144
and electricity, 140–145
Cannizzaro, Stanislao, 88, 115
Carbide, 486
Carbon, abundance of, in earth's crust, 721
atomic orbitals in, 436, 437
boiling point of, 261
bond energy for, 372
burning of, 29
charge cloud model for, 252, 253
electron in-a-box diagram for, 436
electronic configuration for, 418, 437
energy levels in, 418
flame color for, 389
heat capacity of, 337
heat of sublimation for, 462
ionization energy for, 403
isotopes of, 220
reactions of, 68–70
sp^2–sp^2 bond in, 441, 442
Carbon atom, charge cloud model for,
252, 253
Carbon–chlorine, bond energy, 372
Carbon dioxide, boiling point of, 22
bond angle in, 274
bond energy, 375, 376
bond length in, 274
charge cloud model for, 377
density of, 22
dielectric constant for, 187
enthalpy of dissociation for, 376
enthalpy of formation for, 360
heat capacity of, 338
melting point of, 22
molecular structure of, 440
molecules isoelectronic with, 273
percent of, in air, 723
pi bonding in, 440
production of, 27, 29
rate of effusion for, 305
Carbon-hydrogen bond energy, 369, 370,
372, 374
Carbon–hydrogen compounds, 264–266
Carbon monoxide, boiling point of, 22
combustion of, 349, 358
density of, 22
enthalpy of combustion for, 358, 360
enthalpy of dissociation for, 376
enthalpy of formation for, 357
heat capacity of, 338
melting point of, 22
molar volume of, 326
molecules, isoelectronic with, 273
percent of, in air, 723
production of, 29
Carbon tetrachloride, boiling point of, 502
dielectric constant for, 187

enthalpy of dissociation for, 462
heat of vaporization for, 502
melting point of, 502
Carbonate ion, atomic orbital model for, 554
bond angle in, 553
bond length in, 552, 553
hybrid orbital model for, 554
hydrolysis of, 737
Lewis structure of, 554
pi bonding in, 553
Catalyst, *701
and activation energy, 708
adsorption on, 709
and reaction rate, 710
Cation, *512
Caustic soda, 101
Cell, Daniell (see Daniell cell)
dry, 130
electrochemical (see Electrochemical cell)
Cell potential, 610
Cell reaction, reversible, 599–602
Celsius temperature scale, *296
Cementite, 486
Centigrade temperature scale (see Celsius
temperature scale)
Cermet, 495
Cesium, crystal structure of, 475
heat of sublimation for, 462
Cesium chloride, boiling point of, 507
crystal structure of, 514, 515
enthalpy of formation for, 507
enthalpy of solution for, 574
heat of fusion for, 507
heat of vaporization for, 507
melting point of, 507
Cesium chloride lattice, 514, 515, 536, 537
unit cell for, 518
Chadwick, James, 3, 221
Chain reaction, *711
Change, 5–7, 11–13
chemical (see Chemical change)
physical, *12
Characteristic property, *19
Charge, conservation of, 171
electric (see Electric charge)
from friction, 171
moving, 170
transport of, in solution, 145–147
unit of, on electron, 150, 151
unit of, for faraday, 151, 152
Charge cloud, 233, 234
arrangements with carbon nucleus, 253
charge density of, 237
oscillation of, 319
proton in, 234
radius for, 237, 244, 245
shape of, 233, 234
Charge cloud model, 233–235
assumptions for, 238, 243
and atomic orbital model, comparison of,
443, 444
geometrical structure of, 254
kinetic energy in, 286
one–electron, 239–241
one proton–one electron, 236–238
one proton–two electron, 243–245
potential energy in, 286
two–electron, 239
two electron–one nucleus, 243–245
two proton–two electron, 238–242
Charge clouds, merging of, 239, 240
Charge density, *237
Charge flow, 160, 161, 171
and chemical change, 160
and heat, 141–145
measurement of, 141–143
and temperature change, 141–145, 160
(See also Current, electric)
Charge/mass ratio, 149–151
Charge separation, *170, 171
and energy, 159–199
in solution, 729
Charged objects, 162–168
Charles, Jacques, 294
Charles's law, 294
Chemical and electrical structures, 229–281
Chemical bond, 430–449
in crystals, 465

charge on, 153, 213–215
delocalized, *442, *464, 464–468
in high-vacuum discharge, 209
kinetic energy of, 235
localized, 464–466
in matter, 209
movement of, in metallic conductor, 468
in nuclear atom, 230
outer, 458
in photoelectric emission, 209
self-energy of, 236–238
in thermionic emission, 209
Electron affinity, *524
Electron beam, 406
deflection of, 207, 208
mass of, 208–210
velocity of, 208–210
Electron charge cloud (see Charge cloud)
Electron cloud (see Charge cloud)
Electron emission (see Emission, electron)
Electron-in-a-box diagram, 414, 415, 436
Electron pairing, and magnetism, 258
Electron transfer, 510, 595–623
and electronegativity, 522–528
at hydrogen electrode, 615, 616
and oxidation number, 578
Electron-transfer reaction, 595, 596
Electron wave, characteristics of, 445
description of, 407–410
orientation of, 409, 411
shape of, 411
size of, 411
three-dimensional feature of, 400, 401
Electronegativity, 522–528, *523, 535
bond energy in, 524
enthalpy of formation in, 524
periodicity in, 525
Electronegativity difference, 526
formulas by, 527
Electronegativity scale, 526
Electronic configuration, *417
and energy level, 418
Electroscope, 169, 170
Electrostatic charge, by friction, 201
Electrostatic effect, cause of, 171
Electrostatic force, 187–192
Electrostatic system, *167
Electrostatics, *162
Elektron, 162
Element, chemical, 26–32, *28, *31
metallic (see Metal)
Elements, symbols of, 98
transmutation of, 3
Emission, photoelectric, 203, *204, 232, 395
thermionic, *202, 203
in vacuum (see Discharge, high-vacuum)
Emission of radiation, *390
Emission spectra, 390–392
End point, *648
Endothermic reaction, *351
Energy, of alpha particle, 198, 199
analogy for, 362, 363
and charge separation, 159–199
chemical, 155
conservation of, 176, 354
and dielectric constant, 189, 190
in dielectric material, 193
and distance graph for electrostatic systems, 191, 192
forms of, 176–179
kinetic (see Kinetic energy)
potential (see Potential energy)
in proton–electron systems, 234–236, 238–242, 246
relation of, to force and distance, 188
storage of, 195
and structure, 339, 340
transfer of, 195
from zinc and copper sulfate, 130
Energy barrier, 705, 706
Energy conversion, 177–179
Energy level, *397
in atoms, 405
and electronic configuration, 418
in elements at. no. 1–20, 416
sequence of, 416
Energy-level diagram, 413
Energy source, electrical system as an,

193, 194
Energy transfer, 126–128. 141, 176, 177, 193, 194
in cells, 611
Energy transition, 407
Enthalpy, *351
and solutions, 377–379
Enthalpy change, 351, 651–653
and free energy change, 652–654
in neutralization, 676, 677
and volume change, 379
Enthalpy data, additivity of, 354
Enthalpy diagram, 353
for free radical reaction, 712, 713
Enthalpy of combustion, 349–351, *361
Enthalpy of dilution, *377
Enthalpy of dissociation, *361
and crystal energy, 538
Enthalpy of formation, *361
for gaseous atoms, 463
as periodic property of chlorides, 430
Enthalpy of fusion (see Heat of fusion)
Enthalpy of neutralization, 676
Enthalpy of reaction, 349–353, *351, *359, 404
sign convention for, 352
Enthalpy of solution, *377, 574–576
and ion size, 575, 576
Enthalpy of sublimation (see Heat of sublimation)
Enthalpy of vaporization (see Heat of vaporization)
Entropy, *659
and organization, 658–661
Enzyme, 710
Equation, chemical, 101–103
Equilibrium, chemical, 624–650
and free energy change, 643–647
calcium sulfate–water system, 631
dynamic, 715, 716
electrochemical, 639–643
Equilibrium constant, *642, 644–646, 650
acid (see Acid, ionization constant for)
Equilibrium constant for bases, 681
Equilibrium state, *638
Equilibrium vapor pressure, *329
Escape rate, of gas, 302
Ethane, charge cloud model for, 265, 266
enthalpy of combustion for, 360
enthalpy of dissociation for, 371
enthalpy of formation for, 369, 370
heat capacity of, 338
molecular geometry of, 553
molecules isoelectronic with, 273
Ethanol, boiling point of, 740
density of, 740
dielectric constant for, 187
heat capacity of, 725
heat of fusion for, 726
heat of vaporization for, 726
melting point of, 740
reaction of, with sulfuric acid, 671
solubility of, 740
Ethanol–water system, freezing point of, 561
Ethylene, boiling point of, 273
density of, 305
enthalpy of combustion for, 360
molar volume of, 326
molecular geometry for, 439, 553
molecules isoelectronic with, 273
orbital description of, 439
pi bond in, 439
rate of effusion for, 305
sigma and pi bonds in, 440
Ethylene dibromide, 46
Ethylene glycol, 725
Eutectic mixture, *489
Eutectic point, *489
Evaporation, *330
Exclusion principle, 242, 243, 412
in compound formation, 262
Exothermic reaction, *351
Experiment, 3, *5, 7, 8
control for, 5
controlled, *6
isolation for, 5
Experimental science, 5–7
Explosion, *128
Expression, *102

bond angle in, 435
heat of fusion for, 729
heat of vaporization for, 334
ionization constant for, 689
melting point of, 729
Hydrohalic acids, 685, 686
Hydrolysis reaction, 734–737
Hydronium ion, structure of, 670
Hypobromous acid, 688
    ionization constant for, 689
Hypochlorous acid, 688
    ionization constant for, 689
Hypoiodous acid, 688
    ionization constant for, 689
Ice, crystal lattice for, 732
    density of, 723
    dielectric constant for, 187
    structure of, 730, 731
Idea, 3, 7
Ideal gas, *313, 313–315
Ideal gas law, *314
Imagination, 4
Immiscible substances, *47
Incandescence, *388, 392
Incomplete reaction, 624–628, *628
    barium ion and hydroxide ion, 630
    hydrogen ion and acetate ion, 630
    lead ion and chloride ion, 630
    nitrogen gas and hydrogen gas, 630
Inert gas (see Noble gas)
Infinite dilution, *378
Infinite separation of charges, *191
Initial state, *5
Insoluble substances, periodic relationship
        among, 566, 567
Insulator, electric, 495
Interaction, 122
    in solution, 58
    in systems, 49
Interference patterns, 398
Intermetallic compound, 489, 490
Internuclear distance, 529
Interstitial solid solution, 484–487, *486
Iodine, abundance of, in seawater, 727
    covalent radius for, 534
    enthalpy of dissociation for, 361
    van der Waals radius for, 534
Ion, *146
    electric charge on, 171
    origin of, 171, 172
    polyatomic. 551–554, *552
    positive, *213
        in gases, 210–213
        mass of, 212
Ion beam apparatus, 211
Ion concentration, measurement of,
        619–621
Ion-ion interaction, 589
Ion product constant, *681
Ion size, and crystal lattice, 536
    periodicity in, 536
Ionic bond, *262, 523
Ionic charge, determination of, 519
    magnitude of, 519
    and oxidation number, 578
    periodic property of, 521
    in solution, 547–551
    type of, 519
Ionic compound, 501–546, *504
    formula for, 521
    molten, 504
    properties of, 504
    in solution, 547–582
Ionic crystal, attractive force in, 508
    cleavage in, 517, 518
Ionic equations, 558, 559
Ionic radius, 528–535
    for elements, 530
Ionic solution, *146
Ionic system, rates of reaction in, 695, 696
Ionization constant, acid (see Acid,
        ionization constant for)
Ionization energy, 401–405
    apparatus for determining, 402
    and atomic number, 420
    for atoms, 522
    diagram of, 522
    first, *402

for ions, 522
and orbitals, 417–419
periodicity of, 421
Ions, aqueous solutions of, 552
    in chemical systems, 171
    conduction by, 145–147, 172
    in crystals, evidence of, 509–512
    formation of solutions of, 570–574
    identification of, 565–569
    independence of, in solution, 555–558
    interaction of, with other ions, 562–564
        with solvent, 560–562
    nomenclature of, 551
    packing of, in crystals, 512
    separation of, 565–569
    in solution, 547–582
Iron, abundance of, in earth's crust, 721
    boiling point of, 22
    crystal structure of, 474, 475
    density of, 22
    electronic configuration for, 418
    energy levels in, 418
    first ionization energy for, 467
    galvanized, 104
    heat capacity of, 725
    heat of sublimation for, 462
    heat of vaporization for, 503
    melting point of, 22
Iron–air system, 5
Iron filings, 15–18
Iron oxide, 101
Iron rust, 6, 11, 101
Isoelectronic molecules, *266
Isopropyl bromide, 719
Isotopes, 218–222, *220
J-tube, 289, 290
Joule, *144
K_{eq}, 642
K_{sp}, 647
K_w, 681
Kelvin temperature scale, *296
Kernel of atom, *250, 460
Kilocalorie, *113
Kilogram mass, 14
Kinetic energy, 173–182
    average, in gases, 331, 332
        in liquids, 331, 332
    conservation of, in collisions, 315
    of gas molecules, 297–301
    in liquids, 316–318
    for molecules at two temperatures, 707
    in solids, 316
Kinetic model of matter (see Kinetic-molecular
        theory)
Kinetic-molecular theory, 282–341, *318
Kinetic-molecular theory of gases, 296–298,
        *298
Krypton, boiling point of, 334
    crystal structure of, 474
    electronic configuration of, 418, 420
    energy levels in, 418
    first ionization energy for, 420
    heat of vaporization for, 334
    melting point of, 420
    nuclear charge and boiling point of, 321
Krypton tetrafluoride, 421
(l), 102
Lattice, crystal, for ionic compounds, 514–516
        for metals, *476
Lattice energy (see Crystal energy)
Lavoisier, Antoine, 36
Lead, boiling point of, 22
    crystal structure of, 474
    density of, 22
    extraction of, from ore, 487
    heat of sublimation for, 462
    melting point of, 22
    molten, 487
Lead iodide, boiling point of, 503
    heat of vaporization for, 503
    melting point of, 503
    precipitation of, 562
    volume change in formation of, 380, 381
Lead nitrate–potassium iodide system, 562
Lead oxide, 101
Lead shot, 15–18
Lead sulfide, 101
Le Chatelier, Henri, 634